ÉDOUARD MANET, *The Races at Longchamp, Paris*

THE FIRESIDE BOOK

OF Horse Racing

Edited by DAVID F. WOODS

SIMON AND SCHUSTER / NEW YORK / 1963

ACKNOWLEDGMENTS

The editor wishes to express his gratitude to the following individuals and publishers for permission to include in this volume the following material:

Profiles of the race horses Alsab, Azucar, Count Fleet, Discovery, Seabiscuit, War Admiral and Whirlaway by John Hervey, and Gallorette by Joe H. Palmer from the American Race Horse series, reprinted by permission of the Thoroughbred Owners and Breeders Association.

"I Want to Know Why" by Sherwood Anderson. Copyright 1919 by Eleanor Anderson. Copyright renewed. Reprinted by permission of the author's agents, Harold Ober Associates, Inc.

"I Ride to Win" by Eddie Arcaro. Copyright 1951 by Eddie Arcaro and reprinted by permission of the author.

"The Name of the Game" from Across the Board by Toney Betts, the Citadel Press, 1956. Copyright © 1956 by Anthony Zito. Reprinted by permission of the Citadel Press.

"Lost Horse" by William Boniface. Reprinted by permission of the Baltimore Sunpapers.

Selection from Rivers of Damascus and Other Stories by Donn Byrne. Copyright 1931 by Mrs. Dorothea Craig, the author's widow, and used by her permission.

"Keep Off the Rail" by Calvin J. Clements. Copyright 1950 by Popular Publications, Inc. Used by permission of the author's agents, Littauer and Wilkinson.

"The Wounded Admiral" by Bob Considine. Copyright 1937 by King Features Syndicate, Inc. Used by permission of the author.

"Zev Beats Papyrus" by Elmer Davis. Reprinted by permission of The New York Times. Copyright © by the New York Times Company.

"Call Me Horse" by John I. Day. Reprinted by permission of the author.

"Apprentice" by Price Day. Copyright 1935 by the Curtis Publishing Company. Reprinted by permission of the author.

ACKNOWLEDGMENTS

"The Groom's Story" by Sir Arthur Conan Doyle. Reprinted by permission of the Estate of Sir Arthur Conan Doyle.

"Eneas Africanus" by Harry Stillwell Edwards. Copyright 1920 by Harry Stillwell Edwards. Reprinted by permission of the J. W. Burke Company.

"The Look of Eagles" by John Taintor Foote. Reprinted by permission of the publisher, Appleton-Century.

"Come On—My Horse!" from *Farewell to Sport* by Paul Gallico. Reprinted by permission of Alfred A. Knopf, Inc. Copyright 1941 by Paul Gallico.

"Racing for the Rubles" by John Godley, Lord Kilbracken. Copyright © 1958 by Time Inc. Reprinted by permission of the author.

"Morning at Saratoga: The Vanderbilt Barn" by Frank Graham. Reprinted by permission of the author.

"My Big $61,908 Ordeal" by Ernest Havemann. Copyright © 1963 by Time Inc. Reprinted by permission of the author.

"The Rocking-Horse Winner" from *The Portable D. H. Lawrence*. Copyright 1933 by the Estate of D. H. Lawrence. Reprinted by permission of the Viking Press, Inc.

"What's It Get You?" by John P. Marquand. Copyright 1935 by the Curtis Publishing Company. Reprinted by permission of Brandt & Brandt.

Excerpts from "Right Royal" by John Masefield. Reprinted with permission of the publisher. Copyright 1920 by the Macmillan Company. Renewed 1948 by John Masefield.

"A Room at the Barn" by John McNulty. Copyright 1953 by The New Yorker Magazine, Inc., and reprinted by their permission.

"Command Performance" from *The Jockey Club* by Roger Mortimer. Copyright © 1958 by Roger Mortimer. Reprinted by permission of the author's agent, John Johnson.

"The Iron Men" by Tom O'Reiley. Reprinted by permission of the American Totalisator Company.

"Saratoga, or The Horse at Home," "The Good, the True and Mr. Leach," "Stymie—Common Folks" and "People Named Stevens" from *This Was Rac-*ing by Joe H. Palmer. Copyright 1953 by A. S. Barnes & Company, Inc., and reprinted by their permission.

"Chase Me" by Don Reed. Reprinted by permission of the Baltimore Sunpapers.

"Seabiscuit vs. War Admiral" and "Maxims from Methuselah" by Grantland Rice. Reprinted by permission of the Baltimore Sunpapers.

"Gentleman from Sheepshead Bay" by James Roach. Reprinted by permission of *The New York Times*. Copyright © the New York Times Company.

"Little Miss Marker" from *Blue Plate Special* by Damon Runyon. Copyright © 1932, 1960 by Damon Runyon, Jr., and Mary Runyon McCann. Published by J. B. Lippincott Company.

"A Guy like Sande" by Damon Runyon. Copyright 1930 by International News Service and reprinted by its permission.

"Swaps–Nashua" by Evan Shipman. Reprinted by permission of Triangle Publications, Inc.

"A Very Pious Story" and "Clockers Are Little Men" reprinted from *Out of the Red* by Red Smith, by permission of Alfred A. Knopf, Inc. Copyright 1948, 1950 by Walter W. Smith.

"At a Paris Race Track" from *The Street I Know* by Harold E. Stearns. Reprinted by permission of the publisher, Lee Furman.

"Seeing Nellie Home" by Raymond B. Tomkins. Reprinted by permission of the Baltimore Sunpapers.

"The Redemption Handicap" from *Old Man Curry* by Charles E. Van Loan. Copyright 1917 by Doubleday and Company; copyright renewed 1945 by Emma C. Van Loan. Used by permission of Mrs. Virginia Van Loan Updike.

"Upset Beats Man o' War" and "Man o' War vs. John P. Grier" by Fred Van Ness. Reprinted by permission of *The New York Times*. Copyright © by the New York Times Company.

"He Lies Where He Longed to Be" by Tom White. Reprinted by permission of the Baltimore *News-Post*.

"Chinaman's Chance" by David F. Woods. Reprinted by permission of the author.

Appendix selections from *The American Racing Manual*. Reprinted by permission of Triangle Publications, Inc.

In a more personal vein, I am grateful for the help, patience and advice of many friends—in particular, Peter Schwed, my editor at Simon and Schuster; also Scott Sullivan, Patricia Read, Marshall Cassidy and the Jockey Club, Ralph L. Woods and, of course, the one who did the drudgery of typing and indexing, my wife Mona.

DAVID F. WOODS

This volume could reasonably be dedicated to any one in a starting field that would include, among others, Granny Rice, Joe Palmer, John Kieran, John Gaver, Frank Graham, Bill Corum, *et al.,* but I am sure they would all scratch in favor of a walk-over for

JOSEPH B. STEVENS

Contents

Triple Dead Heat, the Carter Handicap, 1944 [JONES PRECISION PHOTO FINISH]

List of Illustrations

Foreword

EDDIE ARCARO

My riding career was fired with an ambition to be on the front end as often as possible. Here I find myself, in a brief writing career, just where I feel most at home—on the front end of a book, and most appropriately a book on horse racing. This rather extraordinary collection of racing stories, and other material, by Dave Woods gives me a particularly nice feeling that someone has at last finally assembled at least a cross-section of the many things about racing that we in the sport have experienced and enjoyed. In my active riding days, most of my reading was necessarily limited to a study of past performances in the *Daily Racing Form*—particularly of horses I was to ride, and those I was to ride against. If someone at that time had told me that the author of *Sherlock Holmes* had written a racing story I would have thought he was confused and probably was referring to Spencer Drayton, head of the Thoroughbred Racing Protective Bureau; and many others would have agreed with me. However, in this anthology I have found some of the best writing of the best writers has been about the best of sports—horse racing. This *Fireside Book of Horse Racing* conveys much of the excitement, the humor, the glamour, the lure, and the delights which so many people have found in the world of racing. If I may be permitted a final word of advice—a tip from the horse's mouth—this is just as good reading under a palm tree in Florida, an orange tree in California or a maple tree at Saratoga as it is in front of my Long Island fireside.

Alsab

JOHN HERVEY

Alsab comes first sentimentally and alphabetically. Normally the eight fine horse profiles in this volume—Alsab, Azucar, Count Fleet, Discovery, Gallorette, Seabiscuit, War Admiral and Whirlaway—would be listed under the names of the authors, John Hervey and Joe H. Palmer. However Messrs. Hervey and Palmer would be the first to acknowledge that for the sake of balance and order it is appropriate to list the accounts of these great Thoroughbreds by the name of the horse rather than by the author. Both writers always did believe that the horse made the writer look good, and if the horse wasn't any good then neither Mr. Harvey nor Mr. Palmer wrote about him.

Around the back stretch of many a race track it was often said that "Sarge" Swenke did as good a job training Alsab's owners as he did with the horse. Some of the truth of that can be read between the lines in the following account of that remarkable racer's career.

CONCLUDING the narration of his career through 1941 in our previous volume, we summed up Alsab as follows:

"The future of this colt will be more eagerly looked forward to than that of almost any other 'since Man o' War.' Should he sustain his two-year-old prestige in the classics of 1942, he will take rank among the great Thoroughbreds of all time."

Now, reviewing his three-year-old performances, it may be said that what was predicted has come to pass. Today, this son of Good Goods and Winds Chant is definitely accorded a niche in the racing Hall of Fame from which he never can be deposed. Age for age, combining his two campaigns of 1941 and 1942, they stand unequaled in turf history.

What, in the minds of many critics, adds to his stature is the fact that his has been no primrose path. On the contrary, adversity has beset him, he has felt "the slings and arrows of outrageous fortune" again and yet again. What he has won, he has fought for against heavy odds.

There have been times when it seemed that the tide had definitely turned against him, that "his day was over." But not so! With indomitable courage and defiant determination he has returned to the charge, wrested victory from defeat under circumstances that seemed insurmountable, and retired at the last, triumphant.

As we peruse the pages of the past seeking for another such instance, we fail to find it. Yes—Alsab is an "only," in the full sense of the term. There has been no other career like his in the annals of racing. The longer and more closely it is studied, the more deeply it impresses with that sense of greatness which alone has enabled him to do what he has and earn the reputation he enjoys.

A year ago, we left Alsab enjoying an all-too-brief rustication in Kentucky at the conclusion of his two-year-old campaign, which had extended from February to mid-November, comprehending no less than 22 races, of which he had won 15, the last ten in succession. His final start, on November 12, had been at Pimlico in the Walden Stakes. His victory brought his winnings for the season up to $110,600, which placed him at the top of his age division. It had been announced that he would be sent to Kentucky and let up, entered in the three-year-old classics of 1942 (he had been ineligible to many of the leading events for juveniles in 1941 and obliged to stand aside while they were being won by colts of inferior class) and carefully prepared for them. He had earned, and would receive a good long vacation and an opportunity to rest, recuperate, grow and strengthen in anticipation of the strenuous ordeal which they would constitute.

But hardly had he arrived in the Blue Grass and had an opportunity to stretch his legs ere he was once more sent upon his way. The program had been completely changed. He was allowed less than two weeks of let-up and was then shipped to Florida, taking quarters at Hialeah. He did not reach Kentucky from Maryland until November 16, and he was not sent out to a farm to enjoy a real rest, but kept at the Keeneland track. There he was a center of interest, being inspected by throngs of visitors every day and surrounded by a continuous stir. And on the 29th he departed, having at no time been outside the racing environment and atmosphere. It was announced that he was being entered in the $50,000 Widener Handicap and other events of the Florida winter season, would at once re-enter training and be got ready for them. One can imagine the colt, if his Biblical education had not been neglected, soliloquizing: "Is thy servant a dog that he should do this thing?" When he arrived in Kentucky, a reporter described him as "a tired-looking colt." He was to look still more so before spring.

The chronicle of Alsab's adventures in Florida during the next ten months is not luminous with the halo of victory. It was obvious that his thirteen-day stopover at Keeneland en route from Pimlico to Hialeah had not done much to neutralize the effects of a ten months' campaign and 22 sweatings for the brass through his two-year-old season. Nobody was more interested in his welfare than his breeder, Thomas Piatt, who had received only $700 for him when he was sold as a yearling at Saratoga but who felt as much concerned for his future as if there had been two more ciphers attached to that sum. Sizing him up with a fatherly eye, he shook his head and said to those who asked him about the colt:

"Alsab is in poor shape. He is thin in flesh, his coat looks dry and dull, he has no snap or life, he's dead on his feet and my opinion is that he is far from what he ought to be if he's going to get anywhere very soon."

Which was quite correct.

Alsab began his Peninsular campaign on February 7 in the Bahamas Handicap, at seven furlongs, started favorite in a field of ten at 6½ to 10 and ran sixth, behind a lot of horses that he should have laughed at even though he was handicapped at 128 pounds (McCreary); the winner being American Wolf (114), with First Fiddle (115) four lengths back; time, 1:24⅗. On February 14, he was out again in a $1,500 allowance race at one mile. This time he was carrying 126 pounds (Arcaro) and again a hot favorite at 7½ to 10. In a field of six he ran fourth, beaten some seven lengths by Bright Willie (118), Sir War (114) and Incoming (102). The time, 1:36⅗, lowered the track record from 1:37, flat.

The Flamingo Stakes (former Florida Derby) followed on February 28. Alsab's form had been so poor in his two previous essays that, while he was obliged to take up 126 pounds (Vedder), Bright Willie (120) was now selected at 2¾ to 1, but Alsab was heavily back at 3½ to 1. Sixteen started, and how Requested took them into camp by a margin of four lengths without being brought to a drive will be found related elsewhere. As for Alsab, he struggled in third, beaten eight lengths. Time, 1:50⅖, race and track record 1:48⅕, by Brevity.

Alsab had now suffered three humiliating defeats. All told, at the track and throughout the country, an immense amount of money had been bet on him and gone up in smoke. The query: "What's the matter with Alsab?" that had first been heard, gave way to bitter comments and criticisms. He was not only booed along the quarter-stretch, but the press teemed with caustic squibs of which he was the target. It was in vain that those who still stood by him tried to make themselves heard, to the effect that this was not the real Alsab and that he was being woefully mismanaged. The derisive cry: "Take him off!" that had greeted his last performance was a concrete expression of the estimate that prevailed.

The response to this was the semi-official announcement that as the colt was obviously not in form, he would not be started for the $50,000 race, set for March 7. This struck the realists as the first glimmer of logic that had attended his campaign thus far. But it was almost at once recanted. "Alsab," ran the revised announcement, "will be started in the Widener. If his owner's judgment were alone to be consulted, he would remain in the stable. But this colt belongs to the public, rather than to his owner. The public expects him to start and it must not be disappointed. He will go to the post."

Such statements are seldom convincing. They are recognized as, for the most part, mere formulas which may mean anything or nothing and

Alsab   [UPI]

are put up as a sort of defense mechanism, advantage of which may be taken as circumstances admit. As we shall see, later in the season when such an announcement was eagerly expected by the public, it was not forthcoming and the colt stayed in the stable, though an immense crowd had gathered to watch him perform.

The extent to which the public demanded the starting of Alsab in the Widener was reflected in the odds. He was at 78½ to 10, five other horses in the field of 17 being preferred to him by the patrons. This turned out pretty straight shooting, as Alsab (109) ran fifth behind The Rhymer (111), Best Seller (112), Olympus (107) and Our Boots (121). The time, 2:05⅕, marked the slowest Widener ever run, by a wide margin. Alsab, due to his age, had been next to the bottom weight. He had been well up most of the way and excellently placed to make his finish run but faltered in the stretch.

The criticisms now became scorching. It was vain for those who had come to his defense previously to attempt to make out a case for him. The scoffers held sway. He was denominated a false alarm; an exploded wonder; just another sky-rocket two-year-old that had failed to go on. His unfashionable breeding and "deficient" pedigree were moralized upon by the oracles that interpret the bloodlines of sensational horses—*after* the event—and those who had felt aggrieved the fall before because of his lack of Newmarket and Ascot quarterings rose to remark: "Didn't we tell you so?"

While on the other hand, those who were convinced, beyond the possibility of any such comedy of errors as the curtain had just fallen upon to contradict, that Alsab was one of the greatest colts within their experience, ground their teeth in rage and exasperation, conceded that it might all be over with him, but were not ready to abandon hope as long as any ground for it remained.

There was one solace. Alsab was still sound. And, while gaunt and scraggly, he was showing no disposition to go sour or dishonest. It seemed amazing, but it was so. Not only this; after leaving Florida he seemed to brighten up, to look, act and feel more like the old Alsab, incredible as that might appear.

Five weeks were now granted him in which to take a new lease of life, during which he was moved to Maryland and there, on April 13, at Havre de Grace, picked up activity in the first running of the Chesapeake Trial, an allowance race of $2,500 at six furlongs framed as a try-out for the $15,000 Chesapeake Stakes to be run five days later. In each, he was defeated by Colchis, just then at his peak, but in each Alsab showed that he was well on the up-grade and

that, if all continued to go well, his critics might soon be having some bad moments. In the Trial, under 126 pounds (Schmidl), he ran Mr. Clark's gelding to a half-length in 1:12⅖, coming from far back; Colchis (118) winning in a hard drive. Bright Willie (114), the favorite, ran unplaced. In the stake itself, ridden by Basil James at 122 pounds, he again laid far back most of the way, then was cut loose but failed to reach, Colchis (116) winning by a length; time, 1:46⅗, race and track record 1:43⅗ by Cavalcade. For this race, Alsab had been made the favorite, at a shade below even money, with Requested (119), who finished third, second choice at 2½ to 1. Eleven started.

There was now one of those revulsions of opinion that are perennial and surprise nobody but the inexperienced. While he had been cleanly beaten in both his races at Havre de Grace, the stock of Alsab, which long before had taken a nose dive for the Kentucky Derby, began to boom! And when, on April 28, the Derby Trial was run at Churchill Downs, with eight starting and he (James) dividing top weight (118 pounds) with Sun Again, the much-fancied colt from Calumet Farm, he slightly outsold the latter, being at 16 as against 17 to 10. His showing was a disappointment. Well placed for the finish drive, he responded sluggishly and was three and a half lengths back as Valdina Orphan (111 pounds) defeated Sun Again by a neck; the mile being run in 1:36⅘. James sent him on an additional furlong, which he completed in 1:54 and after it was over there was little hope left for him in the big race, unless his form vastly improved.

So open an affair did the Derby seem that while the Greentree Stable's pair were strong favorites at about even money, Alsab and Requested were each at five to one, With Regards being almost on a parity with them, at 54 to 10. James was again riding Alsab, and he was far back in the field of fifteen until the race was half over, then was taken the overland route and, circling all the rest, got up in the last stride to snatch second money from Valdina Orphan by a head, as Shut Out won going away.

The wise men were not satisfied with the result of the Derby. They had not figured Shut Out as the probable winner, but his stablemate Devil Diver. The latter had run a poor race to finish sixth while the former had come through and saved the day. But the time was relatively slow and heads were wagged and, it was proclaimed, the result meant little. . . . Who would win the Preakness, a week hence? Well, it was anybody's race. But Alsab was the dangerous horse. He had actually raced himself into condition after a regimen that should have hung his hide on the fence—instead of which he was looking better than at any time since the season opened. He was manifestly rounding into form, and if he improved but a trifle from Churchill Downs to Pimlico, why, it would be nothing but Alsab.

The event proved this logic, doubtful as it might appear, to be explicit. Alsab won the Preakness before one of the largest crowds (42,000) that have gathered to witness any of its fifty-two runnings; thereby acquiring $58,175, the net to the winner, plus an award of $1,500 to his nominator, plus a replica of the historic Woodlawn Vase. He also started favorite at 20½ to 10, with the Greentree pair at 24 to 10 and Sun Again third choice at 5½ to 1. He also did the trick in the most convincing fashion. With ten starters, he was running ninth after six furlongs had been covered and, at the end of the mile and with but 3/16 yet to go, was still only seventh. But when James asked him to race, seeming indifferent to what it meant, he came out around the entire half-dozen in front of him, running them down one by one, and galloped past to win by a length, out in the middle of the track, with Requested and Sun Again dead-heating for place, Colchis right behind them and Shut Out closely following, the front five having almost no daylight between them, so compactly were they wedged together.

The caliber of the performance was beyond cavil. Alsab had run the 1 3/16 miles in flat 1:57, to lower the record for the stake, 1:58 1/5, held by High Quest since 1934, and almost equal that for the track, set at 1:56 3/5 by Seabiscuit when he defeated War Admiral in their memorable match in 1938. The pace from the start had been strong, with the fractions in :23 2/5, :47, 1:11 2/5, 1:37 1/5.

And so, after losing eight straight races, Alsab had at last entered the winner's circle as a three-year-old. In the most dramatic style and with a decisiveness leaving no room for doubt or quibble. And the public rose at him. His victory was greeted with an immensity of acclaim beside which the reserved praise that had been apportioned Shut Out for his Derby triumph became only a faint echo, as of something that might well be forgotten.

Another chapter had been added to the rags-to-riches romance of the $700 colt whose career had passed the bounds of credulity so long ago that the commonplace no longer figured on his daybook. And now it was ho, for Belmont Park, the Withers and the Belmont!

Two weeks elapsed between the Preakness and the "American Guineas"; and Alsab, as might be expected, passed them in the full blare of publicity, which attended his every move, almost his every breath. Then, on May 23, the field of nine paraded to the post, with most of the contenders at Pimlico and Churchill Downs conspicuous by their absence, though the race would net the winner $15,500 and a sumptuous piece of plate, as well as a place upon a historic honor roll that had received its first blazon almost seventy years ago. Alsab 7½ to 10 was the quotation, Fairaris second choice at 31 to 10 and the only one granted even a faint chance to bother him. This imported English colt had been exhibiting meteoric speed and in his previous race had just cantered six furlongs in 1:10 2/5. Bred in lines which caused the lovers of exotics to flutter with ecstasy, they inclined to the opinion that stranger things might happen than for him to put the native son in his place.

Bright Willie dashed to the quarter in :23 1/5, the half in :45 1/5 and the three-quarters in 1:11, where Fairaris was an open length behind and Alsab a fast-coming fourth. As they rounded into the stretch James was rousing him and he began running very fast, so much that as Bright Willie faded he rushed past Fairaris as if the Briton had come in on a forged passport to win in big gallop by 2½ lengths from Lochinvar, who also finished fast to take the place by a nose, with the full mile in 1:36 1/5 as against the race record of 1:35 4/5, held jointly by Snob II (1922) and Johnstown (1939).

Though he had won but two out of his ten races since his campaign opened, this triumph placed Alsab at the head of the season's money-winners to that date, and he was now but $3,000 off the $200,000 mark. He hardly took a long breath as he posed in the enclosure and "Sarge" Swenke, smiling broadly as he led him out of it after Mr. Sabath had led him in, said proudly: "There's nothing that wears hair can beat this colt!" . . . And, truly, it looked that way.

But that "uncertainty of racing"—as old as time, as perennial—was due right now for another extravagant demonstration.

May 23 was Withers Day. June 6 was Belmont Day. Through the two weeks intervening, the enthusiasm over Alsab mounted to delirious heights. The odds tell the story: at post time for "America's only real Derby" the board said: Alsab 2 to 5; Shut Out 3½ to 1; Lochinvar 10¼ to 1; as for the other six in the background—the word being used advisedly—you might have any of them at from 25 to 55 to 1. At the finish, it was Shut Out by two lengths in 2:29 1/5, with Alsab making a long and unsuccessful stern chase, but losing ground steadily all through the home stretch to finish thoroughly beaten. He had tried hard and honestly, given his all, but was unable to get up. Amazement reigned in the grandstand and was reflected in the press next morning.

Five days later, on the 11th, the announcement came that Alsab was suffering from a blind splint, which had affected his running in the Belmont, though unsuspected at the time. A couple of days later he was fired for it, thrown out of training and declared from the approaching Dwyer Stakes, in which it had been expected that he and Shut Out would meet again. From his stable came the report that he was recovering from the firing nicely, and as soon as practicable would be shipped to Chicago and take quarters at Arlington Park, where he would resume galloping and be prepared for the Classic, to be run there on July 25.

"It can't be done," was the reaction of the hard-boiled—and, surely enough, it couldn't. On Classic day, Alsab was far indeed from fit to go to the post, being only just well started back on regular galloping. But he *was* galloping again—and going sound. And as his subsequent performances reveal his comeback to have been accomplished through one of the most expertly successful exhibitions of the training art of which we have knowledge, it will be of interest to chronicle here just how Swenke proceeded in the task, so ticklish and so tremendous, that confronted him. As said before, the Belmont was run on June 6 and just about one week later the firing iron was applied to Alsab's ailing foreleg. He arrived at Arlington Park on June 21, in advance of the opening of the meeting, but did not begin regular speed work until July 9. The way in which he was gradually returned to racing form is shown by the following calendar:

July 9—half in :53; July 11—five furlongs in 1:09⅗; July 13—five furlongs in 1:03; July 16—five furlongs in 1:05; July 19—half in :49; July 22—six furlongs in 1:14; July 25—six furlongs in 1:12 (with the note: "Alsab is rapidly rounding into good form"); July 28—mile in 1:40, "unattended and well in hand." He was then transferred to Washington Park, where the meeting began August 3, and on August 6 was sent five furlongs in 1:02⅘, well in hand; the announcement being made that his return to the post would take place on Saturday the 8th in the Hinsdale Handicap, at $2,500 overnight purse at six furlongs.

When he emerged upon the quarter-stretch, Alsab was greeted with cheers—and when he finished fourth, after having been made a hot favorite at 19 to 10, he was greeted with hisses. But only those misled by flamboyant publicity had expected him to do more than that. He was thin in flesh, looked secondhand, and the leg which had been fired showed a sizable bare spot which was perceptible from any seat in the grandstand. He was carrying 120 pounds and giving much weight to a fast aged field; it was his first race in two months after a sojourn in the repair shop; and, more than that, he is not a sprinter. The swift Jamestown three-year-old Defense (108 pounds) won cleverly in 1:11, after a first half in :45⅘, Sales Talk (106) and Woof Woof (117) second and third, close up. Alsab, fourth, was beaten about three lengths. He was sluggish going away and James hit him repeatedly with the whip, but at the half he was still last. From that point, he made up a lot of ground.

It seemed sad when the boos and hisses went up from thoughtless punters who had lost money they should never have bet on him. But he pulled up sound and cooled out well and those who were watching him passed around the word: "Wait until next time!"

Next time proved to be August 15, when he was saddled for another overnight handicap, the South Chicago, worth $3,500, at seven furlongs. The field was a very fast one, he and With Regards were each given 120 pounds and the latter made the choice at four to five, Alsab second at 17 to 5. He was ridden by J. Richards, and the race he ran was brilliant. A distant last for half a mile, he began to pick up his horses rounding the upper turn. He experienced some interference when making his run but got to Sales Talk, the leader, in the fast furlong and, despite the latter bearing over on him under pressure, literally pushed him out of the way to win by half a length in 1:24⅕, the quarters having been run in :22⅗, :45⅘, 1:11⅕. As he was giving Sales Talk a year and 19 pounds, and that colt was one of the fastest sprinters racing on the Chicago tracks, there was but one conclusion: Alsab is himself again!

Another race completed his preparation for the American Derby, to be run on August 29; this being the Dick Welles Handicap, $5,000 added, at a mile, on the 20th. For this he was given the heavy impost of 128 pounds (Woolf), With Regards (122), King's Abbey (112), Aletern (108), Some Man and Bayridge (each 100) opposing him. This time he got away well, showed much more speed through the early stages, never being far back, took command on the turn and, gradually wearing down King's Abbey, beat him half a length, very easily, in the fast time of 1:36⅕, with quarters in :23⅕, :46⅘, 1:11⅗. He had started favorite at six to ten, and this time received an ovation.

Alsab now seemed a certainty for the American Derby. Shut Out was not coming west for it; Valdina Orphan and Rounders looked outclassed; so did With Regards. There was nothing else in sight that was granted even a remote chance. In short, it appeared a foregone conclusion. And such, in fact, it proved.

Before a crowd of 35,000, which had broken the track record by betting over $1,000,000 for the first time in Washington Park's history, Alsab dominated the Derby field of seven with masterful ease. At the end of the first mile he was fifth, was not asked to race until rounding the far turn, then rushed through his horses and took the lead before entering the home stretch to win going away by 3½ lengths as if merely coasting. He carried 126 pounds and gave five pounds each to the next three colts, With Regards, Anticlimax and Rounders (121 each), Valdina Orphan (126), King's Abbey (118) and Aletern (121) being far astern. A heavy storm had left the track very slow and the time was 2:06⅗ with the race record 2:04. When Woolf brought him back to scale Alsab was received with tremendous cheering, a shawl of red roses was draped over his shoulders, Mr. and Mrs. Sabath stood at his head, Trainer Swenke at his side. High dignitaries spoke through the microphone in praise of his achievement and presented the gold trophy provided for him. The net value of the stake, $60,850, lifted him into the $250,000 class with winnings of $269,465. He had been out of the hospital just a month before, and what the future might hold for him was best expressed by a question mark. Perhaps never before had such a question been answered in such a way.

There are limits to the capacities of the greatest racers, though often, from the manner in which they are used, it might seem that no suspicion of the fact is entertained at home. Alsab had already raced four times at Washington Park, within the space of three weeks—this on top of a bad leg, the firing iron and two months away from the post. But this was not sufficient. Another week, and he was seen at the post, on the closing day, in the field of nine that came out for the $25,000-added Washington Park Handicap, for all ages at 1¼ miles. Assigned 121 pounds (A. Robertson), and asked to give concessions ranging from seven to 21 pounds each, exclusive of what the scale required, to the others, he was made favorite at nine to ten. The task proved too great as, after a gallant but unavailing charge from sixth place at the end of the first mile, he fell short by a length of the six-year-old Marriage, to whom he was giving seven pounds of actual weight and 15 pounds under the scale. It was a very fast race, with the mile and a quarter in 2:02⅖ (track record 2:02), first mile in 1:36 (track record 1:35⅗).

The consensus was that Alsab had run a grand race—but that he was having too much of it, so soon after having held membership in the Down and Out Club. Those who expressed this opinion, howbeit, were in for a real shock when, the handicap having been run on Monday the 7th, they read the announcement in Wednesday morning's papers that the colt was being shipped that day to Providence where, on Saturday, he would oppose Whirlaway for the $25,000 Narragansett Special! . . . As the most trenchant comments came under the head of "unfit for publication," none will be reproduced. From only one source came expressions of pleasure. That was the Narragansett Park management. There had suddenly been dropped into its lap, as from a clear sky, the most blood-stirring event of the season—the first meeting between the two horses at that moment the most sensational before the public! Which meant one of the biggest days in the history of Narragansett Park and everything thereunto appertaining.

Whirlaway had last started on August 29 at Garden State Park, where his race had been but a canter. It had been his only start in over a month. He had been quartered at Narragansett for some time preparing for the Special and was expected to strip for it at razor edge. What show could Alsab have against him, when he would not arrive at the track until Thursday evening, after a severe race on Monday and a hurried shipment across almost half the breadth of the continent? . . . It seemed fantastic. . . . And it was.

Alsab was popularly credited with having two owners and a whole cluster of trainers and managers and the amazing things done with him were difficult at times to elucidate by outsiders. Though in the end, it was Sarge Swenke who, along with the colt, had to bear the heat and burden of the day. Mr. Sabath, however, came forward to declare that in the present instance he was the responsible party. The decision to send Alsab to Providence on a hurry-up crusade against Whirlaway was his, and he would stand for the consequences. . . . Then, as the race drew closer and closer, the fantastic character of the adventure began to loom before him. It kept looming larger and larger. Until finally, with 30,000 people jamming the park and excitement over the "dream race" they were about to witness at the boiling point, it became a dream. Forgetful of his Floridian platform, or perhaps no longer caring whether Alsab belonged to the public or not, he scratched him from the Special.

The colt, he explained, had a bad "ship" from Chicago; there had been no chance to ready him properly for the extreme effort that he must make; and, in justice to him, as also those who would be wagering upon him, he should be withdrawn. This decision, though creating an uproar and the most unkind criticism when it was announced to the multitude, was, from the sporting standpoint, absolutely correct. Mr. Sabath had made a faux-pas at Hialeah; he in effect canceled it out by refusing to make another one of the same sort, now. Let him be awarded such credit as he deserves.

As it turned out, his decision made money for the association instead of costing it a lot. For when the management, after Whirlaway had won the Special in fine style, announced that it would give $25,000 for a match between the two colts the Saturday following, and that both had accepted the offer, it was getting the benefit of two great attractions instead of the one that otherwise would have been all.

The conditions of the match were, a dash of a mile and three-sixteenths (the same distance as the Special); weight for age; winner to take the entire purse of $25,000. Race day proved a perfect one, the track was never better and a crowd of 35,000 people assembled to witness what was officially designated as the Narragansett Championship. It was announced that the entire profits of the event would be donated to War Relief.

Weight for age meant 126 pounds for Whirlaway, to be ridden by Woolf, and 119 for Alsab, ridden by Carroll Bierman. Woolf, who had been riding Alsab, asserted that he would be no match for Whirlaway when asked for his opinion by the reporters. Bierman, who had not ridden Alsab since the fall before, when he had run his record-breaking two-year-old mile in 1:35⅖ in the Champagne Stakes, expressed great confidence in his mount. Alsab's final work for it had been a mile and a quarter in 2:07⅕ on Wednesday. Whirlaway had not been asked for anything more than seven furlongs in 1:29⅖ on Friday, the day before the race.

The preliminary interest in the match, and the analysts' diagnoses, had almost entirely hinged upon the fact that both colts raced in the same manner, staying back in the early running and then coming from behind to do their work in the stretch. It would now be necessary for one of them to go out and set the pace, leaving the other to use his habitual tactics. That this would favor the latter—be a great advantage—was the expert opinion so there was added intensity of excitement as the two rivals entered the stalls, the question upon every lip being: Which one will take the track?

They got off almost immediately and in another instant the answer came: It was Alsab! Bierman was using the same strategy that had served him well a year ago. The three-year-old jumped past the four-year-old, took the lead and set out to make every post a winning one.

In doing so, however, he was wasting nothing. Alsab was not cut loose. Instead, Bierman took him under restraint and settled down to ride a wait-in-front race, taking him just well clear of Whirlaway and keeping him there, though the pace was extremely slow for such horses. The first quarter was run in but :25⅖, the half in :50⅖, at which point Alsab had an open half-length on his pursuer. The pace then began to pick up and the third quarter was run in :23⅘, making the 6 furlongs in 1:14⅕.

Alsab had slightly increased his lead in running the third quarter and now had an open length's advantage, Woolf meanwhile keeping Whirlaway in behind him and using him as a windbreak. The distance to be raced had called for the take-off at the head of the home stretch, hence the fourth quarter, which brought them back to that point, was run around the upper turn. Woolf had begun to ride his mount and he had closed a half-length of the space as they whirled into the stretch with the mile in 1:38⅗, making the fourth quarter in :24⅖.

Strung up to the tensest pitch of excitement, the vast crowd rose in their seats to watch the decisive struggle. Alsab has but a length's advantage as they enter the last furlong, Woolf has swung out with Whirlaway and is beginning one of those powerful rides that have won so many big races for him in the past. Bierman, crouched low upon Alsab's withers and leaning far out along his neck, is lifting him along vigorously. He too has unusual finishing power and every ounce of it is now coming into play. The pace grows furious—it will be such a finish as seldom has been seen. Slowly Whirlaway creeps up and up in his furious, almost frantic forward surge. They are nearing home and he has reached even terms. But he cannot go on past. He has met an adversary that will match everything he can unleash and that is as purely game as ever they make them. Pandemonium reigns. Whirlaway had been a tremendous favorite at 3 to 10, while against Alsab 16 to 10 had ruled. The backers of the long-tailed hero fairly raise the roof in their adjurations to him to "Come on!" At one point it seems for an instant that his nose is in front, but if so he cannot keep it there. Alsab, unflinching, unyielding, unconquerable, will not have it so. They race under the wire so closely coupled that while the names of both colts are shouted, the cry of "Dead heat!" rises loudly. It is a photo finish, *in excelsis,* and the tension is almost unbearable while the negative is developed. Now it is seen dropping down from the eye-in-the-sky to the judges. They confer briefly. Then a number is flashed. . . . It is Alsab's! He wins by the tip of his nostril, as the enlargement of the photo, soon placed on view, clearly shows. The time is 1:56⅗.

The $700 colt by the obscure young sire whose services went begging has defeated the ultra-aristocratic scion of the English Derby winner

Alsab in an early morning workout [UPI]

that cost $225,000 to import and whose stud fee alone is $2,500. He has done so not in the hard but in the hardest way. He has gone out in front of the horse that has astounded the world by winning nearly $500,000, has set his own pace, led from post to finish, and, when challenged, has run the last three-sixteenths of the mile in 17⅘ seconds, which means a rate of faster than 24 seconds per quarter. When Whirlaway ran his dazzling Kentucky Derby in record-breaking time (2:01⅖) he came the last quarter in flat :24. But that rate of speed would not conquer Alsab—and in this we get one of the clear indications of his class.

The result is not popular, though Alsab receives rounds of applause as he poses after the announcement. It had not only been a Whirlaway crowd—almost the entire country had been for the son of Blenheim. The most noted selectors had gone down on him to a man. But it was impossible to offer alibis, which rather aggravated the matter. The loser had run one of his grandest, gamest, fastest finishes, coming from behind the pace in his chosen style. He had received a ride that 99 times in 100 would have put him over. There was nothing to do but to accept the result. But for enthusiasm—except in the camp of the winner—it was lacking.

From Narragansett, Alsab was vanned to Belmont Park for the great fall meeting, where he had three of his most important season's engagements—the Realization, 1⅝ miles, to be run on September 29; The Jockey Club Gold Cup, two miles, to be run on October 3; and the New York Handicap, 2¼ miles, to be run on October 10.

The average length of these three races is practically two miles, the trio totaling 5⅞ miles. They were all to be run within less than two weeks—twelve days, to be exact. We doubt if turf history can show anything similar to the record that Alsab established in them. Two he won, and in the other he ran a close, contending second. Only one was for his own division, the Realization, the other two being for all-aged horses. Certainly no other American three-year-old has ever withstood so severe a test in such an extraordinary manner. We doubt if foreign racing records, for their part, will reveal one. Particularly when it is borne in mind that these were the 18th, 19th and 20th races, respectively, that Alsab had been asked for since the season opened.

For the Realization, he was opposed by the great filly Vagrancy, the queen of the season, Trierarch, Buckskin and Lochinvar; and he conceded them, in rotation, 11, 16, 15 and 12 pounds. Waiting to make his run near home, he then came from third place to win going away, as he willed, from the filly, by 3½ lengths. The time, 2:42; record for the race, and American record for the distance, 2:40⅘, by Man o' War in 1920. It is not improbable that Alsab could have equaled or beaten this had there been anything to carry him. The net of the race to him was $7,900. Woolf rode.

This race was run on Tuesday. The following Saturday he was saddled for the Gold Cup. The event showed that it was asking too much of him so soon after the previous long, fast race. He looked jaded in the paddock and was even quieter and less demonstrative than ever. The excitement was running high, for Whirlaway was facing him again, together with The Rhymer, winner of the $50,000 Widener back in March at Hialeah, Alsab running unplaced to him. Bierman was again riding Alsab, at 117 pounds, the three older horses each carrying 124, they including also Bolingbroke, fresh from a defeat of Whirlaway in the Manhattan Handicap in new American record time for a mile and a half.

It had evidently been figured by his stable that Alsab should duplicate his Narragansett performance, as he went right out on the pace while Whirlaway stayed back. After allowing The Rhymer, on sufferance, to show the way the first mile, Alsab sped to the front and at the turn for home was leading Whirlaway by 1½ lengths. The latter then cut loose and outran him through the stretch, but it required all he had to win by three parts of a length; the time, 3:21⅗. This being, with the exception of Market Wise's record of 3:20⅘, established the previous year in the same event, the fastest two miles run thus far in this country.

So confident had Whirlaway's partisans been of his invincibility that they had sent him to the post at 5½ to 10, with Alsab at 28 to 10.

In 1941, Whirlaway, like Alsab in the present instance, had won the Realization, then lost the Gold Cup, but had drawn out of the New York Handicap, declining the issue. Now "Linden saw another sight," for while Whirlaway had been assigned 130 pounds for the heart-searching test of two miles and a quarter, it had been accepted and his backers sent him to the post at even money, though he was having to take his luck in a field of 12 horses, giving them from nine to as high as 34 pounds each. From that standpoint the only comparable assignment was the 121 pounds of Alsab. While receiving nine pounds' actual weight from Whirlaway, under the scale he was getting but two pounds, as that called for the pair to carry 117 and 124 pounds respectively. The only horse allowed even a vague chance of beating them was Bolingbroke (116 pounds), he being at six to one.

So many of the leading riders had been grounded for offenses that it was difficult to make replacements. Jack Westrope was finally secured for Whirlaway, while Bierman was again upon Alsab. Lochinvar led off, going to the first quarter in :25, and then, amid wide-eyed astonishment, the favorite was seen sailing to the front; which, once he had taken it, he proceeded to make his own. Rating along he was at the half in :49, the mile in 1:37⅗ (over a second faster than the time at that point a year before, when Fénelon in winning had broken the record for the entire distance), sped on to the mile and a quarter in 2:03⅖, mile and a half in 2:29⅖ and completed the two miles in 3:21.

But now it was apparent that "the avenger was upon his trail." While Whirlaway had been giving this grand exhibition, Alsab, exactly reversing the parts the two played in the Gold Cup, had been laying back, biding his time and, furlong by furlong, gradually picking him up. The Belmont Park track is a mile and a half in circuit, hence the race had been started from a point near the head of the back stretch. Upon getting back to this point, Whirlaway held a lead of a length over Bolingbroke, with Alsab at the latter's headstall. Soon he gave him the go-by and challenged the leader. The two raced around the big upper turn in a furious duel, with Alsab, outside, forcing the pace and Whirlaway beginning to show the effects of it. Into the home stretch they turned lapped, and as soon as straight Bierman called upon Alsab for another rally. He responded gamely and, as Whirlaway began to yield ground, forged to the front. That the favorite was beaten was evident—but now a new element was injected into the struggle and in a moment more the 27,000 spectators were swept by a fresh whirlwind of excitement. The gaunt, ghostlike form of the French-bred gray four-year-old Obash, carrying but 106 pounds and ridden by Don Meade, was seen coming on the outside with such speed that he drew closer to Alsab at every stride. Only fifth into the stretch, and earlier much farther back, he was now leaping forward like a hound that runs down a tired deer.

Was it possible? After subduing Whirlaway was the almost-triumphant three-year-old about to have the victory snatched from him by a 70-to-1 shot? A dead lull succeeded the maelstrom that had reigned in the grandstand as in fascinated suspense the watchers saw the drama surge into this astounding phase. Could Alsab, after having raced Whirlaway to defeat, in his turn be defeated? Bierman calls upon him for still another supreme effort and with the courage of a lion wounded but still fighting he races on and on. It looks every instant as if Obash must pass him—but no, he cannot, and they pass the post with Alsab winner by a nose; Whirlaway, tired

but still trying, a close third, his nose almost at Alsab's heels. The time, 3:47⅕—just a fifth-second off the American record of Fénelon made a year ago when he had defeated Market Wise in this handicap; he being then four and carrying 119 pounds, or two pounds less than the heroic three-year-old.

As he is led into the winner's circle, Alsab shows the strain that he has endured but lifts his head high as he stands within it. We may without exaggeration denominate his achievement the grandest that any American three-year-old has ever placed to his credit. It would be so, viewed in isolation. Considering all that he had previously done, it stamps this plain bay colt, whose form at no point indicates the prodigious powers that are concealed within, as one of the titans of turf history.

For dramatic effect, it would be fitting if the curtain could at this grand climax be dropped upon the play. Its hero would have seemed well to deserve such a recompense for all his labors. But three more races are still to be put behind him before his year's work is done.

On October 21, after a ten-day respite, Alsab was seen at Jamaica among the six that contended for the $15,000-added Gallant Fox Handicap, 1⅝ miles. The occasion was one of the most eagerly anticipated of the late fall, as in it he and Shut Out were to meet for the first time since the Belmont Stakes, back in early June. The Equipoise colt had of late been on the ailing list, his trouble being much the same as that from which Alsab had suffered: a blind splint. It had been necessary to strike him from his engagements at Belmont's recent fall meeting, but now it was believed that he would be in shape to meet his rival for the title of champion three-year-old of the season. Each colt was handicapped at 125 pounds; the six-year-old Marriage was carrying 121; Bolingbroke 113; the four-year-old filly Dark Discovery 100, and the five-year-old Paul Pry 98 pounds. Alsab was quoted at even money, Shut Out at 18½ to 10. The race proved a tremendous upset. Shut Out made no show, finished fourth, beaten some eight lengths, and pulled up lame. Alsab, instead of running away with the money, proved unable to concede 24 pounds and a year to Dark Discovery and that filly, at 18 to 1, defeated him by a length after leading most of the way; the time 2:44⅕, track record 2:43.

Ten days later, he was at Empire City trying for the $25,000-added Westchester Handicap, 1³⁄₁₆ miles. Again carrying 124 pounds (Bierman) and making great concessions to the opposing seven, he was deemed a sure winner and was at 11½ to 10, but could not quite get up and was left in third place by Riverland (114) and Tola Rose (108), though the finish was thrilling, with a neck and a nose only separating the three. In this race, he appeared to be climbing when he went away and did not flatten out for a long while, being last at the end of the first mile, and fifth into the stretch, but coming from there with a rush. In order to start him in this race, he was scratched out of the Pimlico Special, run three days before, in which the public had been breathlessly awaiting what promised to be another match between him and Whirlaway, though he had been promised as a certain starter almost to the day of the race. Apparently Alsab had ceased "belonging to the public," altogether.

His grand finale for the season took place at Belmont Park, on November 11, in the $10,000-added Victory Handicap, 1¼ miles, the feature event of the special Victory Meeting held there that week. Here again, the desire of the public to have Alsab and Whirlaway meet once more before going into winter quarters was balked; as, while Alsab was on the ground and ready, Messrs. Wright and Jones refused to bring Whirlaway to the meeting, though it was being held for the purpose of raising funds for War Relief, all profits being devoted thereto. Instead, the champion money-winner was that same day raced in an unimportant event at Pimlico against a small field of mediocre class where a certain victory awaited him. Thus, each of the two rivals had in his turn defaulted, but Alsab stood the winner in two out of their three encounters.

In the Victory Handicap he made his farewell with one of his grandest performances—one which thrilled the nearly 30,000 persons present as had few others of their lifetimes. Seven were starting, he was carrying 126 pounds (Woolf) and conceding from 12 to 24 pounds each, actual weight, to his six older opponents, but was at 7½ to 10 in the betting, with Bright Gallant (111) second at 5 to 1, Tola Rose (111) third at 8 to 1, with Marriage (111) at 9¾ to 1, The Rhymer (114) at 14¼ to 1, Boysy (113) at 14½ to 1, and Bon Jour (102) at 27½ to 1, making up the party.

Alsab, as in his previous start, seemed in difficulty getting away, fell back to last, and at the first furlong pole stumbled so badly that he uncrossed Woolf's reins and came near unseating him. Marriage had taken the lead and bowled along to the quarter in :24⅕, half in :47⅘ and three-quarters in 1:12⅕, at which point he had a clear lead over Tola Rose, with Alsab still trailing the field, and, apparently, in some difficulty. Woolf now went to work on him but he was slow to respond and at the end of the mile in 1:37⅖ was fifth but now began to move into contention, coming around wide. As they entered the stretch, Tola Rose assumed command but Boysy was almost head and head with him and Alsab, hard ridden, had locked them and was ready to challenge. A bruising race home resulted, Tola Rose being the first to falter, which left Alsab and Boysy to fight it out, with the lightweight Bon Jour coming forward to join them. Nothing, however, could prevail against the iron will and terrific speed of Alsab, who had the race safe at the last sixteenth pole and came on to win by three parts of a length from Boysy, with Bon Jour lapped on him to his saddle-girths.

The time marked a truly superb effort by Alsab, being 2:02⅕, while he himself was timed in 2:01⅘, with the first mile in 1:38⅕ showing that he had run the last quarter in :23⅗, a rate of speed seldom or never seen in a race of a mile and a quarter. Considering the lateness of the season, the fact that it was Alsab's 23d start, and that he was finishing the most severe campaign of modern times by a three-year-old Thoroughbred, we must regard his performance as one of absolute grandeur.

It is therefore unpleasant to record that he pulled up quite lame, having wrenched a front ankle when he made his stumble shortly after getting away. On this account, he was unable to accept the offer by New Orleans of a $20,000 purse for a race between him and Whirlaway in December, but instead was sent to Kentucky and turned out, to receive the first real let-up that had been accorded him in two long years, during which he had compiled the following record:

Year	*Age*	*Races*	*First*	*Second*	*Third*	*Unpl.*	*Earned*
1941..	2	22	15	3	1	3	$110,600
1942..	3	23	9	7	3	4	234,565
Totals		45	24	10	4	7	$345,165

Alsab stands fourth among the leading money-winners of the world, and is the only one of the quartet that has raced but two seasons. For 1942, he stands second to Shut Out ($238,972) by the narrow margin of but $4,407. His winnings for his two- and three-year-old seasons lack but $4,495 of equaling those of Whirlaway ($349,-661) at the same age—despite his enforced lay-up of two months in midsummer of 1942.

Just previous to their match at Narragansett Park the measurements of both Alsab and Whirlaway were taken. Both were found to be of the same height, 15 hands, 3 inches, and the same weight, 1,000 pounds. Their length, over all, was almost identical, being 6 feet 10 inches for Whirlaway and 6 feet 11 inches for Alsab (measured from poll to base of tail). Whirlaway, the older horse, girthed 74 inches and Alsab 72; he was also an inch broader of chest, 17 as against 16 inches. Each had a forearm 19½ inches in cir-

Alsab after his victory at Belmont Park, November 1942. Jockey G. Woolf up. Owner Al Sabath congratulates the winner, while trainer A. Swenke looks on. [UPI]

cumference at the swell, a 39½-inch stifle and a 17-inch gaskin. Based upon this one might imagine that they were run in the same mold and closely resembled each other. That is, if "figures cannot lie." The fact is, however, that they resemble each other not at all in appearance, being of strikingly different form and style as well as manner of running. But beneath their superficial exteriors, they possess in common the attributes which have made them forever famous.

I Want to Know Why

SHERWOOD ANDERSON

Good stories, like tips on a horse—good tips—come from the strangest sources. This one by Sherwood Anderson was recommended to me by my son David, who came across it in a course on short-story writing at Loyola College. It is in a textbook, Understanding Fiction, *compiled by Robert Penn Warren and Cleanth Brooks, Jr., of Yale University. It is cited for scholarly purposes for the excellence of theme treatment by Mr. Anderson.*

Sociologically, the use of the word "nigger" is today completely and quite properly unacceptable. However, I have no qualms about including "I Want to Know Why" despite this fact, because if ever the word was used with affection, understanding and admiration, it is in this fine race track story.

WE GOT UP at four in the morning, that first day in the East. On the evening before we had climbed off a freight train at the edge of town, and with the true instinct of Kentucky boys had found our way across town and to the race track and the stables at once. Then we knew we were all right. Hanley Turner right away found a nigger we knew. It was Bildad Johnson who in the winter works at Ed Becker's livery barn in our home town, Beckersville. Bildad is a good cook as almost all our niggers are and of course he, like everyone in our part of Kentucky who is anyone at all, likes the horses. In the spring Bildad begins to scratch around. A nigger from our country can flatter and wheedle anyone into letting him do most anything he wants. Bildad wheedles the stable men and the trainers from the horse farms in our country around Lexington. The trainers come into town in the evening to stand around and talk and maybe get into a poker game. Bildad gets in with them. He is always doing little favors and telling about things to eat, chicken browned in a pan, and how is the best way to cook sweet potatoes and corn bread. It makes your mouth water to hear him.

When the racing season comes on and the horses go to the races and there is all the talk on the streets in the evenings about the new colts, and everyone says when they are going over to Lexington or to the spring meeting at Churchill Downs or to Latonia, and the horsemen that have been down to New Orleans or maybe at the winter meeting at Havana in Cuba come home to spend a week before they start out again, at such a time when everything talked about in Beckersville is just horses and nothing else and the outfits start out and horse racing is in every breath of air you breathe, Bildad shows up with a job as cook for some outfit. Often when I think about it, his always going all season to the races and working in the livery barn in the winter where horses are and where men like to come and talk about horses, I wish I was a nigger. It's a foolish thing to say, but that's the way I am about being around horses, just crazy. I can't help it.

Well, I must tell you about what we did and let you in on what I'm talking about. Four of us boys from Beckersville, all whites and sons of men who live in Beckersville regular, made up our minds we were going to the races, not just to Lexington or Louisville, I don't mean, but to the big eastern track we were always hearing our

Beckersville men talk about, to Saratoga. We were all pretty young then. I was just turned fifteen and I was the oldest of the four. It was my scheme. I admit that and I talked the others into trying it. There was Hanley Turner and Henry Rieback and Tom Tumberton and myself. I had thirty-seven dollars I had earned during the winter working nights and Saturdays in Enoch Myer's grocery. Henry Rieback had eleven dollars and the others, Hanley and Tom, had only a dollar or two each. We fixed it all up and laid low until the Kentucky spring meetings were over and some of our men, the sportiest ones, the ones we envied the most, had cut out—then we cut out too.

I won't tell you the trouble we had beating our way on freights and all. We went through Cleveland and Buffalo and other cities and saw Niagara Falls. We bought things there, souvenirs and spoons and cards and shells with pictures of the Falls on them for our sisters and mothers, but thought we had better not send any of the things home. We didn't want to put the folks on our trail and maybe be nabbed.

We got into Saratoga as I said at night and went to the track. Bildad fed us up. He showed us a place to sleep in hay over a shed and promised to keep still. Niggers are all right about things like that. They won't squeal on you. Often a white man you might meet, when you had run away from home like that, might appear to be all right and give you a quarter or a half dollar or something, and then go right and give you away. White men will do that, but not a nigger. You can trust them. They are squarer with kids. I don't know why.

At the Saratoga meeting that year there were a lot of men from home. Dave Williams and Arthur Mulford and Jerry Myers and others. Then there was a lot from Louisville and Lexington Henry Rieback knew but I didn't. They were professional gamblers and Henry Rieback's father is one too. He is what is called a sheet writer and goes away most of the year to tracks. In the winter when he is home in Beckersville he don't stay there much but goes away to cities and deals faro. He is a nice man and generous, is always sending Henry presents, a bicycle and a gold watch and a boy scout suit of clothes and things like that.

My own father is a lawyer. He's all right, but don't make much money and can't buy me things and anyway I'm getting so old now I don't expect it. He never said nothing to me against Henry, but Hanley Turner and Tom Tumberton's fathers did. They said to their boys that money so come by is no good and they didn't want their boys brought up to hear gamblers' talk and be thinking about such things and maybe embrace them.

That's all right and I guess the men know what they are talking about, but I don't see what it's got to do with Henry or horses either. That's what I'm writing this story about. I'm puzzled. I'm getting to be a man and want to think straight and be O.K., and there's something I saw at the race meeting at the eastern track I can't figure out.

I can't help it, I'm crazy about Thoroughbred horses. I've always been that way. When I was ten years old and saw I was growing to be big and couldn't be a rider I was so sorry I nearly died. Harry Hellinfinger in Beckersville, whose father is postmaster, is grown up and too lazy to work, but likes to stand around in the street and get up jokes on boys like sending them to a hardware store for a gimlet to bore square holes and other jokes like that. He played one on me. He told me that if I would eat a half a cigar I would be stunted and not grow any more and maybe could be a rider. I did it. When father wasn't looking I took a cigar out of his pocket and gagged it down some way. It made me awful sick and the doctor had to be sent for, and then it did no good. I kept right on growing. It was a joke. When I told what I had done and why most fathers would have whipped me but mine didn't.

Well, I didn't get stunted and didn't die. It serves Harry Hellinfinger right. Then I made up my mind I would like to be a stable boy, but had to give that up too. Mostly niggers do that work and I knew father wouldn't let me go into it. No use to ask him.

If you've never been crazy about Thoroughbreds it's because you've never been around where they are much and don't know any better. They're beautiful. There isn't anything so lovely and clean and full of spunk and honest and everything as some race horses. On the big horse farms that are all around our town Beckersville there are tracks and the horses run in the early morning. More than a thousand times I've got out of bed before daylight and walked two or three miles to the tracks. Mother wouldn't of let me go but father always says, "Let him alone." So I got some bread out of the bread box and some butter and jam, gobbled it and lit out.

At the tracks you sit on the fence with men, whites and niggers, and they chew tobacco and talk, and then the colts are brought out. It's early and the grass is covered with shiny dew and in another field a man is plowing and they are frying things in a shed where the track niggers sleep, and you know how a nigger can giggle and laugh and say things that make you laugh. A white man can't do it and some niggers can't but a track nigger can every time.

And so the colts are brought out and some are just galloped by stable boys, but almost every morning on a big track owned by a rich man who lives maybe in New York, there are always, nearly every morning, a few colts and some of the old race horses and geldings and mares that are cut loose.

It brings a lump up into my throat when a horse runs. I don't mean all horses but some. I can pick them nearly every time. It's in my blood like in the blood of race-track niggers and trainers. Even when they just go slop-jogging along with a little nigger on their backs I can tell a winner. If my throat hurts and it's hard for me to swallow, that's him. He'll run like Sam Hill when you let him out. If he don't win every time it'll be a wonder and because they've got him in a pocket behind another or he was pulled or got off bad at the post or something. If I wanted to be a gambler like Henry Rieback's father I could get rich. I know I could and Henry says so too. All I would have to do is to wait till that hurt comes when I see a horse and then bet every cent. That's what I would do if I wanted to be a gambler, but I don't.

When you're at the tracks in the morning—not the race tracks but the training tracks around Beckersville—you don't see a horse, the kind I've been talking about, very often, but it's nice anyway. Any Thoroughbred, that is sired right and out of a good mare and trained by a man that knows how, can run. If he couldn't what would he be there for and not pulling a plow?

Well, out of the stables they come and the boys are on their backs and it's lovely to be there. You hunch down on top of the fence and itch inside you. Over in the sheds the niggers giggle and sing. Bacon is being fried and coffee made. Everything smells lovely. Nothing smells better than coffee and manure and horses and niggers and bacon frying and pipes being smoked out of doors on a morning like that. It just gets you, that's what it does.

But about Saratoga. We was there six days and not a soul from home seen us and everything came off just as we wanted it to, fine weather and horses and races and all. We beat our way home and Bildad gave us a basket with fried chicken and bread and other eatables in, and I had eighteen dollars when we got back to Beckersville. Mother jawed and cried but Pop didn't say much. I told everything we done except one thing. I did and saw that alone. That's what I'm writing about. It got me upset. I think about it at night. Here it is.

At Saratoga we laid up nights in the hay in the shed Bildad had showed us and ate with the niggers early and at night when the race people had all gone away. The men from home stayed mostly in the grandstand and betting field, and didn't come out around the places where the horses are kept except to the paddocks just before a race when the horses are saddled. At Saratoga they don't have paddocks under an open shed as at Lexington and Churchill Downs and other tracks down in our country, but saddle the horses right out in an open place under trees on a lawn as smooth and nice as Banker Bohon's front yard here in Beckersville. It's lovely. The horses are sweaty and nervous and shine and the men come out and smoke cigars and look at them and the trainers are there and the owners, and your heart thumps so you can hardly breathe.

Then the bugle blows for post and the boys that ride come running out with their silk clothes on and you run to get a place by the fence with the niggers.

I always am wanting to be a trainer or owner, and at the risk of being seen and caught and sent home I went to the paddocks before every race. The other boys didn't but I did.

We got to Saratoga on a Friday and on Wednesday the next week the big Mullford Handicap was to be run. Middlestride was in it and Sunstreak. The weather was fine and the track fast. I couldn't sleep the night before.

What had happened was that both these horses are the kind it makes my throat hurt to see. Middlestride is long and looks awkward and is a gelding. He belongs to Joe Thompson, a little owner from home who only has a half-dozen horses. The Mullford Handicap is for a mile and Middlestride can't untrack fast. He goes away slow and is always way back at the half, then he begins to run and if the race is a mile and a quarter he'll just eat up everything and get there.

Sunstreak is different. He is a stallion and nervous and belongs on the biggest farm we've got in our country, the Van Riddle place that belongs to Mr. Van Riddle of New York. Sunstreak is like a girl you think about sometimes but never see. He is hard all over and lovely too. When you look at his head you want to kiss him. He is trained by Jerry Tillford who knows me and has been good to me lots of times, lets me walk into a horse's stall to look at him close and other things. There isn't anything as sweet as that horse. He stands at the post quiet and not letting on, but he is just burning up inside. Then when the barrier goes up he is off like his name, Sunstreak. It makes you ache to see him. It hurts you. He just lays down and runs like a bird dog. There can't anything I ever see run like him except Middlestride when he gets untracked and stretches himself.

Gee! I ached to see that race and those two horses run, ached and dreaded it too. I didn't want to see either of our horses beaten. We had never sent a pair like that to the races before. Old men in Beckersville said so and the niggers said so. It was a fact. Before the race I went over to the paddocks to see. I looked a last look at Middlestride, who isn't such a much standing in a paddock that way, then I went to see Sunstreak.

It was his day. I knew when I see him. I forgot all about being seen myself and walked right up. All the men from Beckersville were there and no one noticed me except Jerry Tillford. He saw me and something happened. I'll tell you about that.

I was standing looking at that horse and aching. In some way, I can't tell how, I knew just how Sunstreak felt inside. He was quiet and letting the niggers rub his legs and Mr. Van Riddle himself put the saddle on, but he was just a raging torrent inside. He was like the water in the river at Niagara Falls just before it goes plunk down. That horse wasn't thinking about running. He don't have to think about that. He was just thinking about holding himself back till the time for the running came. I knew that. I could just in a way see right inside him. He was going to do some awful running and I knew it. He wasn't bragging or letting on much or prancing or making a fuss, but just waiting. I knew it and Jerry Tillford his trainer knew. I looked up and then that man and I looked into each other's eyes. Something happened to me. I guess I loved the man as much as I did the horse because he knew what I knew. Seemed to me there wasn't anything in the world but that man and the horse and me. I cried and Jerry Tillford had a shine in his eyes. Then I came away to the fence to wait for the race. The horse was better than me, more steadier, and now I know better than Jerry. He was the quietest and he had to do the running.

Sunstreak ran first of course and he busted the world's record for a mile. I've seen that if I never see anything more. Everything came out just as I expected. Middlestride got left at the post and was way back and closed up to be second, just as I knew he would. He'll get a world's record too some day. They can't skin the Beckersville country on horses.

I watched the race calm because I knew what would happen. I was sure. Hanley Turner and Henry Rieback and Tom Tumberton were all more excited than me.

A funny thing had happened to me. I was thinking about Jerry Tillford the trainer and how happy he was all through the race. I liked him that afternoon even more than I ever liked my own father. I almost forgot the horses thinking that way about him. It was because of what I had seen in his eyes as he stood in the paddocks beside Sunstreak before the race started. I knew he had been watching and working with Sunstreak since the horse was a baby colt, had taught him to run and be patient and when to let himself out and not to quit, never. I knew that for him it was like a mother seeing her child do something brave or wonderful. It was the first time I ever felt for a man like that.

After the race that night I cut out from Tom and Hanley and Henry. I wanted to be by myself and I wanted to be near Jerry Tillford if I could work it. Here is what happened.

The track in Saratoga is near the edge of town. It is all polished up and trees around, the evergreen kind, and grass and everything painted and nice. If you go past the track you get to a hard road made of asphalt for automobiles, and if you go along this for a few miles there is a road turns off to a little rummy-looking farmhouse set in a yard.

That night after the race I went along that road because I had seen Jerry and some other men go that way in an automobile. I didn't expect to find them. I walked for a ways and then sat down by a fence to think. It was the direction they went in. I wanted to be as near Jerry as I could. I felt close to him. Pretty soon I went up the side road—I don't know why—and came to the rummy farmhouse. I was just lonesome to see Jerry, like wanting to see your father at night when you are a young kid. Just then an automobile came along and turned in. Jerry was in it and Henry Rieback's father, and Arthur Bedford from home, and Dave Williams and two other men I didn't know. They got out of the car and went into the house, all but Henry Rieback's father who quarreled with them and said he wouldn't go. It was only about nine o'clock, but they were all drunk and the rummy-looking farmhouse was a place for bad women to stay in. That's what it was. I crept up along a fence and looked through a window and saw.

It's what give me the fantods. I can't make it out. The women in the house were all ugly mean-looking women, not nice to look at or be near. They were homely too, except one who was tall and looked a little like the gelding Middlestride, but not clean like him, but with a hard ugly mouth. She had red hair. I saw everything plain. I got up by an old rosebush by an open window and looked. The women had on loose dresses and sat around in chairs. The men came in and some sat on the women's laps. The place smelled rotten and there was rotten talk, the kind a kid hears around a livery stable in a town like Beckersville in the winter but don't ever expect to hear talked when there are women around. It was rotten. A nigger wouldn't go into such a place.

I looked at Jerry Tillford. I've told you how I had been feeling about him on account of his knowing what was going on inside of Sunstreak in the minute before he went to the post for the race in which he made a world's record.

Jerry bragged in that bad-woman house as I know Sunstreak wouldn't never have bragged. He said that he made that horse, that it was him that won the race and made the record. He lied and bragged like a fool. I never heard such silly talk.

And then, what do you suppose he did! He looked at the woman in there, the one that was lean and hard-mouthed and looked a little like the gelding Middlestride, but not clean like him, and his eyes began to shine just as they did when he looked at me and at Sunstreak in the paddocks at the track in the afternoon. I stood there by the window—gee!—but I wished I hadn't gone away from the tracks, but had stayed with the boys and the niggers and the horses. The tall rotten-looking woman was between us just as Sunstreak was in the paddocks in the afternoon.

Then, all of a sudden, I began to hate that man. I wanted to scream and rush in the room and kill him. I never had such a feeling before. I was so mad clean through that I cried and my fists were doubled up so my fingernails cut my hands.

And Jerry's eyes kept shining and he waved back and forth, and then he went and kissed that woman and I crept away and went back to the tracks and to bed and didn't sleep hardly any, and then next day I got the other kids to start home

with me and never told them anything I seen.

I been thinking about it ever since. I can't make it out. Spring has come again and I'm nearly sixteen and go to the tracks mornings same as always, and I see Sunstreak and Middlestride and a new colt named Strident I'll bet will lay them all out, but no one thinks so but me and two or three niggers.

But things are different. At the tracks the air don't taste as good or smell as good. It's because a man like Jerry Tillford, who knows what he does, could see a horse like Sunstreak run, and kiss a woman like that the same day. I can't make it out. Darn him, what did he want to do like that for? I keep thinking about it and it spoils looking at horses and smelling things and hearing niggers laugh and everything. Sometimes I'm so mad about it I want to fight someone. It gives me the fantods. What did he do it for? I want to know why.

"I'm very sorry, sir. When I urged my horse on, I had no intention of discouraging yours."

DRAWING BY MIRACHI   [© 1958 BY THE NEW YORKER MAGAZINE, INC.]

An International Horse Race

ANONYMOUS

Over a period of twenty years as a turf publicist, I was constantly galled at the attitude of many people in high places on attendance at horse racing. True, Franklin Roosevelt did interrupt a conference to listen to the broadcast of the War Admiral–Seabiscuit race; Vice-President Curtis was an avowed horse-player; Mrs. Harry Truman was an occasional incognito at the races, and George Humphrey ran his horses in his daughter's name while serving as Eisenhower's Secretary of the Treasury, but they were modern-day exceptions. The following, therefore, was particularly pleasing to me, when I discovered that Andrew Jackson and Martin Van Buren had long ago made horse racing the Sport of Presidents, along with George Washington. The account is taken from an 1876 edition of Wallace's Monthly, *a publication under the aegis of the forebears of Henry A. Wallace, former Vice-President of the United States.*

My first visit to Nashville, Tennessee, was in the early summer of 1868. After reaching the hotel, getting a room, and performing my ablutions—it was late dinnertime, and most of the guests had completed the meal and retired. While thus quietly seated, nearly alone, I observed a large, and remarkably fine-looking gentleman enter the room and cast his eye over the few remaining guests, as if looking for someone. He whispered a word to the head waiter, near the door, and then started directly towards where I was seated. He was a large man, of very commanding presence, and his whole appearance at once indicated a man of distinction and mark, even among the great men of the day. His face was large and smoothly shaven, with kindliness and good feeling beaming all over it, while there was a merry twinkle playing about under his great shaggy and snow-white eyebrows that told unmistakably of his fondness for a good, hearty laugh. The whole appearance and especially the face impressed me as that of a remarkable man; but I had not time for further observation till he was at my table, and inquired if I was Mr. Wallace?

Upon receiving an affirmative answer, he gave me his hand, and with it his name, Balie Peyton. This was a most agreeable surprise, for, of all the distinguished Tennesseans then living, there was no one I was so anxious to meet as the Hon. Balie Peyton. When as a boy I had read of him as a politician and statesman in the days of Jackson, and as a leader of the opposition to his administration in the counsels of the nation. At a later period, I had read of him as one of the great breeders and race horse men of his generation. It appeared hardly possible that the man who had filled so large a place in public affairs, thirty or forty years before, should still possess so many of the marks of vigorous manhood, but the "three-score and ten" years sat lightly upon him in a hale and vigorous old age. He explained that he had but five minutes to stay, and he improved that time by pressing me to pay him a visit at his home, near Gallatin, to all of which I gladly acceded, and indicated the time at two or three weeks from that day.

The few days of my sojourn with Mr. Peyton were literally filled up with racing and political reminiscences of a past generation. In many of these General Jackson was a prominent actor. Notwithstanding our veneration for his pure patriotism and unsullied virtues, it may as well be said that, next to love of country, came his love of a horse race. To our northern minds this may not be a pleasant remark, but we must remember the difference in the habits, surroundings, and associations in which we are placed. When he was President he kept something of a racing stable at Washington, and Mr. Peyton tells an excellent anecdote about Mr. President, his Secretary of State, Mr. Van Buren, and himself, going out one morning before daylight to see the President's horse run a trial. He was very fast, but a vicious, unmanageable brute, and got in the habit of bolting and going into the fence. Mr. Van Buren, knowing nothing of the danger of being run over on such an occasion, took up a position in rather an exposed situation, and the President called out to him with a little mixture of profanity, "Get behind me, Mr. Van Buren, or you will be run over." This became a standing joke in the political campaign, when it was charged Mr. Van Buren was running on the strength of "Old Hickory." But I must not tarry to even allude to any of the interesting and amusing things that were told in a way that was perfectly inimitable, as my purpose is, at present, to give but a single incident.

When General Taylor won the battle of Buena Vista, Mr. Peyton was one of the active, leading minds who brought him forward as a candidate for the presidency. The memorable phrase that he "was a Whig but not an ultra Whig," had more of Mr. Peyton in it than was generally supposed. In the campaign, as is well known, the Whigs were triumphant, and according to usage then well established, the leaders must be provided for. Mr. Peyton had a fancy for a tour in South America among the Andes, and the mission to Chile was raised to a first-class mission, and Mr. Peyton was duly appointed to fill it. He found the people of Chile, from the highest to the lowest, and from the oldest to the youngest, a nation of gamblers. No difference whether it was a game of cards, a cock fight, or horse race, everybody was ready to bet his last penny on the issue.

One of the chief Secretaries of the government affected great knowledge and experience in racing matters. He kept race horses himself, and was known throughout the country as one of the most successful and accomplished of all who frequented and patronized the turf. He was a kind of Napoleon among the racing men of Chile, and some time after Mr. Peyton's arrival in that country he improved an early opportunity to escort the American Minister, on a great occasion, to witness a contest between some of the most famous horses of the country. The winner belonged to the Secretary, and Mr. Peyton, not being greatly impressed with the racing powers of the Chile horses, made some remark, diplomatically conveying that idea. The Secretary at once wished to know if Mr. Peyton thought there were any better race horses in the United States? Mr. Peyton replied, somewhat apologetically, that the American race horse was larger and stronger, could carry more weight, and he thought had more speed. The Chilean, in his anxiety to catch what he supposed was a novice in racing matters, dropped all the diplomatic formulas and came right to business, forthwith challenging Mr. Peyton to bring on his American horse for ten thousand dollars a side, owners to ride. To this latter stipulation Mr. Peyton demurred, as he weighed one hundred and eighty pounds, and the Chilean only about one hundred and twenty. After a sufficient amount of diplomatic hesitation, however, he accepted the terms, and sent up to his plantation, in Tennessee, for a couple of great, strong race horses that he had bred himself, and knew all about their qualities for generations back. There was a little stir in diplomatic and official circles, as soon as it was known that a match had been concluded between the great racing Secretary and the American Minister, but the people did not take much interest in it, or treated it as a joke till the arrival of the American horses, when it at once became the excitement of the day, and the sporting event of the nation. The original stakes were put up. The race was to be a dash of four miles, and the great discrepancy in the weights of the distinguished riders, and the possible inexperience of the American, made it a sure thing, in the estimation of the masses, and indeed the whole Chile people, that the Napoleonic racing Secretary must win. There were many foreign vessels in port, particularly English and American, and they were all ready to back the American horse. As a matter of national feeling the Americans would back their representative, and the English, having unbounded confidence in the superiority of the descendant of the English Thoroughbred, brought out and invested their guineas most liberally. The other foreign vessels took their cue from these two nations, and it was the purse of the foreigners against that of the Chileans. The aggregate amount at stake was simply enormous. Instead of Mr. Peyton being a novice in racing matters, and not knowing how to ride, as the Chileans supposed, he had had a most extensive and successful experience in the saddle. When a schoolboy, he told me, he had received more whippings for running off from school to ride races, than for all other causes put together. He was sought for far and near for his skill and judgment as a rider. By this skill he was able to discount a considerable portion of the sixty pounds overweight he was required to carry.

At last the day arrived, and the whole Chile people were early assembled to witness and speculate on the great contest between the Chile and the American horse. The sailors were out in force, and all employments were suspended. Notwithstanding the vast amounts that had already been wagered, there were still a few more dollars left, and the foreign element was able to meet and cover them. The track was cleared and the riders mounted; Mr. Peyton being on a great, strong son of imp. Leviathan, dressed in a closely fitting jockey suit, looked the perfection of developed manhood and grace; the Secretary, dressed in the style of the country, was mounted on a gray horse of great local reputation for both speed and bottom. Like the horses of the country, he was under size, and had never been tested with a genuine race horse. They got word from the judges on the first trial, and away they went. Mr. Peyton took a strong, steady pull on his horse from the start, while the Secretary was disposed to hurry the pace. Thus they went, side and side, for about three-quarters of a mile, when the great raking stride of the Leviathan began to tell on the little gray and the Secretary did not appear disposed to hurry the pace any more. Soon after they entered on the second mile Mr. Peyton began to discover the Chilean was in trouble, and instead of hurrying the pace, he was laboring hard to maintain it at the present rate. After half a mile spent in breaking the heart of the little gray, but coaxing him to his best efforts, and yet unavailing, Mr. Peyton began to let his horse extend himself gradually, and after a number of desperate efforts had been renewed, over and over again, by the Secretary, to keep up, Mr. Peyton let his horse open out to a full, running gait, listening for the footsteps of the little gray, that he might know the effect of this diplomacy upon him. He could distinctly hear the last of the Secretary, and a suppressed oath occasionally, but the sound of the footsteps became less and less distinct, till, at the completion of the second mile he looked around to see where his adversary was, and as his eye fell upon him, he was pulling up his horse dead beaten. As soon as the Secretary saw Mr. Peyton looking at him he dropped all diplomatic courtesy, and rising in his stirrups and shaking his fist at him fiercely, he shouted, at the top of his voice, "You go to h - - l." Mr. Peyton galloped on the remaining two miles. The foreigners and sailors cheered most vociferously. The Chileans were so greatly astonished they were speechless for a time and all Chile was bankrupt.

Although the Democratic newspapers made a great ado about the disgrace that had been brought on American diplomacy by a Minister abroad engaging in a horse race, and riding the race himself, and although the people of Chile learned a very severe lesson, neither appeared to have any salutary effect on another American Minister to the same government. When General Kilpatrick went to Chile he took some trotting horses with him, or sent back for them after he had been there some time. One of these, as I understand, belonged to the Clay family, and the General matched him to trot five miles against a running horse, both in harness, and both to pull the same weight. For the first three miles the runner went away from the trotter but at that point the trotter began to come up, and beat the runner home. Of this latter match I have no particulars, but from these two instances in Chile, in the past years, and a very notable one, still abroad, I think our diplomatic corps has shown some ability in the gaming interests.

DRAWING BY ALAIN

I Ride to Win

EDDIE ARCARO

I've said it many times and now I can say it in print: "Eddie Arcaro, one of the greatest athletes of our time." The little guy has everything including, as they say along the rail, good mounts. This excerpt from Eddie's book is interesting because it concerns the first of his record-holding Kentucky Derby winners. Someday Eddie has to sit down and write the real story of "How to Ride to Win." I'm moving over, as many a jockey has, to let Eddie through.

THE WINTER-SPRING RACING SEASON of 1937–38 saw the great Earl Sande moving eastward with what looked like an out and out lock to capture the Kentucky Derby. This was the colt Stagehand that Sande was training for Colonel Maxwell Howard. Stagehand had won not only the rich Santa Anita Derby under Sande's training but also, competing against older horses, the $100,000 Santa Anita Handicap—the first and only horse to win those two big California pots. It looked as though Earl, who had not been having too much good luck since he retired from the saddle and embarked on a trainer's career, was about to break his jinx. Sande had ridden three Kentucky Derby winners and with the Negro jockey Isaac Murphy held the record for that accomplishment. And here he was now, training the colt that had rocketed into favoritism on the strength of his sensational California form. Sande also had a second string to his bow in The Chief, also owned by Colonel Howard, and a right fair performer in his own right, but no Stagehand, of course.

I was in Florida during this winter and, of course, knew Stagehand only by reputation, but like everyone else, I was convinced he must be a great horse to do what he did on the Coast. That Handicap victory, although achieved under light weight, put the convincer on me. Three-year-olds

are not in the habit of beating older horses at a mile and a quarter so early in the year.

Florida's Kentucky Derby preview, as they call it down there, is the Flamingo Stakes raced at Hialeah. It was formerly called the Florida Derby and is at a mile and a furlong for three-year-olds, of course. The winner this year turned up in a horse named Lawrin, a son of Insco and Margaret Lawrence, owned and bred by the Kansas City, Missouri, clothing merchant Herbert M. Woolf, and trained by that canny conditioner of horses who was later to become world famous in his profession, Ben A. Jones, also from Missouri, from a town called Parnell. Wayne D. Wright had the Lawrin mount in the Flamingo. I finished second aboard Hal Price Headley's Bourbon King, Greentree not having any three-year-olds deemed ready to start in this Florida event.

By the way, I was the winner of the Jockey Award at Hialeah this winter. The presentation was made by the late Joseph E. Widener, at that time head of the Miami Jockey Club. And my good fortune continued when the racing scene shifted to Tropical Park in Coral Gables. Here I won the Tropical Handicap with Tatterdemalion and my second straight Viscaya Stakes, this time with Sweet Patrice.

By the time the campaign opened in New York,

Greentree had a trio of three-year-olds which had been named for the early spring specials, including the Derby. They were Gangplank, Redbreast, and Perfect Peace. But they did not show enough in either trials or races to warrant Derby consideration.

Ben Jones, who had moved Lawrin from Florida to Kentucky for a crack at the Derby, was after Wayne Wright to come down to ride the colt, but Wayne was committed to ride Caballero II in the Excelsior Handicap at Jamaica on the same day the Derby was to be run. Wayne was reluctant to give up this mount when in his opinion Lawrin had no chance in the Derby. Caballero won the Excelsior, by the way.

So Jones contacted me and offered me the mount on the son of Insco. Although I had never ridden Lawrin, I was even less enthusiastic than Wright. To me, and nearly all other competent observers, Stagehand appeared a cinch. As for Lawrin, there had been whisperings down in Florida that he was not sound.

Since Greentree had nothing to run in stakes races on Derby Day, I knew it would be a simple matter to get permission to ride Lawrin, but I was sure it would be a useless undertaking. However, I was prompted to give it some thought before definitely declining the mount. In the first place, I had learned a long time before that whenever one horse seems a cinch to win a big race, the trainers of the contenders are less worried about the outcome than they are when a race appears wide open with any number of strong possibilities. Second, I had learned through the years to respect and admire Ben Jones's keen judgment. I had known Jones while I was riding in the West, where he had the reputation of being one of the shrewdest horsemen in the business.

Jones had been widely acclaimed for his ability to get horses "up" to certain engagements. He had given a recent demonstration of that ability by working Lawrin into top shape for his Flamingo success. I reasoned that if Jones thought he had some sort of chance in this Derby, then maybe I should hitch my star to his. Again I relished the thought of taking part in the Derby. I'd not forgotten the tense excitement as the field parades postward for that race. I guess it's the ham in all of us. The carnival spirit of Louisville at Derby time does that to you.

Ben kept the phone wires hot calling me to say that I mustn't sell Lawrin short—that if I would come down, he could arrange a fancy retainer. I wasn't interested in the retainer part and told him that if I decided to come down, I would do so for the usual 10 per cent of the purse, or just my expenses if Lawrin got nothing.

The Derby Trial was run on Tuesday before the Derby, and in it Lawrin was beaten only a nose by The Chief, the second string in Colonel Howard's bow. The time was 1:35 and some change for the mile. Ben called that night and said that with good luck Lawrin would have won the race. Besides, he confided to me, he had run Lawrin in bar plates which would be removed for the Derby. A bar plate, by the way, is a bar of metal that is supposed to keep the shoe from spreading. Bar plates are known to slow down some horses.

The outcome of the Derby Trial and Jones's constant pleadings prompted me to accept the mount on Mr. Woolf's horse, even though my decision was made with some reservations.

And then the hard luck that had been dogging Sande struck again. Stagehand came down ill and would be forced to pass up the Derby. That left him with a fair entry in The Chief, but it elevated the hopes of the other trainers, even though Lawrin's stock did not rise materially. Stagehand's defection sent the punters scurrying for bets on Belair Stud's Fighting Fox and Calumet Farms' Bull Lea. They were the ones most in demand now.

On the Thursday before the Derby I breezed Lawrin over the track, but I still couldn't tell much about what kind of a horse he might be at post time on Saturday. Jones endeavored to convince me that the colt had more than an outside chance and that when it came dusk on Saturday, I would have ridden the winner of the Kentucky Derby.

One thing that Jones told me sticks out in my mind to this day. He said, "Eddie, I'm going to tell you one thing that you must remember. Any time you decide to make a move on Lawrin in the Derby, he'll give you an eighth of a mile in eleven seconds. Remember that."

I am setting down the facts leading up to Derby Day, May 7, 1938, in their chronological order without trying to glamorize them. In the first place, I would not even have been at Churchill Downs if Wayne Wright had not refused the mount. And, for another thing, I had been prompted to make the trip chiefly because I enjoyed the fanfare of the Derby scene. Through it all, though, I knew I was going to do my best, and if Lawrin would do his, then we would have some sort of chance, maybe, at that.

So here it is, Derby Day again. Those good citizens to the number of some 65,000 are fidgeting and fussing, awaiting the clarion notes of the bugler that will bring out the field of aspirants for the prize so rich in tradition, so steeped in glory. They have been waiting hours for this one moment. Trainers have been waiting months, of course. And breeders—some of them—a lifetime. But it is the fans who have made this Kentucky's day of days and one of America's most thrilling spectacles.

In the jockey room the air is as electric as elsewhere. Someone has just made the observation that all the Derby riders are maiden jockeys in the Derby. No boy riding in today's Derby has ever won the race. That facts lifts the morale of all the lads.

The Downs jockey room looks just as it does on any other day. No flags are flying here as in the stands. This is a dressing room, and there are the same body odors and leathery smells as on any other day in any other jock's room in the country. The valets are polishing boots; the custodian of the room is hanging up the colors in the lockers. The valets are spreading out on a long numbered table the tack for the jockeys. The table is made up of a number of squares containing numbers, just like a giant checkerboard. The numbers correspond to the program numbers and the valets place the tack there to be carried by them to the saddling enclosure.

Jockeys are sitting around, some playing cards. "Hearts" is the popular pastime. Others are snoozing on the wooden benches that face the lockers. Each jockey has his locker for his personal effects. The long wooden bench is a community seat. In one section of the room soft drinks are obtainable. Or sandwiches, if a rider feels hungry. Today many visitors have been able to get by the guards. (At all tracks the jockey room is well policed and only those properly accredited can get in.) Boys are jogging up the stairs after their engagements in early races. They throw off their silks and don new ones. The silks are the property of the owners, of course. They have been registered by them and each set differs from the others in some respect—in cap, sleeves, collar, cuffs, design on front or back, or in some other way. That's to help the onlookers spot the horses in the running of the race. Also as an aid to the professional chart callers, or the public-address and radio men.

As the hour for the 1938 Derby slowly nears, the Derby jockeys are awaiting the call. Over there is Jimmy Stout, a product of the sidewalks of New York, clad in the red-dotted white jacket of William Woodward's Belair Stud, already twice carried to Derby victory—by Gallant Fox and Omaha. Stout's mount is Fighting Fox, a full brother to Gallant Fox. He knows that he's on one of the favorites—the one they'll all have to beat in this run for the Roses. Irving Anderson, a cherubic-faced lad, is in the Devil's red and blue of Calumet, colors that I carried for Mr. Wright's stable for three years. He's on Bull Lea, a contender for sure.

In another corner is George Woolf, the Iceman, destined to become one of the great money riders of all times, later to lose his life under the flying hooves of a field of horses. Woolf is on Co-Sport. Jackie Westrope is here. I used to ride races for Jackie's dad out at Caliente. Jack's mount is The

Chief, now that Stagehand is out of it. Tough break for the "Rope."

Sonny Workman, a husky blond boy and one of the idols of my early riding days, is attired in the blue and white silks of Hal Price Headley. He is to ride Menow, the Futurity winner of the year before. That's a jinx. No Futurity winner had ever won a Derby, but this horse is going to be out there on the front end, winging, as far as he can go. Everyone concedes that. He's the speed of the party, is Menow—but a mile and a quarter? Ah, there's the rub. Will he be able to carry that speed those ten furlongs? There are many doubters. But the cunning Workman and Menow will have to be watched. Nothing will outrun them in the early part.

Maurice (Moose) Peters is sporting the sapphire blue and gold of Foxcatcher Farms. He's to be up on Dauber. They have been saying that this might be the horse to come on when the early speedsters are calling it a day. Lester Balaski, a New Orleans-born boy, is in the silks of Myron Selznick. He's on Can't Wait. Alfred Robertson, quiet and unassuming, is resting in a corner nook. He's Mountain Ridge's jockey. Young Freddie Faust is the other Derby rider. He's up on Elooto, and he's any price.

There are some emotions stirring in this roomful of young boys and men, you can be sure of that. The older and more experienced hands are poised and cool, the youngsters fidgety and nervous. The pop-eyed kids who are just breaking in are ogling these stars of the jockey firmament gathered here today—as one day some among them may be—to employ all their skill and craftsmanship on the finest horses in the land, some to do battle on the broad ribbon of Churchill Downs in a test of speed and endurance.

Ten boys are to leave this steaming jockey room, clad in their brilliant silks. Only one of them is coming back the smiling hero.

Those ten boys, I among them, are now summoned to the saddling enclosure. Down creaking wooden stairs they walk. At the paddock level literally thousands are seeking a glimpse of the horses they are backing in this great race. All seems confusion in the various stall compartments that have been assigned the Derby starters. Owners and their friends are chatting with trainers and stable hands. And now we Derby jockeys stride up to our appointed places.

Mr. Woolf's friends are introduced and all extend their hands for a clasp as a gesture of wishing you good luck. Ben Jones is the busiest man in the party, attending to tying cinches and surcingles on Lawrin. A stable hand is helping him, and a pony stands at attention outside the stall. Presently Lawrin is saddled up and taken by the head by the pony's rider and led around the walking ring in the paddock. Jones draws me aside. He reiterates what he has already said about Lawrin. "Any time, Eddie, you make a move on this colt, he'll give you an eighth of a mile in eleven seconds. Go out there and hurry back!"

The bugle blows. "Boots and Saddles." A captivating air that sends tingles up and down the spine. I suddenly think of Ruth at our apartment in Forest Hills, ear glued to the radio. The folks over in Newport are tuned in, too. They wired this morning that they were rooting.

The band is playing "My Old Kentucky Home." Where else in all this land is there a moment so spine-tingling, so packed with tension, as when the field parades to the post in this great classic? It will never grow old with me. I love every bit of it.

Lawrin has drawn the rail post position. That can or can not be an advantage. Menow, it has all been figured out, should take the lead on this field. If he should come over at the break, he could pile you up on the fence. In cantering up to the post I'm thinking only of getting my horse away from there. Indelibly etched in my mind is what Jones has told me. I keep repeating it to myself: "Eddie, he'll give you an eighth in eleven seconds, any time you decide to make a move with him."

There is a long delay at the post and one of the chief offenders in breaking up the starts is Lawrin. He has gone through the stall doors on a couple of occasions. When they would get him back in his stall, another of the fractious ones would kick up. The tension mounts as the seconds go into minutes and the minutes seem like hours. Actually this post delay consumes only four and a half minutes, as I was to learn later, but it seems like an eternity before the starter presses his button and shrieks, "C'mon, c'mon!" The 1938 Derby is under way.

When he yelled that, I was ready, and Lawrin came out of there ahead of the bunch by perhaps a length, but as we flew past the stand Lawrin was dropping back, and as we passed the finish line the first time, I thought I was surely going right into that pole. I was knocked back to next to last—only Dauber was behind me.

Perhaps that shuffling back I received at this point of the race was the deciding factor, although I must add that on this day and in this race Lawrin was the best horse. When I was knocked back, I naturally found myself on the rail, and I never left that position for the entire race. As I was getting through at the top of the stretch, Dauber was making his move also. Had I elected to come out at this point and go around horses, it's pretty certain that Dauber would have

run me down in the stretch. In my opinion, saving all that ground on the inside proved to be the difference between winning and losing.

In reporting this Derby, the late Damon Runyon said, in part:

At the first turn Menow moves out in front and holds the lead almost to the mile post where they turn for home. Fighting Fox is dropping back like a fat policeman chasing a nimble schoolboy.

The Kentuckians begin cheering wildly for Headley's horse. Few spectators are paying much attention to Lawrin, but there he is, close on the pace all the way, with the great race rider Eddie Arcaro holding him steady and waiting to make his move.

He is third when they straighten away for home, and suddenly out of the pack comes Lawrin to take the lead from Menow. In the meantime, Dauber, with Maurice Peters driving with might and main, is coming through fast. He passes Can't Wait and sets sail for Lawrin, but Arcaro knows he is coming, and he gives the Missouri colt a championship ride the rest of the way.

Eddie Arcaro's ride on Lawrin is a masterpiece from start to finish. Every move he makes is perfect. He lets Menow and Fighting Fox run their heads off in the first quarter and he keeps back there fifth, with plenty of racing room and always within striking distance to the last turn.

He seems to know exactly how much horse he has under him. When he makes his decisive move, it is sudden, but sure. The way Lawrin responds is a caution. He just roars to the front. Mr. Woolf and Ben Jones can thank Mister Arcaro for this Derby.

The race was worth $47,050 to the winning owner.

When I wheeled Lawrin into the winner's circle, Ben Jones was grinning from ear to ear. He roared up at me, "I told you so. I told you so!" Now he was pumping my hand. Mr. Woolf was excitement personified. Governor A. B. (Happy) Chandler was winking at me from the judges' stand. "If not a Kentucky horse, a Kentucky boy rode him!" he shrieked out.

Many nice things were to happen to me in later years, but looking back in retrospect, I guess this was my most thrilling experience. After all, you win your first Derby only once.

When I reached the jock's room, among a sheaf of wires I found this one:

"Congratulations! Hurry Home! Ruth."

I am quoted in the newspapers as saying, after I read that telegram, "Me for home and my sweetie—and that bubble water."

I suspect I was quoted accurately.

Azucar

JOHN HERVEY

John Hervey's fine portrait of Azucar justifies the inclusion in this collection of the story of the steeplechaser-turned-runner. Azucar also earns a place as the winner of the first Santa Anita Handicap, although he is not offered here as the best of a series of fine Thoroughbreds to win that race. The horse and the race were simultaneously boosted to fame and fortune. The horse matched the setting and, oddly enough, the subsequent history of the race. which has always attracted important foreign horses.

ONE of the fascinations of racing is its eternal and ever-changeful variety. With centuries of history behind it, thoroughly organized, its modes and methods the result of many generations of experience and conduct, the horses that are its *raison d'être* a distinct and definite breed and type, into which no new blood elements have been introduced within the memory of men now living, it is nevertheless always productive of something quite new and entirely unforeseen.

One might at first suppose that within its strictly defined scheme and boundaries there no longer existed scope or opportunity for anything more than incidentally new, novel or out of the way. But such a supposition would be wide of the facts. The reverse is the case—and of the truth of that statement the career of the extraordinary Azucar is a salient example.

Last July he bade farewell to flat racing, after at his home city of Detroit he won the first running of the Michigan Handicap, a stake newly introduced, with an endowment of $3,000 added money, the conditions being: for three-year-olds and upward and the distance stated a mile and a sixteenth.

Carrying the top weight, 117 pounds, he laid back in the early running, but assumed the lead as the field swung into the home stretch and, always holding at bay the lightweight Carl S., with but 98 pounds up, he won cleverly by a neck, the pair being three lengths ahead of Paradisical, third, with four others behind them, in-

cluding the favorite, Tempestuous, winner of several stake events during 1936 and 1937. The time was 1:44⅕; track record 1:43⅖.

His owner, F. M. Alger, Jr., of that city, had announced that in case he won, Azucar, now nine years old, would never again be started in a race on the flat. Owing to that, and to his previous career, great interest centered in his performance and when he came through with a victory, there was applause from the grandstand and a feeling of satisfaction among sportsmen. For Azucar goes into our turf history as one of its extraordinary performers, whose record has had no parallels and, it seems entirely probable, never will have.

Foaled in 1928, Azucar, bred in the Straffan Station Stud, County Kildare, Ireland, was foaled the property of the estate of Edward (familiarly known as "Cub") Kennedy, who had died in 1925. The life story of Kennedy would in itself afford material for an interesting chapter. As a boy he had begun with nothing; when he died he left an estate which was probated at a million and a quarter dollars but was worth considerably more, and it was written at the time that this immense fortune was "entirely the result of his own efforts."

These efforts were almost exclusively made in the field of livestock buying, selling and breeding, which also included that of racing upon both the Irish and the English turf. In 1904 Kennedy mated the brood mare Darkie, by Thurio, with the stallion Bay Ronald. Darkie was at that time fifteen years old and had up to that time nothing to her credit but two insignificant winners of small races and she had cost Kennedy a trifling sum, but the produce of the mating was Dark Ronald, first a race horse of high class and then a remarkable progenitor and today considered one of the chief glories of the Hampton line.

In 1909 Kennedy was watching Dark Ronald race in the Doncaster Cup. He had sold him as a yearling, but his interest in the horse remained, naturally, very great. He was the favorite for the cup and should have won it, but broke down in the race and finished third. The winner was Amadis, who got up in the last strides and just nosed out the French horse Roi Hérode. Kennedy liked the gray Frenchman so much, despite his having been beaten, that he bought him, but he went amiss early the next season and never raced again. He was then sent to Ireland and began service at Straffan Station in 1910.

One of the first mares he covered there was Vahren, by Bona Vista, who was much the same in class at that time as Darkie a few years before. She was thirteen, had been breeding for some years and thus far had very little to show for herself. Nevertheless her foal by Roi Hérode was nothing less than The Tetrarch, one of the most remarkable stallions of modern times—and how Roi Hérode and The Tetrarch between them resuscitated the almost extinct Herod line in England and placed it, as a going concern, among the foremost, is one of the most familiar facts of modern breeding history.

In 1917, the keen-witted Kennedy mated his beloved Frenchman, Roi Hérode, with Nicola, by Symington, a home-bred mare that was also out of Vahren, dam of The Tetrarch. Thus he obtained the colt Milesius.

After winning the Coventry Stakes at Ascot, an offer of $100,000 was made Kennedy for Milesius. He refused it, upon which a blank check was placed before him and he was told to fill it in at his own price—but this also he refused, declaring that the colt was not for sale. This proved one of "Cub's" few large errors of judgment, as Milesius failed to go on and a year later if placed upon the market it might have been very difficult indeed to get $10,000 for him.

However, Kennedy's refusal to part with Milesius was productive, among other things, of Azucar. For the stallion was taken home to Straffan Station and placed in the stud, where, owing to his master's fondness for him, he was kept on after that gentleman's death by his heirs. It cannot be said that he made a success as a sire, however, and had not fate, destiny, or what you will, sent his son Azucar to the U.S.A., as we shall proceed to relate, he would today stand recorded as a failure.

Among the mares at Straffan Station, to which Milesius was bred in 1927, two years after Kennedy's death, was Clarice, a daughter of Picton, of the Bend Or line, and from Clarilaw, by Persimmon, back of which the chain of dams ran directly to Old Maniac, by Shuttle, the celebrated matron from whom Man o' War also descends in tail-female. The produce was a chestnut colt, foaled March 24, 1928, which, when a yearling, was sent to the Doncaster sales in September and brought under the hammer, $5,250, the buyer being Joseph E. Widener, who was then strengthening his stable for the coming season on the English and French turf, where, as well as in this country, he had been racing for an extended period.

Mr. Widener raced him as a two-year-old in England as the "Clarice colt," starting him eight times. His form was good, and he won the Gosforth Park Biennial, gave Pomme d'Api eight pounds and ran him to a length for the Fulbourne Stakes; and in the Woodcote Stakes ran third, beaten a neck and a head.

It was as a three-year-old that he received the name which he was to make famous subsequently upon this side of the Atlantic—Azucar, which is a Spanish word, meaning "sugar." He ran five times that season in England but failed to win. In the London Cup he was third, his best showing. Mr. Widener then decided that his usefulness both as a flat racer and on the British turf was at an end but that as a steeplechaser in the U.S.A. he might prove useful. So he was brought here to appear in his new role; having, in the interim, been added to the list of geldings.

His first campaign as a leaper, that of 1932, was not extensive, as he started but four times, winning one minor event, and in the Charles L. Appleton Memorial Cup splitting Arc Light and Beacon Hill, from which he was receiving 13 and 23 pounds respectively. He was also second in another purse event. This was not a bad beginning and he was even then singled out by the followers of the jumpers as a horse that with more experience in fencing might make a stir. He showed high speed between jumps and his size and strength were excellent assets.

In 1933 he again appeared but four times, though his form was improved, as he won the Appleton Memorial, carrying 138 pounds, and ran second in the Broadhollow, at Belmont Park, splitting Irish Bullet and Arc Light. He also won a purse event. As before he was unplaced but once.

He was now recognized as one of the best 'chasers in training and in 1934 verified this opinion by winning the Corinthian Steeplechase at the Belmont spring meeting, in which he carried 153 pounds and scored in 3:42⅖, a new record for that noted event. This race was run on

June 2, and about that time Mr. Widener decided to give up his steeplechasing stable and sell its members, instructing J. Howard Lewis, who was training them—Mr. Lewis had for a long term of years handled all Mr. Widener's cross-country horses and ranks as one of the most successful trainers of 'chasers of modern times—to dispose of them at the first opportunity. Hearing that Azucar was for sale, Mr. Alger offered $8,000 for him, which was accepted.

Mr. Alger, a devotee of sport between the flags, had in mind when buying Azucar two objects. He had watched the gelding closely and believed that he might be made the best jumper in America. But beyond that he indulged the idea of trying for the Aintree Grand National with him if he came on as expected. In pursuance of this plan he placed him with trainer Matt Brady. The latter was then racing, among others, the horses of the Catawba Stable (Mrs. E. J. West), which included Mr. Khayyam, winner the previous season of the American Derby, Wood Memorial and Chesapeake Stakes, and just then one of the leading handicap horses in the East.

One morning Brady worked Azucar and Mr. Khayyam together and to his great surprise the 'chaser beat the handicap star and classic winner—and did it rather handily. The trainer immediately communicated the result to Mr. Alger and recommended that he convert the gelding back to flat racing, for which his prospects were promising. The advice was followed and after a few weeks spent in his transformation, Azucar was reintroduced to the public at Saratoga, where he ran with success, beating some good horses.

That he was good enough for some stake engagements was manifest and Mr. Alger began making them for him in the big fall handicaps of the Maryland terrain. On September 29 he came out for the Havre de Grace, worth over $8,000 to the winner, for which he had been allotted 108 pounds. Discovery, top weight at 126 pounds, was an overwhelming favorite, but could only run third and in a whipping finish Azucar was beaten a nose only by Faireno (122 pounds), the nine furlongs being run in 1:50⅘. In this race Azucar was ridden by Johnny Gilbert and the display he made impressed the experts with a high idea of his future possibilities.

This opinion he made good in the rich Maryland Handicap, run at Laurel on October 27, and also worth over $8,000 to the winner. For it he had been assigned 114 pounds and he was top weight of the field of seven. His victory was decisive, as he won without being ridden out by half a length from Good Goods, Identify third, running the mile and a quarter in the fast time of 2:02⅖ (track record 2:02).

The excellence of the performance and the successful transformation so rapidly effected in the status of the Irish gelding made him one of the most-talked of Thoroughbreds in the country and as Mr. Alger had announced that he would be sent to California for the winter campaign, and specially pointed for the first $100,000-added Santa Anita Handicap, the interest centering in him became general throughout the turf world. He had been saddled for the Washington by trainer A. G. Wilson, but was later turned over to J. Rushton for his adventure in the gold rush.

Subsequent to his victory at Laurel, Azucar was taken to Narragansett Park for the $28,000 Narragansett Special, run four days later. Having acquired a sensational reputation, he was well taken care of by the handicapper, being required to shoulder 126 pounds. Nevertheless he was heavily backed to win, but ran fourth to Time Supply, Mr. Khayyam and High Glee, beaten three and a half lengths. After arriving on the Pacific Coast he ran first at the San Francisco Handicap, on December 8, assuming 122 pounds and showing poorly to finish eighth as Top Row (109 pounds) won in record time for the mile and a sixteenth, 1:42. This was his last race for 1934, during which he had started 11 times, once as a jumper and ten times on the flat, winning five races, second in two, third in one and $14,280 in money.

New Year's Day, 1935, found him among the field for the stake named in honor of the day at Santa Anita, an event endowed with $5,000 and also at 1¹⁄₁₆ miles. Twelve started, he was not considered to have a real chance, being at about 20 to 1, but came through to win cleverly by a length, under 114 pounds, in 1:43⅕. He then was laid by for a month, reappearing February 2 in the $5,000 San Carlos Handicap, for which he drew 117 pounds and ran fourth, but close, two and a half lengths back of Jabot (109 pounds), the winner. One week later he was out again in the rich San Antonio Stakes, starting favorite at 11 to 10 and again running fourth, this time to Head Play. It was a weight-for-age race, in which he carried 128 pounds, and as before, while three horses beat him, he was close by.

This race was run on February 9 and two weeks elapsed before the $100,000 handicap, which had stirred up tremendous interest throughout the entire American sporting world. It was certain that twenty or more horses would start and that both the gross value and winner's net would be the largest in turf history thus far, American or foreign. The event had been avowedly built up about Equipoise, who, now seven years old, was making his farewell to the public in it before his permanent retirement to the stud and was the top weight at 130 pounds; his old adversary Twenty Grand, making an effort at a

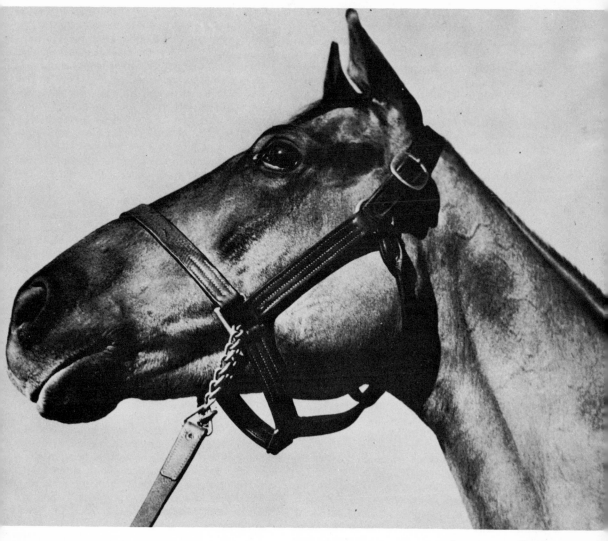

Azucar [UPI]

successful comeback after three years of absence from the course, coming next with 128 pounds, and Faireno third with 120, tied with Mate at the same weight.

When the field was summoned to the post on February 23, before an audience of over 30,000 spectators, it comprised an even twenty horses, making the gross of the stake $125,700 and the net to the winner $108,400. A statistician, after making computations, announced that the score of starters had earned, up to that moment, a net total of $1,767,833, and that six of them had won over $100,000 each, while two (Equipoise and Mate) had won over $300,000 each.

Though Equipoise was known to informed turfmen to be merely a relic of his former glory,

the public would not believe it and he was an immense favorite at 17 to 10, Ladysman (117 pounds) being second choice at 52 to 10 and Ted Clark (103 pounds) third at 63 to 10. Nothing else in the field was at as good as 10 to 1. Azucar, who had drawn an impost of 117 pounds, was at 12½ to 1.

There was a delay of four and a half minutes at the post and when the flag fell Ted Clark set off to make a runaway race of it at a pace not calculated to last over a mile and a quarter. With High Glee several lengths arear and Time Supply third, the son of Chatterton scudded to the quarter in :22⅘, the half in :45, and the three-quarters in 1:10 flat, then kept on to the end of the first mile in 1:36 (track record 1:36⅘), at which point he was still three lengths ahead but was beginning rapidly to come back to his horses.

As they rounded the last turn and started down the stretch, a general closing up and shifting of positions took place. Azucar had gotten off fourteenth, and at the end of that furious six furlongs was still back in eleventh place, but then when George Woolf picked him up and asked him to move, his answer was superb. In running the next quarter mile he had swept past six other horses and into fourth place, the burst of speed he displayed being extraordinary, as the official time of that quarter was 26 seconds and in it he had made up over a dozen lengths.

Sustaining this meteoric flight, he dashed past Ladysman, Time Supply and Top Row, all of which had given the tired Ted Clark the go-by and as they entered the straight had assumed a lead of two full lengths. From there he was complete master of the situation and, keeping steadily on, won by the same margin without being ridden out, the placed horses finishing as named and the time 2:02⅕, a new track record and one that has not since been equaled or beaten at Santa Anita.

For a race with so large a field of horses, for so great a sum of money, and upon which a gigantic amount had been wagered, the contest had been truly run. Of the superiority of the winner there was absolutely no doubt.

We have since had two other Santa Anita Handicaps, but neither has netted the winner as much as the inaugural, so Azucar remains the winner of the richest race ever run for, anywhere in the world.

The triumph of Azucar on that memorable day flashed his name around the world. And with it there accrued the penalties attached. A seven-year-old gelding, but yesterday a steeplechaser, had won the richest race ever contested and in it fairly beaten a field of nineteen horses, the pick of all America. Nothing more astounding was ever inscribed upon the pages of turf history. But how could any seven-year-old gelding, fresh from brush-topping, ever live up to such a reputation?

It requires only a short period of meditation to produce the answer: It can't be done. And the after-career of Azucar demonstrated the correctness of that classic verdict. Subsequently, during 1935, he ran five races—and won none of them. Detroit was naturally proud of him and wished to do her best by him. He was the great magnet of interest when, on Memorial Day, in the Alger Memorial Handicap, he first appeared before the home folks. But he fell an easy prey to Stand Pat when trying to carry 128 pounds and give that good horse 9 pounds. Two weeks later, in the Derby Week Special, his next effort, he was again beaten by Stand Pat, but both of them were beaten by Head Play. In the Pontchartrain Handicap he was also third, beaten by the two three-year-olds Paradisical and Sun Portland.

Meanwhile the Detroit management had been trying to arrange an ultrasensational "grand special" in which it hoped to bring together the five or six best horses in training, but most especially, Azucar, Discovery, Head Play and Cavalcade. A purse of as much as $50,000 was at one time talked of; but eventually breakdowns and other exigencies caused it to dwindle to a two-horse race between Discovery and Azucar, with $11,200 to the winner and $2,500 to the loser—who proved to be Azucar, as Discovery, then at the peak of his form, left him down the stretch as he sailed under the wire in track-record time for the nine furlongs.

The next week he faced Discovery once more in the Stars and Stripes Handicap, at Arlington Park, together with a formidable field of others. A curious crowd surrounded him in the paddock, attracted by the presence of so remarkable a horse, found him looking dull and stale and he ran in the same fashion, finishing fifth. It was his last race of the year. Soon after, it was reported that he had shown himself to be ailing and his retirement for the season was announced. He had run nine times since it began, won two, been second twice, third three times and unplaced twice and earned $117,950.

New Year's Day of 1936 saw Azucar officially eight years old. Could a horse so old, with a record like his and sure of the attentions of the handicappers wherever he went because of it, be expected to make much more history? Surely his future lay in his past! Which was true to a certain extent—but far from wholly so. During that campaign Azucar ran no less than 20 times, almost invariably in stake events.

He was "good" only in the winter and early spring while racing in California. There he won the San Felipe Handicap, worth $2,100, at Santa Anita, in which he started at 20 to 1 and ran a mile in the fast time of 1:36 with 114 pounds up; also the Fashion Stakes at Bay Meadows, in which he ran a mile in 1:37⅗ with 121 pounds up, the stake netting him $4,225. In the Bay Meadows Handicap, while beaten by Special Agent (117 pounds) he ran second with 124 pounds in the very fast time of 1:43 for the 1⅟₁₆ miles.

But undoubtedly his most remarkable performance was in the second $100,000 Santa Anita Handicap. Eighteen started, as before the picked horses of the country. When half the race was over Azucar was thirteenth; then, as in the year previous, he began to move forward with increasing speed and at the wire he was fourth, lapped on Rosemont, third, who was lapped on Time Supply, second, lapped on Top Row, the winner. He was carrying more weight (118 pounds) than any of them and at the finish was going so fast that, had the distance been a furlong farther, in the opinion of many of those who saw the race, he would have won. He also ran third in the Marchbank Handicap, at Tanforan, to Indian Broom and Top Row, when the former horse set a world's record of 1:47⅗ for nine furlongs.

On returning east, Azucar was unable to reproduce his Californian form. He ran third in the Governor's and Alger Memorial Handicaps at Detroit and fourth in the Pontchartrain, but late in the fall showed a surprising recovery by forcing Roman Soldier to run in 2:02⅗ in order to beat him in the Washington Handicap at Laurel, with a lot of good horses behind them— this being the same event with which he himself had started his stake-winning career two years before. The books closed on him as having won but two of his twenty starts, second twice, third four times and 12 times unplaced and earnings of $14,525.

The lastingness and durability of the Irish-bred horse has become one of his essential attributes and perhaps no Thoroughbred ever foaled in the Emerald Isle has surpassed Azucar in those regards, for with 1937 he entered the nine-year-old class still sound, strong and well. Mr. Alger decided this time to omit a California expedition and, instead, send the famous old fellow to Florida, where he began his campaign at Hialeah in February. His first efforts seemed to indicate that he was thoroughly raced out, but he still had surprises in store for racegoers.

On March 6 he was one of the fifteen starters in the $50,000 Widener Challenge Cup Handicap and, still paying the penalty of what he had done two years before, was top weight in the field at 120 pounds. As usual getting off very slowly, he was ninth at the end of the first mile in 1:36⅕, then began to come and while he was able to finish fifth only, as Columbiana won in the very fast time of 2:01⅘, he was only three lengths and a half behind her. The official chart says of him that he "closed an immense gap and ran a winning race." He was giving from five to 17 pounds to everything in front of him. We believe turf history may be searched in vain for such another exhibition by a nine-year-old race horse. It excited admiration among all who witnessed or read of it.

Azucar was given a good rest after this race and did not start again until in May, at Pimlico, where he ran third in a handicap to Finance and Purple Knight, and in the Dixie Handicap of $10,000 was unplaced. He next ran second in a $2,000 handicap to Dark Hope, still at Pimlico. Mr. Alger then brought him home to Detroit and stated that as soon as the veteran could win another stake event—which he was sure he would do—he would retire him from flat racing. His first effort there was in the Alger Memorial, in which he had already once run second and once third. He had been given 115 pounds, while Whopper was top weight at 126 and a hot favorite. The big five-year-old from the Headley stable went at once to the front and led all the way, but just lasted to win by half a length from Azucar, who, says the chart "was wearing down the winner at the close." After a rest he was started in the $10,000 Frontier Handicap, in which, with 116 pounds he ran third to Infantry (108) and War Minstrel (98), with ten horses behind him.

Finally, on July 3, as related at the beginning of this sketch, his hour came and he won the Michigan Handicap from a field of six. It was his 58th start in America, of which he had won 14, been second and third each 12 times and earned $159,525. In England his earnings had been approximately $3,500, making his total a trifle over $163,000, of which over $150,000 was won at the ages of from six to nine years. We believe there is no other similar instance in turf history.

After his farewell upon the flat, Azucar was put back at steeplechasing and made several starts but without success. It is said to be the intention of Mr. Alger henceforth to accord him the honorable estate of a life-pensioner. Individually, he is a bright chestnut, stands over 16½ hands tall, is of rakish, powerful build and possesses one of the best sets of feet and legs ever given a Thoroughbred. His action is long-striding, he was not a quick beginner and it was at the back end of a race that he demonstrated his capacities.

The Name of the Game

TONEY BETTS

It may be Toney Betts was accused of being delirious when he wrote the following, an excerpt from his book Across the Board, *or that I will be for having selected it for this anthology. Nevertheless, I make no apologies, because he wrote what he saw and he went everywhere on a race track where there was anything to see and write about. His is an uninhibited excursion into the compulsions of a horse player, the people he met in racing and on the fringes, and some enlightening bits of what goes on between races and before and after.*

In the autumn of that insane racing season, I decided to submit to the surgery I needed so badly. One 4 A.M. I was closing up Tiger Lil's, down the block from the *Daily Mirror*. The place was owned by Barbara Kelley, willowy, red-headed, full of animation, with a face so like Katharine Hepburn's she could be a ringer for the actress. Through Big Bill Dwyer I knew her husband, Frank.

Barbara had gone to her home town, Saratoga, to visit relatives and had left Frank to mind the store, with orders for me to mind Frank. They lived in Jackson Heights, Queens, near Physicians' Hospital, where a long-time friend of mine, Dr. Alexander Kaye, was chief surgeon. I asked Frank to drive me to the hospital, for I had a hunch not to delay any longer. I explained to Frank we'd have to look sober when we met the admitting nurse. A couple of months before, I had gone with a load on to another hospital where Dr. Kaye also operated, and had been chased.

Frank and I conned the admitting nurse, a girl with bobbed auburn hair whose soft blue eyes were full of sympathy for a suffering patient.

For the register she asked my occupation.

I gave Frank the glad eye as I said, "Gambler, poet and lover."

"Did you notice he put the lover third?" Frank quipped.

"That's not out of the money," she smiled.

And now we knew we were home; the nurse was a horse player.

I was checked into a double room and stayed there for forty-six days, wishing four roommates good luck after their operations. I was released on Christmas Eve, trimmed down to mere bones, less than a hundred pounds, the winner of the sweetest of all daily doubles. I'd never squawk again about photo finishes on the race track. These were the photos that counted.

Under a spinal, I was conscious of every snip. Whatever it is nature gives us when we're on such spots we forget to fear the thing we had feared. Nature's hidden wonder is protective coloration, which she gives to lower animals in color itself and to higher animals as speech. . . .

"They're off," I said to Dr. Kaye. "Pick up a scalpel and make a muscle-splitting incision down to the peritoneum."

"Stop practicing surgery without a license," he said.

Now came a general exploration. Then the scalpel, dipped in carbolic, incised the appendix.

"At the half," the surgeon said.

"It's like calling a Jersey wire-office and hanging on for a description," I commented.

In the stretch, the retrograde method for removal of gall bladder, the placing of a clamp on the ampulla, stripping surrounding fat and thereby bringing into view the cystic artery and duct, a ligature then being passed around the cystic duct and the artery and the tying-off for both.

"I told you a year ago you had a stone and this had to be done," the surgeon said.

"Stop playing the red board," I said, with just about all the breath I had left.

The stone was half the size of a golf ball and as pock-marked. My birthstone. Science hasn't found out how these things start.

A few days later there was a claim of foul. A silent stone had slipped from the liver into the common bile duct. This happens to surgeons only when they have a dear friend on the table. It was the toughest half of the double. But I wasn't worried. I was in the hands of an old pro.

The champions in surgery are like the champions in sports. They are cool in the clutches. When I was rolled back into the room, members of my family were there. Big Bill Dwyer and Dan Parker rushed over later in the afternoon. My brother Vincent, a race track cashier, then in an Army uniform, showed up with Jim Jennings, the boxing writer on my paper. I bet Jennings how long it would take for the bottle of blood in the transfusion to empty. It was the blood of my other brother Joseph, a lieutenant in the New York Police Department, and it gurgled at the end as I lost the bet. I just couldn't beat the law.

My sisters, Mrs. Loretta Contino and Mrs. Gloria McGivney, were helping Big Bill Dwyer with his coat and he ranted: "Do you see this hat? My friend who bought it for me is crazy. Longy Zwillman. I meet him on Park Avenue and he treats me to a forty-dollar hat. If I ever get in the money again, I'll never pay forty dollars for a hat."

Dwyer, the man who lost ten million on the horses, was concerned over $40 being spent for a hat.

The bottles of blood were followed by bottles of glucose and other nutrients. That night I went into a haze, and a plumpish, Irish Catholic nurse looked me straight in the eye and I knew what she was thinking, for she had hinted at it before. . . .

No, Peggy, please don't be calling a priest. I've gone this far without formal religion and what will God be thinking of me dogging it at the end, using Him only in the pinches? Please, Peggy, let me play out the hand and if I'll be meeting my Maker today, I'll take what's coming to me. . . .

Later that night the Horseman of Death was trying to make a hangout of my bedside and I conned him gently. . . . "Look, why don't you leave me alone? Not for my sake, but for my daughter's. She needs a father. Haven't you made enough orphans in the war? Come on, get a move on, will you please?"

In the morning, my rally astounded Dr. Kaye. The crisis was over. For several days there had been more tubes in my stomach than in the bedrock under the East River. The drug called penicillin was just coming into civilian use and I exhausted the hospital's supply.

The hospital's first chef was a horse player and he cooked contraband steaks my friends brought in, even though I had put him on a few losers. He left to go to work at the Turf Restaurant on Broadway because it belonged to Jack Amiel, a horse owner who later went partners in food and drink vending with Jack Dempsey. The chef thought the information would be better there than at the hospital. I hope he cashed in when Amiel won the Kentucky Derby six years later with Count Turf.

I had known Dr. Kaye since the Oral Days. A man with both an air of distinction and a democratic manner, dark, with searching brown eyes, and small, capable hands. I kept thinking of that morning when he had entered my room and said, "We've got to make another trip to the starting gate."

"What are the odds?" I said.

"In my book you're a one-to-ten favorite," he said.

"I heard different," I said. "They tell me the fix is in. I heard the Jockey Club got to you."

"Did you get the morning line?"

"They got me ten-to-one underdog in 'Gallagher's.' "

"Go ahead and take all you can," he said. "And tack me on for a wing of the hospital. It's a big overlay."

A couple of months later, I was riding in a Pennsy parlor car to Baltimore, reading Ferenc Molnar's play *Liliom,* enjoying the intoxication of sobriety. I had been assigned to cover a public hearing of the Maryland State Racing Commission involving seven steeplechase jockeys, a trainer and a jockey's agent, who had fixed a race at Pimlico. I was off the sports desk, and happy to be outdoors again.

At the start of a long convalescence, the patient takes inventory of himself. I felt like Liliom, the man God gave another chance on earth. As the landscape I loved rolled by, I wondered if I, too, would make the same mistakes in this new life. We all do. All of us are Lilioms.

But most of all I felt about racing the way Liliom had felt about life, that there were two rule books, one for the rich and one for the poor. When you're rich and get drunk and forget where you drank, you're suffering from Korsakoff's syndrome, and you rate sympathy. But if you're poor, then you're just a drunken bum.

So, here I am, across the board across the years, still trying to beat the races.

It looks big. I'm at the track every day and suckers say, "What do you know?" I say, "Nothing." They don't believe me. There's an inside to the game, for sure. I say those who know don't tell and those who tell don't know. Still they don't believe me.

If there's an inside, a newspaperman is the last to know. Suppose you pick six winners in a row today. Tomorrow you pick six losers in a row and they call you a bum. Maybe the touts have got the right idea. Maybe. But I can't tout. I can't cool out a sucker. I've got to blow my top, blow it bad.

Touts work with other people's money. O.P. That's what they call it at the track. O.P. All the way down the line, O.P. But I like to bet my own, go broke with my own. A tout's a harlot in his heart; won't admit he's a tout, the way harlots won't admit they're harlots. There's a tout who puts the bite on everyone he knows and he doesn't pay. When he makes a score he's got the gall to bawl out a guy he owes who needs the money. The tout says, "Show me somebody I ever paid and I'll pay you." Touts like that should be hit in the head, right square in the head.

The world is divided into right guys and wrong guys and one right guy outweighs a thousand wrong guys, and that's why I'm not bitter. I'm really not bitter. Listen, mistah, I mean I'm not bitter. I go back to the old dope book. Class will tell. Everything begins and ends with character.

Old pros never cry. Even when they get hurt they don't cry. A high-class man can be hurt only by a low-class man. The low-class man can't look down at anybody, and he has no feeling and can't be hurt, anyway.

Class, class, class. If I like a guy I say he has class. If I don't like a guy I say he's got no class. If I don't know about a guy I just say I got no figure on his class. All of it scored in the strings, no brass, no drums. This is all I know for sure: you can't please them all. If you spend, you're a sucker; if you save they say you go for nothing.

A right guy looks me in the eye and says, "Are you all right?" I say, "I'm all right." He knows I'm not all right. I make a loan. After I pay I can come back for twice as much. A right guy doesn't worry how long it takes you to pay if he knows you intend to pay. This is the school I go to in the Oral Days. I don't think of putting the bite on the wrong guys that drifted in with the dirty, rubbery tide of mutuel tickets.

A wrong guy tells the world and its mistress and expects me to tie my hands when I sit at the typewriter. I don't like my hands tied when I sit at a typewriter. And I write with a hammer, not with a whistle. This is the way the world ends, this is the way the world ends, not with a whimper but a bang.

Across the board across the years, I'm playing horses and I go for forty straight days without a winning day. All I got is a job and a few friends, and how long can you keep going to friends? I walk around in a haze of photo finishes. A nose is a nose is a nose. I can't keep my mind off the race track.

I pluck a book from the Governor Winthrop secretary. It's crammed with four years of *Daily Racing Form* monthly chartbooks. The bully books force out T. S. Eliot's *Four Quartets*. I don't always know what he's trying to say, but I love to hear him say it.

This is such a bad day that I can't even read Hemingway. Why does he sound so tough? Did his mother dominate him as a child? There I go now, drifting back to Freud. The Jazz Age's father-confessor gets a big figure, but I find a flaw in the speed chart. Why does Freud keep talking of the Oedipus complex when Oedipus Rex himself doesn't have an Oedipus complex? Endocrinology TKO's Freud in the second round.

My heart's in the highland, my heart is not here, my heart's in the highland a-chasin' the also-rans. I put down the poetry. All newspapermen should read poetry. Poetry keeps your ear in tune with the active voice. Always the active voice, the voice active. And poetry teaches you how to keep it short, keep it short.

Fox jumped over lazy dog's back. Keep it short, keep it short.

I try music to keep my mind off the horses. I take my daughter to the City Center on Fifty-fifth Street off Sixth Avenue. They're running a spring opera meeting. The stake event this Sunday afternoon is *Madame Butterfly*. I'm trying to forget about the race track, and the tenor-throated cad who jackpots the Japanese girl is named Pinkerton.

I'm looking at my daughter and thinking of the time she is about to graduate from grammar school and I'm trying to win out her higher education on the noses of horses. Two days before graduation day I cut into the paycheck for a tough $10. I beat a daily double. I have $496 going into the fifth race, and I want to bet $500. I borrow four dollars from Ken Kling, creator of that rollicking cartoon, Joe and Asbestos. Now, don't get me wrong. With Kling I'm a $200 man, maybe more. But all I need is four dollars and if the horse loses I want to punish myself.

In hooked horse players there's a bit of masochism. If this horse loses I want to order a seven-course dinner and send back every dish. I want to walk home. Walk, you sucker, walk. This is a two-year-old that's never started but he comes from a smart stable and clockers tip him to me.

The colt goes off at two to one and he's out in front till he bucks his shins. Pop goes Papa's graduation-day parlay. It doesn't really hurt until the next race when I make a five-to-one shot a fuzzy in the figures, but I'm broke and can't bet on him—and he wins.

That's the story of my life, the life story of all horse players. I have to borrow to buy my daughter a wrist watch, wholesale. At a party I arrange for her in a restaurant I ask her why there's no patron saint for horse players and she straightens me out.

"But there is, Daddy, there is," she says. "St. Jude—the patron saint of the hopeless cases."

Maybe her prayers are answered. A few days later I put across a twenty-dollar parlay on the last four winners and the payoff is in the thousands. I take out a little white card with the initials of the creditors alongside the amounts long due. The small creditors, the shortstops, have a priority. Another winning day and I'm circling off large creditors, the longstops.

Winning streaks never last as long as losing streaks. Now I'm getting daily-double exposures against me. Parlays are winding up in photos I don't care to hang on the wall. Round robins won't take wing, and I fail in one-horse punch plays, too. I'm working with short money again, but the shortstops are paid and most of the longstops. I tear up the little old white card and start a little new white card.

That's how it's been across the board across the years.

A friend tells me he's sorry I get whacked out, but I'm riding too high; I've got to fall the way he falls, the way they all fall. He says I need control. It's all right to speed up when I'm in front but I don't slow down when I'm behind.

My friend is Sammy Engelberg, rangy, smiling, honor student in speed-chart handicapping and a wizard pricemaker. He gives the figures away. He would rather be right than rich.

Now he is about to explain a betting method: You don't go for more than 10 per cent of the bankroll any day. Colonel E. R. Bradley, I remember, blueprints a similar plan for me one evening, while we are chatting on the veranda of the United States Hotel in Saratoga. But I don't follow it, I ask Sammy what I use for winners. I'm not worrying about money so long as I still got friends.

I ask him, do I use a wind meter? Because I know he's given the wind to every two-dollar bum and his brother. But humbly, out of the goodness of his heart, he says I shouldn't sell the wind short. When he is in the anti-aircraft in World War II, he remembers, anemometers are general issue. I remind Sammy shells have no pinhead jockeys to guide them and no flathead stewards to take down the number.

The struggle never ends. Speed or class?

But few seem to care about condition. One way or the other, it's always in the figures. Yet a horse with a big figure might have a bigger knee. That's where condition comes in. Newspaper handicappers use figures plucked mostly from speed charts. The *Form* papers and scratch sheets classify. Me? I'm strictly an angle handicapper, most of the angles obtuse.

"Well, anyway," says Sammy. "I don't care how you work. But you can't go broke in one day. You've got to be there tomorrow."

Now Sammy agrees that the only chance you have is with parlays. But he wants to know how many horses I want to put in a parlay. He's thinking of the day when we put up a few dollars apiece on a seven-horse parlay and it breaks in the middle. I got a hunch on Sammy and the wind that day and he comes up with six winners.

I'm thinking of Little Jonas, a big bettor who died some time ago. He invests 10 per cent of his bankroll daily on parlays. But Jonas gets the commission, the 5 per cent juice from bookmakers on losers, and that helps plenty at the end of a long season. The small, olive-skinned Jonas beats The Game with the kickback on the L's; but the strain of heavy betting wears him down.

He's in Las Vegas taking house-prices in a room for himself and his speed-chart counselors. That's strong, too. Morning-line prices, strong enough to steal for. Little Jonas goes to Los Angeles and takes a plane to New York to see his family. Three hundred miles out he suffers a heart attack and the plane returns to Los Angeles and they rush him to a hospital, where he passes away.

I go along with the Ten Per Cent Plan. I play horses as if I'm at a dice game, where they lay six to five on sixes and eights; three to two on nines and fives and two to one on tens and fours. Four straight passes, in a parlay, figure anywhere between 22 to 1, with sixes or eights, and 80 to 1, with tens and fours. I like dice games where you can bet as high as you want, man to man. With strangers, not with friends. I can't gamble against friends.

But in most highly organized dice games, where the house runs the book, they put a limit on a winner. What I like best about a race track is that there is no limit on a winner. You can take home the grandstand. But the trouble is I try to take home the grandstand in one day when I should be taking it home, seat by seat, to the end of a season.

I like the new Ten Per Cent Plan. My losses are limited and my winnings unlimited. If I start a parlay and the first horse loses I quit. I forget about the second horse. Stay stuck, sweat it out, wait. Who gets even on the last race? Track owners. I know men who go for fortunes trying to get even.

Bookies don't like to handle parlays and daily doubles. If it's no good for them, it must be good for me. I'm not going to flat-bet myself to the finance companies while bookies ride in Caddys. I find doubles dynamite when I use a key horse at around three to one with two, three or four long shots at the other end. It figures more than a parlay. But when I like two long shots I make a parlay, which pays more than the double.

Parlays, in round robin order, are a power play. When I try to give a handbook a round robin he hollers, "What are you trying to do? Stick me up?" In the old days I make round robins over untapped telephones, when the action is big and bookies juggle with my money, making straight bets on the round-robined horses and getting 5 per cent from other offices on the L's.

Now I make round robins at the race track. A card comes up, say, where I like Zev, Alsab and Nashua. I have $60 to put in action and I'm going to make three parlays, $20 a shot. I bet $40 on Zev in the second race. If Zev loses I've got $20 left to start a parlay with Alsab in the fourth, winding up with Nashua in the sixth. If Zev wins I collect $120. I bet $80 on Alsab in the fourth. Of this $60 is for the parlay with Zev and $20 starts a new parlay winding up on Nashua in the sixth. I save $60 to finish the parlay that begins with Zev and ends with Nashua.

I make six $100 parlays with four horses.

Here, instead of betting two-thirds of the ticket on the first horse, I bet one-half on the first horse or $300 to work out the flight of round robins. To find out how many parlays I can make I go to the digit below the number of horses. Say I go crazy and like eight horses on a card. I multiply eight by seven and divide the 56 by two, making 28 parlays for this round robin.

The day Sammy picks six winners with the wind we should be making 15 parlays. Six horses times five divided by two. That's what we should be doing, or would have done if I only think of it. Always the big little if.

I test the Ten Per Cent Plan with a $500 bankroll. Action the first day calls for $50 on the daily double. I lose. On the second day I must bet 10 per cent of the $450. I pick out a parlay, a horse in the fourth with a horse in the seventh. My own daily double; the track owners are not going to regiment me in the first and second race. I lose $45. I slow down but I'm still in action. Now for the next nine days I must make $25 parlays; and if I score I raise the original bankroll. Always be there tomorrow, be there tomorrow!

The Ten Per Cent Plan I can manage with thousands as well as hundreds. I can juggle, starting with 20 per cent of the original. With a $1,000 bankroll, the parlay cycle runs $200, $150, $100, $100, $100, $50, $50, $50, $50. With a $2,000 bankroll it starts with $400; with $600 on $3,000; $800 on $4,000. The first parlay is $1,000 when you work with a $5,000 bankroll. The parlay is always the theme, always the cycle to complete, and I can break a $10,000 bankroll down to $1,000 cycles, and last a long time and have a lot of fun, with a chance for a big score in between.

I don't have to polish off a parlay the same day. If I like one horse today I can parlay him with a horse I like tomorrow; the next day, or a horse I like three days from now. I can also arrange these parlays on a weekly basis, looking for stake events where I know all the jockeys are trying.

Well, I'm carrying out this Ten Per Cent Plan and I'm down to the bottom of the deck and I bail out on a daily double at big numbers. Be there tomorrow, be there tomorrow! If I stick to the old plan I'm whacked out days ago. Now I circle off all the creditors, shortstops and long-stops, and I'm out of hock for the first time in many years. It's a funny feeling and I'm walking around in a pleasant fog. I don't lose my head and I surprise myself when I stick to the Ten Per Cent Plan.

I go bad and yank myself out of the box, the way a baseball manager does with a pitcher that's got nothing on the ball, and I consult the Delphic oracles of the dope book. I look for Kingston Sam Astatas, thin, kindly, truthful, a crack classi-fier whose hole card is betting on winners to repeat. But I say to Kingston Sam, only class horses run two races alike; and I can't tell you exactly what class is but I think maybe it's con-sistency. Cheap horses beat one another contin-ually.

"Over the track." That's what Kingston Sam keeps saying, "Over the track." That's what all handicappers are saying across the board across the years, the speed charters, the classifiers, making their big plunges on horses over the track, over the track.

I look up Max (Mop Top) Fogel, who used to be with the Speed Boys. He checks in from New England for a short visit. We go over the dope and he bets around favorites, especially in the mud. He's a good man in the mud, like Ed Soule. But, brother, I can't con you. They're all good when they've got a little help, and better when they're working with other people's money. They play loose cards, then go for gin. With their own they knock with nine points and are undercut.

Pick-Your-Nose Willie, a speed-charter, is out of heavy action since the Kefauver investigation shuts down his outlet, getting morning-line prices from Eddie Dopkin in Chicago. These are the New Orleans figures we get in the old days from one of Kingy Schwartz's beardmen. Now there's Canadian figures. A syndicate is playing with comeback-money orders. I check and it looks like the wind. Who needs them for the wind?

Sammy's brother, Memphis, offers me the wind years ago. Memphis Engelberg says to me, "Tell me what kind of a speed chart you want and I'll order it for you. Do you want one that converts to time or one that converts to pounds?"

Memphis is one of the sweetest souls I ever meet across the board across the years. He holds the distinction of being the only member of the armed forces in World War II whose GI card shows, "occupation: handicapper."

I see my friend Eddie Burke from the days of the books and he says, "The P.C. is so high you got no chance if you take less than eight to one. Wait for a spot at eight to one or better. I tell you the fifteen per cent must whack out General Motors. It's silly, anyway. What they've got to do is build tracks with no P.C. on the tote. Crowds will run over 100,000 daily and the track owners and state can make money on the admissions alone. High admissions, that's all, pay the tax as you enter, instead of them giving you eight-five dollars worth of action on a hundred-dollar bet in the mutuel machines."

There's no exit. Whom can I follow? Maybe the system player in the paddock who reads the trainer's lips as he is giving instructions to the jockeys. But that system player is going bad, too. How do I get out?

An old neighbor, a Brooklyn opera impresario, Alfredo Salmaggi, says to me one day when he's going bad: "One week-a from Saturday night we get outta with *La Bohème*." But there's no such sure thing on a race track. Sometimes it drives me to whiskey. But that doesn't help. Tomorrow morning you see your troubles through a microscope. What's the answer? The key to knowledge has a question mark at the end of it.

I ask Al (The Brain) Winderman, champion of the speed charters, the Colonel James of the new generation, beating The Game with his own money. Al The Brain is soft-spoken, with the eyes of a mystic, and he says: "It takes about twenty years to learn how to play horses, and then I don't know whether it's worth the trouble. There's easier ways of making a fortune, and you don't run into unlucky streaks where you almost go out of your mind. If I didn't have my wife Ginger and the kids, I think I would have jumped into the ocean the time I was doing so bad at the Atlantic City meeting.

The Brain studies day and night. Observation is his long suit. He watches objectively every horse in the race. How many racegoers watch any horse but their own? The Brain watches all, even when he's got a big bet on one. Such objectivity amounts to genius.

He times horses with two watches, one in each hand, and manages to look through binoculars as an added stunt in these acrobatics. The Brain sits in the stands near the finish line with a crew of assistants. They keep voluminous records. As The Brain times, a crewman synchronizes a camera shot of the finish. The Brain's strength is in punch plays on two-year-olds. The two-year-olds are the most honest horses. When horses grow older they get smart, pull themselves up. There are dishonest horses, too.

I am out early on the opening day of a meeting, and I see The Brain walking around the racing strip, measuring the track's cushion. The depth of the cushion affects the speed. The Brain takes his work, but not himself, seriously, and he says to me, "Well, you got me with the goods and I'll have to give you the gismo. After that all you'll need is time, patience and money.

"You should know by now there's more slightly used speed charts around than broken-down horse players. It's easy to fix one up, with high or low numbers. After you do that—you need a track variant, and that differs from race to race. The composition of the soil and the moisture it contains affects a track's speed. I check the sprinkler wagons all afternoon, because I know the speed varies with every drink. Tracks near the seashore may change in speed with the tides. And the big thing, hard to figure, is the degree of attention the track had in the morning with harrows, levelers or scrapers.

"I started playing horses in the early twenties, when Morvich was a two-year-old, in fact. What numbers I had on him! Well, in those days the tracks had individuality. So did The Game. Nowadays the tracks are speeded up for track records and big headlines. The soil is mixed freely with sand, and that acts as a sieve for water, and horses sometimes hang out faster time when a track is sloppy than when it's dry. Mud doesn't last long the way it did in the old days when the soil contained more clay, which absorbs moisture.

"Speed-charters, to tell you the truth, are classifiers, only they use a basis in time to arrive at classifications. Classifiers who ignore time can only compare horses out of the same race, and when they must figure them with horses out of other races they don't have a guide, like speed-charters."

The Game doesn't change. George (Pittsburgh Phil) is saying, "If you can classify horses you can beat races."

Class dismissed at Prosperity College. But I

know all along what The Brain really has on The Game—iron nerve. I remember the day he sells his automobile to bet on a private equation at Belmont Park. This is just a little experience in the life of a man whose iron nerve stands out like Winston Churchill in the Battle of Britain! He's vain about his figures but he blushes when I remind him of his iron nerve. That's the gismo within the gismo.

I remind The Brain of the time he is at Santa Anita working with a big crew. Mario the Sheik is in the infield, standing on a bench with a wind meter in hand. Dr. Charles Strub, boss of the track, flanked by a platoon of private eyes, rushes to see what's going on. He suspects the Sheik is getting set to flash information to Continental News Service, maybe working with a walkie-talkie to speed information for the bookies. The Doctor says to the Sheik, "What's going on here?"

"Nothing. I'm taking the wind."

"The wind?"

"How can The Brain work without the wind?"

"The Brain?"

"You mean you don't know The Brain?"

Dr. Strub cracks a smile and says, "There are many brains on a race track."

The Sheik says emphatically, "But there's only one Brain. Al The Brain, from Brooklyn. He's got to have the wind. He puts plenty of money in the mutuels."

"You don't tell me," Dr. Strub laughs. "I've got movie producers out here who bet thousands without looking at a program."

So, after this consultation with The Brain, and the privilege of getting secret figures from a Sphinx who doesn't even tell his wife what he's doing until the horses are nearing the starting gate, I lose control.

I go bad again, but with the best of it, The Brain's figures, and he happens to be going bad at the time. I go off the Ten Per Cent Plan. It's the human system that beats all betting systems.

Pat O'Brien, brilliant young turf writer with the *Blood-Horse,* says to me in the press stand, "You've tried everything but the absolute strength of The Game—making book!" But you need luck with that, too. Even The Brain needs luck, like the day he's broke at Saratoga and he meets a friend just in time to borrow money to bet on a 20-to-1 shot that wins in a photo.

Sholem Aleichem has a word for it, *schlimazel,* one who never does anything right. In one way or another, aren't we all *schlimazels?* On a race track there's a procession of *schlimazels.* Moisha Workouts, the master of the Eastern Parkway Foxhounds, and his whipper-in, Benny the Bagel Maker. Moisha lives in a room that looks as if he has a subrent from the Collyer brothers, clips

of workouts strewn all over the floor. Benny argues with him that you can't beat the races checking workouts, because clockers who get up with the milkman for twenty dollars a day aren't going to give you all the right works, and anyway horses don't run to their works.

Harry the Shipper Schlepper pulls angles on horses that ship into New York from out-of-town tracks. "They didn't come here to ride the subway," he says. Sometimes he's right, but a shipper-schlepper is better off when it's a New York horse going out of town. "But them handbooks call a policeman when you hit them with four-figure mutuels," he says. "They say you're fixing races."

The most intense *schlimazel* is Itchky the Pastry Baker, putting in hellish hours at an oven, taking his salary, betting it all on one horse, parlaying down the line, then back to the oven for a new bankroll. "I listen to guys with holes in their shoes," he smiles. He quits the runners for the pacers and now I call him Adios Itchky the Pastry Baker.

Most of the time I bet on my opinion. Die with the dope, as Nick F. used to say, die with the dope. Even if your opinion is bad it's better than shuffling around, getting caught in the switches. One day the speed charters come up with winners; the next day the classifiers come up with winners; and some days nobody comes up with winners, except a sweet old lady in the grandstand holding a ticket on a $1,384 daily double, and she's smarter than the speed charters, the classifiers, the owners, trainers, jockeys, clockers.

What do you need to know? I recall the day I'm at Bowie. I go there with a bankroll I get pawning a pair of binoculars. I lose the expense money the paper advances me. I stay a few days after the assignment ends. I got to get out of hock. I'm in the clubhouse celebrating my forty-first birthday. I play four and one in the daily double. This is what you need to know. I'm sitting at a table marked "41." I press the bet. Mrs. Josephine O'Hara, the lovely lady-president of the track—more ladies should run tracks—gives me a birthday party.

My daily double wins. I bet on another winner, then a loser, then a winner, and in the last race I spot a Canadian horse that is 50 to 1 in the morning line. I am cured that year betting on short-priced horses. I won't take less than two to one. Maybe, here and there, a solid eight to five. I won't take three to five the next Pope is an Italian. I keep studying the hidden form on this long shot. Speed, with no speed in here to go with him. Two easy races over the track. It's near the wind-up of the meeting. They can't wait any more.

Canadian horsemen are clever mechanics. They infiltrate the mutuel lines, betting small sums on long shots, picking up more than they would by making a big plunge in the pools. I tell my friends at the table this horse will take the track and never come out of a pull. He will win pricking his ears.

They think I'm crazy on this craziest day I ever spend at a race track. I give the horse to dimpled, puckish George Dixon, the columnist who is my Washington beardman, and he must have spread it around to Congress and the Cabinet, and maybe a comeback-money order comes from No. 10 Downing Street, on Rise to Follow; and he wins by ten lengths and pays only 30 to 1. I'm out of hock for the first time in years.

Dixon comes to the table with George Allen, court jester for Presidents, and he says to me, "I just bet Allen you could make him laugh." I say to Dixon, "Who can't laugh after a day like this at the races?"

Dixon wants Allen to hear the story about the handicapper and the crayons. I tell Allen about the handicapper who marked off speed horses with blue crayon, middle-of-the-pace horses with green crayon, and stretch runners with brown crayon. A friend looks over the multicolored form chart and asks, "What's the red crayon for?"

The handicapper says, "That's not crayon; that's my blood."

Allen laughs and pays off a bet that night—dinner at Harvey's.

I have action and fun across the board across the years, and I'm sitting home one Sunday afternoon and having action and fun in a way I neglect across the board across the years. I don't know. All I know is I don't know. I'm improvising on a typewriter as if it's the piano at the old house in Brooklyn . . . and I'm thinking of my mother and father giving me their hard-earned money for music lessons and me sending a beard into the Book on the Block to bet two-if-four . . . Bach to Bach. . . .

Maybe I should stick to music. . . . Maybe . . . . I know in my secret heart I would rather orchestrate like Richard Wagner than win a billion dollars on horses. But if I make that career in music I play horses, anyway. . . .

"Other men just lose their money by luck—you got to figure out
how to do it."

DRAWING BY HOFF   [© 1958 BY THE NEW YORKER MAGAZINE, INC.]

NATIONAL
JOCKEYS
HALL OF FAME

1

2

3

4

5

6

7

8

9

10

11

12

13

14

15

16

17

1. *Ted Atkinson*
2. *Eddie Arcaro*
3. *Steve Brooks*
4. *Laverne Fator*
5. *Mack Garner*
6. *Edward (Snapper) Garrison*
7. *John Patrick Loftus*
8. *Johnny Longden*
9. *Linus (Pony) McAtee*
10. *James McLaughlin*
11. *Walter Miller*
12. *Isaac Murphy*
13. *Joe Notter*
14. *Earl Sande*
15. *Carroll Shilling*
16. *William Shoemaker*
17. *Tod Sloan*
18. *George Woolf*
19. *Raymond "Sonny" Workman*

18

19

Lost Horse

WILLIAM BONIFACE

Bill Boniface, turf editor of the Baltimore Sunpapers, has spent most of his sports writing trying to pick winners for subscribers and making deadlines with late-bulletin results. I like this story because it gave Bill an opportunity to write the kind of story he prefers and it proves he is more of a sentimentalist than he cares to admit.

For the first time in more than 200 years, Maryland's Belair Stud, home of first Governor Ogle, is down to one Thoroughbred and an unwelcome one at that. But he's there only because he's lost.

Prince Simon, American-bred horse who became the leading three-year-old of England in 1950 and who returned to this country a conquering hero aboard the *Queen Mary,* presents a touching picture as he stands proudly alone among the stubby shorthorn cattle now overrunning Belair's stables and pastures.

The Prince would have been crowded off the 2,500 acres some weeks ago if he had anywhere to go. But he doesn't. He's truly a horse without an owner.

It's a strange twist of fate which puts this oncefamous race horse whose competitive spirit and stout-hearted performance in the English Derby thrilled the queen and 150,000 of her subjects, in such a humiliating position.

He was given away by William Woodward, Jr., just five days before the wealthy sportsman was accidentally killed in his Long Island home last fall. The 37-year-old master of Belair never got around to telling anyone to whom he had given the horse.

So far, the person who was to have received the gift has not claimed Prince Simon. Whether the rightful owner be a man, woman, or child remains a mystery and the Prince remains Belair's uninvited guest.

Since he's taking up room which could stable and graze three or four shorthorns, a farm hand was tempted to ask: "When are they going to get him out of the way?"

However, the dignity and pride with which nine-year-old Prince Simon struts before visitors seems to reply, "This is my heritage. I belong here."

Nothing could be more true. The very stable Prince Simon now shares with beefy, waddling cattle has been the home of no lesser Thoroughbred greats than Gallant Fox, Omaha (both Kentucky Derby winners), Johnstown, Fighting Fox, and more recently, Nashua.

What will happen to Belair's last horse?

It is hoped this story will bring forth the owner. Otherwise, trustees of the Woodward estate still have to find a good home for the gelding or have him humanely destroyed.

After being acclaimed throughout England as the best horse never to win the English Derby—he lost by a nose to Galcador in one of the roughest "darbies" in history—Prince Simon was returned to this country to stand at stud at famous Claiborne Farm in Kentucky.

"He was not a complete failure at stud," explains Bill Davison, manager of Belair Stud. "He was somewhat impotent, however, and Mr.

Woodward decided to dispense with his services. He was shipped to Belair last fall and he had him gelded.

"Mr. Woodward flew in here the Tuesday before he was killed and talked about giving Prince Simon away, but the subject changed before he said to whom he had given the horse. I'm waiting for the New York office to let me know what to do with him."

When Prince Simon leaves Belair it will mark the end of an era in the breeding of American Thoroughbreds. An era which began 206 years ago with the importation of a British-bred mare, Selima, to Belair estate.

When bloodline experts go back far enough they find the name Selima in the pedigrees of many famous members of the great Belair stables of the last 35 years.

The mare was foaled in England April 30, 1745. Five years later she was purchased by Colonel Benjamin Tasker and shipped across the Atlantic aboard a four-masted ship. She was unloaded in Maryland and led by a halter along the long, dusty road to the colonel's Belair Stud Farm in Bowie.

Lord Godolphin, from whom Selima was purchased, had reported to Colonel Tasker that the mare was in foal. But the colonel's wait was unavailing. Upon discovering the mare barren, the colonel placed her in training.

Her first race in this country was at Annapolis, then the home of the Maryland Jockey Club and where George Washington is reported often to have attended the sport. She won a match race over Creeping Katie, owned by Lawrence Butler.

When Selima was seven, she was retired to Belair Stud, where she produced six foals. Her most noted colt was Selim, who was purchased as a yearling by an Annapolitan, Samuel Galloway. Selim made his first start at four and his last at 13. Until he was nine years old he was undefeated. That's when the majority of races were at a four-mile distance.

Selima was Belair's first Thoroughbred. Apparently Prince Simon will be its last.

Selima was a British-bred mare who came to Belair to prove a champion in a new land. Two centuries later, Prince Simon, an American-bred horse, left Belair to become an English champion. Stories of the champions who came in between the two would fill several volumes.

When Prince Simon leaves Belair's picturesque, vine-covered brick stable, only a few dim reminders of the fabulous past will remain.

Unmovable as long as the stable stands is a bronze tablet made 30 years ago by an English sculptress, Kathleen Wheeler. This handsome work of art—cemented into the wall—shows Selima with a foal at her side. She is depicted as a fine old brood mare, gazing absently across the pasture while her foal nibbles grass at her side.

Also, the stable entrance and yard are decorated by three iron jockeys dressed in the famous white-and-red polka-dot silks of the Woodward family. Time and weather probably will erase the colors but never the memories.

Incidentally, the prized shorthorn bull now occupying the stall which once confined Gallant Fox is named Rosemer's Sensation.

"Stanley, there's a Mr. Bookie here to see you."

DRAWING BY **FRANK RIDGEWAY**   [© 1956 BY THE CURTIS PUBLISHING COMPANY]

Rivers of Damascus

DONN BYRNE

The most popular turf reading consists of the Daily Racing Form, *but the literature of racing is found among the works of many fine writers not ordinarily associated with the sport. Donn Byrne's story is appealing for its literary quality and for his adept treatment of the subject.*

Now, if he had been a white man, with his little spare body, his powerful hands, his light legs and wizened face, you might have taken him for what he was, a jockey. But as he was colored, you would hardly think of that. One is apt to forget the black man's light, strong legs, his beautiful hands for a horse's mouth, his strange, caressing way with animals. Besides, one's experience of jockeys is that they are invariably well-dressed in that exaggerated mode that passes for smartness on Broadway and Piccadilly. But this one was dressed in a French suit, baggy trousers with gussets, waisted coat, and shoes that turned up at the toe like a Turk's slippers. His favorite seat was on the Promenade des Anglais at Nice, where he sat on a public wooden bench and sunned himself like a cat because there was nothing else for him to do. His name—none remember it now—was Les Armstrong.

Now, a Negro in Nice is not something to look and wonder at and perhaps shoot, if you have a spare cartridge, as he would be in Ireland. From Martinique, from Madagascar, from Algeria they come and are welcomed as free men and brothers. They dress like the smarter sort of Frenchman, and often are "princes in their own country." But this poor chap, sitting on the smartest promenade in the world, dressed in a suit of cheap French reach-me-downs, was Virginian American and proud of it. To him a khan of India or a bey of Algiers was a "nigger." He was an American. He did not proclaim it in an arrogant manner, for there was no arrogance in him. As he sat there

on the Promenade des Anglais reading his Continental edition of an American paper, picking possible winners at Auteuil, and wondering which of the surreptitious French bookmakers he could trust with his ten or twenty francs, there was about him the dignity all small gentle people have. A Moor of Tunis in white burnous, with prayer carpets for sale, approached him. There was a quiet superiority in the little jockey's "Nix, guy, nix!" that put him, who was a sheik in his own country, as all Riviera Moors are, into his proper plane of color.

And yet if he had not been so loyally American, as indeed it would have been to his advantage not to be, one could hardly have blamed him. For it was only two afternoons ago that paying his fifty centimes, or half a nickel, he had gone into the Jetty Casino, on the off-chance of picking up a little on *petits chevaux*. The throbbing drum and the moaning bassoon of the band playing the blues had drawn him in curiosity to the dancing-floor. There they circled slowly around, English peer and demi-mondaine, American millionaire and shady countess, professional gambler and his female lure, Egyptian prince and fair, postwar Englishwoman, little Provençal shopkeepers who love to dance. And honeymooners from Scotland, or Birmingham perhaps, who are thrilled to the core at being one with the mad, bad life of France; and who will bore their grandchildren with descriptions of how wild grandpa and granny were when young. The little jockey looked on with pathetic face, for he loved dancing. A slim Creole instructress from Martinique, whom he had spoken to once, took pity on him.

"*Voulez-vous . . . ?*"

"Why, doggone, I'd just love to. You sure are one decent girl!"

They had made a half circle when the band stopped. It would go on again in a second or two if the applause warranted. High above the clapping of hands, a woman's voice rang out abruptly.

"Look here. I'm not going on if this thing's allowed."

The little jockey turned around. A hard-faced brittle woman was pointing at him. Les Armstrong didn't know her, but he knew her type. He had often seen it flash from limousine to baccarat rooms in furs and diamonds. He flushed and turned to the little instructress.

"You excusez me, mademoiselle. One moment."

He went toward the hard-faced woman, making up a little speech as he went: "Ma'am, if you want me to, I won't dance on this floor again. But, if you don't mind, I'll dance this dance, because this little professional girl asked me to. Ma'am, I'm sorry, I'm real sorry."

But he never got a word of it out, for the woman's escort, a burly man of six feet two, caught him a vicious crack with the right fist on the side of the head. It was a fat man's punch, untimed, all elbow; but it was heavy. It caught the little one-hundred-and-fifteen-pounder on neck and ear and smashed him to the floor as if he had been picked up and hurled. It stunned him. Attendants, detectives, what not, rushed over. In all the commotion Armstrong could hear the fat man's voice say:

"I'm an American, sir! And we don't stand for these guys dancing on the same floor as white women."

The little jockey knew that, American or not, if he had been a French Negro, by now the fat man would have been led off by police to be placed in jail, unbailed. The interpreter was bawling in his ear.

"You wish make no complaint? No, you no wish make complaint. No, he make no complaint."

"No," said Armstrong quietly, "I don't want to make no complaint."

He tottered up and away, leaving the little instructress, her blazing eyes filled with tears, her body crisp as a tiger's, without a word of farewell. Somebody pushed his hat into his hand. He slunk past the loud boule table, and out into the mellow sunset.

"I ain't ever going into that joint never any more."

He walked along the promenade blindly.

"I had no right to dance on that floor nohow. . . ."

"Doggone, what could I do, when that little girl asked me . . ."

"Them black Frenchmen dance. Nobody says a word. . . ."

The worst of it was he had recognized the big man who struck him. He had seen him at the Longchamps races, and later outside Monte Carlo. A year before when the English hunter, Devan Pride, had won a big race with himself up, the fat man had pushed through the crowd when Armstrong was on his way to the scales with his saddle over his arm. "Attaboy!" he had shouted. "Attaboy! You showed them Frenchies what an American boy can do!"

"He ain't no American. . . .

"Ain't I heard that guy outside the Café de Paris knocking America to a bunch of Englishmen and saying he was so sick of it he couldn't live there any more? Yes, boy, I did."

He stood and looked at the flaming Esterel. There were tears in his eyes. His heart was more hurt than his ear and neck were.

"He ain't no American. . . . No American would hit a little guy like me. . . ."

The truth of the matter was that he was ill—more ill than even he knew. At times his face would take on a brownish gray color and his knees tremble for no reason. But this would pass, and he would feel all right again.

Years of sweating down to keep his weight down had taken the vitality out of him; and homesickness, that thing that gnaws like a rat, had eaten his heart. Because he had never accustomed himself to read anything but newspapers, and because that dingy little room of his in Old Nice was so lonely, his nights would be passed in bars a little more sordid and less artificial than those of Paris.

Hither would come, when the tables of the Casino closed, women in diamonds and men in evening clothes for a cocktail or a dance or a look at the underworld. Once when some of them were present he keeled over.

He came to in a second or so. A burly man with the red face of a butcher, and wearing a white carnation in his dinner jacket, was holding his wrist. Little Armstrong didn't know it, but the beefy citizen was Sir Michael O'Callaghan, the Dublin surgeon known to all Ireland as "Big Mike."

He had come south "to cut the tripes out of some Grand Jook, begob!" but the colored jockey was getting for nothing the thought and sympathy that had cost the Romanoff half an emerald mine.

"Boy, you're sick," he roared.

"Yes, sir. I knows."

"Do you? What's wrong with you?"

"No, sir. I don't."

"Why don't you go home?"

"Yes, sir. Why?"

"What do you do? Follow the races?"

"Yes, sir. I follows the races now. I was a good jockey once. Some folks as knew," he added quietly, "said there was none better."

Big Mike thought an instant. Only those who knew him intimately, knew how deeply religious he was, would have caught the meaning of his next remark.

"Well, boy, there's a good time coming soon."

He dug his hand into his pocket where his baccarat winnings were: pulled out a thousand-franc note. The little jockey shook his head.

"I don't want to hurt your feelings, no, sir, but I ain't got as far as that yet. It sure was good of you—"

"Well, you'll have a drink on me," said Big Mike. "Garsong," he shouted in his abominable French, "apportez un poo brandy quicko!" He patted the colored man on the shoulder and left him. There was nothing else to do.

"If that big man had been home folks, now," the jockey would talk to himself afterwards on his seat on the promenade, "I sure could have taken his money. I couldn't let no stranger say an American boy had taken his money. No, sir. Doggone, that guy sure was a white man."

He had been born outside Norfolk, Virginia, and his early days had been happy. His father he remembered as a cheery, fat, small man, always laughing; his mother had been a raw-boned Louisiana woman. But his father died when he was eleven, and the mother removed to New Orleans. There his mother went bad, taking to drink and a saturnine Jamaican who saw to it that she kept him in the state to which Jamaicans of the better sort are accustomed. The Jamaican, who bore the name of Horatio Wilson Jones, beat little Les on every possible occasion. Hence his dislike of New Orleans and his love for Virginia where he had been happy as a child. The only refuge was the race track, where he made himself useful, running errands for grooms and handlers. One day, as a joke, he was given a leg up at exercise on a five-year-old selling plater. He went around the track as if he had been cradled in pigskin.

Now, anybody can acquire a good seat on a horse, even—I have it on competent authority—a Knight of the British Empire; but hands are indubitably the gift of God. And hands little Les had. So in the course of a few years he was taken on as apprentice, and later on rose to the dignity of having a black plate with his name on it in white letters—Les Armstrong. Within a couple of years he had won two or three sound races. And then he began "pulling the hat trick," which means winning three races in one day. He did it two or three times a season, so his future was assured.

He went North to New York for the summer season at Empire and Jamaica and Tuxedo, where for various reasons he didn't do so well. There is a great deal more in racing than meets the eye. And wizened white jockeys cannot be blamed, if you look at the matter from the human standpoint, because they are not enthusiastic about a colored jockey winning. In my own most sporting country, in a large field, I should be tremendously surprised to see an English jockey win a race, no matter how good his mount is. But that is for psychologists.

An owner gave him the chance to come to Paris for the season, to ride there and at the seaside courses, at Deauville. Armstrong had heard of the great Paris races, of the fine horses, and the flower of European society, the beautiful midinettes, the royalty on the lawn. "Doggone, I'll go," he laughed. "I sure wants to see this Paris."

He found out very soon that little interest was attached to the horses. They were an adjunct to the betting machines. For flat racing, few out of the multitude cared. Hurdles and steeplechases were the popular idea of what the racing should be, the jumps being thrown in to make the gambling a little more thrilling, as deuces are made wild in a poker game. Of how a horse was bred few cared. To whom the horse belonged mattered a lot. And owners' instructions were often very puzzling. One had the impression of them meeting the night before the race, in the Casino. "This poor Gaston," the Alphonses would say, "this poor Gaston, my old, has not won a race at the meeting. Impossible! But I, who speak to you! His pleasure here will be spoiled, utterly spoiled. Also his legitimate will say: 'I told you so! Why didn't you stick to politics?' Gaston must win tomorrow. No! No! Gaston, we insist!" All this may be untrue, but one got the impression. Also, Gaston won.

With the four-year-olds and five-year-olds over the hurdles Armstrong was singularly successful. He seemed to know to an ounce what a horse could do. Warily, waiting for the exact second, he would nurse his mount along, that touch of the nervous muscular hands telling the horse that he knew what he was doing, until the most nervous, fractious, ill-treated racer knew that it was in the hands of a comrade and a master. Owners might rave, bettors tear their beards and weep, as French bettors will, but until his moment arrived, Les never moved, and then, a touch of the little finger on the reins, a tightening of the knees, and his husky friendly: "Horse, let's go!" and he would sweep along to take his easy win or certain place, as the mount was worth. The sight of the fluttering silk, the black face and black hands pounding up from behind came to be a recognized feature of certain race courses. *"Le noir, il gagne, il gagne encore,"* they would shout on the lawn, "the black wins, wins again." It was as though he were the color on a roulette wheel.

And at steeplechasing, too, he lifted three or four of the big plumes, and a host of minor ones. For some reason or other the horses took to the colored American jockey. They liked his hand, they liked his confidence, they knew he was a master in his craft.

Then Armstrong's luck turned.

He was riding, for a French owner, a big brown gelding called Mistral, a son of Chimney Sweep, a fine fencer and a horse with a great heart; and coming to the last hurdle, he felt that little give in the stride that told him his mount had gone lame.

"Doggone!" he said. "This baby's gone and hurt himself."

His eyes shifted, pivoted in his still head, to the mounts beside him. He noticed the falter, the half-stride lost at the hurdle. From the lawn in front the crowds were shouting "Mistral! Mistral!"A big English gray beside him began to stretch. He leaned over and showed Mistral the whip. The big dun never quickened his stride.

"Doggone," Armstrong said, "he ain't got nothing no more."

The shouts came louder. *"Tuez-le! Tuez-le!* Kill him! Kill him!" And some voice was calling in English: "Beat him up, Les! Beat him up!" Armstrong slackened his reins.

"Another race another day, boy," he said to the big chaser.

He was halfway across the lawn when the owner accosted him, a huge, burly man with a huge curling, black beard like that of an Assyrian king, oiled and perfumed. His black eyes were like snake's eyes, alive with venom.

"Vat you do?" he shouted. "Vat you do?"

"I pulled up your horse, monsoo, because he'd gone lame."

"Vy you pull up, ha? Vy you pull up?"

"I said: because your horse had gone lame."

"Couldn't you get a place, ha? No? Yes, you get a place?" He leaned over half smothering the little jockey with his exquisite beard. People began to gather, chattering.

"I guess I could have, if I'd killed that horse, but I ain't going to kill no horse for no owner, no, sir."

The Frenchman's fingers contracted, like the claws of a hawk. They suddenly descended on Armstrong's shoulder, ripping the silk jacket from his back, leaving him a ridiculous figure in a sleeveless gray woolen shirt, with black arms like brittle sticks, among the concourse of chic women and men dressed in gray cutaways and black stocks with diamonds in them. The owner waved the torn jacket in the air.

"Ainsi aux caguins!" he bellowed. "Thus treat rascals." He might have been the chief executioner of an antique commonwealth holding up a bleeding head. "Thus perish traitors!" It was all ridiculous!

"I don't care," Armstrong said. "I ain't going to kill no horse for no man. A win is only a win," he said, "but a horse, well, a horse is a horse."

It was ridiculous, but—

Caesar's wife must be above suspicion, but what must Caesar's jockey be? The cold attitude of that righteousness is terrifying. To pull a horse, to slacken up, all this is right if the owner says it is. But, to be under the suspicion of not obeying the owner's orders is the chief sin of the racing world, the penalty for which is the chief penalty of the racing world—no mounts.

He may be all right and he may not, say owners; he's a nice fellow, he's a good rider, but this is a hard enough game as it is, without taking extra chances—

All the mounts he got now were rank outsiders with which he was expected to do miracles, but miracles are not done on race courses unless the stage has been carefully set beforehand. The vanishing favorite of a race course must be as carefully prepared as the Vanishing Lady in vaudeville. The other mounts he got were horses conditioning up, who hadn't a chance in the race, but were out for exercise. Added to this, his luck had definitely turned. Riderless mounts seemed to like getting in his way in preference to other jockeys'. And three times he took a toss trying to jam through at fences, where, had he had a decent horse, he would have waited his time. Little by little his name disappeared. That thing the French denote as luck, and which we more sensible folk call the phenomenon of the law of averages, had left him. And when that thing leaves a man definitely, he is in a bad way.

There is something about French money, too, that lacks power. It hasn't the efficient look of a five-dollar bill, nor the crisp solidity of a pound. It has a consumptive, appealing look that makes you extremely generous with it, so you part with it saying: after all, it's only francs. It is only when they are gone that one considers that those flimsy notes might not have been so anemic after all. Also, if there is one person who is more foolish about money than a prize fighter, it is a jockey, for the fighter has usually sense enough not to bet on fights.

So after a while of barren racing and money given into that most heartless of all human contraptions, the Totalizator, Armstrong felt himself poor.

"Doggone," he said, "I must ride me a winner."

He went South to Pau. The local papers greeted the Parisian jockey with a column of eulogy. But after he had been down the field three consecutive days, the papers were silent, if the public weren't.

"Doggone," he puzzled, "I must have passed a funeral, or a cross-eyed woman, or something."

At Marseilles it was the same story. No winners and plunging on the pari mutuel, until he discovered with a shock that he was down to his last thousand-franc note. A thousand francs is roughly fifty dollars; but 50 is a good masculine sum with which much can be done. A thousand francs—well, all you can do with it is spend it.

He had, as all men have, one song he was fond of singing. It was the only song a white man had written for Negroes that the Negroes love: "Carry me back to old Virginny." That was the song he whistled or sang as he tested girths and leather:

Carry me back to old Virginny,
There's where the cotton and the corn and taters
    grow;
There's where the birds warble sweet in the
    springtime,
There's where this old darky's heart am long'd
    to go.

There never had been anyone to work for, barring owners for whom one rode, and his only experience of cornfields was to see them as he passed in trains, but he would sing the little song as though the words translated a life of personal experience:

There's where I labored all day in the cotton,
There's where I worked in the fields of yellow
    corn—

But this he understood—

No place on earth do I love more sincerely
Than old Virginny, the state where I was born.

Night would steal over Marseilles, the last rays of the sun bless Notre Dame de la Garde; along the ancient Prado the lights would come up one by one, the Cannebrière blaze suddenly, and he would feel that he was in a strange city, stranger than any he had known. Here people were interested in ships, not in horses.

He moved along the quays of the Vieux Port, and like an answer from heaven to a breathed prayer he saw on the counter of a freighter the name *Elisha Hopkins,* Baltimore.

"Doggone," he said, "Baltimore, Maryland."

If it had occurred six weeks before, when he had money in his pocket, and no sense that his luck was black out, he would have gone direct to the master and bargained for a passage home, or made friends with the doctor, as the ship's cook is familiarly called, who was probably one of his own race. But bad luck brings timidity.

"I'll just sneak aboard and lay low, and when the boat's off, I'll come out and tell the stewards I'm an American boy out of luck, and everything will be all right. Yes, boy!"

He did manage to slip up the gangplank, and work into a lifeboat under the tarpaulin. It had

been raining, and the boat, for all its cover, was half filled with glutinous water, in which he knelt shivering. But the hawk-eyed mate noticed something amiss, and had the cover off.

"Come out o' that," he directed. He was a florid Scandinavian type. Armstrong came out.

"Stowaway, hey?"

"Boss, I'm an American—"

"That's what they all are."

"I'm trying to get back home," he said. "I'm sure sick of this France."

"You'll be sicker before you're through, my lad." He motioned up two policemen from the pier. Armstrong trembled.

"You ain't going to turn me over to the cops, boss," he pleaded.

"You didn't think I was going to give you flowers, did you?"

"Boss, you wouldn't do that to an American."

"I done it to fifty, kid. You're the fifty-first." The mate was cruel. He was one of those men in whom cruelty is a vice, as drugs and drink are in other men.

"I guess," Armstrong gave in, "I'm out of luck."

"Look-a-here," the mate gave him a baffled wicked glance that made him shiver. "You're in luck. That's what you are. What I does to stowaways, when I finds them aboard at sea, though I says it myself, it's a shame. They don't exactly die, but they ain't any good after. You believe it, nigger. You're in luck."

So the police took him, speaking words to him he couldn't understand, and the judge, in a language he couldn't understand, gave him a month. They kept him sewing mail bags and coats for Moroccan soldiers, while he never spoke. Warders with beards and warders with fine mustaches saw to it he worked: "*Allez-houp!*" they would call, as to a broken-down cab-horse. Occasionally his little song would come to his lips in a quavering nostalgia.

There's where the birds warble sweet in the
    springtime,
There's where this old darky's heart am long'd
    to go.

But "*Silence, le noir!*" they would shout, and he would bend over his sewing again, his eyes blinded.

They fed him on fish, which he could hardly eat, so nauseating did he find it. They gave him a cough, which can be cured, and a broken heart, which cannot. And on the thirtieth day they took him out and gave him his own clothes again. They led him to the door of the jail, where he stood blinking for an instant in the sunlight. They pushed him along. "*En route!*" they called. "Off with you now," and they added, out of the kindness of their hearts, "*Au revoir!*"

On leaving Marseilles he walked eastward toward Italy, not for the reason he needed carfare, but for this: that he feared that everyone on the railroad carriage would know he had been in jail. For each of us, white, black or yellow, has his degradation point. It may be drink or drugs, or nobbling a horse, or cheating at cards. With the little jockey it was having been in jail. It put him in his own mind on the level with those of his race who used razors in brawls, of the traveling Negro hoboes who are accused of brutal crimes. His thought went back to the laughing father in Norfolk, whom he remembered so dimly, so affectionately.

"I'm glad the old man croaked," he said. "It sure would have hurt him bad, to know his boy was a bum."

"Yes, boy, that's all you is." Tears came into his eyes. "You is a bum, a plain bum."

He trudged along the long road to Nice, a withered black speck of broken humanity, by the Mediterranean, bluest of all oceans, catlike, indifferent. It which had seen Tyre and Sidon, the crowning cities, go; Greece crumble; Rome pass—not one breath, or chime of sympathy came from that harsh Latin sea. Atlantic, our mother, would have breathed comfort. And the sullen supercilious Alps, they had seen so many pass by. The greatest Caesar, gallant Eugene of Savoy, Napoleon. What did they care for the black speck on the road? Some ancient hoary mountain may have blinked in its sleep, remembering how centuries ago the black folk were Lords of the Isles of Lerius and the scourge of the littoral, and thought: Have these bronze supple men gone too? Have they come to this? Everything passes, everything grows tired, everything breaks. Only we, born of ice and fire abide—we and the stars.

He had an impression that in Nice his troubles would cease. There was a city with Americans; Nice was a city with races—some of the biggest stakes in France were run for there. It would be a month or more before the races began, but he would lie up and get well—get rid of this cough, doggone!—and luck must change. There were two desires in his heart—to get back to Virginia, and to ride a great horse to victory before he went, for when he went back, he knew, it would be going from fair to fair with the trotters and pacers. He would never swing a leg over pigskin any more.

Armstrong found Nice a pleasant town. Here and there were bars behind which were men who had been in America, French waiters who had picked up a good deal of the American language and a certain aptitude in mixing cocktails, and returning to France had been raised to the episcopal rank of bartender. Though few of these had been farther south than New York, it set the blood warm in his veins to talk about Empire race track, and Butler's horses, and Jamaica. And they had heard of Ral Parr's great string in Kentucky, and Man o' War, whose immense stride was a miracle. To these ex-missionaries, now bishops, of the catering world, he would discourse on the temperament of the horse.

"There is something about a horse, doggone, look-a-here. If a horse is a mean horse, he's just naturally mean. If a man is mean, it may be his relatives, it may be his wife, it may be he ain't a well man. But a horse ain't got no relatives, ain't got no wife, and if a horse is sick, you call the vet. Then if it's proven to you that a horse is born mean, then you got to get around that some way. Look-a-here, a man may be yellow, and you never find that out in all your life. But if a horse is yellow, you find it out the first time you're in the home stretch and the favorite's creeping up on you. You says: Horse, here's where you pay for your oats, and if he lies down and dies, boy, you know he's a dog. A horse ain't no actor. Me, I knows horses, but I don't get men."

And then he would say, in a queer tone of voice, very different from his enthusiastic tone of before:

"Horses remember you!"

One day a piece of luck came his way. A 50-to-1 shot rolled home at Marseilles, on which he had ten francs. So he could still go around his accustomed haunts.

At all these places he was welcome, because at two o'clock in the morning he gave an air of disreputability to the place that was worth money. Most of the night bars were intensely respectable, the proprietor insisted on it, and his wife more so, for little Jean-Baptiste, or Pierre-Marie, when he grew to be a marshal like Pétain, or a premier like Poincaré, mustn't be ashamed of his origin. So the pretty ladies were dragooned like a girls' school. If they wished to be rough, let them go outside. But they drew customers, and Armstrong's shiny black face made the bar look like a hell-hole out of some hack writer's novel. *Ex Africa semper aliquid novi.* Africa always provides a novelty.

They were very decent to him, by and large. The pretty ladies never bothered him, for they had wisdom enough to see he was a clean little cuss, and they liked him for it. Also they understood in a vague way that a man who is interested in horses is interested in little else. They bothered about his cough. And were vituperative on the subject. Why did he allow himself to be made a fool of? *Tiens, tiens!* It was a shame. Ah, those rascals!

And often they would ask him to sing his little song, and he would give it in his fair tenor, always preserving the rhythm but sometimes leaving out the body of the music to emphasize the words.

No place on earth do I love more sincerely
Than old Virginny, the state where I was born.
Carry me back to old Virginny
There's where the cotton and the corn and taters
    grow;
There's where the birds warble sweet in the
    springtime,
There's where this old darky's heart am long'd
    to go.

Carry me back to old Virginny
There let me live till I wither and decay;
Long by the old Dismal Swamp have I wan-
    dered,
There's where this old darky's life will pass
    away—

And sometimes there his voice would take on
a quaver, or sink into a whisper, and he would
say: "I ain't feeling much like singing tonight,
folks, if you don't mind." And the barkeeper
would nod, for he too in America had had his
moments of nostalgia, and the pretty ladies would
look sad, and not speak, but apply themselves to
their grenadines or bocks, drinking daintily as
birds.

Whenever one thinks of France in a far country, as for instance in America or Ireland, one
thinks of roulette wheels, and it comes as a
distinct blow to know that roulette is not allowed.
Roulette is gambling. *Petits chevaux* are allowed.
But that is not gambling, that is piracy. Baccarat
is allowed. But that is not gambling; that is just
over the hills to the poorhouse. If you want the
Royal and Ancient Game of Roulette you have
to leave France and go to Monte Carlo.

He had looked forward to seeing this roulette,
to seeing the strained faces of the players around
the baize, to see the wheel a blaze of color, and
hear the whir of the ball, the hoarse cry of the
croupier: *"Rien ne va plus!* No more bets!" or
the announcement of the result: *"Quatorze
gagne, rouge pair et manque!* Fourteen wins, red
evens and below the line." The click of chips, the
rustle of bank notes, all the strain of the hot,
crowded rooms, heavy with stale air, all this he
wanted to see, for there are three things we all
wish to know about in this life: Love, Death and
Monte Carlo.

At the desk they refused him entry. An official
who spoke English much better than he did,
punched him all around the ring in machine-gun
French. He kept smiling that insincere, chilly
smile which tells you there is nothing doing.

"I guess there's worse'n me comes in here,
boss," Armstrong said. "I guess when all's said
and done, I'm the honestest of the bunch."

His objurgation moved them not. Three men
had cursed them that week, one as he jumped to
death from the upper Corniche Road; one as he

shot himself in a back room at Mentone, and one
as he went overboard from a small rowboat he
had hired into the black Mediterranean. All three
had called God to witness their end, and yet no
heaven had opened, nor had the Casino been
consumed like the cities of the plain.

He was wandering into the sunshine, where
the palms sighed and the pigeons drummed, and
going toward the Café de Paris, where he wondered would they refuse to serve him, when a
large hand descended on his shoulder.

"Ain't you Les Armstrong, the jock?"

"Yeh. I'm Armstrong."

"I thought I was right," a hearty, insincere
voice roared. "Boy, I got something for you.
Come right here."

Armstrong studied the red-faced, hearty-voiced
man. He had once been an American, he was
one no longer, which was one up to the Western
republic. For his voice was loud; his feet were
not in his own house.

"Come right along, boy," Armstrong was encouraged. "I got something you'll love."

"Is it, is it a mount?"

"Yeh, it's a nice big horse for you to ride."

"I sure likes a nice horse," he said. "Is it a
good horse?"

"Ain't no better."

"Is it a square ride?"

"Do I look like a guy," the ex-American demanded hotly, "who would want to pull some
dirty trick? I ask you, do I?"

If he had asked you or me, who are six-footers,
and handy with the mitts, we should have answered: You sure do! and awaited the results
with interest. But if you are a small underfed
jockey, out of luck, you don't have much *joie de
coeur* in matching wallops. So Armstrong gave
the soft answer that turneth away wrath.

"I ain't meant nothing, boss. Doggone, you
know. In this horse business a jock has got to
be careful."

"Kid, you're all right. You're the guy we want.
Come right with me."

He brought him over to the striped awnings
of the Café de Paris. A huge dark fat man was
sitting before a glass of Perrier. He was not
jollily fat, as many fat men are, but fat in a sin-
ister way, like some adipose evil thing in the
depths of the sea. He had small black eyes that
seldom moved, but have the keen edge of knives.
He was scrubbed to the perfection of cleanliness,
his spatulate, grubby hands were beautifully
manicured. On one hand shone a great diamond.
The other held a cigar. He never moved. His
eyes just shifted slightly.

"Well, Chief," his scout called, "I got the guy
we want."

The Chief slowly pivoted his eyes, as a search-
light is pivoted, on the little jockey. He moved
them away again.

"Yeh, Chief," the ex-American told him, "this is the kid. You can sit down, Armstrong," he condescended.

The little jockey was not very comfortable, for out of this immense fat man there exhaled an atmosphere of evil. It was not very hard to place him. You will see him, or one of the eleven or twelve like him, at various casinos during the season, at Biarritz, at Deauville, at Hamburg, at Cannes. They are the ones who are called the professional gamblers. Whence they come God knows. They speak English and French well, almost perfectly if that were possible, but French or English or American they are not. This swarthy one will be an Egyptian, perhaps; and this one a Greek, perhaps. They always win.

They win for this reason—that gambling to them is a business, and they have toward money an attitude that is neither yours nor mine. When you or I bet a hundred pounds or a thousand dollars on a fine horse, we bet it because we like the horse. We know of no better horse in the race. We have confidence in the jockey. The course suits both of them. And when we lose, we have lost money. We have lost something that cost us work and effort. A little share of power is gone.

But to these men money is not money but a commodity, as fish is to a fishmonger. There are so many counters on a table. They are not money. They are counters. What they spend outside is money. What they lose or win at the tables is a commodity. They exchange the commodity for money to spend, or invest money in the commodity. But of risking big sums they are not afraid, as we would be, and as they know we are. Also they have developed a sense of luck. When their luck is going bad, they will leave the table where they are risking tens of thousands, and go to a small table where you risk ten francs. This is known as "running the bad luck out." They are not alone. They have ancient vile old women who play for them at smaller tables. They have young girls, beautiful, perfectly groomed young girls to sit beside and encourage losers, suckers, that expressive term, whose vanity will not let them be quitters before the bright sympathetic eyes of the young girl. If you will ask me, I believe they are virtuous, these girls, to use that sweet old-time word, but they have sold their souls to the devil. The Tribunal of Heaven, I make free to believe, prefers their sisters of the street. Such is the gambler.

"Baron Ganzoni here," the scout explained, "has a horse for the Grand Prix de la Ville de Nice, and he wants you to ride. He'll walk it."

"I don't know," said Armstrong, "any Baron Ganzoni racing. And about walking that course, I heard of four that'll do it."

"Well, this hoss is by Spearmint out of Moyra's Pride. His name is Kilkenny Boy."

"But that horse," Armstrong said, aghast, "that horse belongs to a English dook."

"It did, kid, it did," the scout soothed him. The gambler leaned forward on the table. When he moved the slightest bit he breathed heavily, like some horrible animal coming at you in the dark of a hideous dream. "He don't no more. Listen, this horse is the goods."

"I know he's the goods," the jockey answered. "I don't see yet how he's your Chief's."

"Well, I'll tell you, kid. This English dook has no money, see, and he figures out he's had so much bad luck there's some good coming. So he sails into Monte for the baccarat with what dough he can collect, and right away he runs into the Chief.

"Well, you know baccarat. It makes an airplane look slow. In a while there's only the dook and the Chief in the game, and this dook's luck is certainly gone flooey. If it was raining, and the dook in the middle of the street, boy, if luck was rain, this guy would be bone dry. And before he knows anything he has nothing. He ain't the sort of guy to pull bum checks or rough stuff like that. He gets up.

" 'What? No more?' says the Chief. And he smiles dirty. Boy, the Chief's smile would make a rabbit furious.

" 'I'm cleaned out,' says the dook, 'but I've got a horse at Marseilles that ought to win the Grand Prix at Nice. That's worth a hundred and twenty-five thousand francs in stakes. He won at Marseilles easily and he got a very poor ride. I don't even know how good he is, and weight won't stop him!' The Chief looks at me and I tips my mitt that what the dook says is O.K.

" 'Supposing,' says the dook, 'I match his luck against yours. Between himself and stakes and bets he's worth three thousand pounds. If you care to, put that up in a bank and I'll go you. You take the horse or I take your money.'

"The Chief looks at me, and I nods, it's O.K. The Chief puts up a quarter of a million francs on the table.

" 'Bank of a quarter million francs,' says the croupier.

" '*Banco!*' says the dook.

"So the Chief deals him two cards, and takes two. You know this game. The nearest to nine wins. You can draw a card if the other guy hasn't a eight or a nine.

" 'I'll have a card,' says the dook.

"The Chief turns up his cards and they's two picture cards, worth nothing. Boy, I nearly fainted. I'm standing behind the dook, and I sees he's got an ace and a two spot, making three, and the Chief chucks him a five.

" 'I've got *huit,*' says the dook. The money was won.

"The Chief pulls a card from the box, and looks at it for a moment before putting it down.

" *'Noof!'* says he. 'Nine!'

"And that's how we gets the horse!

"Now here's where we get a raw deal. We brings the horse from Marseilles and tries to get a trainer, but this dook, see, he may be short of jack but he's got a lot of friends. And all the trainers say: Sorry, but we ain't got no stalls. And all the jocks down here, Mitchell and Atkinson and Head, and the French guys and the Eye-talians, they all got mounts for the race. Kind o' cold and distant, just because the baron, see, he ain't in with the racing gang. Wouldn't that get your goat? So then I remembers you. And I says: Bo, what are you worrying about? Here's a guy will look back and laugh at 'em.

"What do you say, kid? What do you say?"

If he had not been so out of luck, he, too would have said: Sorry, but I got a mount for this race. But nobility, and contempt for sharp practice, are perquisites of the reasonably rich. It is easy to be noble with a sound balance at your bankers. But try it on two bits.

"Well," he thought, "the horse and me is on the square anyhow." And aloud he said: "I'll go it."

The ex-American pulled a wallet out of his pocket.

"Well," he said, "just to show you what I think of you, I'll pay you the winning jockey's fee now." And he handed him 200 francs. "That's how I do things, see? And there'll be the same on for you with this pari mutuel, see?"

"Now, look-a-here, kid, no cracks about this, see? If the gang thinks we can't get a regular jock, boy, they'll leave this horse alone on the machines. They'll hardly put a cent up. And guy, we'll just take their shoes off. So put it away in your dome, and forget it till the day of the race. We'll show these dooks and dooks' friends they can't be cold and haughty with us, see?"

Well, that was legitimate. That didn't come into the infernal region of pulling or doping a horse. That was withholding stable information. There was nothing wrong about that.

Ganzoni, the gambler, spoke for the first time in the interview. His heavy glucose voice rumbled out: "Are you in good shape to ride this race?"

Armstrong's heart sank for a moment. Had they noticed he was ill? Were they going to take this mount from him? Had the man's infernal eye plumbed through clothes and flesh and bone to the stricken organs beneath? Those horrible coughing fits which shook him until he was covered with sweat, and had to lean against something for support—did they know of those? It was only that morning when he was tying a shoe lace he had fallen on his face, and lain there for an hour, unconscious.

But sick and all as he was, he knew he had a good race in him still. He was certain of that as of—

"I'm all right, boss. You needn't worry."

Now, you may laugh at the Var race course as much as you like. You may say it isn't a race course, it's a motion picture. You may say, put an Irish hunter at those jumps and he will take them in his stride. Barring the act of God or the king's enemies, a half-bred handy horse will walk it.

For the act of God and the king's enemies seemed to have selected the Nice race course as their favorite winter resort. Here are hurdles a plow horse will take. Here is an Irish bank that the hunter Pelican would skim over with the Meath hounds. Here is a stone wall a green five-year-old will take. Here is a water jump that is a great test of jumping, for a cow. It is all tremendously simple.

Yet lying hidden beside each fence are two small ghoul-like figures with a stretcher, small, wizened-faced men with cynical expressions and cigarettes, trolls, gnomes, the meaner sort of earth elementals, as a mystic might put it. And their stretchers are always in use. Of course everyone laid on those stretchers, next day the papers will tell you, is in a fair way to recovery; but if you notice you don't see them racing again. The kind-hearted foreign customers might not come to the race course again, if they heard a jockey was killed. So that in France jockeys never die.

For all that the jumps are low, they are narrow, real estate in Nice being what real estate in New York is in a minor way. The fields are big, fifteen or twenty horses starting in a steeplechase. There you will not find the beautiful timing of the Irish meets, the nursing of the horses, the course craft, the burst in the home stretch. The horses in a big race are there to win. Four abreast and six behind, they take the narrow jumps together. So that the act of God and the king's enemies figure largely in the French racing equation.

Apart from racing, barring sweet Leopardstown—Leopardstown of the Irish heart, green turf and soft brooding hills!—there is no prettier spot on earth for a race course. Beside you, you can hear the Mediterranean chime on the pebbly shore. Back of you, the little Var drowses downward from the Alpine gorges. Eastward the coast sweeps toward Monte Carlo in a bold reckless line. The red sails of the fisher folk show daintily on the peacock-blue sea. The higher Alps are furred with snow. It will be crimson for a minute when the sun drops westward back of the Esterel. The gray sleeping towns of Roman days daydream, like an old sheep dog by the fire, in the bluish hills. And somewhere chimes a sweet old bell in a monastery calling the Fathers to lauds. . . .

The second race was over. The beautiful six-year-old mare, Carina, had carried off the La

Turbie hurdle race from a field of sound starters. At the Totalizators people were swarming to have their bets paid. On the lawns mannequins, with faces made up as in some exotic play about Arabia, pass to and fro in clothes that represent more value than their bodies and souls. Here passes an Indian rajah, dressed in European clothes, with a brown sealskin waistcoat and a huge watch chain, looking very much like a retired saloonkeeper, but for his dark skin. He is entitled to a salute of twenty-one guns from His Majesty's government, as they will call it; but the meanest Frenchman here jostles him as if he were just "George." Here are two Egyptian princes, dressed in flaming Oriental costume, that seem tawdry somehow, in bad taste in this setting. Here is an Irish marquess, dressed like a farmer, leaning on an ash plant and wishing that "he was in Dublin this minute, so!" Here is an ex-king of a European state, looking very much like a cad. Beside him is a great Second Avenue safe-blower, "resting," looking one's ideal of an Italian prince. Through and over and past them swarm the common or garden people. French folk, vivacious, excited, chattering, like small birds in a tree; English people, striding like male and female Juggernauts, happily unconscious of the comments of the trodden French; Americans, notable by the huge frames of the men, and outwardly tolerant of and inwardly a little awed by this color and glory. Nearby in the field a band plays a quick fox trot.

A fat and not scrupulously clean man climbed a ladder by the starting board, and began clicking runners and jockeys up for the big race. Number One went, Velvet, Mark Baldwin's fast chaser, with Poivier up. So went Carbusy; so went Sainte Nitouche, "Little Puritan" it would be in English, by Quaker out of Moralité; Viouret of the gray, and great strain of Roi Hérode; Helicopter, that excellent fencer; so went Parakeet, who never looked much in a race, but was always in the running; so went Hans, who was to run in the Grand National in England, Daniele riding him—

Number Ten went up, Kilkenny Boy. There was a pause until the jockey's name was shown, "L. Armstrong" painted roughly in black letters on a piece of white planking. There was no glint of recognition in eyes that would have been charmed by it six months before. "Armstrong. *Connais pas!*" "Never heard of him!" A man went by selling the *"premier jaune!"*—the yellow slip that gives probable pari-mutuel results. They turned from the board to rush on him. . . .

In the jockeys' room Armstrong was received with coldness, while he worked into boots and breeches, and pulled on the flaming crimson silk jacket and cap that Ganzoni had chosen for his colors. Only Fred Rankin, the English jockey riding Viouret, an old enemy, came up and shook hands.

"I'm glad to see you up again," he said, "but I hate to see you on this job."

"I hate it myself, Fred, but doggone, you know how it is, when you're out o' luck, boy, you got to take what you can get."

"I got the winner, myself," Rankin said. "I wish it was another race, and you had it."

"They tell me this horse is good."

"He's good for home—— Listen, darky," Rankin's voice was sincere, "you're not looking well, why don't you go home to that place you're always singing about?"

"Old Virginny. Believe me, Fred, when I gets me a good winner, you won't see my heels for dust. Oh, boy, and how!"

"Well, good luck, darky!"

"Good luck, Fred."

They went down to the scales, Armstrong carrying his heavily weighted saddle. Outside the band had broken into the great hunting song:

D'ye ken John Peel with his coat so gay,
D'ye ken John Peel at the break of day,
D'ye ken John Peel when he's far, far away,
With his hounds and his horn in the morning?
Yes, I ken John Peel and Ruby, too—

Armstrong walked swiftly to the paddock. A French stable boy whipped the cloth from the big chestnut and took the saddle. The jockey took the snaffle and looked at the horse. His heart swelled.

"Doggone, boy," he said, "you'se a horse."

His eyes roved along the sweet line of body; the hind quarters, powerful as artillery; the legs delicate as a flower's; the pretty feet. The head was so small, so lovely. The nose could go in a cup. The eyes were a gentleman's eyes. They looked with wonder at the dark face above the crimson racing jacket. But the Irish chaser felt the masterly, knowing hands, and sensed everything was right. The jockey smiled with a dazzling show of white teeth.

"Boy," he said, "you'se a champeen horse. That's what you is, a champeen horse."

A burst of happiness came to him, and with it a flow of false strength. He tested girths and stirrups and sang as he tested them; not with any nostalgia now, but with happiness.

Carry me back to old Virginny,
There's where the cotton and the corn and taters grow;
There's where the birds warble sweet in the springtime,
There's where this old darky's heart am long'd to go—

The horse, knowing with the mystic sense animals have, that the merry heart is the good heart, turned and nuzzled him.

"Quit your kidding, horse," Armstrong re-buffed him with mock severity. "This ain't no picnic. This is a race."

No place on earth do I love more sincerely
Than old Virginny, the state where I was born.

He took the reins and slid his left foot into the iron. The stable boy caught his right knee and swung him into the saddle.

Ganzoni lumbered up.

"I know nothing about horses——"

"Yeh," Armstrong agreed.

"But it looks a good horse."

"What do you say, kid, what do you say?" the ex-American boomed heartily.

"I says: Anything that beats this horse wins; and I says: I ain't seen anything like this horse."

"He's at tens," the scout whispered hoarsely. "And the Chief's put on some dough for you. There's some jack coming to you, kid, if you comes in first."

"It's finding money." Armstrong grinned.

He followed the other horses through the gate into the course. A thrill he had never known, when he was popular and lucky, ran through him as he passed the stand and lawn swarming with people. The buzz of comment, the white faces, the flash of field glasses, it was all a throbbing, swarming mass of excitement. He loosed the chestnut for a dash down the field. The big horse broke into his beautiful stretching canter. The wind whipped into Armstrong's silk jacket like a pleasantly cold shower. They skimmed a hurdle like a swallow.

"Doggone, boy," Armstrong grinned, "you're it." He pulled the horse in and returned to where the others were waiting. Velvet, the big black horse that Poivier was riding, vicious and eager; Sainte Nitouche, quiet as a mouse. Viouret, quiet and watchful, with Rankin up. Immense Hans, with his Italian rider, stupid, relying on his great stride to carry him home. The silken jackets were a strange mad jumble of color in the Midi sun-shine. Green and crimson, brown, blue with white spots, purple, orange—they shifted and mixed as the horses moved. A man in a slouch hat raised a white flag half a furlong away. Horses pranced, turned, curveted. Riders cursed in English, French, Italian. Of a sudden, like a figure in a country dance, they turned their backs on the starter, and cantered downfield; and then, as if answering a command of some invisible master of ceremonies, they each turned again and came forward gently in a line that was at first a little ragged, gradually grew even as the horses stretched out. Their hoofs thumped like drums on the sunburnt turf. They swept on, like a squadron on parade.

Then with an abrupt movement, the starter whipped the fluttering white flag to his feet. The crowd roared. On the lawn a bell rang madly. The crowd roared again. In a dozen languages they called the world-old cry:

"They're off!"

For an instant on the left-hand side of the riders the stand appeared, an anthill of swarming folk, a flash of a thousand field glasses. And then it whipped out of sight like something seen from an airplane. The first hurdle showed; its white rails, its stiff, bristling bush. The horses took it leisurely, carefully. Back of them, the crowd cried:

"They're over."

They swept along the right-hand course, fight-ing for position now. Américaine, the sweet little mare, galloped along, first of the field. Behind came Savvice, the huge Italian jumper. Parakeet and Hans raced together. Viouret lay easily on the rails. Back of the field Armstrong held his mount. The Irish chaser was fighting for his head, not understanding why this rush of mounts should take precedence of him. He was not yet the cunning old racer that appreciates a yard here, an effort saved there. He was still the wild free hunter that loved horn and hounds.

But "Doggone, boy," Armstrong was soothing him, "take it easy. This ain't no waltz. This is work." And, "Easy baby, easy, I'll say when." And the big horse eased down, galloping sweetly, confidently. They took the second hurdle. Ahead the course forked to left and right. They swung to the right-hand side; Américaine still led. Entente, an outsider, swirled along, in a mad rush. None paid any attention to him. The battle was not on yet. They swept toward the first water jump, a hedge with a treacherous dike on the far side. The little mare skimmed it. The outsider faltered, took it clumsily, came down. He rolled over on his jockey. The jockey lay still. Carbusy's iron caught him on the head, where he lay. A woman near the rails screamed like a rabbit caught by a stoat. The field swept on.

But for the slow thunder of the hoofs all was silence. The jockeys were still as clay figures set on moving platforms. Their eyes never left the ground ahead of them. Their eyes were half-closed, wary as eagles'. Their hands were still. Their peaked wizened faces showed under the silk caps like creations of some artist with a morbid twist in his mind. They galloped on. Be-hind them the mountains rose, before them the sea chimed. About them, hemming them on all sides, were dark rings of people, on the rails, on the tops of motorcars, in trees. They paid no heed. They might have been riding between land and stars.

Big Hans, ugly-headed, splay-footed, with his clumsy, deceptive, dangerous stride came creep-ing up on the favorite. Rankin's voice came from the side of his mouth.

"If you cross me, you Wop, I'll cut your face

off with the whip." But his eyes never moved. His hands never moved. They took the hurdle easily. The little American mare fell behind. Now the race began to quicken. Velvet and Viouret, Hans and Parakeet began dueling for position. The biggest of the hurdles rose before them. The leaders took it carefully. Armstrong heard the crash and thump behind him as more of the field came down.

Suddenly Parakeet began to slow up. They passed him. *"Estropié!"* his rider called. "He's gone lame."

They huddled the left-hand side now, going toward the big bank with the hedge. As they went for it, each called on his horse. "Hip!" Rankin shouted, and brought his hand down sharply on his horse's ribs. "Ey-ah," shrilled the Italian jockey, and Hans rose like an airplane. The Frenchman sent Velvet over, with a vicious dig of the heel. Armstrong gathered Kilkenny Boy gently. The big horse slowed a little, then suddenly drove forward. He gathered his hind feet prettily in midair. They were over.

Now the field had broken into three parts. Ahead were Hans and Viouret, with the big black, Velvet, sparring for mastery. Behind them a few lengths Armstrong lay, quietly biding his time. Back of him four lengths were the rest of the field. They scrambled over the earthen ditch. They swung toward the dike. They took it easily, Velvet and Viouret gaining a little at each jump on Hans, but Hans regaining it each time with his powerful deceptive stride. At the stone wall Viouret faltered and almost fell, regained, went ahead. The Irish jumper cleared without laying an iron on it. They swept toward the grandstand to take the water jump. Big Hans rushed forward. They could see Daniele try to steady him. The horse seemed to bolt forward through the air. There was a crash as he came on his knees. And for an instant, Daniele appeared in the air, shot out of his irons as from a catapult. He turned over in midair and came down on his head. There was a long moan of horror from the grandstand. Daniele, he was done!

From the corner of his eye Armstrong could see the Italian where he lay, limp on his back, his hands outstretched as on a cross, a froth of blood on his mouth and nostrils. Behind thundered the field. Ahead, riderless, big Hans loped. Velvet and Viouret galloped on behind the other on the rails, each awaiting the moment for the other to crack. They swept around to the right again to cross the line of hurdles the second time. They quickened a little. Armstrong let Kilkenny Boy out a little. He mustn't make the leaders suspicious, but he mustn't let them get too far away. The wind had been right behind him coming down the field, bellying his silk jacket out in front, and now as he turned the wind, the jacket whipped close to his body, and

he had a feeling it was raining. He looked down. His jacket was wet with perspiration. His hands were wet. The reins where his hands held were wet.

"Doggone," he said, "that Italian guy, he must have made me sick."

He knew he was trembling in the saddle. His arms had no strength in them. He was afraid for an instant that the horse might feel there was something wrong.

"It's all right, boy," he said. "It's all right. Just a little weak, that's all."

They skimmed the hedge. He pulled himself together with a great effort as they came for the double fence, some inner reserve of strength giving his fingers the touch to steady the chaser, time him and send him over flying. They swept around again toward the ditch and hedge. Very hazily the leaders appeared to him, as though they were hazy horses in a hazy dream. Everything seemed furry. The landscape had an ethereal look, as though at any moment it might dissolve into nothingness. And queerly enough, the sea made a loud chiming in his ears, high above the thunder of the hoofs and the shouting. For a fraction of an instant this would endure, then would come superclear lucidity. Ahead of them was the last jump, the bank and hedge, and the stretch home. Viouret was slightly ahead of the black horse, Velvet. He saw Velvet's jockey loose his right hand. The whip would be going soon. Rankin's head moved slightly, ever so slightly, to the left. He sat down to ride Viouret home.

"Boy," Armstrong whispered, "now we go."

With the old cunning, the old craft, he swung out to the left. His knees gripped a little closer. He went down on the chestnut's neck as they thundered to the jump.

"Over, boy!" he called. And they were over like a rocket.

But the last effort seemed to have taken all out of him. He was empty, it seemed, empty of vitality, of everything. He could hear crack-crack-crack-crack of a whip before him, beside him, now behind him. He had passed Velvet. Now he was racing beside the favorite, now he passed him. Ahead of him loomed the black mass of the grandstand, the circle on top of the winning post. A great roar came to his ears, and curiously enough, above that the chime of the sea.

He heard the swish of Rankin's whip, the crack of it. The favorite crept up, crept, crept . . .

"Horse," he called in agony, "I'm done. You must win yourself." His fingers caught the mane to avoid falling off.

The big chestnut felt the favorite come along, come up to his forehand, come up to his neck. With an immense burst of fighting speed, he hurled himself forward, the stand, the favorite, the winning post were passed in four gigantic strides. Armstrong faintly heard the roar of the crowd as he won, clearly heard the insistent chiming of the sea, of a sea.

With the wisdom all good horses have, the chestnut slowed up, cantered, walked. He stood for an instant to give the little jockey a chance to sit up. He turned toward the paddock. A stableboy ran up and led him into the weighing enclosure. Ganzoni's scout met him with a frown.

"You cut that a bit fine," he criticized.

"Did I?" Armstrong said dully.

"Yeh," he said. "The Chief's sore. You might have lost us our dough. He says you rode a bum race, and he ain't going to come through with no bonus for a bum race."

"No?" He turned to the stableboy. "Give us a hand down," he said. He tottered on his feet when he was on the ground. He managed to get the saddle off. He turned to the horse for a moment.

"Boy," he said—he probably didn't know what he was saying—"boy, I'll see you again."

He walked toward the chair, and sat down in it mechanically, his saddle in his lap. He tipped the scale down.

"All right," said the weightsman. But Armstrong didn't hear.

"Get up."

But he didn't move.

"He's fainted," Rankin, who was waiting his turn, suggested. "That darky's sick."

They carried him off and laid him on a couch.

"He's cold and stiff," somebody remarked.

"He's dead."

Ganzoni bustled forward, roused out of his lethargy.

"But I win my race," he called excitedly. "Don't I win my race?"

"Yes, you win your race," the officials told him. "But what about your jockey?"

"Him! He's nothing to me." Ganzoni lifted his shoulders. "Besides, I paid him in advance. But there's no objection?"

"What objection could there be?" they assured him. "He weighed in."

The gong rang. Everything was all right. The Totalizator could pay. New jockeys appeared. New horses were brought out. The day merged into the short Mediterranean twilight. The moon that had just been a vague shape in the east became an immense silver penny while as yet the sun had not gone down. A little mistral sprang up, and the Mediterranean, sleek as a cat, turned like a cat, and struck back in small vicious snarling gray waves. The mountains became forbidding. The band, because there were so many Americans at Nice that year, played a medley of American songs, giving to them that faint twist of unbelief and cynicism with which French bands will always treat songs of sentiment.

Carry me back to old Virginny, [*it played*]
There's where the cotton and the corn and taters grow;
There's where the birds warble sweet in the springtime,
There's where this old darky's heart am long'd to go.

And two small ghouls, smoking cigarettes, removed the last of the jockey to an unseen place, where he would be kept until dark. Thence they would remove him to the house of the friendless dead. And lest his name should be forgotten, they had chucked on his chest the piece of plank from the starters' board with "L. Armstrong" on it in hasty, uncouth letters.

"No place on earth do I love more sincerely," the band seemed to sneer, "than old Virginny, the state where I was born."

But the band might have saved its irony. He had ridden and won a great race. Also, he was in Virginny now.

A PORTFOLIO OF DRAWINGS
BY ROBERT RIGER

My Flame—Valenzuela up

"Tack"

Willie Hartack

"Mr. Fitz"

At the Starting Gate

Keep Off the Rail

CALVIN J. CLEMENTS

During World War II I was drafted into the Army. They took one look at my civilian record and gave me a ticket to Fort Riley, Kansas, a cavalry post inhabited by seventy thousand men and six thousand horses. I mucked out stalls there but never rode a horse and have been on a horse only once in my life. Nevertheless, and perhaps because of that, I have a deep admiration for the men who do ride. They are courageous athletes, their season is year round and they are exposed to more temptation than any other professional performer. I like "Keep Off the Rail" because it's about a jockey.

HE ELBOWED his way closer to the paddock railing and stood between two women holding umbrellas. He saw the first horse being led into a stall. It was the filly, Miss Elsie, with the familiar blaze across her brown nose.

"She hates this slop," he thought.

She could have changed, though, in the two years since he'd ridden her. Time can make a difference in horses as well as men.

He moved away from the railing, along the muddy path toward the paddock gate. There were puddles of water on the path and he felt the water seep through the cracked leather of his shoes. The hole in his sock chafed his heel.

"I'd like to see Mr. Marshall," he said to the guard at the paddock gate.

The guard looked surprised. "I'm supposed to look for 'im?"

"He came in with Miss Elsie."

"You gotta have a pass."

"The name is Joey Grecco," he said.

"It's supposed to mean somethin', maybe?"

The guard scratched a wart on his nose and stood aside for a young girl in slacks and a transparent lemon-yellow raincoat. The girl didn't look at Joey as she passed by. He was part of the bleak sky that hung over Belmont, part of the yellow spongy mud through which she gingerly picked her way.

"Look—" Joey began.

"You gotta have a pass. That's what I'm here for, to keep you bums out. You gotta have a pass." The guard's eyes followed the girl.

Joey said, "This bum gave you ten bucks when your old lady had twins a few years back."

The guard looked carefully at Joey's face, at the frayed collar, the baggy pants and muddy shoes. He scratched the wart again.

He stood aside. "Okay. You wanna walk around?"

In the paddock area horses moved restlessly in their stalls, warily eyeing the riding equipment in the arms of arriving grooms. Owners and trainers stood together, talking in low tones. A few jockeys had appeared on the scene, their bright silks contrasting sharply with the grayness of the day.

Joey moved through the private drama he was once so much a part of, and tried to ignore the curious glances thrown his way. He approached the Number Eight stall, where Kenneth Marshall stood. Marshall was a big heavy-set man who dwarfed the pale young rider in orange silks beside him.

Joey said, "Could I see you a moment, Mr. Marshall?"

The big man stopped speaking to the jockey. Through thick-rimmed glasses he considered Joey with a frown.

"Grecco." He didn't sound pleased.

"I don't know how to say this," Joey started. He was about to say that things had changed, that he had changed. But had he?

Kenneth Marshall said, "If you're thinking of riding Misfit in the Stakes today, forget it. I've got a boy."

"Misfit's in over her head," Joey said. "With luck, she finishes third. You can't get away from it. Third-place peanuts—if she's lucky."

"Meaning," Marshall said, "you'll do better?"

"I broke her in," Joey said. "I always got a couple of lengths more out of her than she had. We got along. Sometimes it's like that."

Marshall was silent as a colored boy and a wizened stump of a man carried some equipment into the stall. The man placed a saddle cloth on Miss Elsie, and when she shied, her hoofs lashing at the rear wall, the colored boy held out his hand, murmuring soothing, nonsensical words to her. The filly quieted then, and cautiously nuzzled the palm of his hand.

There was a wallet in Marshall's hands now. "If I can help you out, Grecco . . . perhaps a few dollars?"

"I don't want it that way," Joey said. "I want to ride."

Marshall shrugged and put the wallet away. He turned to the boy in orange silks.

"Break her in front," Marshall said. "Try to keep her there. If she gets the slop kicked into her face too much she'll quit."

The jockey nodded. "Sure, Mr. Marshall." He tapped his leg nervously with his bat.

Joey shifted his feet. "My license was okayed this morning," he said. "I wouldn't ask you if I thought I couldn't win."

"Look, Grecco," said Marshall, turning. "I don't like to say no, but that's the way it's got to be." He made a futile gesture with one hand. "Besides, Misfit will be carrying a hundred and five."

"I'm one-three."

"You always had trouble making one-twelve."

"I've been on a diet," Joey said. "It's no trouble making weight when you're broke. No trouble at all."

They led the horses out of the paddock, across the short path to the walking ring. Marshall remained behind, watching from the paddock.

"Have you ridden since you left me, Joey?"

Joey shook his head.

"Then how do you know . . ." Marshall hesitated, looking at him.

"Things are different," Joey said, wondering if they really were.

"But you haven't ridden?"

"No."

"Then I can't take the chance, Joey. I'm sorry. Really sorry. But look, I know you have a family. I have a hundred I can spare. Take it. Pay me back when you can."

"The hell with your hundred," Joey said. "The hell with everything."

He was a dozen steps away before he realized Marshall was calling him.

"Wait for me by the clubhouse," the man told him. "Maybe we can work something out, Joey."

He stood on the stone steps that led into the clubhouse. It was raining again and he was cold and he put his hands into his pockets to warm them. He watched the horses file past, down the lane toward the racing strip, the jockeys hunched forward on their mounts, their colorful silks clinging wetly. He picked out the brown and white of the King Ranch, the Wheatley yellow and purple. He saw Atkinson in green and gold.

Great name, Atkinson. Great rider.

Joey Grecco had been a great rider, also. His name wasn't too well remembered because he hadn't been up there very long. A year. One year on the big circuit. He had booted home close to two hundred winners. Great kid, they said. Great rider. Never a poor ride, never pocketed. In fact, it was amazing how he consistently rode in the clear, well away from the jammings at the rail. Smart operator, Grecco. That was before they had caught wise.

He remembered the day. There are days you don't forget, and that was one of them. It was at Aqueduct. He was riding Last Chance, the two to one favorite. She'd broken slow from the gate in a field of eighteen. In the stretch the horses were fanned from rail to rail with Joey close up on the inside. There was an opening ahead of him along the rail. Narrow, but an opening. Last Chance answered to the whip. He was booting home the winner. He knew it. The crowd knew it, and roared for him to come on.

Joey didn't go through the narrow slot.

The stewards were polite. "A bad ride," they'd said; they meant it mustn't happen again. The crowd wanted to know how much Joey got paid for the boat ride.

He tried to explain to the other jockeys in the locker room. He told them about a dirt track in Arkansas the previous year, guiding a nervous colt through on the rail, the colt's forelegs crossing, the sickening moment of catapulting through the air. He told them about the jagged sliver of wood on the rail that had ripped away half his face. Plastic surgery had given him back a face, had erased most of the scars. He gave them the full story, and they listened to him and they understood. But they didn't understand about the other scar.

Only Joey Grecco knew that the smooth, white

railings at Jamaica or Gulfstream weren't smooth and white after the accident, that in the jams at the turns you found yourself looking down at the same weathered railing that had torn into your face. Always there was the gnarled and knotty rail and it froze you in the saddle until you were just so much dead weight the horse was carrying.

"It's nothing solid you can fight," he tried to tell them. If you could only reach out and touch it, grab it with your hands and hold it tight, maybe you could tear it apart. But you can't. You can't touch it so you can't fight it. They didn't seem to understand.

Too late he realized it would have been wiser for the story to be left untold. Jockeys are human. Once they knew his weakness he found himself against the rail whenever the other riders considered his horse a threat. Only with a really good mount could he earn a win.

Owners are human, too. It was natural they should wonder about the close ones he lost, natural they should think back and try to remember if he had swung outside and lost when he could have taken the railing and won. The bids for his services grew less and less. . . .

Worst of all was the loss of Misfit.

Before all the trouble, Marshall had asked him to ride Misfit, a high-strung filly that seemed destined for the plater class. Their first time out Joey had ridden her with his hands. He had talked to her, babied her, coaxed her, and he had brought her home in front. Eight in a row he went on to win aboard her. Before the year was out, Misfit had stepped up into the stakes class. But, finally, Marshall was like the rest of the owners:

"I hope you'll understand, Joey. I don't like to do this, but my string isn't a rich man's hobby. With me it's a living. If it wasn't I'd let you go on riding until you licked this thing, this phobia of yours. You understand, don't you, Joey?"

He understood, and the solution was simple. Get away from the tracks. You were twenty-five and had a wife and kid but you were the size of a twelve-year-old and they laughed when they looked down at your four-ten and called you 'sonny' and wanted to know what you could do. They laughed again when you said you rode. You got tired of laughing with them.

He stepped aside and a mud-splattered jockey swung carelessly past him and into the clubhouse. Marshall came up the path then, walking with the pale-faced boy wearing his colors. The boy, Joey noted, was carrying plenty of mud across his blouse, mute testimony that Miss Elsie had not stayed out in front.

Marshall came over to Joey.

"I'll give it to you straight," he said. "Things haven't been going too well for me. It would mean a great deal if Misfit came through today.

As you said before, she's in over her head, no better than third on form. So maybe I should gamble those peanuts against first money. Misfit was a better horse with you up. No one can deny that. We'll see if it still works that way."

Joey said, "Thanks, Mr. Marshall."

"It's only a five-horse field, anyway, at a mile and a quarter . . ." Marshall didn't finish. He didn't have to. Joey knew what he meant. A small field and plenty of distance. No problem for a rail-shy jockey. Plenty of time and plenty of space to pick your spot.

"If you come through," Marshall continued, "I'll have a fifteen thousand purse and you'll have your ten per cent. But we'll have to call it quits after that. That may sound callous, but I doubt if one race would prove anything. Perhaps a hundred wouldn't."

"You mean you could never be sure whether I was giving you a fair ride or playing cute and watching out for my own skin."

"I didn't say that."

Joey nodded. "It's okay. You're giving me a chance to make some dough and I appreciate it, Mr. Marshall. I won't let you down."

Marshall placed a big hand on his shoulder. "I'll make all the arrangements, Joey. Incidentally, I saw Mary seated near the walking ring. I didn't have time to stop and say hello, so you'll give her my regards, won't you?"

She was sitting on a wooden bench beneath a tall maple. She was hatless. Her dark brown hair was damp from the rain and hung straight and there were tired lines about her mouth. But she smiled as Joey approached and suddenly she was very young and very pretty.

Joey said abruptly, "I told you not to come."

Her smile faded. "Joey, I had to. I left little Joey with mother—"

"I told you not to come," he repeated.

Her dark eyes searched his. "Did Mr. Marshall . . ."

"He's letting me ride Misfit," Joey said, "but it's only a chance to pick up a check. One race and that's all. If I win, it still won't make any difference."

"But, Joey . . ." She looked up at him uncertainly. "That doesn't seem quite fair."

"It's fair enough if you're looking at it from Marshall's side. He's got trouble keeping his string off the auction block. Why should he take chances with a broken-down jockey?" He kicked bitterly at the mud underfoot. "One race and I'm through for good. I'd never be able to get up the nerve it would take to ask him again."

She rose from the bench and slipped an arm through his. "Darling, you shouldn't be thinking like that before a race. If you win, perhaps other owners might think of using you. Or perhaps Mr. Marshall might change his mind. Anything can happen."

"Sure, Mary, a hundred things could happen," he said listlessly, without conviction.

"I'll be waiting down at the winner's circle—"

"I don't want you looking on."

"Joey—"

"Forty thousand people will be watching," Joey said. "I can muff this one. I can muff it bad. I don't want you there listening to the crowd if I do."

She leaned close and tenderly kissed his cheek. "I never hear anything but the cheers," she whispered. "I'll be at the winner's circle waiting for you. Good luck, darling."

It was like a dream. The feel of silks in his hands again, the sweaty damp smells in the locker room, the faces that stared, strange, familiar, some friendly, others cold and impersonal.

The goggles broke the spell.

They were lying on the bench. Chalk had been carefully rubbed across the outer part of each lens, narrowing the vision. Blinkers for the jockey.

Chuck Davies came over, a thin graying track veteran with the haunted expression of a man fighting his weight. He shook hands with Joey. "Glad to see you back, Grecco." He indicated the glasses. "Don't mind that business. Some moron was looking for a laugh."

"I don't mind," Joey said. "It's funny. I'm screaming."

He sat on the bench in front of his locker and pulled his boots on.

"Big comeback race, eh, kid?"

Joey looked up at the pint-sized swarthy man in green silks who smiled down at him. It was a thin smile, the humor all in the razor-thin lips, none in the flat black eyes. Al Feeney. You had to go far to find a more skillful rider, or a dirtier one.

Joey nodded mechanically and began to polish his boots.

"Too bad you had to pick this particular race to prove you ain't yellow, kid."

Joey tossed the shoe rag into the locker and straightened. "You talk like there's something on your mind, Feeney, and I'm lousy at riddles. Get to the point."

"You've got a punk memory, kid." The smile was thinner. "Maybe you forgot I was set down for six months on your account."

Joey recalled the incident. It had been in a cheap claiming affair and Feeney had hooked his boot, pulling Joey's mount out of fourth money and edging himself into it. It had been a cheap and petty trick, with nothing at stake except a two-hundred-dollar share in the purse. When Joey started to file an objection Feeney had pleaded with him to forget it, but it was Marshall's money at stake and Joey felt morally

bound to protect the small purse. The stewards had not only allowed the claim but, weary of Feeney's trickery, had set him down for six months.

"When you use dirty tactics you take the risk of suspension," Joey said curtly.

"A lousy two hundred bucks," Feeney said, "and you had to play crybaby. I said it'd cost you when I was reinstated, but I found you'd gone yellow and left the tracks."

Joey fought down his rising anger. At the moment, Feeney was not important, the coming race was.

"Look, Feeney, after the race I'll talk to you, argue or anything else. Right now I have a few things on my mind."

Feeney nodded. "Okay, kid. Just wanted to let you know I didn't forget. Take my advice and stay far behind me with Misfit. Things can happen on a sloppy track."

Feeney picked up the goggles. He grinned. "Now here's what I call a good idea!" His black eyes flicked around the room to see if he was gaining attention.

The few jockeys who were riding in the coming race were already dressed and sitting at the far end of the room. They were sipping coffee, carefully studying their cups. Chuck Davies was grimly staring out a window.

"A good idea," repeated Feeney. "They work real fine on horses and there's no reason they can't do the same for the rider."

Joey looked carefully from the glasses to Feeney. "You wouldn't be the comedian who did that, would you?"

"Now, what ever gave you that idea?"

"Wipe them off," Joey said softly.

Feeney's mouth worked into a sneer. "Who's being the comedian now, yellowback?"

Two years of bitterness went into the punch that Joey threw. It smashed Feeney squarely on the mouth and sent him staggering back across the room to crash into a locker.

The other riders were between them then, but Feeney made no attempt to move away from the locker. Instead he glared over at Joey, his black eyes smoldering with fury as he wiped a trickle of blood from his chin.

"Try passing me today, Grecco, and you're a dead pigeon," he said. "I may lose but I'm going to make damn sure you'll be further back."

Chuck Davies handed Joey his blouse. "A crumb," Davies said. "A natural-born crumb. Pay no attention to him or you'll be leaving your race in this room. . . ."

"Did you hear me, Joey?" It was Marshall speaking. The riders were up and Joey sat stiffly in the saddle. His hands shook. Beneath him was Misfit, an ebony mare with the ancestral beauty and power of War Admiral in her finely bred lines. Something of Joey's nervousness passed to the mare and she pawed the ground and whinnied. Under his touch she trembled.

The winning combination, he thought bitterly. A nervous jockey and a nervous horse.

"Did you hear me, Joey?" Marshall repeated. "Lay off the pacer. And stay clear of the rail. It's a river out there."

He nodded, only half hearing, and they were moving around the walking ring and he was looking down at the people leaning over the railing. A fat man chewing on a black cigar was regarding him without expression. Next to the fat man a blonde girl with startling white teeth against her tanned face was smiling up at him.

"He'll need careful pacing," Marshall was saying. "But I guess I don't have to tell you that."

He nodded again and they moved out. He was only half conscious of the parade past the grandstand, of skirting the barrier at the quarter pole. Once or twice he heard his name in the sounds from the stands. Then he stood in the irons and jogged Misfit over to the inside rail where blackish pools of water rippled in the stiff wind.

He glanced down at the whitewashed railing. It was smooth and clean and glistened with drops of rain. He felt no particular sensation, no sharp fear. But, then, the rail never bothered him before a race. It would be in the jams at the turns, or in the stretch when the field made their final moves that the old fear would come, a cold paralysis starting in the pit of his stomach, numbing him.

"Grecco, you look like you got two minutes to live. Loosen up. It's only a horse race!" The assistant starter grinned up at him and took Misfit's bit. As they moved toward the starting gate, Joey adjusted his goggles.

"Now look, old girl, take it easy." The assistant starter took a firmer grip on the bit as Misfit shied away from the barrier. "Now look, old girl."

It happened suddenly, without warning. A sheet of newspaper, blown across the track, plastered itself against the barrier with a wet smack. Misfit reared and the assistant starter lost the bit. Joey went floundering across the mare's neck, then he was face down in the cold, brown mud, and the frightened mare was running off. People laughed, but Joey heard none of it. He was listening to the mare's hoofs pound away her race, his race.

When he got to his feet Misfit was rounding the clubhouse bend with the outriders attempting to head her off. Two attempts to halt her failed. It wasn't until the mare had covered half a mile that they managed to pocket her. A half mile of precious strength wasted.

Today, he thought dully, today his race was over before it had begun. It had to happen today.

"Tough luck!" the assistant starter said. "But she may still have it in her. I've seen her come in breezin' after a mile and a quarter an' ready to go again. It was a cheaper race, though," he added.

Joey watched the outriders trot back with Misfit wedged between them, the mare shying and fighting the bit, her eyes rolling wildly.

"All right, Grecco. Up!" The command came from the head starter. The mare wasn't to be scratched, then.

He remounted, and he and Misfit moved over to the starting gate and into the Number Three slot without further trouble.

"Remember, yellowback, a guy can get hurt if he ain't careful."

Joey glanced only briefly at Feeney in the second post position and made no reply. The flag was up. His mind mechanically plotted the coming race, weighing the individual horses, Blue Star with Feeney aboard going to the front with speed to spare, the others trailing, Misfit prodding along in the rear, conserving her strength for that final-stretch run.

The starting bell went through him like a knife, and five animals plunged from the gate, seeking firm footing in the slop, fighting for position. At the clubhouse bend Joey found himself eating mud, a dead last.

When he saw Blue Star running fourth, he realized the pace was faster than he had expected, very fast for a sloppy track. The lead had been taken by the early speedsters who hoped to burn out Blue Star before the stretch was reached. A slow track, a killing pace. Joey's hopes rose. Misfit was always at her best under these conditions.

He held his weight against the mare's mouth, content to remain two lengths behind Blue Star as they worked down the back stretch and neared the far turn. When Blue Star made her bid, Joey brought his bat down against Misfit's side. There was no response.

He cursed himself for a fool. In the past he had always hand-ridden the mare. She was stubborn to the whip.

He leaned forward, high in the irons.

"Come on, baby, show me what's left." He whispered other words to her, endearing words, silly words, and he saw the silken ears flatten as they had so often in the past, felt the surge of power beneath him, the lengthening strides. And suddenly they were rounding the stretch and the early leaders were dropping behind. It was Blue Star and Misfit then, Blue Star in the lead by two lengths. Misfit moving up.

Nearing the quarter pole, with the roar of the crowd in his ears, Joey knew the race was his. A half length behind the favorite and still moving up. Pass Blue Star on the right, clear of the rail, clear of any interference. The race was his. He had come through for Marshall.

One race won't prove anything, Joey—perhaps a hundred wouldn't.

"Wrap this one up, baby," he whispered. "Wrap it up the hard way." He guided the mare to the left then, toward the railing, and Misfit surged forward. They were a neck behind Blue Star, the rail on one side and Blue Star on the other, and suddenly Blue Star was pressing in, roughing it, forcing Misfit closer to the rail. Joey felt the railing scrape his boot. He glanced down and ice filled his veins.

The weather-beaten railing, knotty and scarred and ugly. His hands were putty, unfeeling. He sensed the reins going slack, the mare faltering. He opened his mouth to speak to her but no sound came. Then he saw Feeney's face turning toward him, the venomous hate in the black glaring eyes. He saw the whip in Feeney's hand, ready to lash at him, heard its ugly whine. He lacked even the power to flinch.

A whip lash in close quarters? Those things can't be helped.

It caught him across the cheek and the pain exploded somewhere deep in his brain and traveled down his spine and into his arms and legs. He fought his way back through the pain, an eternity of agony.

"Wrap it up, baby!" Somehow the words came through gritted teeth, and his hands were alive now on the mare's neck. She moved ahead and the eighth pole flashed by and they were head and head with Blue Star. Joey saw the insane rage in the dark face of the rider alongside, a rage that swept all caution aside. The whip snapped back, this time directly at him, with no attempt to mask the ugly intentions. He shielded his face along the mare's neck and took the lash across his arm.

He felt the whip again, across his neck, then his shoulders, then his back as he drew away. "Wrap it up, baby!" A moment later they thundered across the finish line a length to the good.

He stood high in the irons and galloped her past the bend to ease her wind, before trotting back to the winner's circle. Mary was there with Marshall. They were smiling, and a photographer was asking him to hold his bat aloft.

He dismounted, removed the saddle and weighed in. When he stepped off the scales, Mary caught his arm. He saw she was smiling through tears.

"The stewards have already corralled Feeney," Marshall said. "I think he will be set down for good. As for you, Joey—" He held out his hand. "Will a handshake do for a contract?"

"Look—" Joey said.

"I know what you're going to say," Marshall interrupted. "You're going to tell me you came through, not despite Feeney's tactics, but because of those tactics, that it gave you something to fight against and you forgot the rail."

Marshall poked a long finger against Joey's chest. "Anyone who can ride an eighth of a mile like that against a whip can overcome anything—even himself. Don't tell me you can't!"

"But—"

"No 'buts'," Marshall snapped. "You're going to ride my horses from now on. And I'm willing to bet the rail won't mean a damn thing to you any more."

"You'd win your bet," Joey said. "I rode that last eighth with my cheek along Misfit's neck, watching the rail as I rode." Joey grinned at Marshall, then down at Mary. "And it didn't mean a thing. I could've kissed it."

"You're my boy, Joey." Mary spoke the words softly as she squeezed Joey's arm but someone near the circle heard them, and the words were picked up in the stands and repeated there and shouted down to Joey.

He turned around and grinned toward the crowd.

The Wounded Admiral

BOB CONSIDINE

It has been about a quarter of a century since Bob Considine filed the story of War Admiral's Belmont Stakes victory. He had the touch then, of drama, the same touch he has today reporting his exclusive interviews with the great leaders of the world. Considine's scope is fantastic, but we like to believe his enthusiasm for sports is as keen as the day he filed his first sports story for the Washington Post, *the phoned-in result of a high school contest.*

Bleeding from a great gash in his right front leg, split at the very start of the race, War Admiral, the courageous son of Man o' War, was crowned with the wreath of racing immortality at Belmont Park yesterday.

The little dark-brown colt, with the Derby and Preakness already to his credit, won the 69th renewal of the grueling Belmont Stakes as only he and his deathless pappy could win them. He was in front a few yards from the barrier, four lengths in front in the back stretch, and finished the punishing 1½-mile ordeal "looking back."

Well behind him, plowing along in his scarlet wake, thundered the cream of America's Thoroughbreds, but the eyes of the greatest crowd in the history of New York racing were only for the winner, and to him the 35,000 spectators extended a roar that boomed through the leafy countryside.

Sceneshifter, trained by Earl Sande, was second, three lengths behind the Sam Riddle colt, unbeaten this year. Vamoose, a rank outsider from the Falaise Stable, was third. Pompoon, believed by many to be the only horse in America able to give War Admiral a race, finished sixth. Colonel Ed Bradley's Brooklyn, the dark horse of the race, was fourth—but the colonel's day wasn't ruined. He bet Jerry Loucheim, owner of Pompoon, $10,000 to $11,000 that Brooklyn would beat out the son of Pompey.

The incredible War Admiral, carrying 126 pounds, eight more than Man o' War toted when he set the track mark in 1920, not only bettered his sire's standard, but also equaled the American record in adding the Triple Crown to his string of victories.

He ran the mile and a half in 2:28⅗, one fifth of a second faster than Man o' War's record set in the Jockey Club Gold Cup race of 1920. His time equaled the American record of Handy Mandy, who carried only 109 pounds, made at Latonia, June 25, 1927, and eclipsed the mark of 2:29⅕ for the Belmont Stakes established by Peace Chance in 1934.

The Admiral, wild at the post, kicked his right front leg just above the hoof as he fought his way out of the starting block. For one startling moment he nearly fell, while little Charley Kurtsinger fought madly for his balance. His sharp rear hoof, propelled by the sturdiest muscles in horsedom, had taken a fearful chunk out of the rear of his forequarter.

But there was no quit in him. He was behind, and it infuriated him. Jock Whitney's Flying Scot had catapulted out of the block a head in front of him.

With one enormous punch at the perfect loam of the track, War Admiral shoved those eager nostrils out into the cool dustless air which is sucked in only by the leaders. He came up and looked Flying Scot in the eye, and then burst past.

He was on the outside, far from his favorite position on the rail, but it was of no moment. By the time he had led the procession to the first turn he was a length and a half ahead. Kurtsinger bore him over close to the rail. And from there it was the same old story, the story he first told at the Derby: the story of a horse that refused to be licked.

His foot was soggy with blood, but as he rounded that first bend and flattened out for the long back stretch the Admiral went out to four lengths ahead of the pack. Sceneshifter, coming up from seventh, took second place from Flying Scot in a heavy rush.

Bobbing along, with his peculiarly short and choppy stride, the Admiral maintained his four-length advantage down the weary furlongs of the back stretch, and the pack behind him was as rooted in their positions as merry-go-round Thoroughbreds. But as they hurled into the final bend, and Kurtsinger kept that numbed but ceaseless leg ticking off these flying yards, Pompoon and Brooklyn went out for him.

The beautiful Pompey colt, beaten by only a lip in the Preakness, pounded from sixth to fourth in the big bend, with Brooklyn at his side. The big fashionable crowd, which wagered well beyond a million dollars during the day, set up a chant for the two horses whose hoofs were scattering the red wake of the leader.

But Pompoon wasn't up to it. Winded and wanting, he dropped back as they followed the Admiral into the stretch. Brooklyn forged up as far as Vamoose, the third horse, but Vamoose wouldn't let him by. The all but unknown horse, whose sire—like Brooklyn's—was Blue Larkspur, fought off the challenge of its half brother.

But no one saw this little internecine drama. No soul in that crowd that was so large that hundreds huddled on the grandstand roof could see anything except the little dark-brown colt that romped along far out in front. War Admiral, nine to ten in the betting, was winning his greatest race, the closest thing America has to the English Derby.

And he was doing it with a leg whose bloody leakage left a thin coating of carmine on the groomed and manicured racing strip. The numbness must, by this time, have enveloped his entire side, but not his heart. The Admiral finished easily, and, if one kept his eyes off that gory hoof, looked so full of run at the end that he might have rerun the race without trouble.

Kurtsinger, a huddling pigmy in the black and yellow silks of Old Man Riddle, let his charge lope as he wished, after they had blistered under the finish wire. Then he walked him back, into the teeth of the crowd's great roar—and steered the exciting little fellow into the unsaddling enclosure.

He pricked up his ears to the whirr of the newsreel cameras and looked a little wildly at the clattering news cameras. Kurtsinger got off him and rubbed his nose until he was quiet, and three kindly-looking people came up near to him.

One was Mrs. August Belmont, and the others were Mr. and Mrs. Sam Riddle. War Admiral watched curiously while Mrs. Belmont presented the great Belmont Trophy to the Riddles—and then a groom led him back to his stable, and here and there along the path you could see the blood that still dripped from his leg.

Count Fleet

JOHN HERVEY

The only untold story I know concerning Count Fleet was of the man at Belmont Park on that day in 1943 who plunked down $66,000 in cold cash at the hundred-dollar mutuel window—all to win on Count Fleet in the Belmont Stakes. There were so many pasteboard tickets the man carried them in his shirt-front. Of course, Count Fleet won but the injury which was to retire him occurred in that race. And the man? Well, he received 5¢ profit on each of the $66,000 he bet.

EXTRAVAGANT epithets have been applied to famous race horses time out of mind. In the effort to describe them and fitly to characterize their achievements, the repertoire of laudation, it might well be said, has been worn threadbare.

We have been assured that they were marvelous, wonderful, amazing, phenomenal, unequaled, peerless, incomparable, prodigious, transcendent, unmatched, glorious and superlative; that they and their performances were so beyond precedent that they marked new epochs, established new standards of greatness and gave them places in the equine Valhalla so exalted that they "stand alone"—in the words of the campaign orator, "Without a rival and without a peer." . . . And so on and on and on, until the vocabulary of adulation has been exhausted.

Yet, truth to tell, of the numerous Thoroughbreds which thus have been honored, when at their apogees, few today remain much more than "folks in history." Only students, researchers, breeding specialists and, here and there, an old-timer given to that habit known as living in the past—which, as we all know, is most decidedly unprogressive and reprehensible!—knows or cares anything about them. Otherwise, they are little more than lay figures; "names in pedigrees" and the like.

Bearing this in mind, also remembering that even as stars of the first magnitude—meaning those in the heavens—differ in glory, so likewise do those of the turf. It is perhaps well to be conservative rather than "waste a wealth of praise" upon the latest and most brightly shining orb that glorifies the course. Otherwise, in a few seasons it may all have to be taken back, or revised downward, when another animal of similar estate comes knocking at the door, burdened with gigantic money-winnings, gold and silver trophies, collars, shawls and blankets of roses and other posies, sheaves of track, stake or world's records (or all three) and demanding due honor as the greatest of the great.

Generations ago that wisest of racing critics, the late W. S. Vosburgh, laid it down as an axiom that the safest line to follow is to concede that the newest turf idol is assuredly the greatest, for by so doing one is always sure of voting with the majority. And, as all men know, it is the majority that rules. As racing goes, enthusiasts have short memories. They require new gods to worship, and if, a season or two hence, these deities show feet of clay, by that time still newer ones will have displaced them.

We have been led to these reflections while surveying the one pre-eminent performer of 1943 whose claims to recognition as "the horse of the year" so far surpass those of all rivals as to leave them down the course. His achievements were so dazzling, his record so splendid, that not only does he stand out—he throws into the shade all other Thoroughbreds of 1943, without regard to age, sex, or other qualifications.

Just where is he to be ranked among our turf titans? How shall he most correctly be characterized and his performances assessed? What is his title to high distinction, when judicially considered?

In trying to answer these questions we shall endeavor to conform to the records while holding in mind the fact that the records by no means tell all. It may be true that figures never lie, but in and of themselves they are never final. There are many things in racing which they do not and cannot express—and to leave this out of account is perhaps the greatest, as it is also the commonest, error that critics of racing and race horses can commit.

If we take the record of Count Fleet, as expressed in figures, a mere glance at it is sufficient to disclose a capacity absolutely first-class.

Up to the time he disabled himself in winning the Belmont Stakes on June 5, making it necessary to throw him out of training and declare him from many of his richest three-year-old engagements, he had started in 21 races, won 16 of them, second in four of the others and third in the remaining one, earning the sum of $250,300. Of these races, 15 were run as a two-year-old, with ten wins; the other six were run as a three-year-old and all were victories.

Now, this is by no means an unequaled record, nor one that is unsurpassed. Man o' War, for instance, at the same age, ran 21 races, won 20 of them and was second in the remaining start. His earnings were almost precisely similar, being $249,465—though it should be borne in mind that back in 1919–1920, when he was racing, purse and stake values were far lower than nowadays. As a matter of fact, five of the stakes won by Man o' War were not renewed in 1942 (complete returns for 1943 are not available at this writing) but reckoning the values of the others and adding the exceptions of 1919–1920 thereto, the son of Fair Play would have won $411,010 in his two- and three-year-old form, instead of the $249,465 which he actually did— though that was sufficient to make him the leading American money-winner up to that time. . . . It is such facts as these which so greatly qualify the validity of the assertion that "figures never lie" when we are trying to weigh the achievements of race horses. As does also the accompanying fact that Man o' War raced on through his entire three-year-old season and not merely until June.

So exalted does the reputation of Man o' War remain, though it is now almost a quarter of a century since he retired from the turf, that he has become by common consent the yardstick by which aspirants for the highest turf honors are measured; while, furthermore, comparisons between him and Count Fleet have been made profusely since the latter leaped into such prominence.

Curiously enough, those who have questioned the supremacy of Man o' War among modern American race horses have been insistent upon the contention that "he never beat a good horse." One which, however, has not been accepted at face value because he beat many of high class and did so in the most commanding style. Now, precisely the same contention has been made as regards Count Fleet. We may say that Man o' War never, as a two-year-old, met so brilliant a colt as Occupation, by whom Count Fleet was given two of his five defeats at that age. But again, when three Count Fleet met nothing that was within pounds of top class, the utter inability of his opposition to extend him, even when the time was moderate to slow, "placing" them in a definite manner.

We may more justly compare Count Fleet with Man o' War's son, War Admiral. The parallel between them is indeed much closer and includes a singularly identical climax; for, in winning the Belmont Stakes of 1937 War Admiral, like Count Fleet, injured and incapacitated himself, it being necessary to throw him out of training for an extended period. While, up to that time he had, at that age, started in and won five successive races, including the Triple Crown of Kentucky Derby, Preakness and Belmont, in all but the Preakness literally losing his fields. As a two-year-old War Admiral had started in six races, won three, twice second and once third. All in all, the analogy between him and Mrs. Hertz's colt is much closer than with Man o' War, as will readily be seen when the tables of their performances are compared.

COUNT FLEET					
	Races	First	Second	Third	Unpl.	Earned
Two Years	15	10	4	1	0	$ 76,245
Three Years	6	6	0	0	0	174,055
	21	16	4	1	0	$250,300

WAR ADMIRAL					
Two Years	6	3	2	1	0	$ 14,800
Three Years	8	8	0	0	0	166,500
	14	11	2	1	0	$181,300

The difference in winnings at two years lies in the fact that much more use was made of Count Fleet at that age than of War Admiral. The latter was started in none of the season's Futurities, because the costly oversight of not engaging him in any of them had been committed.

However, in his three-year-old season War Admiral, after having been on the shelf since his victory and injury in the Belmont, run June 5, returned to the post late in the fall to start in and win the Chesapeake Stakes and Pimlico Special, both against aged horses. But so badly crippled was Count Fleet in the Belmont that his campaign ended then and there.

Count Fleet [MORNING TELEGRAPH]

For the two-year-old performances of the son of Reigh Count, together with his ancestral and other background, the reader may refer to the volume of *American Race Horses* for 1942. We will resume the chronicle of his career where we left off, he having been retired to winter quarters at his birthplace, Mrs. Hertz's Stoner Creek Stud, Paris, Kentucky.

At that time he stood just 15½ hands high and weighed around 900 pounds, but by January 1, 1943 he had reached the 1,000-pound notch. Had there been any racing in Florida, he would probably have been sent there early in the winter; but war conditions precluding this, he was shipped to Oaklawn Park, Hot Springs, Arkansas, to return to training and be edged up for strong work. Arriving on January 27, he was first clocked in his work on February 19, when he breezed three furlongs in :38 and a half in :52⅘. He remained there four weeks longer, being then shipped east to Belmont Park, where he arrived on March 19. His fastest move at Oaklawn, six furlongs in 1:17⅕, had been made about a week before.

The colt's campaign for 1943 had been planned with the purpose of his bow being made in the Wood Memorial, at Jamaica, on April 17, and as this was now near at hand, tightening-up was forthwith in order. Beginning conservatively with a breeze of three furlongs on the 22nd, he thereafter speedily became the sensation of the morning hours and the subject of a succession of headlines in the newspapers. On the 23rd, he was sent six furlongs in 1:16⅖, "hard held," then on the 26th set the clockers agog by moving a mile over the Belmont training track in 1:40⅖, the half being done in :48⅖, six furlongs in 1:14⅖ and seven furlongs in 1:26⅖. All through the final eighth he was being slowed down. Considering his moderate preliminary trials this exhibition had a thrilling effect. But it too was forgotten when only four days later, on the 30th, he reeled off the fastest mile (or so it was averred) ever clocked over this oval, which is seconds slower than the Belmont main course and one seldom used by trainers for fast trials. Ridden by his regular jockey, Longden, Count Fleet sped to the first furlong pole in :11⅘, quarter in :24⅘, three furlongs in :35⅘, half in :48 flat, six furlongs in 1:12⅖, seven furlongs in 1:25⅖ and full mile in 1:38⅗. He was being taken back through the last furlong and, under strong restraint, went on to finish out nine furlongs in 1:52.

From the moment the winter books had been opened on the Kentucky Derby, Count Fleet had ruled a top-heavy favorite. As early as March 1 he had been at but five to two. His odds now began to grow shorter and shorter and the prediction was made that if all continued well with him he would go to the post at Churchill Downs the shortest-priced choice in Derby history. His next trial was eagerly awaited and was staged on April 3, still over the Belmont training track, and was a nine-furlong effort in 1:55, first mile in 1:41⅖, Longden having him under double wraps. By this time, the attention centered upon him had become such that the management at Jamaica, where the spring meeting was just getting under way, secured him for a "public trial" on April 9, between races. When introduced to the crowd he was loudly cheered and rewarded his admirers with a mile in 1:39⅖, then eased off the nine furlongs in 1:53⅗, with fractions in :11⅘, :24⅕, :48⅕, 1:00⅖, 1:13⅗ and 1:26⅖.

While his debut for the year had all along been designated as the Wood, on April 17, with no preliminary race, a change of plan was made and on Tuesday, April 13, at Jamaica, he was saddled for the St. James purse race of $3,000, distance one mile and 70 yards. His assignment was 122 pounds and he was asked to give from eight to 14 pounds each to the seven that opposed him, they including Bossuet, Towser, Four Freedoms, Famous Victory, Eurasian, Eye-for-Eye and Joe Burger. The track was sloppy from a shower. Such was his prestige that at post time he was at 15 cents to $1.00; with Bossuet second choice at 7½ to 1. Carried very wide on the first turn, he was then steered in near the rail by Longden, and, picking up the leaders in a leisurely and confident manner, he was challenging Bossuet at the turn for home, drew past him when ready and won in a gallop by 3½ lengths "with ridiculous ease." Despite the mud he ran the first mile in 1:38⅘ and full distance in 1:42⅘; track record, 1:40⅘. Net of the purse to him, $1,950.

The furor created by this performance was unqualified. It brought interest in the Wood Memorial to the boiling point and over 20,000 people jammed the Jamaica enclosure when the field of eight paraded to the post for it on Saturday, the 17th. Though the track was fast, the weather was cold and raw. The sum of $196,192 was wagered upon him, which made his odds one to four. He was carrying 126 pounds, as were all the others except Twoses with 121. Drawing the No. 4 stall, he met interference when the gates were sprung, as Modest Lad (No. 2) cannoned into Vincentive (No. 3) and the latter was forced over on him, but Longden quickly got him clear and he at once went to the leader, Blue Swords, headed him at the quarter in :23⅗ and, taking a fine burst of speed, opened up three lengths on him in running the next quarter, which took him to the half in :46⅘. Thenceforward he rated along at will, and with Longden taking a stiff hold of him all through the home stretch, he was at the three-quarters in 1:11⅖, ran the mile in 1:36⅖ (track record 1:38⅖) and won in a canter at the wire with the time for the full 1¹⁄₁₆ miles 1:43. The record for the event was 1:45⅕, and track record 1:42⅗, by the four-year-old Sting with 106 pounds up. The net value of the stake to Count Fleet was $20,150, its endowment of added money having been raised to $25,000 in 1942. This was the 19th running of the stake.

The Wood Memorial is generally recognized as the preview, or dress rehearsal, for the Kentucky Derby insofar as the eastern candidates are concerned. Its result, therefore, left the impression in the minds of those who had witnessed it that nothing could block the pathway of Count Fleet—that his victory at Churchill Downs was a foregone conclusion. For among the western aspirants there was nothing, with public form in evidence, fit to bother him. Only one disturbing fact remained. When roughhoused leaving the gate in the Wood he had received a nasty cut on his left hind coronet and pulled up bleeding from the wound. However, no trace of soreness developed and after a day's rest he was shipped to Louisville, on the morning of Monday, the 19th, by Trainer G. D. Cameron, who pronounced the injury negligible.

Saturday, May 1, being Derby day, he had two weeks in which to prepare for the great event. Colonel Matt Winn had sturdily refused to strip any of its glamour by reducing it in value; the Derby again carried its $75,000 endowment. When advised to declare it off, he had snorted in contemptuous indignation. So again Louisville prepared to entertain a Derby crowd, which might be reduced in numbers, as the difficulties of wartime transportation were being reinforced by official threats and rumblings regarding pleasure driving, special trains or planes; in fact, any and all modes and manners of reaching the course from far or near. The main concern of those intent upon getting there was really not so much the method they might have to employ, or the hardships attendant; but whether the overshadowing prestige of the favorite might not reduce the field so materially as to leave him little opposition. It was, therefore, something of a surprise when no less than nine other colts were saddled to start, making a field of ten; about double the number which had seemed probable.

After his arrival in Kentucky, Count Fleet encountered a spell of wet weather and a continuously muddy track to train over, "Dogs up" being the order of the day. Nothing, therefore, in the way of notable work by him was done until his formal distance trial for the Derby on the Tuesday preceding the race; when, over slow and sticky footing he received it between races for the public's benefit. It was well worth seeing, as he did his full mile and a quarter in flat 2:07,

the fractions rated in :24⅘, :49⅖, 1:15, 1:40⅕ and 1:53⅗. This was done with such facility that the colt appeared little more than romping; he was out in the middle of track and under a strong hold all the way.

If the transportation authorities frowned upon the race, the weather man did not. Forgetting his previous bad manners, he was on his holiday behavior and served up a fine day and track. The restrictions upon travel had a noticeable effect, not only upon the size of the crowd but upon its character. The galaxies of persons, male and female, famed in all walks of life and from all parts of the country, which customarily gave the occasion tone and flavor, were not in attendance. But one governor was present—this being Kentucky's own Keene Johnson, who declined to absent himself and presided in person over the official ceremonies. But the Blue Grass did its noblest to show its loyalty to its Blue Ribbon day and institution. Resorting to all possible means of "getting there," from "shanks' ponies" upward, an attendance estimated from a low of 45,000 to a high of 60,000 passed the gates of Churchill Downs. A drop from 1942 was expected in the betting, and this was turned in when a total of $1,801,899 passed through the machines as against the $1,983,011 then recorded. Under the circumstances, it was so much smaller than had been anticipated that Colonel Winn was justified in announcing another extremely successful Derby, with which he was entirely satisfied.

The prediction that Count Fleet would be the shortest-priced favorite in Derby history was not quite verified. At post time the board quoted 1 to 2½ against him, which by one-half point only fell short of the one to three that had ruled against Hindoo in 1881, Halma in 1895 and Agile in 1905. Had he got to the post, without doubt Warren Wright's colt, Ocean Wave, would have ruled second choice; but he was scratched after being carded as a starter. Only three days before, Ocean Wave had won the Derby Trial Stakes from a big field, running the mile in 1:38⅕ through muddy going and leaving Slide Rule, second, nine lengths astern. Previously through a winter and spring campaign of nine other races he had won six and been second in the other three. But he had gone into the Trial with a suspicious leg, came out of it lame and, as it was to prove, would race no more in 1943, if ever. Blue Swords, therefore, on the strength of his second in the Wood, became the second choice at nine to one, with Slide Rule third at 10¾ to 1 and Gold Shower (a colt that created a flutter by working a mile in 1:35⅕ at Belmont Park just before being shipped to Kentucky) fourth at 12 to 1.

To attempt anything like a circumstantial description of this, the 69th Kentucky Derby, as a contest, would be to essay the impossible; for the reason that it proved, to all intents and purposes, a one-man show. Breaking from the No. 5 stall, Longden took Count Fleet to the front after Gold Shower had attempted to stay with him to the quarter in :23⅕ and half in :46⅗, the latter than falling back two lengths at the three quarters in 1:12⅗. Reaching the mile post in 1:37⅗, without trying to move farther than an open length away from Blue Swords, who had come forward into the place, Count Fleet swept into the stretch and down through it in commanding style, doing the nine furlongs in 1:50⅗ (track record 1:49⅘) and passed under the wire, with speed in reserve, three lengths in front of Blue Swords. The field behind them seemed utterly demoralized, for Blue Swords had six lengths on Slide Rule, third, and that colt as many more on Amber Light, fourth, while great gaps separated the stragglers in the rear guard. Seldom, indeed, in a classic race, did one behold so many colts so badly beaten. The time for the mile and a quarter was 2:04; race and track record 2:01⅖ by Whirlaway in 1941.

Posing in the winner's enclosure, Count Fleet seemed little the worse for his exertions. Trainer Cameron stood beside him and up above Governor Johnson made the speech of presentation, and the magnificent gold cup, a replica of that won by the winner's sire, Reigh Count, 1928, was tendered to Mrs. Hertz. That lady, a picture of happiness, was unable to make her way back to her box because of the throng of friends and admirers that besieged her. It was indeed a proud day for her and Mr. Hertz. On only three previous occasions in the long history of the Derby had it been won by a colt whose sire had preceded him in victory. The first occasion was in 1902, when Alan-a-Dale triumphed, he being by Halma, the victor in 1895. Next came the father and son Bubbling Over (1926) and Burgoo King (1932); followed by Gallant Fox (1930) and Omaha (1935).

Resting over Sunday, on Monday, May 3, Count Fleet departed from Louisville to arrive next morning in Baltimore and take quarters at Pimlico awaiting the Preakness, due for decision the Saturday following. There had been rumors around Churchill Downs the morning after the Derby that all was not well with him, but his appearance upon arrival at "Old Hill Top" belied them, as he never looked or acted better. And as for the Preakness, never had it seemed so utterly at a favorite's mercy. The remorseless manner in which the Count had smashed up the Derby field had established the opinion that nothing in or out of it could hold him an argument—and the main question concerning his appearance was the shortness of his odds. That and the other one: What will be willing to face him?

The manner in which these questions were answered was instructive. On Preakness Day, May 8, it was with difficulty that a trio of colts could be marshaled against him—while as for his odds, they were the shortest ever known—15 cents to $1.00—and virtually the same as the one to seven quoted against Vanguard far back in 1882, sixty-one years before—at which time the stake now so famous as the "second leg" of the American Triple Crown was a merely local event worth but $1,250 to the winner. Though Blue Swords had definitely outrun all the fielders in both the Wood and the Derby, there was a misplaced confidence abroad in the ability of the Maryland colt Vincentive, winner of his last two starts at Pimlico, within the previous ten days. George Woolf, premier big-money jockey, had been secured to ride him and he was backed down to 6:15 to 1, as against 10 to 1 Blue Swords. New Moon, the fourth member of the quartet, was friendless at 48¾ to 1.

Pimlico's proximity to the nation's capital brought over from there many notables, titled and otherwise, while numerous others from points throughout the East were visible in the clubhouse enclosure. As the location of the track makes it easy of access to Baltimoreans, few of those who wanted to see the race from the city and thereabouts found trouble in reaching the park. The attendance, given out in round figures at 30,000, lacked little of the normal.

If the Derby was so destitute of features, as a contest, what may be said of the Preakness? Almost nothing. It was an absolute one-horse race—that, and only that. Count Fleet shot to the front like a skyrocket when the get-off came, and thereafter his flying form, steadily increasing the distance between him and his ineffectual pursuers, drew farther and farther off from them. At the quarter it was three lengths, at the half it was four, at the three-quarters about the same, at the mile it was five, and through the stretch he came swinging, with long, hurtling leaps, apparently effortless in their propulsion, to win, hard held, by eight from Blue Swords, who left Vincentive five more behind him, with the very late-rising New Moon just visible at the horizon.

So amazingly easy was his effort that until the time was hung out hardly anybody realized that it was merely because he had been kept under restraint that Count Fleet had not broken records. The fractional time of the mile and 3/16 was :23⅗, :47⅖, 1:11⅘, 1:38⅕, 1:57⅖, with the Preakness mark the 1:57, flat, established by the great Alsab in 1942. Mrs. Hertz was called to the stand to receive the congratulations of President Harry Parr III of the Maryland Jockey Club, together with the replica of the historic Woodlawn Vase which that organization annually presents to the Preakness winner.

The net of the stake to Count Fleet was

Count Fleet as a two-year-old—Jockey J. Longden up [UPI]

$43,190. That of the Kentucky Derby had been $60,725. Thus in the two events he had earned over $100,000, exclusive of cups and breeder's cash awards. Counting his two previous wins at Jamaica in the Wood Memorial and St. James purse, together with his two-year-old credit of $76,245, he had already topped the $200,000 mark with a total of $202,260—and it was but May 8! Stimulated by this exhibit, the statisticians unleashed their comptometers and were producing figures to show the new hero far on his way to eclipse the money-won record for a single season, $308,275, by Gallant Fox, back in 1930; when the famous son of Sir Gallahad had monopolized the classics.

Trainer Cameron had announced that if all went well in the Preakness, he would not follow the usual precedent of reserving his charge for the Belmont, to be run four weeks thence, but would point him for the Withers, due to come up on May 22, just two weeks later. Twenty-four years before, or back in 1919, Sir Barton had brought off the only sweep ever executed in the Derby, Preakness, Withers and Belmont. Cameron was confident that Count Fleet could duplicate the achievement. In accordance, the colt was vanned over from Pimlico to Belmont Park, on Monday the 10th, to prepare for an outing in the American Two Thousand.

The prospect was for another bloodless victory; for among the eligibles there was nothing with the slightest prospect of giving him trouble. Being, therefore, at the top of his form and with only a mile to race, nothing was asked of him during the intervening fortnight more notable than a gallop of five furlongs in :58⅗ on the 15th and another of seven in 1:28⅕ on the 18th. He stripped for the Withers looking cherry-ripe and found facing him but two opponents, Slide Rule and Tip Toe, they alone having the temerity to sport silk. The odds were truly farcical, being 5 cents to $1.00 against him, or 20 to 1 *on*. Rain had left the track muddy and threatening weather and transportation restraints reduced the attendance from what it otherwise would have been.

Had the going been good, sensational time would have been expected. As it was, that recorded lacked little of being so, for the Count, dashing off to a three-lengths' lead at the quarter in :26, flew to the half in :46⅖, three-quarters in 1:10⅗ and finished, in Longden's lap, in flat 1:36; the Withers record being 1:35⅘ by Man o' War, established in 1920, which was first tied by Snob II in 1922 and again by Johnstown in 1939; a fast track prevailing on each of these occasions. The net value of the stake was $12,700, with a piece of plate to the winner.

By this time, the immense superiority of the son of Reigh Count over the three-year-olds of 1943 had become so evident that, together with his meteoric style of racing and the facility with which he negotiated all kinds of tracks, fast or slow, wet or dry, had won a truly extravagant acclaim. The feverish state of affairs produced by the war, which tended to exaggerate everything in any way striking or unusual, did not fail to affect his status. As has previously been remarked, he was elevated to a position analogous to that held by Man o' War; while perfervid enthusiasts did not hesitate to relegate even that phenomenal horse to a secondary position.

The drama, however, was now due for a sudden termination. One so unexpected, and so condign, that it came like a thunderbolt crashing from the unflecked blue.

The two weeks that elapsed between the Withers and the Belmont saw him working a mile and a quarter over a muddy track, on May 27, in 2:07⅘, first mile in 1:41⅖, and losing a plate in the journey; and the same distance, in his formal trial for the Belmont, on June 1, in 2:04, the first mile in 1:36⅗, with fractions in :23, :34⅖, :46⅖, :58⅗, 1:11⅖ and 1:24⅕, he being pulled up all through the final quarter.

The effect was what might have been looked for. Though the famous fixture was carrying $25,000 added money, the second colt would receive $5,000 and third $2,500. Of all the long list of eligibles nothing could be persuaded to oppose him but Fairy Manhurst, thus far the winner of but two overnight races, and Deseronto, a winner of one small purse event in a dozen starts. Under the New York State laws regulating betting, nothing is allowable in the way of odds shorter than the 5 cents to $1.00 that had prevailed in the Withers. In consequence these were again the quotations—had there been no restrictions the Count might perhaps have been barred from the betting, or ruled at no more than a penny to a dollar. As it was, in order to comply with the law and pay to his backers a five-cent premium, the Westchester Racing Association was out the sum of $15,912.02.

It was the first time since the season opened that Count Fleet was starting over a fast and perfect track. So, excitement reigned in the crowd of something over 20,000 that he had attracted, as to the possibility of a new American record for a mile and a half, the distance he was now to run. The standing one was the 2:27⅗ of the five-year-old Bolingbroke (115 pounds) made the previous fall when that son of Equipoise so unexpectedly defeated Whirlaway for the Manhattan Handicap, over this same track; while the Belmont Stakes record was the 2:28⅗ of War Admiral, scored by that colt in the renewal for 1937. This excitement being intensified when it was reported that Trainer Cameron was understood to have agreed to attempt the task with the brown colt, and for the first time during the season he would be ridden out.

Getting off almost immediately, Longden in his tactics verified this forecast. Leaving the gate at high speed and, quickly dropping his two adversaries far astern, Count Fleet began spinning off the fractions in dizzy style. The quarter was run in :23⅗, half in :48, three-quarters in 1:12⅕, seven-eighths in 1:25⅖ and first mile completed in 1:37⅘. Having started from in front of the stand, directly beneath the wire, as the Belmont course is just a mile and a half in circuit, he was now speeding around the far turn, a dozen lengths in advance of Fairy Manhurst, second. Comparisons were made with the fractional time of Bolingbroke's race and they showed that the first mile had then been run in 1:37 flat; while War Admiral, in his Belmont run, had done the distance in 1:37⅕.

Could the lag be picked up through the half mile still to be traversed? Thus far, Longden had just been letting his mount rate along within himself; so predictions were heard that a new record was about to be chalked up.

Rounding the upper turn, Count Fleet moved beautifully, and, completing the nine furlongs in 1:50⅖, swung for home. From the head of the stretch to the wire at Belmont Park the distance is 1,147 feet, or something less than a quarter-mile (1,320 feet), so he was hardly well straight before completing the mile and a quarter, where the watches showed 2:03⅗. Now full twenty lengths in front of the plodding pursuers, Longden, it was observed, was no longer restraining him but had loosed his hold and was preparing for a grand effort. Again hasty references were made to the records and they showed that in Bolingbroke's race the time at the same point had been 2:02⅗, while in War Admiral's it had been 2:02⅕.

For the first time it was realized that Count Fleet faced a supreme test. To equal Bolingbroke's record of 2:27⅗ would mean a last quarter in :24 flat; to lower it, one in :23⅘—in either case a prodigious feat at the end of so long and fast a race. To lower War Admiral's 2:28⅗ would require one of :24⅘—a full second's leeway. . . . Could he do it?

The mile and three-eighths was passed in 2:15⅗ and Longden was seen to be riding the colt—but soon after, it was observed that he was beginning to shorten stride. That he was beginning to tire was apparent and, desisting in his efforts, Longden eased his pressure and let him finish on his courage, which he did amid a hurricane of encouragement in 2:28⅕. While he had failed of a new American record, he had lowered that of the stake by ⅖ of a second. The toiling pair up the stretch were twenty-five lengths behind.

Count Fleet by his magnificent effort had not only taken the Triple Crown but also duplicated the feat of Sir Barton by adding to it the Withers—a feat so difficult that any turfman who has witnessed it once need not expect to see it again during his lifetime.

And so once more Mrs. Hertz descended to meet him as Trainer Cameron led him into the enclosure for the presentation of the massive gold cup signalizing his victory, while serried batteries of cameramen clustered about them and the stands rocked with an ovation as sincere as it was reverberant. The net value of the stake to him was $35,340.

It was an inspiring moment—but one which none of the 20,000 persons that participated could have imagined was to prove the finale for the season of its central figure; and only the future can reveal whether ever again he will be seen in public.

While to all appearances Count Fleet returned to his stable unscathed from his exploit, a few hours later the rejoicing which attended him gave way to gloom and apprehension. It developed that his right fore ankle had been struck during his flight around the course; by some, it was thought when he crossed the chute just before entering the back stretch, by others, when nearing the end of the race, he had suddenly tired and was unable to respond to Longden's calls . . . it being under precisely such circumstances that race horses are most apt to strike themselves. But, wherever or however the injury had been sustained, there it was. The colt walked soundly upon the leg and foot; but the lower portion of the shin, likewise the ankle and the pastern, were filled and feverish.

To the interviewers that besieged him, Trainer Cameron gave out the statement next morning that it was nothing to be alarmed about—mere superficial damage had been done of which no trace would remain a few days hence. It might be necessary to stop the colt in his work for a short time, but he would be ready for the $25,000 Yankee Handicap at Boston on July 4; and for the $50,000 Classic at Chicago, on July 24, without fail. . . . How often have not similar assurances been uttered in similar circumstances, by hopeful trainers and anxious owners, unable to believe that something serious really has happened—and, in a moment's flash, their champion has become a cripple.

The days passed, then the weeks, and gradually it became apparent that Count Fleet's mere superficial injury was, on the contrary, something very serious indeed. After other remedies had been tried without the desired results, it was announced that the tendon was involved and the firing-iron must be resorted to. But, as no thought would be entertained of irreparably breaking him down by any ill-advised effort to bring him back to the post, the colt would be declared from his coming engagements and retired for the season. He remained at Belmont Park thereafter until the early part of October and was then shipped home to Stoner Creek to winter there—where, with complete rest and careful treatment it was the hope that he would come out sound in the spring of 1944 and resume his career of conquest, so cruelly cut short with his supreme achievement.

All lovers of a great race horse will earnestly unite in expressing the wish that this hope will be gratified and that the coming season may witness many more performances by Count Fleet in keeping with those which have raised him to the high distinction which he now enjoys. They will also trust that, if this cannot be, he will be spared the ordeals to which other champions of recent years have been subjected when, mere memories of their once-great selves, they have been forced through a series of inglorious failures to a belated farewell to the course which found them with none left to do them reverence. Indeed, knowing Mr. and Mrs. Hertz as we do, we feel certain that Count Fleet will never meet that ignominious fate.

Zev Beats Papyrus

ELMER DAVIS

I couldn't say whether or not this is Elmer Davis' first piece of international reporting. As a fourteen-year-old youngster living in Wisconsin at the time of the Zev–Papyrus race I was somewhat removed from the orbit of Elmer Davis. I caught up with him, though, during the Second World War, as did many millions of others who followed his brilliant newscasting of the international conflict.

NEW YORK, Oct. 21, 1923

BEFORE a cheering, howling crowd of 45,000 people, packed in the stands and swarming along the rail at Belmont Park, Zev, Harry Sinclair's three-year-old colt, yesterday won a decisive victory over Benjamin Irish's Papyrus, winner of the English Derby.

The American horse was five lengths ahead at the end of the mile and a half. On a sloppy track, particularly wet in the home stretch, where the shadow of the grandstand had kept off the afternoon sun, the running was slow. Zev finished in 2:35⅗, nearly seven seconds under the record for the distance. But of two good mud horses Zev showed he was the better, and contrary to the gloomy prediction of those who said he could not go the distance and that Papyrus would pull ahead at the finish, Zev led all the way and Papyrus, after a last fierce burst at the mile and three-eighths, fell farther and farther behind.

The brilliant weather and the satisfactory race brought to a happy conclusion an international event which at one time, when one mishap after another was changing the preliminary drama to farce, threatened to resemble the late unfortunate prize fight at Shelby.

The selection of Zev as the American contender by the Jockey Club, instead of an elimination race as had originally been intended, embittered feeling among partisans of Admiral Grayson's colt, My Own, and all Washington and the United States seethed with a conviction of injustice. Then, after Papyrus' fast trial on Thursday, Zev broke out with the hives, My Own had to be imported to relieve him in case of necessity, and gloomy observers began to talk of Major Belmont, chairman of the Jockey Club, changing horses as fast as John McGraw changes pitchers.

But Zev ran after all, and in view of his conclusive victory over Papyrus it must be supposed that when he broke out in a rash on Thursday and scared people who had bet on him until they broke out in a rash too, it was with excitement and not with fear.

Zev's victory makes him the leading money-maker among American horses of all time. A purse of $100,000 had been put up for the international race, of which $80,000 went to the winner. Adding this to Zev's previous earnings, he has made about $255,000 for his owner, Mr. Sinclair, who to be sure doesn't need it but can probably use it just the same. This is about $5,000 more than the great Man o' War made before he was retired to stud.

Papyrus got $20,000 for the loser's end. Two gold cups were given in addition, one to become the property of the owner of the winning horse,

Zev leading Papyrus by a length at the mile post [UPI]

the other to serve as a standing trophy for the international race and to be held for a year by each of the annual winners.

Papyrus' defeat, though generally expected—for Zev was a slight favorite in the betting odds clear down to the finish—was an honorable one. First of the English horses to make the transatlantic trip especially for a single race, he faced the handicap of an unfamiliar climate, a dirt track when he had been used to turf, and the handicap of the Volstead Act which, so far as can be learned, deprived him of the solacing bucket of beer which he is accustomed to put away after his day's work.

The mud of an American track, furthermore, is not like the muddy English turf, and Steve Donoghue, who rode Papyrus, said after the race that his horse had slipped continually.

Papyrus wore smooth plates for the race, and, according to racing men, the failure of Basil Jarvis, trainer of the English horse, to equip Papyrus with the clip plates placed the foreign horse at a disadvantage. It is the belief of American racing men that had Papyrus been properly shod he would have run a much better race.

Officials of the Jockey Club could not say too much in praise of Benjamin Irish, Papyrus' owner, who had gallantly taken the chance of sending him over for this race against almost certain defeat.

The Westchester Racing Association, operating Belmont Park, came out of the affair pretty well, too. Though the record-breaking crowd which had been expected failed to turn out, the shortage was almost entirely in the lower brackets of the price list. Box seats, enclosure and grandstand were almost all filled, and there were thousands who came in on general admission, besides a scattering crowd in the infield. Though no official report of the gate was obtainable last night, it was believed that the receipts had aggregated $432,000, and the motion picture rights are worth $50,000 more.

The expense of the race, altogether, will come to about $190,000, so the house is pretty well ahead.

As to the handling of the crowd, it could not have been better. There was no trouble of any sort.

It was a great victory for the stubborn friends

of the American horse, who had stuck to him despite the smoke clouds of whispered rumors about bad condition early in the week, finally brought out into the open by the sudden action of the Jockey Club in bringing My Own up from Washington on the day before the race. Odds against Papyrus, which had begun at three or four to one, dropped steadily until just before the race they were five to four, and some bets were made at even money. But Zev had the advantage of an old guard of supporters who had to stick to him because they could pronounce his name, and their loyalty was rewarded when their champion came through to a great victory.

There could have been no finer day for a great international race. After two days of rain the sky cleared completely yesterday morning, the sun shone and the weather was Long Island at its October best. Before noon long columns of automobiles were moving out along the sadly inadequate boulevards of Long Island, and special trains from the Thirty-third Street station were beginning to carry the crowds down to Belmont Park.

Five races transferred from the Empire City track were also on the card—three before and two after the big event, and there was everything needed to bring out both racing fans and the crowd that feels that it has to turn out for any great sporting event.

An hour before the big race the stands were almost filled and the enclosure in front was packed with thousands of people. It was already evident that however the race might turn out as a race, it was going to be a big success as a fall fashion show. There was a sufficient sprinkling of uniforms—the khaki of Army officers, with several generals among them; the blue of naval officers, convinced that the glory of the Stars and Stripes would have been safer if My Own had been the contestant, but prepared to root for Zev anyway; police inspectors almost as numerous as honorary deputy police commissioners; the blue of city police, the dark gray uniforms and soft hats of a troop of State police; the light gray of special officers employed at the track, and women's frocks rivaling the scarlet and gold of the autumn woods across from the stands.

There were strange costumes, too. Down in the clubhouse enclosure, where every New Yorker who possessed a sense of self-esteem, a pair of field glasses and $22 had crowded in, there were race track fans who didn't look like race track fans but like actors in a burlesque show made up to look like race track fans. Four-inch wing collars were to be seen—a sight that hasn't been unveiled on Manhattan Island for fifteen or twenty years.

Most of the crowd amused itself with the early races, but there were thousands of people in the paddock when the contenders in the big race were brought out and saddled at 3:40, just as the band in front of the grandstand was starting in on "God Save the King," followed by "The Star-Spangled Banner." The paddock loiterers crowded in about equal numbers around Papyrus and Zev. The English horse was accompanied by his stable companion, Bar Gold, ridden by the red-coated, black-capped whipper-in Murray, who was to lead the racers out to the track.

Almost of a size, the horses differed considerably in color, though both are classed as brown. Papyrus is about as near black as a horse can be and still be called brown. His long, flowing black tail was a luxurious contrast to Zev's appendage, shaved until it looked almost like a mule's.

Then Steve Donoghue mounted—Donoghue, the greatest jockey in England, winner of three Derbies in a row. In the purple jacket of Benjamin Irish, crossed by gold stripes, with gold sleeves and cap, he came up on Papyrus and drew his mount in behind Murray's red coat. Then Earl Sande, in the white jacket with green sleeves of the Rancocas Stables, got aboard Zev. Sande had taken part in the first three races of the afternoon and had failed to place, but he seemed unworried. For one thing, in none of those other races had he ridden a Zev.

Surrounded by a squad of gray-clad police, with I. Whitsed, Mr. Irish's solicitor and representative, a carnation in his buttonhole, walking behind Papyrus, the rivals walked out on the track at 3:53, while the whole crowd stood up and shouted.

Fifty yards to the left was the starting line; they walked up the track past it, on down to the last quarter pole, and, then, while Sande struggled to hold in his impatient mount, Papyrus galloped the quarter mile to the finish, warming himself up and giving the crowd a chance to cheer. He reined in, came back slowly, and then, with Zev at the rail, the two horses got into position and a moment later Starter Mars Cassidy let them go.

Papyrus was off a length ahead, but within fifty yards Sande had caught him and forced Zev in front. They rounded the turn, with Zev still leading but Papyrus' head abreast of Zev's tail, and so running steadily came into the back stretch.

Across the track 45,000 people, standing on the turn or cinders of the infield and enclosure—standing, for that matter, on chairs, on the backs of benches, on iron railings, for nobody who sat down could see that race—45,000 people yelled at them as they increased speed slightly on the drier going of the back stretch, which had been four hours in the sun.

Then Donoghue made his first effort to catch up, but his gain was so small as to be imperceptible to the amateurs of racing. Zev was a scant length ahead when Donoghue spurted, was still half a length ahead as they came toward the turn. Then Zev began to gain—Zev, whose enemies said he couldn't go the distance.

Donoghue strove desperately to make up his loss on the turn. As they came toward the stretch, Papyrus was doing his best to respond to the whip, but Zev, unforced, was doing better; Zev led by two or three lengths; the most heroic effort of which Papyrus was capable cut the lead a length for a moment; then the English horse, his aluminum shoes unable to catch firmly in the splashy mud, his strength unequal to keeping up the pace that Zev had forced and held from the beginning, began to slip farther and farther behind.

As they galloped down in front of the grandstand, roaring with "Come on, Zev!" Papyrus lost ground more and more until the native champion shot across the finish line a good five lengths in the lead. A moment later the green-bordered white flag of the Rancocas Stables was being raised above the winning number; and there was nothing more to do except observe the formalities of sportsmanship and courtesy.

Donoghue and Basil Jarvis, Papyrus' trainer, congratulated Sande and Sam Hildreth, who trained Zev; Admiral Grayson congratulated Harry Sinclair, Sinclair congratulated the losers, everybody congratulated everybody else, and part of the crowd—though no large part—started moving toward the exits at once, absorbed in the principal worry involved in attendance on any sporting event in New York—that of getting home ahead of the crowd.

Papyrus is going home Tuesday—back to turf tracks and beer, where he will feel at home. He leaves behind him the memory of a great horse that made a gallant race, and of an owner, a trainer and a jockey who were fine sportsmen and not afraid to take a sportsmanlike chance against heavy odds. Horse racing is a sport which often stirs up bad blood, but this particular horse race seems to have left only good feeling and friendly admiration behind it. One could wish that that might always be said of international contests between amateurs, which have sometimes led to brandished fists instead of clasped hands across the seas.

Zev's victory restores a balance of international sport which had once more been trending rather heavily in favor of Britain. True, the latest British competitors among us, the Oxford debating team, have been losing their debates, but they won a double moral victory in that they forced their American opponents to adopt their method of argument and also their method of decision—by vote of the audience, which is bound to be partisan, instead of the calm conclusion of a small group of judges.

Papyrus, too, had the crowd against him, but since he lost they cheered him with the approval which even a crowd of winners can usually muster for a good loser.

There were many losers in the crowd, of course, but on the whole it seems doubtful if any extraordinary amount of money changed hands on the race. There was too much uncertainty— uncertainty about both horses, and about the conditions under which the race might have to be run. Still, even for those who didn't bet, it was an expensive pastime. Enclosure seats cost $22, and for that the customers saw a little more than two minutes and a half of racing—not counting the other events on the card, of course, which certainly would have brought out no great proportion of this crowd at these prices. That is pretty nearly $9 a minute.

Customers who paid $27.50 for the Dempsey-Firpo fight saw nearly four minutes of action at an average rate of about $7 a minute.

The sport of kings comes too high for most kings in these days of impoverished royalty, but New York made a display of opulence yesterday which suggests that this city is still able to get along.

Call Me Horse

JOHN I. DAY

This little anecdote and the two which follow appear in a compilation by John I. Day entitled Call Me Horse. *The first is a classic tall tale; the other two are of completely different character.*

Back in the old days, the fashionable stables used to get to Saratoga a few weeks ahead of the meeting to rest their horses for the big races there; and of course at night the trainers would sit out on the porch of the United States Hotel and talk and lie about the horses they had trained and seen. One group that was pretty regular was made up of a famous bunch of men, through whose hands had passed most of the cracks of the previous thirty years—men like Sam Hildreth, Bill Lakeland, and Jimmy Rowe. They used to notice an old fellow sitting near them, well muffled up in one of those ulsters that were worn in the first days of the horseless carriage; but since he never showed any signs of butting in, and didn't want to be touted on horses, they stopped paying attention to him.

A few days before the meeting, however, he suddenly got up, came over to them, and said: "Gentlemen, I've been listening to you talk about horses for two weeks, and I haven't heard you mention a horse with class yet!"

They were aghast, because they had been talking about Domino, Sysonby, Colin, Henry of Navarre, and the like; but finally somebody found his tongue and asked: "What in the world do you call a horse of class?"

The old man hoisted himself up on the porch rail. "Well," he said, "I used to race horses out in Montana in the days of Marcus Daly at Ana-

conda an' the other little tracks out there. Purses weren't much, of course, but we had a lot of fun, an' some good horses too. Well, I had a little mare out there that I think was a horse of class.

"At the end of the meetin' there was usually a pretty good race, with a $5,000 purse, an' everybody was shootin' at it, of course. It didn't suit my mare, but it was so much money I put her in. She was a little thing an' couldn't pack much weight, but she'd won three or four races, an' the handicapper didn't have much use for me anyhow, so he put 160 pounds on her. Sixty pounds of that was dead weight, an' the rest was a little apprentice boy that had rid only a couple of times. She liked to sprint, mostly, but this race was at a mile and a half. She couldn't put up with the bumping she'd get in a big field, but there were seventeen horses answered the bugle. She liked to run on the rail, but she drawed sixteenth. She couldn't mud worth shucks, but it came up to rain hard that mornin', an' the track was fetlock deep.

"Well, they broke off in a tangle, an' she got bumped from both sides an' pretty near knocked down. But she got up an' went after the field, an' she looked the leader eye to eye around the first turn an' into the back stretch. An' goin' down the back stretch that little apprentice boy felt his saddle start to slip. He was scared of that big field behind him, so he steered to the outside rail

[99

an' pulled up. An' that mare stopped out there, an' she had a foal. I'd bred her the year before an' thought she hadn't caught."

The old man stopped in a dead hush and looked at the trainers.

"Gentlemen," he went on, "she was what I call a horse of class. She won that race by three open lengths. An' the foal ran second!"

In all my years in racing I never did hear two consistent stories about the great Australian horse Phar Lap. He was undoubtedly a fine horse but he never had a chance to prove it in this country. My own feeling is that the innuendoes surrounding his death were grossly unfair to Phar Lap's ability. The following is a factual account, from Call Me Horse, *of his brief and fatal visit to this hemisphere.*

WHENEVER horsemen get together and begin discussing great Thoroughbreds it's a safe bet that sooner or later the conversation will get around to Phar Lap, the ill-fated Australian gelding that invaded North America in 1932 and raced here but once.

From all reports, that one race, the Agua Caliente Handicap, was enough to convince astute horsemen that Phar Lap must be included in any list of all-time greats.

Not since Man o' War had dominated the racing scene had one horse been so publicized. Phar Lap had defeated everything in Australia and had nowhere to go until his owners decided to bring him to North America. He arrived at San Francisco on January 15, 1932 and was sent to a nearby farm for a ten-day rest and then to Agua Caliente to train for the mile-and-a-quarter Handicap on March 20.

Harry Telford and David Davis, Phar Lap's owners, thought so little of the opposition that they sent the horse over in the care of Tommy Woodcock, a groom. They also brought over Bill Elliott, the stable's second-string jockey, to ride.

About ten days before the race, Phar Lap sustained a quarter-crack and it was cut away and heavy bar plates put on his forefeet. On the day of the race, these were removed and he was shod with steel plates.

The Agua Caliente Handicap was programmed as the 13th event and horsemen were astounded when Phar Lap appeared in the paddock just after the tenth race and walked around. About 20 minutes before the horses were scheduled for mounting, a heavy Australian saddle was placed on the horse and Elliott was put up. Phar Lap was top-weight at 129 pounds and Elliott, weighing but 102, had to make up the difference with lead. Instead of carrying the lead weights in the saddle, Elliott carried them inside his silk jacket.

Before the horses were paraded to the post, Woodcock was overheard giving Elliott his riding instructions.

"When you leave the gate, canter down the stretch," he said, "and when you get on the back stretch, gallop on home."

Elliott carried out the instructions to the letter. As they left the gate, Elliott took a tight hold and as the horses passed the stands for the first time, Phar Lap was last. Going into the back stretch, Phar Lap moved up to sixth place in the field of eleven, and then Elliott turned him loose. By the time the field reached the far turn he was three lengths in the lead and Elliott took hold of him again, thinking he had smothered the opposition. However, Reveille Boy ranged up and as the horses straightened out in the stretch, Phar Lap's lead had been cut to a neck. At the eighth pole, Elliott turned the big gelding loose and Phar Lap quickly moved to a two-length lead, maintaining it to the finish. The time of 2:02⅖ was a new track record.

Two weeks later, on April 5, the turf world was shocked when Phar Lap suddenly died at Ed Perry's Ranch, near Palo Alto, California, where he had been resting for an Eastern campaign. There were reports that he had been poisoned, but after a careful examination, the Hooper Foundation of the University of California announced that colic was the cause of death.

The post-mortem showed that Phar Lap's heart weighed 14 pounds, the heaviest of any Thoroughbred, the average being nine. It is now on exhibition at the Institute of Anatomy in Canberra, Australia.

Phar Lap was foaled in New Zealand in 1926 and was bought at a yearling sale for $800. He was taken to Australia to race and after an ordinary two-year-old season became the best three-year-old Down Under, winning 13 of 20 starts. At four he won 14 of 16, including the two-mile Melbourne Cup under 138 pounds. The following year he won eight of his nine starts, his only defeat coming in the Melbourne Cup with 150 pounds up.

His record was so impressive in his last two Australian seasons that many bookmakers refused to offer a price on him.

Phar Lap derived his name from the Javanese word meaning "lightning." He was called. "The Red Terror" because of his chestnut coloring. He was anything but a "picture" horse. But, from the saddle on back, he was all horse.

His lifetime record shows 51 starts, 37 wins, three seconds, and two thirds for earnings of $332,700.

In Australia, Phar Lap has become a legendary figure. From his one race on this continent the legend has taken a firm hold here.

My third selection from Call Me Horse *answers a few questions that may interest the ladies.*

I N England they list many different colorings of Thoroughbreds, but in this country they are limited to bay, chestnut, brown, black, dun, gray, and roan. There have been many debates as to which particular color boasts the biggest number of outstanding horses, but the more one looks into it, the more he gets back to that old expression, "Good horses come in all sizes, shapes, and colors."

Chestnut is a whole color, and three shades may be named—bright, golden, and red. Man o' War was often called "Big Red" for the reason that he is a red chestnut.

The bay coloring varies considerably in shade from a dull red, approaching the brown, to a yellowish coloring that is near to the chestnut, but it can be distinguished from the chestnut by the fact that the bay has a black mane and tail and almost invariably has black on the limbs.

Two questions persist year after year—whether chestnuts are superior to horses of other colorings and whether grays are inferior. Many opinions but few facts have been offered on the subject, and there is no evidence that there is any link between racing ability and coat color.

There is nothing in research to substantiate the idea that chestnuts are better racers than horses of other colors. A check made of the foals of 1930 revealed that of the first 770 (arranged by dams), no less than 484 were bay, brown, or black, and that only 270, or 35 per cent, were chestnut—and that 16 were gray or roan. Another check, made in 1935, showed that of 135 stakes winners from the 1930 crop, 90 were bay,

brown, or black; 44, or 32 per cent, were chestnut, and just one was gray.

That gray horses are in the minority is only natural. For a time they almost disappeared from the American scene. It was The Tetrarch, often called the "Spotted Wonder" and more often called "the fastest horse that ever lived," that revived the interest in grays. He was by Roi Hérode and was undefeated on the race course, while his son Tetratema won thirteen of his sixteen starts.

Once a ratio between a dominant and a recessive color (bay and chestnut) is established in a breed, the natural operation of the Mendelian laws of heredity will tend to preserve that ratio. But there has never been a ratio which says a horse of a particular color cannot be a good one.

Many Thoroughbreds popularly mistaken for black horses are actually dark brown. Black is not a common coat color for the Thoroughbred, and in almost every case it is traceable to the Byerly Turk, one of the three foundation sires of the Thoroughbred, the others being the "brown-bay" Godolphin Arabian and the bay Darley Arabian. Unlike the gray, where at least one parent must be a gray, the black coat may vanish for a generation or more, and then reappear in an individual horse.

While much has been written and little established regarding what, if any, relation a Thoroughbred's coat color has to his racing ability, there is something more than ordinarily appealing about a gray horse. Not long ago a man named E. E. Fogelson sought to race only gray horses. If one were so disposed today it would be a little easier. There has been a notable increase in the number of gray Thoroughbreds, and indications are that their number will continue to increase.

To produce a gray foal one or the other of the parents must be a gray. Though there is no handy record of the number of gray mares around and thus likely to pass on their coat color, it can be noted that of some 250 Thoroughbreds listed in 1945 in the Stallion Register published by *The Blood-Horse,* ten are grays.

"Your horse is now breaking into a brisk walk."

DRAWING BY CHON DAY   [© 1957 BY THE CURTIS PUBLISHING COMPANY]

"Did your mother ever pay $95.60?"

DRAWING BY HENRY BOLTINOFF

[© 1961 BY FAWCETT PUBLICATIONS, INC.]

DRAWING BY ERIC ERICSON   [© 1945 BY THE CURTIS PUBLISHING COMPANY]

Apprentice

PRICE DAY

Price Day, a Pulitzer Prize winner, was born in Amarillo, Texas, on a ranch where his father raised polo ponies. After graduating from Princeton, he worked—among other jobs—as a pari-mutuel clerk at various race tracks. He is today a senior editor of the Baltimore Sun *and a recognized authority on the Near East and Latin America, in which areas he has traveled extensively as a correspondent. He has given up fiction writing as "poor pay"; and horse racing because you can't beat them.*

PERSONALLY, my feelings about superstition are strong: I'm against it. But in twenty-five years or so on the turf you see a lot of things. Some are funny, and some are messy, and some are sad. And some are tragic and strange and wild. There was one thing once.

It came mighty close to home, but just the same I believe I can see it clearly, most of the time. Sometimes, when I can't sleep nights, though, I lie awake thinking about it, and it gives me the cold creeps.

I'll tell you the story of Jerry Granahan, the jockey.

I come into it because I'm a jockeys' agent, and have been for a number of years. Back of that, I handicapped for a while, and back of that I just hung around, and back of that I was a heavy player. I was headed for the law, but I got left a little money, and started playing the ponies, and—

That part doesn't matter.

Well, a middle-aged jockeys' agent, even one who had a smear of education way back yonder somewhere, couldn't be asked to know it in the original, but there's a Spanish proverb that says: "Give your son luck and throw him into the sea."

I wonder, or rather, I believe I know. After I'd tossed my money, I decided that I didn't want any more excitement, and so I've spent a lot of the last fifteen or sixteen years just sitting in the sun on paddock benches or against stable walls, with the old felt propped down over my eyes, trying to figure things out. Not for any particular purpose, mind; just trying to figure them out because I haven't anything else to do.

If you're like that, and if you live around horse tracks, you do see many things. You see the wildness of a bettor or a whole crowd, or a horse or a whole stable, when they go on a winning spree that looks good to last forever, and that can't be explained by brains or handling or blood or anything else you can put your finger on—or a losing spree that's the same way. And you see jockeys who can't win, and once in a while a jockey who can't lose.

There's such a thing as luck, all right. Sometimes I think there isn't much else. And wherever there's luck—everywhere—there's superstition.

I guess what happens is this: People see all that crazy luck running loose, they see a good part of what goes on in the world being decided by luck alone, and they try to explain it, because it's human to want to have everything tucked away into pigeonholes. That fails, and then comes the next step. They decide that it's all due to fate, and they decide to control fate. They get a bunny's left hind foot, or a horseshoe, or any one of the millions of personal charms you see around. And they believe in those things. Superstition!

There's no sense to it, no sense at all. You can't figure luck. And you can't predict it or force it or charm it. And, good or bad, you can't steal somebody else's luck, or give your own away.

Of course, a lot of people believe different. Whoever thought up that proverb, now—taking the words at face value, he believed different. And so did Jerry Granahan, and he still does, and he'll go on believing different till the day he dies.

And maybe, if I'd been younger and not so set in my head, what happened to old Mike Granahan's kid Jerry would have changed even me over. I couldn't say about that.

When I first knew Mike Granahan, he was sixteen—an ugly, cocky little youngster with green eyes and red-roan hair and a grin that could shake the mortar out from between bricks. I was about ten years older, but we cottoned right up to each other. Maybe it was because we both liked to talk, and the grander and more theoretical the talk, the better. Two Irishmen, you see.

Mike was actually born over there, though he was brought across when he was a couple of years old. He was packed with all sorts of superstitions. He said no, he couldn't remember having seen any leprechauns, but his mother had seen one once. Things like that. And of course luck, to him, was just as real and solid as potatoes. If you had it, you guarded it with your life; and you begged or stole or prayed for it, if you didn't.

Not that Mike ever had to do any begging or stealing or praying. The year after I met him, he rode a whole stack of winners, and it wasn't all good horses or good riding, either, though he was a wild young riding fool. One day that fall, at Latonia, he turned in five winners, just short of a full card. He felt so good then, and so sure of himself, that he up and got married the same day to a Covington girl he'd met only a week before. I helped them run off to Cincinnati.

Jerry was born the next fall, and Mike's wife died then. Her folks heard about it and wanted to take the kid, but Mike wouldn't have any part of that. What he aimed to do was keep the kid right under his arm. He was crazy about him. But I made him see that an eighteen-year-old jock couldn't lug a brownie around to the horse plants, and he finally sent the baby to his sister in Jersey.

Mike kept booting 'em in, year after year, all over the country—not the biggest rider in the game, but one of the steadiest, and one of the smartest.

And by all odds the luckiest. Owners would get him under contract just to ease their minds. They knew that with him up, any breaks that happened to fall would fall their way.

Time went along, fast there and slow there, and Mike and I went with it. Sometimes we were together, sometimes not.

He was still booting 'em in last year, the year I'm telling you about. He was Old Mike Granahan now, though he was only between thirty-five and forty. But he was beginning to look old. For the first time in his life he'd been having to sweat weight off, and it had begun to show in deep gouges down his face. I hadn't seen him since Pimlico, but I'd noticed then.

The kid was about grown, if you can call five feet high grown. Winters, Mike had made him spend in school; and he wanted the kid to go on to college after he'd finished at the plant up in New Hampshire. But ever since he was old enough, the kid had been making the summer rounds with Mike, and learning a lot about horses, because—well, the horses were there.

So when he said, in the middle of a school year, that he was going to quit the books and ride, I guess it wasn't much of a surprise to Mike, or much of a disappointment either. He growled about it a little, to save his face; but I guess, when you came right down to it, he was pretty proud to have his boy follow along.

Mike thought about it for a while, and then apprenticed Jerry for three years to Tom Hall, the trainer.

I recall the first race he rode, at Tropical Park last winter. He was excited—any jockey is, in his first trial. And everybody who knew a horse from an American flag was onto who Jerry was, and was pulling for him to come through on top.

Tom and Mike and I watched it from the rail. As they were at the post, I looked at Mike, and I could see his chaw of tobacco making a little hill in one side of his lean face, and then, so fast you wouldn't believe it, the hill would have done a round trip to the other side and would be back again.

They broke, and they hadn't gone a furlong before it happened. Why did it happen? Why does a coin come tails? That's as good a reason as I can give. Jerry's horse, on the inside, took a couple of little skips sideways and jumped over the rail into the infield and began gamboling around like a silly lamb.

Mike's tobacco stopped in one cheek and stayed there.

And when we saw Jerry, he didn't have much to say, but a thing like that in his first race tasted about like iced pork chops, you could tell.

After that, the name "J. Granahan" appeared often in the jockey lists, but it wasn't often near the top in the charts next morning. The horses weren't to blame, and Jerry wasn't, and nobody was. It was just a whole lot of rotten racing luck.

We moved over to Hialeah soon after that first ride, and the forty-five days there were not better. Bowie wasn't much better either. Or The Graw, or Pimlico, or Belmont, or Aqueduct. And the early meet at Empire City was drawing to a close, with the breaks still leaning away from Jerry.

Mike wasn't with us, after Pimlico. He had headed out to Aurora to finish the meet there, and the owner he was riding for planned to concentrate in the Middle West that summer, so I had the kid pretty much on my hands at the New York tracks.

I did have some help in handling him, though. I'd known that Tom Hall's home was in Yonkers, if you can say trainers have homes, and I'd known that he had a daughter: I'd seen her picture—pug-nosed, about five, with big freckles and with light-colored curls hanging on her shoulders. But now it turned out that that picture was taken some time back. She still had the pug nose, but the freckles were little now, just a dust of them across the bridge of the nose, and the curls had been lopped off, and she was about twenty. She and Jerry met, and took to each other pronto, and for a while he forgot about his luck.

But you can't forget luck like that for very long.

I recall the twentieth day of the Empire meet —the next-to-last day. Things had gone specially bad in the afternoon, and when I found Jerry sitting in a restaurant that night, alone, he looked up when I spoke to him, but he didn't even nod.

So I took a chair, and he sat across the table from me, stowing steak and potatoes into himself with both hands. He plastered butter an inch deep on a hunk of bread, gobbled it down, and called the waiter.

"Bring me a lot of cream cheese and jelly," he said.

I shrugged my shoulders and said, "It's your life."

"It's my life, all right," he said, "and I'm sick of it."

"You'll be sicker," I said, "when you can't make the weight any more."

"So what?" he said. "I'll be driving an ice truck in another ten days, and I never heard of an ice company that cared how much you weigh."

I ordered a cigar, and waited for him to get it out of his system .

"The grippe in Florida," he said, "set down for ten days in Maryland, and a sprained wrist the first day at Belmont. And I'm on the little she-pig that's sure to take the Fashion, and two days before the running she pulls up lame as a handicapper's brain." He'd lighted a cigarette, but without taking one drag from it he mashed it out on the slippery remains of the cheese and jelly. "And when I do ride a winner, what happens? Look at today. Disqualified!"

"I know," I said.

" 'Course, I haven't had the measles—not yet."

"You had measles when you were a weaner," I said. "You can't get measles more than once."

"You mean most guys can't. I can, I'll lay you ten to one."

"Take it easy, kid," I said.

"Take it easy!" He leaned toward me. "Take it easy! Now, isn't that nice? Listen, do you know that I'm jinxed so bad that these monkeys in the plant will walk miles out of their way to keep from brushing against me? Afraid that they'll catch it, and I don't blame them. I'm poison, that's what I am, poison. Even to myself, I'm poison."

"I hate to see you crabbing like this, Jerry," I said. "Your old man wouldn't—"

"And the old man's another thing I'm sick hearing about. 'Course he wouldn't crab. He never had anything to crab about. He could go to the post on a three-legged mule, and halfway down the stretch it'd turn into Cavalcade."

"It wouldn't be sure to," I said. "It just might."

"Who's the old man, anyway? What's he ever done for me?"

The kid was nervous and sore.

"He gave you those hands," I said, "and he put that clock in your head."

"Yeah! And what good's that to a broken-down rider?" he barked. "I hate horses."

I wanted to laugh, because it's pretty hard to be a broken-down anything at nineteen; but I didn't laugh.

"No, you don't," I said. "One day away from them and you'd be wanting to get back so bad you'd go crazy."

"I'm going crazy anyhow!" He snapped the words out.

"Take it easy, kid," I said.

He put his big brown hands on the white table top in front of him.

"What's the matter with me, Jim?" he said. "I'm a good jockey. I've got the build and I've got the head and I've got the guts and I've got everything it takes. I ride hard and clean, and I ride smart."

"I know it," I said.

"I should have lifted a hundred down in front, and I haven't lifted fifteen. Why do I have such lousy luck? Why can't I give it away?"

I didn't say anything, and he didn't say anything else for a good while, either. He just sat there looking at his hands, and I chewed my cigar and watched him. His face right then seemed even younger than it did most times, and that was plenty young. Or maybe it wasn't the face alone that seemed so young, maybe it was the contrast of face and hands. His hands were man's hands if I ever saw any. They were big and wide and heavy; honest, solid hands with long back-sprung thumbs; and as supple and strong as green bamboo.

I had an idea to make him forget himself for a while.

"Why don't you go see Janet?" I said.

His answer was out of his mouth before I'd finished speaking.

"I don't want to see Janet!"

"Why not?" I said.

The wind went out of him, and he spoke listlessly.

"We had a fight," he said.

"You kids—"

"That's another thing I'm sick of," he said, sore again. "I'm sick of being called a kid. I don't feel like a kid, let me tell you! In the last six months I've gone through enough for a guy a million years old, and that's how old I feel, to the minute." He stood up and grabbed his hat from a peg. "And Janet's no kid, either, and this fight of ours isn't any kid fight."

"Take it easy, Jerry," I said.

"Come on," he said. "Let's find the worst movie we can, and go sit through it twice."

The following afternoon I hooked onto Janet myself, at the track. I figured I could talk to her, because she was as sensible a girl as you'll meet. She came by her sense honestly enough; there's not a trainer in the business smarter than Tom Hall. And not a trainer less likely to have had Janet for a daughter, either, when you come right down to it, for Tom is as wide as the side of Madison Square Garden, and about fifty hands high. He could put Janet in his vest pocket and still have room for that golden truck tire he calls his watch. And where Tom is dark-complected, Janet's face is like Grade A milk. But they have the same straight blue eyes, even if Tom's do look a little faded from a lifetime of squinting at the bangtails.

I found Janet this day in the stands, but this was once when she didn't seem to want to chatter about Jerry. I tried to slide the conversation around to him, but she dodged and turned for all she was worth, and finally she smiled and said:

"It's no use, Mr. Conner. You'd just better give up."

So I abandoned the subtle approach.

"I hear you had a fight," I said.

"We have lots of fights," she said, and then she clamped her sweet mouth shut, tight and hard.

I said, "What about?" But she didn't answer; and we watched the finish of the third race.

Jerry was riding in that one, and he came in sixth or seventh.

"Don't be too hard on him," I said.

She looked up at me with those big, clear, blue eyes.

"Mr. Conner," she said, "I like Jerry—"

"You're crazy about him," I said.

"All right, I'm crazy about him." She wasn't a girl to deny facts. "And for all I know, he's the same way about me. But being crazy about each other isn't the only thing there is."

"I'm surprised," I said.

She waved her hand impatiently.

"Don't interrupt me, Mr. Conner. I was about to point out that being in love isn't always worth what you have to go through. Do I get two smiles from him a week? No. Does he ever say, 'Well, darling, you look wonderful'? Does he even call me 'sweetheart'? I'm not asking you, Mr. Conner; I'm telling you. He does not. He comes in and throws his hat on a chair, and he just sits there. Every once in a while he grunts. 'Ugh,' he says. 'Ugh.' " She stuck her square little chin out. "It doesn't make any difference whether I'm crazy about him or not. It doesn't even make any difference whether I'm sorry for him or not."

"What do you mean, it doesn't make any difference?" I said.

Her voice was very low.

"It doesn't make any difference in my being through with the whole thing," she said.

But I discovered that she'd talked Tom into promising to take her up to Saratoga, just the same—she could have talked him into taking her over Niagara Falls in a barrel, if she'd put her mind to it. And maybe, I thought, it'd all clear up when we got there. Those two kids weren't really the way they were acting; they were just bewildered and lost.

It certainly hadn't all cleared up that day, though.

That evening when I went to the room Jerry and I shared, I found him stretched out on his bed. He had a towel wrapped around him, but that was all.

"You're too old to need a nurse," I said. "Put some clothes on. Do you want to get the grippe again?"

He didn't speak, and I went over and closed the window, for it was a raw evening.

In a minute he said, "I haven't got any clothes."

I told him that now he was crazy.

He said, "Look in the closet."

Sure enough, there was nothing in the closet but my other suit—the brown one—and a pair of low-quartered shoes, mine, and a few other odds and ends, all mine.

"Funny they took only your tack," I said.

"Nobody stole them," he said.

I got it out of him, about two words at a time. He'd given the clothes away. He'd got one of the Negro swipes to come over and cart them away, every stitch. He had carried to the opposite extreme the old idea that a certain hat, say, or a pair of old shoes, is the reason for the owner's good fortune.

"The swipe won't wear them. I told him what was the matter with them," he said. He clenched his big fists, and his voice got high and nervous. "I had to try to get rid of it, Jim," he said. "I had to."

And I'll swear he was about to cry. I knew he wouldn't, but he sure wanted to.

I felt sorry for him, and ashamed of myself. You know how it is when you're dealing with youngsters. You listen to their troubles, and you nod your head and say, "I know," and look as wise as an old granddaddy owl. You're indulgent. You've forgotten how desperate youngsters can get. And then suddenly something happens to wake you up, and you want to kick yourself, because you didn't know for a minute how it was. You didn't know beans.

I didn't even tell Jerry he had no sense.

"Well," I said, "I'll go out and try to dig up something for you to wear. I hope this does the job."

"Thanks, Jim," he said.

The next day we moved up to Saratoga.

Saratoga is a place where it's always seemed to me nothing ought to go wrong. Even the Broadway boys, with their peg-top pants and three-day sunburns, realize that August at the Spa is something special. It seems real, and not only because things as ugly as those hotels are couldn't be anything else but real, either. The Broadway boys realize this in their own way— it makes them nervous.

For my part, Saratoga is the one track I think about when I'm away from it. Horse plants mostly are just where the horses happen to be running at the time, and when the horses are carted away, you forget them till the next meeting rolls around. But somehow you know that Saratoga is always there, and you can close your eyes and see the empty grandstand at night, with dead leaves or snows whooshing and sighing through it, and you can catch glimpses of the great horseflesh you've seen there—Roamer, and Old Rosebud, and Sir Barton, and Exterminator, and that sweet filly, Top Flight, and Big Red himself—and you can see Jim Dandy coming home through the mud in that Travers; a good horse which, with a lot of mud and a lot of luck, did a great thing once.

But the ghosts of great horses and the ghosts of great luck didn't help Jerry Granahan when we moved up that year. No, nor the ghosts of great riders who'd booted 'em in there, either.

First off, he did go and get a cold from lying around naked in that room at Empire City. Nobody else would have, but Jerry did. And in ten racing days he topped just one winner. Of course, he wasn't getting the best horses now, not by a mile, and if it hadn't been for Tom Hall, he'd hardly have had any mounts at all, for I couldn't sell his services often. Tom stood by him. I believe that by this time Tom was the only man besides myself who saw what Jerry had—old Mike's brains and ability. And sometimes even we had to look pretty close. And even Tom couldn't dodge the facts: Jerry was jinxed, and it wasn't square with Tom's owners to put the kid in spots where a little racing luck was needed—not the way he was going.

One morning along about the twelfth or thirteenth day, I was leaning on the rail, just leaning and chewing a blade of grass, when Jerry plodded over and stood alongside me.

"Pigs," he said. "That's all I ever get now. Pigs." He glared at the sandy soil of the strip. "By winter I'll be riding down at Oriental Park," he said.

I said, "I thought they weren't going to run down there this year."

"Yeah; that's what I mean," said Jerry.

After a while, he said, "Maybe some day I'll pull a nag in through a flood and a fire and a sandstorm, and then it'll all be different." But he didn't believe it.

He wasn't seeing Janet much those days. It seemed she was sticking to her guns about being through unless he snapped out of his gloom. And as much as I thought of Jerry, I couldn't help seeing her point. She wasn't quitting on him any more than he was quitting on her.

If he'd let her even try to cheer him up, she'd have stuck to him through hell and high water. But when somebody just grunts—

Finally, Jerry did junk the idea that he could give his luck away. Besides the clothes episode, he'd tried all sorts of little things—touching other jocks on the shoulders, getting them to accept his cigarettes, and so on. And everything had failed. It seemed that the curse wasn't on his person.

But then he got another notion that was just as screwy. He had it all figured out, he told me: Bad luck was just the absence of good luck.

"That makes it pie, doesn't it?" I said.

"Sure," he said. "I got to steal somebody else's luck."

There was a monkey named Bosca who had had a long string of beautiful breaks, and Jerry began watching him like a hawk, tagging his steps all over the place.

The Bosca boy didn't like it—nobody would— and he said so, plenty strong. But I tell you Jerry was almost insane by now.

One day the two boys were working in the

same race, and they came into the stretch looking as though they'd fight it out for show; the first and second horses were as good as in. Jerry was on the rail, with Bosca crowding him hard; and all at once Bosca lifted his pony a couple of strides out ahead and set him down, plunk, square in front of Jerry's—so square and so fast that it was a wonder Jerry wasn't tossed; he had to pull up almost dead. It was about as open a foul as you'll see.

When they came easing back, I was surprised to see Jerry toss his whip down. He dismounted and headed for Bosca. He stepped up to him and hauled off with one of those big fists of his and knocked the monk flat.

Bosca hopped up swinging, but somebody caught his arms, and that was the end of it. That was the end of it, I mean, except that the stewards set Bosca down for ten days and Jerry, who'd have been all right if he had kept his head, for five.

That night I managed to squeeze out of him what had happened. In watching the other boy, he'd noticed that before weighing out for each race he would reach in the pocket of his coat in the jockey's room and touch something there. Every time.

So, once when Bosca wasn't around, Jerry reached in that pocket himself. He found a silver dollar, and he took it.

Of course Bosca knew who had done it. He'd been trying to spill Jerry that afternoon. I expected Jerry to be sore, and as stubborn as fifteen mules; but he was only dejected, and funny and sort of calm. It worried me.

I eased along with him, and after a while he pulled the lobe of his ear—a trick he'd picked up from Mike—and said:

"I might as well tell you. After this meet, I'm through."

"You're talking through your hat," I said.

"No. I mean it. Unless something happens, my last mount here is the last horse I even look at."

"You're quitting," I said.

"The hell I'm quitting, Jim Conner! . . . Listen, Jim, quitting is one thing, and having sense enough to get out of where you don't belong is another thing."

"You can't get out," I said. "Where you belong is sitting on a slab of leather on top of a horse. It's in your blood, Jerry. You can't get out."

He set his lips in a thin, hard line, and his eyes were hard—and unhappy too.

"You watch me get out!" he said. "You watch me!"

It was no joke.

None of it was any joke, and when I heard that Mike Granahan was going to fly east to ride in the Special at Narragansett, I decided to roll over there and see him about Jerry. At least,

that's what I pretended, but I guess it wasn't the whole reason. I guess I wanted to see Mike for the good of my own soul.

And it sure enough was good to see him, with his lined face and screwed-up green eyes and lopsided grin. His hands—the backs of them—were beginning to look like slabs of old bark, and he was just about bald by now, too, and the corners of his mouth were always stained with tobacco juice. No, he wasn't what the little girls are thinking of when they call jockeys "cute," but he sure looked like home and mother to me.

I didn't need to ask how they were breaking for him; I knew that he'd had only four or five better seasons in his life.

"It don't make sense," Mike said. "Me with a unlucky kid."

"Luck never makes sense," I said.

"Yeah? It's made sense to me for twenty years."

"Is it that long?" I said.

Mike said, "Yeah."

We thought about that for a while.

"Holy cats!" Mike said.

And we thought about it for a while longer. Then Mike shook himself, and pulled the lobe of his ear with his big fingers.

"Wisht I had time to jump over there and see him," he said. "How's he look?"

I lied. "Fine," I said.

I didn't tell him that Jerry was going to quit after Saratoga. I did tell him all about Janet Hall, though.

"I remember seein' her last year," he said. "Seemed like she was smart; looks and fire and a good head on her. . . . It's a fine thing for a man to have a wife," he said. "A fine thing."

"I wouldn't know," I said. "But unless Jerry comes out of it, this is one wife he won't get."

Mike tugged at his ear as though he'd pull it off.

"It's tough," he said. He shook himself again, and held out his hand. "Well, I got to snake along." He grinned. "Say, tell the kid hello for me, will you?"

And when I got back to Saratoga, I told Jerry that Mike had said hello.

Jerry was riding even less now, and he looked almost as old as Mike, and he went around staring at the ground most of the time, and dodging everybody he knew.

And the meeting was drawing toward September.

Jerry even dodged Janet. Once in a while you'd see them together, but they were never exactly chattering gaily, and they wouldn't stay together for long. If they'd been older, maybe the spot wouldn't have been so tough for them, but they were just kids.

From Janet's looks, I judged Jerry had told her about his giving up the game. He hadn't told Tom, and I didn't tell Tom—it wasn't up to me to do that.

But Tom caught on that something was mighty wrong.

"All I know is horse," he said to me one morning when we were watching the workouts. "It takes something damn bad in people to make me see that they're riled up." He fished a pipe out of his pocket. "Janet's the one I'm thinking of first, but I'm not forgetting that kid." He chewed the stem of his pipe for a minute. "I'd sure like to see him up on two or three winners in a row," he said.

"That wouldn't do it—not now," I said. "It'd have to be something with a whole raft of luck attached to it, to make him believe in himself now."

"I reckon it would," Tom said.

I knew it would.

Well, I could look back and tell you that when I woke up on the morning of the twenty-ninth racing day at Saratoga—the day before the last—I felt in my mortal bones that the next twelve hours would hold about the strangest thing I ever knew to happen. I could tell you that, but it wouldn't be the truth.

The day that changed Jerry Granahan's life, and mine, too, more than I like to think about, began just like a million other bad days around race tracks. The early morning, as I recall, was cloudy and raw, but with no rain. The dew dried almost not at all, on account of the low clouds, and the gray tops of the stands were darker with it, and the clumps and hedges of the jumping course looked wet and heavy and dreary.

I saw Jerry for just a minute early in the morning.

"This is what they call Granahan weather," he said.

And I can't recall seeing him again, to speak to, until after it had happened, until after the sixth race that afternoon.

The rest of the morning, and the early afternoon, are pretty much of a blank, except that I do remember a wind that came up along about noontime—not a steady wind, but big, spanking gusts. There'd be a chunk of wind, whipping the tops of the trees like scarecrows' arms, and then a calm, and then another chunk.

Jerry was riding in the first race, and I went out under the trees in the paddock and watched them saddle. On my way to the stands I ran across Janet, with a raincoat up around her throat, and we went together to Tom's box and watched the race. It was just another horse race.

We sat there through the second race, and the third, and the fourth. Once Janet said:

"What's he going to do if he quits, Mr. Conner?"

"I don't know," I said.

Jerry had another mount in the sixth. After the fifth, I was called out of the stands for a while, and I didn't get back till the starter was already getting them lined up in the mile chute, far over to the right of the stand.

I have reason to remember that race, and I do remember it, every bit of it, the way you remember things when something that comes pretty close to you is happening or has just happened; something you can't do anything about, so that you just stare like a camera at what's going on in front of you, and you have little snapshots of it forever.

Jerry's horse was a black gelding named Dark One. Not a tortoise—about the second or third fastest horse in the race, in fact, except for one thing. I knew this Dark One from far back, because in his own way he was famous. He was one of the slowest starters that was ever not ruled off the turf for life.

He couldn't win this one, I was certain, for there was a standout in it, named Counterpin. A heavy impost had been dumped on Counterpin, but a lot of difference that would make.

From the amount of time that start took, you'd have thought they were maiden two-year-olds in the month of January. They bounced out, and were led around or shoved back, and then one of them would bounce out again. The starter just couldn't seem to get them standing right.

And then suddenly there was the sound that's the same in any language and on any track, that deep roll of excitement, with a few women's screams riding high on top. They were off.

One horse shot way out in front, with the other eight left for the moment standing still. It was a bad break.

"A break for somebody!" Janet said involuntarily, and then she must have seen what I was seeing through my glasses, for she said "Oh!" The horse in front was a black horse.

"Oh," she said again, about three tones lower, and you could tell from the tone what she meant. She meant she didn't think it would do any good.

But it was enough to put Dark One ahead, and to keep him ahead around the corner, and by that time he had gathered a little of his speed and he swung into the far stretch still ahead, with the others chasing him like a pack of greyhounds.

Halfway down the stretch he was still in front, but the pack was stringing out now, with Counterpin, the favorite, well back. He'd got off from the post about last.

The jockeys' silks made bright blobs of color in all that gray and gray-green, gloomy landscape, and the horses didn't seem to be running; they seemed to be sliding along on a greased track, for it was hard to see their legs moving below the rail.

Toward the end of the stretch I could see one horse running faster than the others back of Dark One.

"Counterpin!" Janet said.

He was slicing right through the middle of the pack, ticking off one horse after another, until at the turn there were only two ponies between him and Dark One.

Dark One was clicking sweetly under Jerry, but I judged that it was all over. Counterpin was just too good.

Counterpin slid against the rail at the turn, and I could see through the glasses that his jock must have caught sight of daylight between the second and third ponies, because the jock moved forward. He was a smart rider, I knew, and ninety-nine times out of a hundred when he moved for a slit, the slit would be there, or else there'd be a foul.

But this time it just wasn't there. There was no foul—that daylight must have closed up all by itself. Counterpin was thrown off stride, and Dark One gained a length on him, making three now, and kept a two-length lead over the second horse.

"I just can't believe it's Jerry they're falling for out there," Janet said. I couldn't, either.

Counterpin recovered fast and took out on the outside, and in no time at all he was past the third horse, and then the second, and they straightened away with Dark One only two lengths to the good.

And then Counterpin's boy made his drive. He was a length back, and then half a length, and then a neck. Then it was a head only, and then they were running nose and nose. And then, a furlong from the end, Counterpin poked out on top.

"It's over now," Janet said.

But it wasn't over.

Listen, now. Suppose you have a day with a funny wind—a gust, say, every four minutes. And suppose you have a crowd of about ten thousand, with perhaps five hundred newspapers among them, counting out racing forms. Suppose a few of those newspapers have been thrown away loose. All right. And suppose you have seven races, with from sixty to seventy-five horses running, all told, over a period of something more than three hours.

And suppose that just one of those papers is blown out on the track, that just once during the day one of them is caught by exactly the right gust of wind and blown in exactly the right direction, at just the right speed and height, to land in one certain spot as sure as though it had been shot from a rifle.

Counterpin was a neck in front now, with under a furlong to go. Dark One was on the rail.

The sheet of loose paper soared out over the outside rail down at the end of the stands, and wallowed around up in the air, spread wide, the way papers do. It hovered there in one spot. The horses thundered toward it, and it settled deliberately in front of them, wavering. And then all of a sudden there was a dip and a swoop, and it plastered itself smack over Counterpin's blinkers. Over his whole face.

Counterpin faltered—not much, but enough. Enough for Jerry to move Dark One into the lead. Enough for him to bring Dark One home a winner.

"Oh!" said Janet. "Oh!"

"Yes," I said.

And then she spoke very low.

"I wonder if that's it," she said.

And she jumped up and ran from the stand.

I followed her, slowly, and leaned against a tree and watched her.

And after a while I saw Jerry come from the direction of the jockeys' room, walking along fast with his chin out and a little lopsided grin on his face and his straw hat cocked over one ear. I hadn't seen him grin like that in a long time, and I don't know whether Janet ever had or not.

Well, sometimes when there's only one single thing wrong between two people, it takes only one thing, something fast and big, to clear it up. And I guess that was the way this was.

Janet saw Jerry, too, and she rushed toward him and they said a few words. And then for a minute they just stood looking at each other, and you could tell they didn't know there was anybody else in the world.

Then Janet put her hand through his arm and they walked toward the stand.

I watched them go, and I wondered.

I didn't believe it. I was too old to change over and believe it then. And I still say that rabbits' feet are no good, and that there aren't really such things as ghosts, and that the idea of transference of luck is so much hot air.

If you ask me for a better explanation, all I say is that I guess somebody has to pay for happiness. Nothing comes free. Things sort of even up in the end, it seems like.

No, I didn't believe it, mad and wild as it was.

But Jerry Granahan would believe it.

I watched the kids go into the stands, and I gave them a couple of minutes, and then I followed them. I had a job to do, and it was the hardest and saddest job I ever had to do in my life, but it was mine to carry out. I couldn't wait too long, either, for I had to get to Jerry before he saw any reporters, or anybody else who knew.

You remember I said I had been called from the stand after the fifth race.

The way that came about was that a clocker

I knew had happened to be passing Tom's box then, and he said my name was chalked up for a telegram. I heard the envelope crinkle in my pocket now as I walked.

I recall clearly the sound of it, and I believe I recall each step across that paddock grass, under the dark trees with their blowing tops.

I'm not a man to talk much about how I feel, but I'm saying I felt bad then.

There had been a mean spill in the third race out at Hawthorne that afternoon—Mike Granahan was dead.

"Ed made almost five hundred dollars playing the ponies last year. Of course, he lost a lot, too."

DRAWING BY GARDNER REA

Discovery

JOHN HERVEY

The only time I ever saw Discovery run was in his pasture, and I saw him many times in his retirement at Sagamore Farm. If I hadn't known him from a summary of his record and from the affection his owner held for him, I would learn fully in reading the following account of Discovery's remarkable racing career. In my first year of racing an acquaintance remarked that a good horse, in addition to needing a good trainer and a good jockey, needs a good owner. Discovery never lacked anything.

THE FIRST GREAT Saga of Discovery was that told when the world was young: the Quest of the Golden Fleece. Minstrels smiting their harps sung to spellbound audiences of the sailing of the good ship Argo:

The singing ship, hewn from Peneus' wood,
That bore the Greeks to Colchis o'er the flood—

that carried with her the heroes and the demigods who had sworn never to return until they brought back with them the wondrous treasure that they sought. In the end their leader, Jason, triumphed—but it was only through the aid of the sorceress Medea, who, by her magic art, enabled him to overcome the barriers that had to be surmounted. The Golden Fleece was protected by walls of fire, by terrible monsters and by enchantments before which even heroes and demigods were powerless without the help that she only could give. It fell to Jason to win her heart and, thereby, the Fleece.

Long before Homer told of the siege of Troy, and ended it with the first description of a horse race ever written, that given as one of the funeral games that celebrated the obsequies of Patroclus, the Quest of the Golden Fleece had become famous and familiar. Like all other classic myths it is a mixture of fact and fable, with, underlying it, an allegory of the eternal quest of humanity for fame and riches. The Argonauts were the first in the endless procession destined to follow in their track as long as time endures. Their saga is the oldest known to man in which adventure and discovery, the search for gold and glory, is the theme.

The sagas of the turf, of which there are and will continue to be many, are all variants of it— and that of the Discovery of the past three seasons is one of the most absorbing of them all. For few have had a central figure so heroic.

Is it just fortuitous—or is it symbolic that Discovery, whose Quest of the Golden Fleece was one attended by feats worthy of a Jason, but surpassing his because no magic arts assisted him to triumph, nothing but his own speed and valor being at his command, wears a gleaming golden coat which, when the sun strikes it in the post-parade, gives back a glow of molten iridescence? That he carries always with him the badge of his order? Its rich undertones are full of warmth and splendor, making it a feast for the eye as a matter of color alone.

It descends to him neither from his sire, Display, nor his dam, Ariadne, for both are browns, but from his still more distinguished grandsire, the renowned progenitor Fair Play, who bore a golden panoply dazzling in its sheen. When Display was racing—and at the peak of his career he stood as the premier money-winning American Thoroughbred with a credit of $256,526— it used to be said that he was not a true son of Fair Play because all the others of that sire's greatest sons carried his color: Man o' War,

[113

Chance Play, Mad Play, Ladkin, Dunlin, Chatterton and others being quoted in proof of the contention. But like many similar claims, those making it overlooked the fact that in addition to Display, such sons of Fair Play as Mad Hatter and Chance Shot had not been chestnuts like their sire, but bay or bay-brown.

However, the color theorists, when their theory is at stake, seldom hesitate but take opposing facts in their stride and forget them. Color, they assert, is that mystic thing, a "dominant," it must be transmitted in a dominant way, and when it isn't, the transmission of other qualities falters. The breeder, they tell us, should fight shy of sons of great progenitors that do not carry their sire's coat-color. Which is really too bad, considering that Bend Or was a chestnut and Ormonde a bay; Boston a chestnut and Lexington a bay; Sultan a bay and Glencoe a chestnut; Diomed a chestnut and Sir Archy a bay; and, to go on far back, the mighty Eclipse a chestnut and his sire, Marske, a dark seal-brown, while Eclipse had a prominent white face and one white leg behind nearly to his hock, and Marske nothing but an almost imperceptible white coronet and that on the opposite foot.

As a matter of fact, while Display did not breed after Fair Play in color or marks, he had many of what we call the Fair Play "characters." And his son, Discovery—one of his first crop of foals which came in 1931 and debuted as two-year-olds in 1933—is in many respects a typical Fair Play. He not only carries the chestnut color and the blazed face; in conformation he resembles many of the most famous members of the tribe, as well as in his manner of racing, his physical strength and rugged constitution, his ability to "stand grief" and to go on and on.

On one score he is, however, of another kidney. The restiveness of the Fair Plays at the post has been and is commonly considered a generic trait, prevalent throughout the family. In Display it was conspicuous, so much so that he became a terror to starters. Discovery is the exact contrary. His post manners are exemplary. Nothing that goes on about him seems more than mildly to interest him. While horses lined up on either side cavort wildly about, he may be seen gazing off at the surrounding landscape as if preoccupied by its charms. He is always in his place, always ready for business, no matter what. He is very fond of his lead-pony and likes to have him close at hand in the paddock, but will be content without him. He has a high order of intelligence and the instincts of a gentleman.

Discovery stands 16.1 hands tall and in racing condition the past season weighed 1,180 pounds. His sire, Display, has a small and very fine head, much of the Oriental type, with a tapering muzzle and dished face. That of Discovery is more masculine. It is full of character, which

its white blaze accentuates. His eye is clear and bright and his ear small for so big a horse, almost daintily cut, and is beautifully set and carried. Bodily his distinctive mark is power. It is revealed at every point. His neck, which is of good length, is muscular and at maturity will be nicely crested, while the throat-latch is clean. His breast is broad and deep, his shoulder well laid, his barrel round and well ribbed-up back to the coupling, which is smooth and strong. His hips and quarters do not "swell with muscle," but are swathed with it in long fillets, so firmly set and molded that beneath his shining coat they look as if wrought in bronze. His stifle is powerful but his gaskin and second-thigh not noticeably so. His limbs are of excellent bone, knees and hocks well articulated, cannons of medium length, pasterns short and strong rather than long and flexible.

Without being a leggy horse he stands well off the ground and, despite his powerful physique, gives no impression of bulkiness—rather the reverse. The grooved muscles of his hindquarter were often remarked, by close observers, as indicative of the equine athlete that he proved himself. His action is that of the distance runner. The stroke very precise and like that of the piston-rod of a locomotive, apparently under perfect control and never, when making an extreme effort, broad and sprawling, and is propelled with great force. The air of Discovery in action is that of the most resolute determination. In some of his best races he has gone immediately out in front, set the pace and won all the way. In others he has been kept back and not made his run until the race approached its climax.

A facile racing-machine, he has shown only one weakness, which he shares with most other present-day American Thoroughbreds—the desire to race at the rail, bred of the circular courses over which all racing is done here, and the propensity to rush for it as he takes command of a field. But of propensity to swerve under a drive he has none.

Both Discovery and his sire, Display, were bred by Walter J. Salmon in his Mereworth Stud, Lexington, Kentucky. Ariadne, the dam of Discovery, is a young mare, foaled in 1926, and a daughter of the English horse Light Brigade, of the Bend Or line and one of the most successful sires of winners among the importations of the last twenty years, while his daughters are proving good producers. The grandam of Discovery, Adrienne, produced the stake winner Andria and was by His Majesty, son of the Futurity winner imported Ogden, a successful sire. His third dam, Adriana, was by another great stallion, Hamburg, son of Hanover, and was the dam of two stake winners, Celandria and Coquette.

Back of this the line runs through a succession

of distinguished brood and race mares straight to the tenth dam, no less a matron than imported Gallopade, one of the most influential fountains of speed in the *American Stud Book,* among others Domino being of her direct descendants. Discovery, therefore, is distinctively "American-bred." On his top line we have to go back to the year 1858 to reach his first imported ancestor, while in the female line we must go back to 1835—more than one hundred years.

Several years ago Mr. Salmon, whose stable had previously been among the most prominent and whose colors were carried by Display throughout his turf career, discontinued racing, but arranged with Adolphe Pons to race in his name such of the colts and fillies bred at Mereworth as seemed advisable. Discovery, as aforesaid a son of Display and one of his first crop of foals, was among the lot of 1931 selected in the fall of 1932 to race the next season as two-year-olds and sent to Columbia, South Carolina, to winter. He was trained by John R. Pryce and an extensive campaign mapped out for him, which began June 3, 1933, at Belmont Park, in an overnight race for maiden juveniles. In this, his official turf debut, Discovery was ridden by A. Robertson and finished fourth in a field of twelve in a five-furlong dash over the Widener straight course, run in :59⅗ and won by Watch Her. On June 8 he again started there in a similar event and ran third to Galabang; the time 1:00.

The campaign thus opened did not close until November 4, at Pimlico, and during its course the colt started some 14 times, to win twice, be thrice second, five times third and four times unplaced, with earnings of $8,397. At the end of the season he had earned a somewhat unique distinction. Looked upon by the critics as a high-class two-year-old and particularly likely to train on into a still better three-year-old, he nevertheless retired without a single stake event to his credit, though placed and a hot contender in no less than five different ones. Both his wins had been in purse races, the first at Arlington Park, on July 6, when carrying 118 pounds and with R. Jones up, he beat eleven others five and a half furlongs, run in 1:06; and the second at Havre de Grace, on September 21, when, ridden by J. Gilbert at 113 pounds he beat a field of five others six furlongs run in 1:12⅗.

As he had not been engaged in the Futurity, he could not contend for it, but he went to the post for a number of the principal juvenile stakes of the year. The trying-tackle subjected him to the acid test, for it included such youngsters as Cavalcade, High Quest, Mata Hari, Far Star, Hadagal, Wise Daughter, Singing Wood, Bazaar and a group of others only less precocious and he was constantly required to meet them.

He throve upon the regimen and was a better colt at the close of the long grind than at any time previously, running second in both his last two efforts, the Kentucky Jockey Club Stakes, $10,000 added, at Latonia, and the Walden Handicap, at Pimlico, the former won by Mata Hari, then at the peak of her form, and the latter by Chicstraw. In his last previous start, the rich Breeders' Futurity, also at Latonia, he had run third to Mata Hari and Giggling; and, just before that, third to Chicstraw and Wise Daughter in the Richard Johnson Stakes, at Laurel. But it was at Saratoga that he first showed his mettle by running third to Bazaar and High Quest in the Hopeful Stakes, in a field of fourteen with many of the most prominent juniors of the year behind him.

Getting off "absolutely," he gradually worked his way through the pack of runners and finally had High Quest under extreme pressure to snatch the place from him by a neck, that colt having been one of the leaders from the start. From The Spa, Discovery had gone to Havre, where, after first winning the purse race already mentioned, he had engaged in the $10,000 Eastern Shore Handicap, from which, however, he was virtually eliminated by an accident on the far turn, High Glee impeding him so suddenly that he almost went down, High Quest then winning from Cavalcade. It was in this race that Discovery and the last-named colt first met. Their only other encounter as two-year-olds was the next week at Laurel in the Richard Johnson Stakes, in which the son of Display, carrying a pound more (113) than the black colt (112) beat him a length and a half to finish third.

It is not generally expected that the members of the Fair Play line will be sensational juveniles. It has been the habit of most of its best members to begin moderately, later on developing into champions. Discovery's campaign betrayed the familiar earmarks of the tribe. And as in the late fall Alfred Gwynne Vanderbilt was on the lookout for a colt that seemed the making of a high-class three-year-old, just after Discovery's second to Mata Hari in the Kentucky Jockey Club Stakes at Latonia, on October 28, that gentleman, on the advice of his trainer, J. H. Stotler, purchased him from Mr. Pons for $25,000; he was transferred to his stable and filled his last engagement, the Walden Handicap, carrying his colors, "cerise, white diamonds, cerise sleeves, white cap"; destined in subsequent seasons to be borne by him to many a "famous victory."

Discovery spent the winter of 1933–34 at Mr. Vanderbilt's Sagamore Farm, in the Worthington Valley of Maryland. There is no better climate in America than that of Maryland for such purposes. Dotted about in the state, from the earliest colonial times, have been cradles of great Thoroughbreds.

The son of Display had not been engaged in

either the Belmont Stakes or the Realization by his breeder, hence remained ineligible to those three-year-old classics, but he was now entered for all the others open to him, as well as in numerous important events for all ages. From the first the policy was pursued with him that has been Mr. Vanderbilt's throughout—of dodging nothing or nobody but meeting all comers under all conditions of track and weather, weight and distance.

To fill his first engagement for 1934, Discovery had to travel but a few miles from Sagamore Farm eastward to Havre de Grace where the race in question, the Chesapeake Stakes, was run on April 28. His work for it had been pleasing but it was not expected that he was ready to beat Cavalcade, who but three days before had won from a smart field, running a mile and 70 yards in track record time, 1:41⅘, with Agrarian second. The result of the Chesapeake verified this form, as Cavalcade won by a length while Agrarian beat Discovery for the place by a short head; time, 1:43⅗ for the mile and a sixteenth and a new record for both the event and the course. The odds had been: even money, Cavalcade; 3½ to 1, Discovery. The unplaced horses were Time Supply, Singing Wood, Time Clock, Jabot, Soon Over and Time Flight. In this race Mr. Vanderbilt's contract rider, J. Bejshak, henceforth to be so closely identified with the chestnut colt, for the first time had the mount upon him. The expert comment on Discovery's effort was: "In the thick of the contention throughout; held on gamely."

One week from that day, Saturday, May 5, brought the Kentucky Derby at Churchill Downs. Cavalcade's two glittering races in Maryland served to make him (coupled with his stable companion Time Clock) a tremendous favorite, the quotations being 1½ to 1. Bazaar, specially prepared for the event was at 5 to 1, and Mata Hari, seeking also to smash the tradition that fillies cannot win it, at 6½ to 1. Peace Chance was at 9¾; Sergeant Byrne, Quasimodo and Speedmore at 10½; and Discovery at 12 to 1. Of the entire field of 13 horses, only four, Agrarian, Spy Hill, Singing Wood and Sir Thomas, were at longer odds. Mata Hari at once went out in front. Discovery, rating along third until six furlongs had been covered, then shot into the lead and, Cavalcade moving through the field at the same time, they turned into the stretch almost head and head, but Discovery's nose in front, the mile being run in 1:37⅖. The duel between the two colts was sustained until inside the last furlong pole, when Cavalcade, upon whom Garner was forced to draw his whip, proved the better and came on to win by two and a half lengths; time, 2:04. Discovery was four lengths in front of Agrarian, third.

An interval of another week, a shipment back to Maryland, and Saturday, May 12 brought the Preakness of 1934. The three successive victories of Cavalcade and the fact that coupled with him for the first time that season would run his stable companion High Quest, in intimate circles said to be as good if not better even than the son of Lancegaye, proved discouraging to other aspirants and the field dwindled down to seven, as aside from Discovery only Agrarian, Spy Hill, Time Supply and Riskulus went to the post. The odds were overwhelmingly in favor of Mrs. Sloane's pair, being somewhat better than one to two *on*. Of the rest, Discovery, at 7½ to 1, was the only one accorded any chance whatever.

High Quest went at once to the front, led all the way and won by a short head from Cavalcade, both being ridden out to the last ounce. Discovery, who had been third all the way, was beaten a short length, after having turned into the stretch on almost even terms with them. Time for the mile and three-sixteenths, 1:58⅕—track record, 1:58.

It was a bruising race, for at the start High Quest and Discovery had cannoned each other, the former being the offender, and both had suffered from it. High Quest emerged from the scrimmage somewhat the worse for wear and soon after his career came to a sudden termination. Discovery kept resolutely on in his efforts to overcome Cavalcade. Being engaged in neither the Withers nor the Belmont, he now had a vacation of two weeks and was then saddled for an allowance race at Belmont Park on May 25, a purse of seven furlongs, for $1,000. With 112 pounds up he was a prohibitive favorite at one to four over War Letter, Rebel Yell, Can't Remember and three others. Though it had been raining and the track was sloppy, Bejshak took him at once to the front and increasing his lead at every stride he galloped home a winner in 1:25, after which he was sent on to do the mile in 1:37⅗, nine furlongs in 1:51⅕ and mile and a quarter in 2:04⅘, in preparation for the American Derby at Chicago the following week. The move was in effect a public trial and was considered a sensational one.

The following Tuesday Discovery was shipped to Washington Park, arriving Wednesday and doing no more strong work prior to the Derby, run on Saturday, the second. Nine started, Cavalcade, by this time a public idol, was at even money, Discovery at 2¾ to 1. None of the others were seriously considered—a correct forecast as the race proved almost a duplicate of the Kentucky Derby, Mata Hari cutting out the work for six furlongs, Discovery and Cavalcade then coming through, turning into the stretch on almost even terms, and well clear of the others. Once again Garner had to go to the whip with Cavalcade and ride him strenuously and once again inside the last furlong he finally assumed the mastery and, coming away, beat Discovery an open length; the time, 2:04, exactly the same as at Louisville, first mile in 1:38⅕. As third, Singing Wood was six lengths behind Discovery.

The black colt and the chestnut had now met four times since the season opened, successively in the Chesapeake, Kentucky Derby, Preakness and American Derby. The finish was always the same. Discovery could bring Cavalcade to the whip but could not outfinish him. Two weeks later they had their fifth encounter in the Detroit Derby at the automobile metropolis, run on June 16. For this Workman was engaged to ride him in the attempt to see whether a change of jockeys would benefit Discovery. It had the opposite effect. With twelve starting he finished eleventh, never having been a factor. Cavalcade won from Plight and New Deal in 1:58⅕ for the mile and three-sixteenths, a new track record for the distance. Discovery had been well backed at 3½ to 1 (Cavalcade was at one to two) on the strength of Workman's presence in the saddle and the fact that in his formal trial for the race at Belmont Park, on Tuesday, he had turned in one of 2:03⅖.

It was the only race throughout the season in which he did not give a good account of himself. All horses have their off days. Few that have raced so strenuously as Discovery have had so few, but apparently that of the Detroit Derby was one of them. That the race was not his form is conclusive.

Whatever may have been his trouble then, he quickly came out of it. Back in the East he was started two weeks later, on June 28, in a seven-furlong allowance race at Aqueduct and, under 112 pounds with Bejshak back on him, he romped away from Fleam and five others to win by four lengths in 1:23⅗; track record 1:23. This effort was in reality his trial for the Brooklyn Handicap, to be run on July 4 over the same course.

This, the first essay of Discovery in an all-aged event—one of the most famous of the American turf, and dating back to 1887—saw him carrying 113 pounds, an indication of the estimation that Mr. Vosburgh held him in, for at the same age and for the same stake the record shows that he had asked Grey Lag to carry but 112, Victorian 112, Friar Rock 108, Eternal 106 and Fair Play only 99! Considering that up to that day Discovery had never won a stake race and that spring had lost five in succession, the compliment paid him was unique. The public extended him a similar one as he was made a four-to-five favorite—perhaps because only three others were starting; but one of them was the grand five-year-old Dark Secret, winner of the same handicap the year before as well as many other notable races. He now had up 126 pounds and under the scale was giving Discovery but one pound. Fleam and Halcyon made up the quartette, the former and Dark Secret coupled being at six to five.

There was no race. Discovery followed Dark Secret, under strong restraint, until the stretch, then given his head, he rushed away from him and won, says the chart, "with ridiculous ease" by half-a-dozen lengths. Time for the nine furlongs, 1:49⅘, first mile in 1:37⅗—track record 1:48⅗. So impressive was the performance that it wiped out the memory of the Detroit Derby and the next prospective meeting of Discovery and Cavalcade, due in the Classic, at Arlington Park on Saturday, July 14, became the subject of consuming anticipation. Mr. Vanderbilt's colt, as before, not being the winner of any of the previous three-year-old fixtures, would receive a concession of five pounds—121 as against 126—from Mrs. Sloane's; and it was the opinion that he would make good use of it.

The two rivals after arriving at Arlington were hindered in their preparation by a spell of wet weather, but on the Tuesday preceding the race were given their distance trials over a sloppy track. Cavalcade did his in 2:06⅘, while Discovery was kept back to 2:11⅗. An immense crowd turned out to witness the Classic and Arlington's velvet oval had dried out from its drenchings to its usual state. Though it was conceded that there would be nothing left for the others but third and fourth moneys, seven colts decided to accept the task of making the field. So great was Cavalcade's prestige that he was at one to three, with Discovery at five to one and nothing else so good as ten to one. The long shot Growler set a terrific pace and did not surrender until nearly a mile had been run, when he abandoned the struggle and Discovery swept past him closely followed, as was his wont, by Cavalcade. The time at this station was 1:36⅗ and when it was reached Mrs. Sloane's great colt had assumed the lead. He was running at a prodigious rate of speed, his rush around the upper turn being meteoric. It carried him into the stretch two open lengths ahead of Discovery and keeping on he sailed home to win by three open lengths in 2:02⅘, while in the closing run Hadagal drew up to finish third, lapped on Discovery.

Little did the vast assemblage imagine as they rose to tender an ovation to the winner that it was the last time he would be seen under colors that season and the final flash of his glory. Or that the chestnut colt that had been obliged for the sixth time since the season opened to bow to him, was soon to replace him in the spotlight. And as the two were not destined to meet again, nor have to the present writing save under circumstances that were futile to decide their relative merits, we may pause a moment here to view them together in retrospect.

Their continuous rivalry as three-year-olds has had two parallels in previous American turf records—that of Duke of Magenta and Bramble in 1878, and of Hindoo and Crickmore in 1881.

The Duke and Bramble engaged four times—in the Withers, Belmont, Travers and Kenner Stakes, and each time the former won. Hindoo and Crickmore met six times, Hindoo winning the Belmont, Lorillard, U. S. Hotel and Kenner Stakes in succession and then being defeated in the September Handicap and a special match by Crickmore. Would Discovery, like Crickmore with Hindoo, eventually have mastered Cavalcade had the latter remained in commission throughout the season? We can only conjecture, as opinion prompts. It is, howbeit, an accepted axiom among turfmen that one horse, after a series of consecutive beatings by another one, will lose heart and, when the pinch comes, refuse to try against him. It being also doubtful if he will ever again be so good as before. That Discovery was made of sterner stuff than that he was immediately to demonstrate.

Going from Arlington Park to Saratoga he made his first appearance there on August 14 in the Kenner Stakes, for which only Somebody and Cleves could be found to oppose him. Giving each 7 pounds, he was quoted at one to ten and merely paraded to win pulled up over a mile and three-sixteenths in 1:57⅕. This he followed on the 25th by the Whitney Stakes, a mile and a quarter. The conditions let him into this at but 105 pounds—an exquisite jest. Only Fleam, Time Clock and Caesar's Ghost cared to face him and he cantered in ten lengths ahead in 2:07⅘ at odds of one to three. As the Travers was another rich stake which he had been left out of when a yearling, he had to remain in the stable while its $14,650 was gathered in by Observant, a colt that he could probably have beaten in a walk.

Having accounted for everything open to him at The Spa, Discovery moved over from there to Rockingham Park for the Bennington Handicap, run September 1, a mile and one-sixteenth, $10,000 added, for all ages. With ten starting, he was made favorite at odds of two to five, though being assessed 124 pounds and conceding everything loads of weight. It was another lucky day for the opposition. At the start he was badly bumped by Flying Cadet, being quite knocked off his stride. Bejshak gathered him together and sat down on him. He came through the field and from a bad last had reached fifth place passing the three-quarter pole, but the effort and the weight told, he was carried wide coming into the home stretch and when Advising Anna, in receipt of 22 pounds, got home two lengths in front of Fleam, receiving 17 pounds, Larranga and Bazaar were also in front of him, his position being sixth. Time, 1:43⅕ (new track record).

Such breaks are part of that ineluctable thing known as racing luck. How wholly false the result was, it required only two days more to develop. As noted, the Bennington Handicap was run Saturday, September 1. Monday found Discovery at Narragansett Park, the new Rhode Island course where the throngs and the speculation were almost beyond belief, lined up with Hadagal, Good Goods, Lady Reigh, Indian Runner and Collateral for the Rhode Island Handicap, $15,000 added, one and three-sixteenths miles, before a Labor Day crowd estimated at 40,000. The Narragansett handicapper had this time been more lenient and he was carrying 117 pounds, as was also Hadagal, recent hero there of brilliant efforts. Despite his reverse of Saturday at Rockingham, Discovery was backed down to even money, Hadagal was at 2¼ to 1, the rest, save Indian Runner (117 pounds) whose quotations were five to one, rank outsiders.

The son of Display, as if determined to wipe all blots from his 'scutcheon, went immediately to the lead. Though Bejshak had him under restraint and was rating him, not asking him to run, he spun off the furlongs one after the other with the precision of clockwork, keeping just well clear of Hadagal, and when that colt essayed to get to him, again and again, moving away with an ease and speed that were amazing. At the head of the stretch an open length separated them and as soon as they were straight Arcaro called upon Hadagal for a grand effort. The son of Sir Gallahad answered gamely, but with futility. Bejshak let go Discovery's head a trifle and he bounded away as if just beginning to race, came steaming home like a locomotive, was taken back as they neared the post and won in hand, his courageous adversary two lengths behind him, on sufferance only. Despite the fact that Discovery was not extended, the timers hung out 1:55—a new world record for the distance, and ⅗ seconds better than the previous one that Sir Barton had posted far back in 1920 at Saratoga. Net value of the stake to him, $11,200—the first really worthwhile plum to fall into his basket.

"How fast would Discovery have run, if extended?" was the general topic next morning among turfmen. With the added query: "Where would Cavalcade have finished had he been there? Could he have met that pace?"

With autumn in the offing the Vanderbilt stable journeyed home to Maryland, where Discovery, on September 15, reappeared at Havre de Grace in the Potomac Handicap, $10,000 added, for three-year-olds, one and one-sixteenth miles. In this event former years had witnessed magnificent triumphs by Man o' War, Sir Barton, Chance Play, Sun Beau and other blazing stars. A great change had come in the year that had passed since the previous September when Discovery was competing in the two-year-old fixtures of the Maryland fall season. He was now to meet colts and fillies which were then giving him weight and handling him with facility. But the card for the Potomac read as follows: Discovery,

128 pounds; Bazaar, 119; Chicstraw and New Deal, each 116; Good Goods, 110; Only One, 106. The chart tells, also, that Discovery won, hard held, by four lengths from Chicstraw. Only One lengths farther back; time 1:45⅕. So sure was his victory regarded that he started at six to ten.

Two weeks later, Saturday, September 29, brought him to the Havre de Grace Handicap, $10,000 added, nine furlongs, all ages. He was asked to assume the top weight, 126 pounds, and make large concessions to a field of eight high-class handicap horses, among them Mr. Woodward's rejuvenated Faireno, five years, 122 pounds, which had been running some fine races, and the ex-steeplechaser Azucar, whose quality was as yet unsuspected on the flat, he getting in at 108 pounds. Yet such had the faith in the colt become that he was a 1 to 2 favorite, with nothing else at better than 10 to 1, while 35 to 1 ruled for Faireno and 17 to 1 for Azucar. It was another day on which Dame Fortune frowned upon Discovery. Leaving the stalls, Bazaar caromed into him; after he had recovered from this mishap, Indian Runner repeated Bazaar's offense. Relegated to last position by these interferences, Discovery had to be hard ridden to show in sixth place at the half and to move on thence into third place as they swung for home, racing widely to dodge other trouble. Giving his best he drew gradually up but fell short a length as Faireno nosed out Azucar in an eyelash finish; time, 1:50⅘. "He should have won," was the expert verdict.

Eastern track managers were now vying with each other in their efforts to lure the handicap horses by offers of events worth up to $25,000 each, or "extra specials." The newspaper headlines teemed with their publicity and, in especial, the getting together of Discovery and Equipoise, the latter champion, on the shelf since the early season, being reported about ready again. Mr. Vanderbilt and Trainer Stotler decided not to be rushed off their feet. It was three weeks before their colt again answered the bugle in what proved to be his *au revoir* for 1934: the Maryland Handicap, run at Laurel on Saturday, October 20, for three-year-olds, $5,000 added, a mile and a quarter.

And here again sportsmanship ruled, for the extreme top weight of 130 pounds had been assigned the colt and while but four opposed him, he was giving them each from 20 to 25 pounds. Little had been asked of him during his lay-up, and his distance trial, given him on Wednesday, was only a breezing gallop in 2:06⅗. He stripped for the race "like a giant refreshed" and the tang of the autumn air made him so mettlesome that when they immediately got off Bejshak found it impossible to keep him back, it being the only time all the season that he took the bit in his teeth and set out to make his pace as he pleased. It was a burning one. He rushed to the quarter in :23, to the half in :46⅕ and then to the three-quarters in 1:10⅖—almost half a second below the track record for a dash of that length, 1:10⅘. Constantly increasing his lead, he reached the mile post in 1:36⅘—track record 1:37⅕, with his rider still trying to coax him back. Into the home stretch and down it he flew, completing the nine furlongs in 1:49⅖—track record 1:49⅗. Not until he was almost at the end of his journey did the pace and the weight begin to have any effect. He then began to slacken up, while Good Goods, to whom he was giving 21 pounds at the same time, made a fine run in the effort to nail him. With a nice exhibition of skill, Bejshak, keeping him well in hand, lifted him along and as the post was passed he was a half-length to the good; time, 2:03. The merit of the performance was appreciated by the 12,000 spectators, who greeted Discovery with round after round of applause on his return to the scale.

It was noticed, however, that the colt, for the first time in his career, pulled up showing distress. That perhaps was pardonable in view of the rate at which he had run, the distance he had gone, the weight he had carried and the fact that he had defied control. Still, it was so unusual that apprehension was excited—and that evening he was found to be running a temperature, with signs of incipient catarrhal fever. Prompt treatment kept this down to a heavy cold. But Mr. Vanderbilt at once authorized the announcement that he would be retired for the season and he was shortly sent to Sagamore Farm and went into winter quarters.

His season's record stood: 16 starts, eight wins, three times second, three times third and twice unplaced, with earnings of $49,555. He had won six important stakes—the Brooklyn Handicap, Kenner and Whitney Stakes, and Maryland, Potomac and Rhode Island Handicaps, and had run second in both the Kentucky and the American Derbies and the Classic. He had broken a long-standing American record. He had carried to victory the highest weight—130 pounds—of any three-year-old of the year. He was generally regarded as the best horse in training at the time he retired, regardless of age or sex.

It is one of the weak spots of the American turf that in its present racing scheme there is no possibility of a great stake horse paying his way unless in handicaps, once he passes his three-year-old form. Weight-for-age events for all ages, once the grand feature of our turf drama, under pressure of commercialism and profit-taking, no longer exist save in a few isolated examples, in number and value so small that no owner is justified in keeping a horse in training exclusively for them. Due to this deplorable fact, in recent years numerous horses, including some of our very greatest, have been forced into the stud at the apex of their fame and when the public interest in them was most intense, their value to racing incalculable. Others have been sent abroad where such engagements are still possible and the renown great that attends their winning.

Otherwise, the horse remaining upon the American turf after his three-year-old season is wholly at the mercy of the handicappers. And what that means is well known. It means that he must enter single-handed into a contest with them all, in which his stoutness is pitted against their avowed purpose of piling ever heavier burdens upon his back until either he is beaten, or broken down, or both. To withstand the ordeal he must be indeed a titan. It is, moreover, one which foreign owners of outstanding "classic" colts are declining more and more frequently. It is becoming very rare, something that isn't done, for such to abide the issue of the handicaps. Only immense confidence in a colt, together with a sheer sporting determination to accept the ultimate hazard, will inspire an owner to the contrary. But as Mr. Vanderbilt had both the confidence and the sportsmanship, he announced that Discovery would race again in 1935 and be seen in the big handicaps. It was an announcement that brought smiles to the faces of the track managers and "great expectations" to race-goers.

With the complete returns of the season before us, we can still better appreciate what that meant than was possible a year before. The records tell us that during 1935 Discovery started in 19 races and that, in his first essay having to shoulder 130 pounds, as the season aged and his reputation and prowess with it, he was finally stepped up to 139 pounds, the highest weight under which any American handicap of consequence has ever been won, and that only once; and that the average weight carried by him in these 19 races was just 130 pounds—a figure, moreover, reduced to that level only by the fact that at rare intervals he was able to start in a weight-for-age event which placed his impost below 130 pounds. Of these 19 races he won 11, was second in two, third in two and unplaced in four and earned $102,545.

This is an exhibit without parallel in turf history, either American or foreign. There is nothing in the annals of England, France or Australia to approach it. Here at home, the nearest approach will be found in the record of Exterminator, the gelding commonly considered the greatest weight-carrying campaigner ever seen. As a four-year-old, however, while Exterminator ran 21 races, or two more than Discovery, in but four of them did he carry as much as 130 pounds, and his top weight was but 134 pounds. Moreover, he won but nine times. Thus Discovery's showing surpasses his. In none of his subsequent campaigns did Exterminator, as an aged horse, start as many as 19 times, nor did he ever win

as many as 11 times in any one season. While on one occasion he was given 140 pounds, he then ran unplaced; and his highest winning weight was 138 pounds.

We may therefore, without any undue encomium, pronounce Discovery to have achieved something never before known. He also narrowly escaped reaching and passing the record of Equipoise, the leading money-winning four-year-old of America. At that age the "Chocolate Soldier" earned $107,735, and, until the performances of Discovery, was the only horse to win as much as $100,000. The most valuable event won by both colts was the Stars and Stripes Handicap at Arlington Park. It was worth $22,300 to Equipoise in 1932 but only $9,000 to Discovery in 1935—this single item tipping the scales against the latter.

These facts are cited as giving a comparative glimpse of the performances of three horses among which we assign no definite superiority, that being something impossible to any reasoned criticism. It would be no discredit if Discovery were to be ranked the last of the trio. That in various regards he stands first must be considered an index of his class.

Discovery never had been an "early bloomer." As neither a two- nor a three-year-old was he nearly so good in the spring as later on and this idiosyncrasy was again demonstrated as a four-year-old. In fact he came to hand more slowly than ever before—and to this must be attributed his defeat in five successive races before he struck that winning stride thereafter to carry him so far. These effects may be briefly dismissed with their enumeration and the statement that he seemed in all of them not really Discovery. The public was beginning to look upon him somewhat doubtfully, when, without warning, like the sun bursting from behind a cloud, he began a career of conquest that dazzled it.

His debut was made May 15, at Belmont Park, in the Toboggan Handicap, and he carried top weight, 130 pounds, in a field of eleven others despite which he was made favorite at six to five, coupled with his stablemate Identify. He finished fifth, less than three lengths back of the winner, which was nothing less than Identify, to the great surprise of the crowd and the critics! Three days later he came out again for the Metropolitan Handicap at Belmont, again as top weight, 127 pounds, in a field of nine. This time he finished fourth as King Saxon, 118 pounds, won from Singing Wood, 114 pounds, by a neck, Only One, 113 pounds, third by a neck and Discovery lapped on him, to his middle. Though fourth only he was beaten less than a length by the winner after being shut off when he attempted to come through, and forced to come out around the leaders. Owing to his previous race, five to one ruled against him.

Discovery just before his 1934 Kentucky Derby race [UPI]

His third effort was in the Suburban, on May 30 and here for the first and only time during the season he again faced his arch-antagonist Cavalcade. The latter, specially prepared for the race and with top weight of 127 pounds, was made the favorite at two to one; Discovery (again coupled with Identify) was at 2½ to 1, and had up 123 pounds. Cavalcade eliminated himself at the start, losing his rider, Discovery ran a grand race, but failed to reach the flying Head Play (114 pounds) by a length and a half, with the time 2:02, equaling that of Equipoise in 1933; first mile in 1:36⅕. The Queen's County Handicap, at Aqueduct, run on June 10, next called him out, again as top weight at 123 pounds. He finished fifth, ten lengths back of the winner, King Saxon, 118 pounds, faltering in the stretch when he looked a possibility. Five days later, June 15, found him in New Hampshire, at Rockingham Park, where, still with the faithful Identify, he ruled favorite for the $10,000 handicap named in honor of the park. He was assigned 128 pounds, the track was muddy, eleven horses started. Near the half, when going well, he seemed almost to stumble and lost considerable ground. Meanwhile Identify was off in front going great guns and continued to the finish an easy winner, while Discovery, regaining his stride, came home fast and just failed to take the place from Dark Hope by a head.

Five successive defeats had now placed Discovery upon the doubtful list. "He isn't the Discovery of old," was the verdict. His reputation was tarnished, beyond doubt. That it would be rehabilitated many doubts were expressed. Wrote one expert: "The handicappers have been rating the Vanderbilt colt too high. He has demonstrated that he cannot carry the imposts they are allotting him and win." Even the experts cannot always be clairvoyant. But what Discovery now immediately launched forth upon resembled nothing so much as a sudden stroke of melodrama. Beginning June 22, between that date and August 10, or in a period of six weeks, he ran up a string of eight consecutive victories in important stake events, carrying higher weights than ever before, running in sensational time and literally squandering his opposition. While in the process, he traveled back and forth across the country thousands of miles. Nothing like it had ever before been seen and it is no wonder that the furor he excited relegated everything else in turf affairs to subordinate positions.

This series of triumphs began with the Brooklyn Handicap. Established nearly forty years before, with a history starred by great names and furious contests, he had won it the previous season, as before related. Upon its roster there was no double winner. Many famous horses after winning it once had attempted to do so again— always to fail. Many others had attempted to win even once, and failed. What reason, then, to expect that Discovery, fresh from five straight defeats, could accomplish anything so unheard-of? Nobody could find any, though he had been let in at 123 pounds and King Saxon was giving him four pounds, the latter carrying 127. But another menace was in the field—William Woodward's Omaha, the champion three-year-old of the season, fresh from his triumph in the American Triple Crown of Kentucky Derby, Preakness and Belmont Stakes. At 114 pounds he looked so formidable that he was the public choice at seven to five, with King Saxon at eight to five, while Discovery was at four to one. Good Goods, Somebody and Thursday made up the field.

That the King, a front runner, would attempt to make every post a winning one was a foregone conclusion. He dashed away at a dizzy pace, taking a lead of two lengths, while Bejshak laid Discovery along behind him and kept him within striking distance. The colt was so full of run that, fast as the King was flying he not only maintained his position, but as the furlongs flew by, began gradually to draw closer to the leader. The half was done in :46⅕ and six furlongs in 1:11⅖. Then Bejshak began loosening his hold of Discovery and his mount's response was thrilling. The great crowd that packed the Aqueduct stands and enclosures in tense silence saw him spring forward and, as it were, take King Saxon by the throat and choke him into submission. They passed the mile post almost head and head in 1:35⅗ (track record 1:36) and turned for home. As they did so Discovery began to come away from the Knebelkamp colt as if the latter had suddenly stopped racing. Crossing over to the rail, the son of Display bounded along to a lead of half a dozen lengths to finish off by himself, not fully extended, in 1:48⅕. He had placed another American record to his credit, as the previous one for a mile and an eighth was 1:48⅖, held jointly by Hot Toddy, four, 110 pounds, and Blessed Event, four, 111 pounds. Omaha, unable at any time to meet the pace, ran home four lengths behind King Saxon, with the rest nowhere.

It is not exaggeration to say that the effect of this performance was prodigious. Discovery had for the first time in history executed a double in the Brooklyn Handicap; he had made the season's fastest horse—supposedly—and its champion three-year-old, look mediocre; he had broken a world's record; and he had never come to a drive!

A claim of foul was lodged against Discovery by Rainey, the rider of King Saxon, on the ground that when he crossed over into the lead, when passing him, he had crowded him into the rail and caused his injury as well as his defeat. After examining it the stewards dismissed it as frivolous.

The next Saturday, June 29, we discover the chestnut colt at Detroit, where he had been named for a race originally known as the Detroit Challenge Cup, endowed with $25,000 and eligible only to horses in effect champions. Its avowed purpose was to bring together Discovery, Cavalcade, Head Play and Azucar, the winner of the $100,000 Santa Anita Handicap at Los Angeles. But one by one the candidates were eliminated by training exigencies and on the day appointed only Discovery and Azucar came out, a purse of $12,500 being offered them, at nine and a half furlongs, weights 126 and 127 pounds respectively. Though run in the mud, Discovery, finishing 30 lengths ahead, did the distance in 1:58¼ to equal the record made there the previous year by Cavalcade. He could have run much faster, being at no time called upon.

Next on his itinerary came Arlington Park, and the Stars and Stripes Handicap, $10,000 added. The July 4 crowd, estimated at 35,000, on tiptoe with excitement, mobbed Discovery in the paddock and followed him to the post with salvoes of applause, also backing him down to three to ten in the Totalisator. There were eight starters, the favorite top weight at 126 pounds, as his Brooklyn and Detroit penalties had not yet accrued, and conceding everything lumps of weight. We will by courtesy call the race a contest. Discovery, kept back until the stretch, came away then without an effort to gallop in six lengths before Chief Cherokee, 106 pounds, and Riskulus, 118. Time for nine furlongs, 1:50⅘; track record, 1:49⅗.

Shipped immediately back to the East, on Saturday of the next week he appeared at Empire City Park for the Butler Handicap, $10,000 added, nine furlongs. Carrying 129 pounds, and at odds at nine to ten, he ran home a length and a half ahead of Only One, 113 pounds, and Top Row, 116 pounds, with Good Goods, King Saxon and Vicar out of it. Time, 1:53; track record, 1:51.

Saturday a week, July 20, brought him to still another scene of action—the new Suffolk Downs plant at Boston, where for the first time the citizens of the Puritan metropolis were being offered the opportunity to see major Thoroughbred racing. The Bunker Hill Handicap, $10,000 added, nine furlongs, was his objective and though allotted 131 pounds, his opposition, including Governor Sholtz, Advising Anna, Gusto and Teralice, was so feeble that 108 pounds (Gusto) was the heaviest weight among them. At odds of five to one *on*, Discovery came rolling home fifteen lengths in the clear but under restraint all the way. Time, 1:51⅘; previous track record 1:53⅗.

The severest test of his career, thus far, was now before him—the Arlington Handicap, for which he had been allotted 135 pounds, and to be run on Saturday, July 27; one mile and a quarter. The colt stayed on at Suffolk Downs until Wednesday the 24th, and was then given an early morning distance-trial of 2:09; shortly afterward he was on the train headed for Chicago, and reached it on the morning of Thursday the 25th. After arriving at Arlington nothing was done but unlimber him gently before the race, for which he went to the post at five o'clock Saturday afternoon. He was making the following concessions to the six horses with the temerity to oppose him: Riskulus, 19 pounds (he the winner of the event the year before); Stand Pat, 20 pounds; Late Date, 25 pounds; Watch Him and Count Arthur each 31 pounds; Skip It, 39 pounds —this in actual weight. In order to get up to 135 pounds, Bejshak was also obliged to pack some 25 pounds of dead lead, in itself no small handicap to a horse otherwise heavily burdened. Nevetheless the 20,000 people present, who cheered the colt enthusiastically when they caught sight of him, made him an overwhelming favorite over the entire field, so complete was their confidence in him.

That his performance that day stands among the most splendid in our turf history is merely stating the fact. Allowing first Riskulus and then Stand Pat to take the lead and set the pace until he was ready to move, but not letting them get at any time more than two lengths away from him, keeping out wide to avoid complications, Bejshak did not ask him to run until rounding the upper turn and then merely let go his head. The manner in which he flew—for literally he seemed to fly!—forward will never be forgotten by those who saw it and a great shout went up as he turned into the stretch almost clear of Stand Pat, in a moment more shot away from him, opened up a gap of five lengths and bounding along won by that margin, beautifully carried but not ridden out.

That the time must be very fast was felt by everybody—but nobody was prepared, save a few watch-holders in favorable positions, for what the timers hung out: 2:01⅕—the fastest mile and a quarter ever run in America, authentically timed, with the sole exception of the 2:00⅘ of Sarazen, at Latonia in 1924, that famous gelding on that occasion being three and carrying 120 pounds. The time by quarters was:—:23, :47, :59, 1:11, 1:23, 1:35, 1:48⅕, 2:01⅕. This will not be found on the charts of the race, which give the fractions as follows:—:23⅖, :47⅖, 1:11, 1:36, 2:01⅕, but was obtained direct from the officials, immediately after the running of the race, by the present historian. It will be seen that the complete time (2:01⅕) of the chart is precisely that of the officials, but varies slightly for the first quarter and a half, and by a full second for the mile; while it omits the time for the five and seven furlongs and the nine furlongs.

That the official watches are to be preferred is obvious. We think the records may be searched in vain for another instance of a mile run in 1:35 around the four turns of a circular course, not out of a chute; or of seven furlongs in 1:23; or of nine furlongs in 1:48⅕—for when Discovery had run in that notch in the Brooklyn Handicap, the race was started out of the chute at Aqueduct for events of that distance. And when we add that the colt was carrying 135 pounds, the sheer splendor of the feat is doubled.

It was recognized and rewarded by one of the most tumultuous ovations ever tendered a winner in Chicago. The vast throng rose and shouted themselves hoarse in acclaim, men and women joining in an almost frantic demonstration.

The next day the hero who had excited this outburst was on his way back East to Saratoga, and, arriving there on Monday, Wednesday beheld him demurely going postward for the Wilson Stakes, one of the few weight-for-age fixtures on the calendar; distance one mile. It was but a formality. Only his chum, Identify, and Psychic

Bid went with him and he left them up the course as he cantered in, with his 126 pounds, in 1:37⅕. An interval of ten days and then he posted another all-time-high by taking up 139 pounds in the Merchants' and Citizens' Handicap, $7,500 added, one and three-sixteenths miles, to equal for the first time the impost carried in the Suburban of 1913 by Whisk Broom II. Encouraged by his ponderous load, five horses kept him company—in the stalls, at least. He was making these concessions: Stand Pat, 22 pounds; Top Row, 22 pounds; Only One, 24 pounds; Good Goods, 31 pounds; Hindu Queen, 35 pounds, but race there was none, as he took command at once, led all the way and won easily by two lengths from Stand Pat and Top Row. Time, 1:57⅖; track record, 1:55⅗.

"Where will he stop?" had now become the cry. Eight stakes in succession, nearly $75,000 earned since the season opened, world and track records strewn about him, weight apparently unable to stop him—Discovery had become, to the public, another "wonder horse," to be mentioned only with Man o' War and Equipoise among those of the past twenty years.

The handicapper, however, give him enough rope, will stop any horse—for there is no horse that can overcome him. We will find that the Eclipses, Ormondes, St. Simons and other unbeaten titans of monumental fame never matched themselves with the handicapper. Neither did Man o' War. And when Discovery threw down the gauntlet to him yet again for the $25,000 added Narragansett Special at the Rhode Island course on August 21, he turned the trick, for the colt was once more allotted 139 pounds and the exactions asked from him were inordinate—24 pounds to Time Supply; 29 pounds to Top Row; 32 pounds to Howard; and 35 pounds to Fidelis.

The outpouring of people to see the race was reckoned above 40,000; over $700,000 passed through the betting machines; over $100,000 of it was wagered on the big race—and so supreme was the belief in the invincibility of Discovery that he was at one to four. It was realized in advance that the menace would come from Top Row, the jaunty litle four-year-old by the jaunty little Peanuts of former days; they had already met twice and Discovery had given him, first 16 pounds and then 22 pounds and left him lengths arear. But 29 pounds? Conservatives placed a big question mark there. And they were only too correct. After a hard race, Top Row, ridden out, beat Discovery by a few feet of daylight; the time, 1:55⅘ for the mile and three-sixteenths—less than a second off Discovery's record of 1:55 made over the same course the fall before under 119 pounds.

Sent down from Saratoga for the Special, Discovery was returned immediately to The Spa, where only three days later the Whitney Stakes gave him another of his scant opportunities to avoid the handicapper. A weight-for-age event at a mile and a quarter, his presence with but 126 pounds on his back, and the pencillers generously offered 1 to 10 against him, there being three others to start. He was laid off the pace until the stretch, then allowed to race home two lengths in front of Esposa in 2:04⅗. It was another double for him as he had won the same event in 1934.

This race was run on August 24, and was followed by the announcement that he would now be accorded a vacation, having won nine of his last ten starts and run second in the remaining one; and that he would next be seen in public in the Hawthorne Gold Cup, to occur on October 5. This meant a rest of six weeks and when after making his third trip of the season from New York to Chicago, he arrived there and stripped for the cup, he showed plainly the benefit he had experienced. Endowed with $15,000 added money and a gold trophy for the winner, and having been previously won by such horses as his sire, Display, upon its first running, then thrice in succession by Sun Beau, and then by Plucky Play and Equipoise, it presented his last opportunity of the season to race under scale weight. That fact did not, very naturally, appeal to the other owners interested and when the starters were summoned from the saddling paddock but three platers could be mustered.

Again the odds were one to ten—and again the contest was purely formal. Discovery, on a cold, bleak day but before a great crowd eager to behold him, galloped the mile and a quarter in 2:04⅖ to lead home Top Dog by three lengths with Bejshak taking him back all the way through the last furlongs. An immense collar of American Beauties was thrown about his neck, there were speeches punctuated by applause and Mr. Vanderbilt received a parchment calling for a golden statuette of his golden colt from whatever goldsmith he might choose to fabricate it. That evening Discovery bade farewell to Chicago for 1935, his three invasions of it between July and October having been productive of three brilliant triumphs, winnings of $28,675 and the gold trophy, not to mention the flowers. Behind him he left the reputation among its race-goers, of being a "superhorse."

The unwearied traveler, now habituated to hegiras surpassing those from Mecca to Medina, was due to make his next appearance at Boston, where on October 16 the grand event of the season was to be staged—the $25,000 Massachusetts Handicap. Though 138 pounds had been allotted him, there was no thought of evading the test and before a crowd of 30,000 assembled chiefly to "see Discovery," whose presence anywhere now meant a capacity house, he took his place at the barrier with the seven opponents that, encouraged by his burden, were willing to face him. His concessions to them ranged from 22 to 36 pounds, with an average of 26 pounds for the entire field. Of them all only his conquerer at Narragansett Park, Top Row, was accorded any chance to beat him. That "little joker" was being asked to pick up six pounds more than on that memorable day, while Discovery had one pound off. The reasoning was that, with a better break by seven pounds, Discovery could not lose. Hence his odds were seven to ten, while Top Row's were six to one.

Was the reasoning correct? There is good cause for believing so. But from the equation in which victory represented the unknown quantity had been omitted another for the moment unguessed. Not a factor, suppositiously, that should be reckoned in at such a time, place or race. Not that one is expected to rear its ugly head when a greater sporting event is at issue. But, nevertheless, one that did—foul riding. Though none was claimed, the patrol judge reported that at a critical point in the race, Frank Mann, riding Stand Pat, and in the lead at the half-mile post, when Discovery attempted to move past him, seized the saddle-cloth of Bejshak, deflected the colt's run, impeded him for a considerable distance and desisted only when further interference was impossible.

Despite this shameful act, Discovery went to the leaders when he got free, locked them, and in one of the most thrilling finishes of the season, was beaten only three feet, Top Row winning by a neck from Whopper, with which colt, in at 108 pounds, hence receiving 30 pounds from him, Mr. Vanderbilt's horse made almost a dead heat. The race was also a very fast one, the track record for nine furlongs being lowered from 1:51⅘ (made by Discovery on July 20) to 1:49⅖, and the first mile run in 1:36⅘ (track record 1:37⅘). There was no doubt of the offense, which was amply verified. The offender was suspended for the rest of the meeting—but as that endured for but three days it can hardly be said that justice was done. Discovery emerged the hero of the race, it being the expert opinion that only the foul perpetrated enabled his defeat.

Another long journey now confronted him, for he was due at the Coney Island course, Cincinnati, on October 22, to fill his engagement there in the Cincinnati Handicap, $10,000 added, a mile and a quarter. The appointed day found him there and over a track much like a mortar bed he cantered home twelve lengths ahead under his weight of 132 pounds, his five opponents being strung out behind him for the best part of a furlong. Time, 2:06⅖.

The last stanza of the saga of Discovery in 1935 was now at hand. His closing essay of the season was made in the Washington Handicap at Laurel, $10,000 added, mile and a quarter. Only four days intervened between it and the Cincinnati Handicap, its date being October 26. While he had won so easily at Coney Island, his weight and the heavy going there, together with his two long journeys, first from Boston to the Ohio city and then to Maryland, had dulled his edge. Moreover, he was being asked to take up 138 pounds and run against several of the tops among the season's three-year-olds, giving them from 19 to 37 pounds each; while aside from this galaxy, which included Firethorn, Count Arthur, Black Helen, Bloodroot and Judy O'Grady, the field embraced Only One, Soon Over and Riskulus, also claiming from him vast allowances.

In justice to the colt, as well as the Messrs. Vanderbilt and Stotler, it should be recorded that no intention of starting him had been entertained and he was sent forth only upon the urgent plea of the management, which, together with the public, had been counting greatly upon his going to the post. Looked upon by them as a Maryland horse, he had not been seen anywhere in that state during the entire campaign and they were clamorous to see him in action. Yielding to this pressure, he was saddled for the race with reluctance. Leaving the stalls he was sluggish and at the half was "absolutely," many lengths behind the leaders. He then gradually warmed to his work and began moving forward, but without avail, as they were running very fast, and when Firethorn won in 2:02⅗, with Count Arthur second and Only One third, he had reached only fourth place, having been obliged to race widely all the way in order to get around the field.

On the Monday following, Discovery was vanned home to Sagamore Farm to be let down for the winter until taken up to prepare for the Santa Anita Handicap of 1936, run late in February. Despite the immensity of his labors, which, aside from his 19 races, had necessitated the traveling of 9,000 miles by rail and van, he had not taken a lame step and so rugged is his constitution that he came through labors that would have finished the average Thoroughbred absolutely unscathed.

It may be said that in the battle of 1935 between Discovery and the handicappers, the colt had got the better of them. He had won under the highest imposts they had piled upon him. He had got the better of them in 11 out of 19 encounters. He had accomplished apparently impossible feats. And he had retired sound, while Mr. Vanderbilt announced that 1936 would find him back on the firing line and ready for the fray. We may, imaginatively, behold the handicappers rolling up their sleeves, spitting on their hands and sharpening their weapons while they passed along the brotherly admonition: "It can't happen here—*again!*" Worsted at their own game, it had come to the showdown. Their ability and their power had alike been defied, with a success hitherto unheard of. It was time to put an end to such presumption.

In 1935 the turf world had been startled by the appearance upon the scene of a new organization, the Los Angeles Turf Club, with a new attraction, the Santa Anita Handicap, whose value to the winner, the veteran ex-steeplechaser Azucar, $108,400, had made it the richest race in the world. It was renewed for 1936, and the promoters had besieged Mr. Vanderbilt for assurances that Discovery would start for it, as his presence was necessary in order that its success be guaranteed in advance. He had yielded to their blandishments.

As the date set for the decision of the stake, again to net the winner over $100,000, was Washington's birthday, February 22, it meant that the long rest which Discovery otherwise would have enjoyed must be abbreviated to about four weeks, or six at most, as he must begin his preparation at home in good time and then be on the scene in California well in advance of the date of the contest. As a matter of fact, after having been in action up to within a few days of November 1, on December 20 he was loaded upon the express car that took him to Santa Anita, where he arrived December 23 and at once began active work for the coming ordeal. On the same day his old rival, Cavalcade, also pulled in from Columbia, South Carolina, where he had been carefully nursed back into what was hoped was a condition that would enable him to prepare for the event and start in it—a hope not destined for fulfillment, as he could not be got to the post. Discovery had spent his brief rustication at Sagamore Farm and unloaded from his transcontinental trip, the longest of the many long ones that he had taken and literally from the Atlantic to the Pacific coast, sound and well; and on Christmas Day, accompanied by his beloved lead pony, he took his first canter over the new California course.

With two months to get ready in, it was, of course, scheduled that he should be seen in public before the big race. This was the intention of the Messrs. Vanderbilt and Stotler. But the Santa Anita management, whose ideas about publicity were tinged by the proximity of Hollywood, and awake to the value of the five-year-old as a drawing-card, were insistent that he be seen in action as soon as possible, and at least twice before the fateful day which, if all went well, might be the decisive factor in making Discovery the world's premier money-winner. Yielding to the pressure brought to bear upon them, his owner and trainer consented to send him to the post for the San Carlos Handicap, $5,000 added, on February 1. Assigned 130 pounds and getting off badly, he ran over the rest in the stretch to win going away at a mile and a sixteenth run in 1:45⅗ over a muddy track, with Ariel Cross

five lengths back and Head Play among the also-rans. He had started at six to ten, as five days before, again to gratify the management, he had been given a public trial between races and run a mile in 1:36, with 125 pounds up.

His support for the Santa Anita Handicap on the strength of these exhibitions now settled into a strong favoritism. He had not, however, thoroughly satisfied close critics in them, as he seemed lighter in flesh than usual, and was slow to leave the starting gate, requiring persuasion to extend himself. A week now elapsed and then again he came out for the San Antonio Handicap, one and an eighth miles, $7,500 added, for which he had been allotted the crusher of 138 pounds. Still, he ruled the choice at seven to ten. Again getting away poorly, and meeting interference, he never got nearer the front than fourth and finished fifth as Time Supply (116 pounds) won from Pompey's Pillar (105) and Ariel Cross (106) in 1:49⅖ (new track record). On the same day it was announced that Cavalcade was definitely out of the $100,000 event. They were never to meet again.

Discovery's performance satisfied the experts that he had gone back and while he would carry but 130 pounds (the fixed top weight) in the big race, his chances for it were none too bright. The rainy season in California was now also keeping the track muddy much of the time and interfering with work as planned. His formal distance trial for the race was given him the Tuesday preceding when he ran it in 2:08 with his weight up, over bad going, and outside the "dogs." To feather his edge, the day before the ordeal he was stepped a half in :46⅗, though the track was still heavy. The public refused to desert him and when the fifteen starters paraded to the post over a track at last called "good," he was carrying "tons of money" at 1½ to 1.

Of Discovery the official report says briefly: "He was bumped at the start, raced on the outside all the way, and although making a brief bid on the back stretch, was never a serious contender." Getting off twelfth, he finished seventh, about five and a half lengths back of the winner.

Overtures to race Discovery at other California meetings were declined and the son of Display was shipped back home to Maryland where it was decided to give him the resting-up that he obviously deserved. And it was almost four months before he again went postward.

The recuperative power of this chestnut horse, it must be allowed, was extraordinary. The manner in which he responded to the treatment accorded him indicated that his greatness was unimpaired; and when, on June 17, he reappeared at Aqueduct in the Inchcape Handicap, at nine furlongs, in what was virtually a public trial for his essay to convert his "double" in the Brooklyn Handicap into a "triple," he took up

135 pounds as if it were a feather and played with Palma (106) and Observant (110), winning off by himself under double wraps in 1:50.

For the Brooklyn he was assigned 136 pounds, or a pound more than Exterminator had carried to victory in 1922, that gelding being the only previous winner under more than 130 pounds. Nevertheless the dread of him was such that aside from his stable mate, Good Gamble (110), only Roman Soldier (126), Ann O'Ruley (96) and Palma (101½) were willing to dispute the day, and on their part it proved but a gesture. Waiting until the home turn to make his run, Discovery sailed past the leader, Good Gamble, and romped in four lengths ahead in 1:50 for the nine furlongs. Net value to him, $10,575. It was the first time in our turf history that a handicap of premier importance had been won thrice in succession by the same horse; always, moreover, with much increased weight: 1934—113 pounds; 1935—123 pounds; 1936—136 pounds.

Viewing with alarm such audacious contempt for tradition and the rules of the game, the handicappers girded themselves for action and when Discovery, one week later, answered the call of "Boots and saddles!" for the $10,000 added Stars and Stripes Handicap at Arlington Park, in which he had carried 126 pounds to victory twelve months before, a "package" of 138 pounds was handed him. The national holiday and the Vanderbilt horse had combined to draw 40,000 people to the beautiful Chicago course and while a field of twelve was opposing him, and to none of them was he conceding less than 16 pounds, while to most he was giving from 20 to 34, he was a roaring even-money favorite, mobbed in the paddock and greeted with cheers when he appeared before the stands. But while he got off well, he at once dropped back, seemed to be anchored, never emerged from the rear guard and finished ninth, as Stand Pat won from Sun Teddy in time (1:49⅗) just a fifth of a second off the track record.

In dissecting the race the pundits argued that the weight could not have bothered him; that it was "just an off day" for him—and that Fallon, who was riding him of late, while Bejshak was nursing a broken collarbone, didn't understand him. Meanwhile the handicappers, avid to earn their salaries and see that nobody, and especially Discovery, "got by," continued blandly to assign him still more terrific imposts, capping the climax by one of 145 pounds, for an event at one of the Metropolitan tracks. Upon which even the patient and game owner of the horse at length revolted, scratched him out of it and spoke a bit of his mind, in perhaps overcourteous phrases, about what they were doing to his racer.

Nevertheless, when the $25,000 Massachusetts Handicap came up at Suffolk Downs, on July 22, Discovery was on hand ready to shoulder his 136 pounds and, coupled with Good Gamble, was made the favorite at 11 to 10. The race he ran was very similar to the previous one. Never getting into contention, he finished eighth in a field of eleven as Time Supply, 121 pounds, won in 1:49⅘; track record 1:49⅖, to which Discovery, then burdened with 138 pounds, had carried Top Row a year before.

Obviously, he was not the same Discovery as of old; obviously the handicappers were at length succeeding in their laudable efforts to "get him down and stamp on him." He had given them some bad quarters of an hour, but like death and taxes, they could bide their time and take their turn.

The outcries of the public, however, were too loud to go unheeded. The public, always ready to admire true greatness, had been loyal to Discovery and had been losing hundreds of thousands of dollars upon him; all, it was affirmed, because the handicappers were setting him impossible tasks. And as the handicappers, in the last analysis, would be out of a job if owners of Discoveries refused to accept their imposts, and the public stayed away from their race tracks in consequence, they began to take back a bit. The courageous, highly-taxed horse was handed "only" 132 pounds for the Saratoga Handicap run at The Spa on August 1; which was indeed magnanimous considering that in thirty-six years of its history it had just once been won by a horse with as much as 130 pounds. Grateful for this rare concession, Discovery, evidently feeling that it would be base ingratitude to do otherwise, won cantering by six lengths from five others to which he was giving from 14 to 30 pounds each; time for the mile and a quarter 2:05; stake value, $8,350; odds, Discovery seven to ten; Bejshak riding. Pleasure of the public. Disgust of the handicappers and the firm resolve to even it up.

And now, before this high object could be accomplished there happened one of those rare phenomena in his career, an engagement in which the conditions fixed his weight, this being the Wilson Stakes, which he had won the previous season and with the same impost, 126 pounds. In recording the result one publication headed it: "Discovery Accepts a Gift"—a neat way of stating that he cantered around in front of St. Bernard and Purple Knight a mile in 1:38⅘ and was awarded $3,475. But only in handling it that way could it be lifted from the repertoire of racing scandals. . . . Discovery actually allowed to carry such a feather!

Then the outraged handicappers got their longed-for chance. Discovery's following engagement, run only three days later, was the Merchants' and Citizens' Handicap, whose renewal the year before he had dared to win under 139 pounds. Now he was called upon to assume no less than 143 pounds. In the entire history of racing, the world around, there was only one instance of a horse carrying such weight as that and winning a first-class handicap; as is well known, Carbine's phenomenal Melbourne Cup of 1890 under 145 pounds, a performance from that day to this standing before the world in lonely and colossal greatness. But in the connection it is worthy of remark that during his entire career of 43 races, Carbine (whose blood Discovery carries) raced in but six handicaps, being used almost exclusively in weight-for-age events. Of the six handicaps in which he started he won three and lost three; and aside from the wondrous Melbourne Cup feat, never won a handicap with more than 128 pounds on his back. These facts are cited to show, by comparison, what incredible tasks the handicappers were setting Mr. Vanderbilt's five-year-old.

Heedless or unknowing what the records enforced, both the public and the experts figured Discovery to carry his 143 pounds and win. Oracular Consensus rated him to do so by a wide margin. There were five starters—and he finished fifth, Esposa, to which he was giving 43 pounds actually, and 38 under the scale, winning over a slow track; the mile and three sixteenths run in 1:00⅖; track record 1:55⅗. Did even the handicappers take pleasure in seeing one of the grandest horses of modern times made thus to look like a lizard? Feeling, we are informed, unfits them for their vocation. And yet—we must still believe them human.

Discovery was now given two weeks of leisure and then, on August 22, dropped into the only other "soft spot" on his season's calendar; the Whitney Stakes, which he had, like the Wilson, won in 1935, at a mile and a quarter. As he got into it at but 126 pounds again, only three others would compete and he ran away with it to win by ten lengths in 2:06⅕; track very muddy; betting, Discovery one to five.

Then followed the race for which the "regulars" at The Spa, as well as others all over America, had been anxiously awaiting; the 56th renewal of the Saratoga Cup, our premier distance event, at a mile and three-quarters, weight for age. Granville, supreme among the season's three-year-olds since the eclipse first of Bold Venture and then of Brevity, had been specially prepared for it, desired by Mr. Woodward to follow in the footsteps of his sire, Gallant Fox. The meeting between the two should decide the kingship of the turf. Which would win? Discovery went down to defeat; the race he ran made him seem below his form, but as a matter of fact he threw a shoe as he was making his move at the three-eighths pole the second time around.

His campaign was now drawing near the end and included but two more efforts. After the cup race he had nearly three weeks' vacation and

then reappeared once again at Providence to make a second effort for the Narragansett Special, $25,000 added, in which a year before under 138 pounds he had been beaten by Top Row. This time it was manifest that something within reason was "coming to him" and his assignment was 130 pounds. But fate ordained that another tremendous performance should not be a winning one. The date was September 16, distance, a mile and three-sixteenths; net to winner, $32,100 —the richest race yet run in New England.

Eight started, and a public still loyal sent Discovery to the post at 15 to 10, with Time Supply (121 pounds) second choice at 31½ to 10 and Rosemont (121 pounds) third at 66 to 10. Discovery trailed the field for almost a mile and at the head of the home stretch was still no nearer the front than third. From that point he gave a stirring exhibition. Drawing past Time Supply and then collaring Rosemont, the leader, he battled with him to the finish in a desperate duel that aroused the 35,000 spectators to frenzies of excitement, for they had wagered over $100,000 on the outcome. All the last furlong the result hung in the balance. The two horses lay close together, locked in furious combat. A few strides from the wire, Richards, flourishing his whip as he plied it upon Rosemont, narrowly escaped striking Discovery over the head, the horse ducked momentarily—and in that moment the race was lost—by a nose! Time, 1:56⅖; track record (American record as well), Discovery's own 1:55, of 1934. Said Daily Racing Form: "Discovery was greater in defeat today than he has ever been in victory."

The prospect of a return meeting between the two contenders was held out by the Havre de Grace Handicap, $10,000 added, to be run at that Maryland track on September 30; but when race day came Rosemont declined the issue, having been assigned the same weight he carried at Narragansett, 121 pounds, while this time—and for the first time (in a handicap) during the season—Discovery was given less than 130 pounds, his allotment being 128. Giving from 10 to 26 pounds to the seven that opposed him, he was made a hot favorite at 75 to 100, but finished fifth while Roman Soldier (118 pounds) won from Where Away (110 pounds) in the very fast time of 1:51 for the nine furlongs run over a track muddy from recurrent showers.

Next morning the reporters filled the public prints with uncalled-for criticisms of the son of Display. He was described as a notional, unreliable performer, that would run only when the mood urged him, otherwise he would not try; together with other strictures which, everything considered, were severe. None of these writers apparently had taken any trouble to ascertain the truth about Discovery—which was that he had pulled up lame, making it necessary for Mr.

Vanderbilt at once to declare him out of the Jockey Club Gold Cup, in which he was expecting once again to meet Granville, this time at two miles, and announce his retirement for the season.

The handicappers had won their battle. They had at length sent him from the race course not only beaten but limping, his steel-and-whipcord underpinning finally yielding under the inordinate strain they had imposed upon it. They had converted him into a target for bitter animadversions in lieu of the eulogies formerly lavished upon him, wherever he went and whatever he did. In the combat of the one against the many he had gone down.

In discussing his horse, Mr. Vanderbilt, also Trainer Stotler, stated that more than once previous to his Havre de Grace effort, Discovery had led them to believe that something was hurting him, but it had been impossible to locate anything. There seemed to be no apparent sore spot; while, when he at last did show up lame, it was difficult to trace the trouble to its exact source.

During 1936, Discovery had run 14 races, in which he had carried an average weight of 132½ pounds. In ten of them he had carried the average weight of 135 pounds. In six of them (all at distances beyond a mile) he had carried the average weight of almost 138 pounds (to be exact, 137⅔ pounds). During the two campaigns of 1935–36 he had run no less than 33 races, only one at a distance of less than a mile, and had carried the average weight of something over 131 pounds. He had raced in New Hampshire, Massachusetts, Rhode Island, New York, Maryland, Ohio, Michigan, Illinois and California, spanning the entire Union in his travels, which aggregated tens of thousands of miles. He had raced over all kinds of tracks, good, bad and indifferent, from early spring to late fall. He had dodged no competitor, no odds.

To the close of 1936, Discovery had started in 63 races, won 27, been second in 10, third in 10, and won $195,287.

We have already said that the turf history of the entire world shows no parallel to his four-year-old achievements. When we add to them his five-year-old career, that statement may be reaffirmed. He was called upon to do things that no other Thoroughbred ever attempted; and if he did not uniformly succeed, his success was such that the voice of detraction should be silent in the presence of a performer so transcendent.

"I don't see him anywhere."

DRAWING BY McCALLISTER [© 1953 BY THE CURTIS PUBLISHING COMPANY]

The Groom's Story

SIR ARTHUR CONAN DOYLE

Perhaps the old cry of "Get a horse!" inspired the creator of Sherlock Holmes to write the following lines. Nevertheless it's an amusing piece and should appeal particularly to the New York Chapter of the Baker Street Irregulars which holds an annual clambake at Belmont Park.

Ten miles in twenty minutes! 'E done it, sir.
    That's true.
The big bay 'orse in the further stall—the one
    wot's next to you.
I've seen some better 'orses; I've seldom seen a
    wuss,
But 'e 'olds the bloomin' record, an' that's good
    enough for us.

We knew as it was in 'im. 'E's thoroughbred,
    three part,
We bought 'im for to race 'im, but we found 'e
    'ad no 'eart;
For 'e was sad and thoughtful, and amazin'
    dignified,
It seemed a kind o' liberty to drive 'im or to ride;

For 'e never seemed a-thinkin' of what 'e 'ad to
    do,
But 'is thoughts was set on 'igher things, admirin'
    of the view.
'E looked a puffeck pictur, and a pictur 'e would
    stay,
'E wouldn't even switch 'is tail to drive the flies
    away.

And yet we knew 't was in 'im; we knew as 'e
    could fly;
But what we couldn't git at was 'ow to make 'im
    try;
We 'd almost turned the job up, until at last one
    day
We got the last yard out of 'im in a most amazin'
    way.

It was all along o' master; which master 'as the
    name
Of a reg'lar true-blue sportman, an' always acts
    the same;
But we all 'as weaker moments, which master 'e
    'ad one,
An' 'e went and bought a motor car when motor
    cars begun.

I seed it in the stable yard—it fairly turned me
    sick—
A greasy, wheezy engine as can neither buck or
    kick.
You've a screw to drive it forrad, and a screw
    to make it stop,
For it was foaled in a smithy stove an' bred in
    a blacksmith shop.

It didn't want no stable, it didn't ask no groom,
It didn't need no nothin' but a bit o' standin'
    room.
Just fill it up with paraffin an' it would go all day,
Which the same should be agin the law if I
    could 'ave my way.

Well, master took 'is motor car, an' moted 'ere
    an' there,
A frightenin' the 'orses an' a poisonin' the air.
'E wore a bloomin' yachtin' cap, but Lor'! Wot
    did 'e know,
Excep' that if you turn a screw the thing would
    stop or go?

An' then one day it wouldn't go. 'E screwed and
    screwed again,
But somethin' jammed, an' there 'e stuck in the
    mud of a country lane.
It 'urt 'is pride most cruel, but what was 'e to do?
So at last 'e bad me fetch a 'orse to pull the
    motor through.

This was the 'orse we fetched 'im; an' when we
    reached the car,
We braced 'im tight and proper to the middle of
    the bar,
And buckled up 'is traces and lashed them to
    each side,
While 'e 'eld 'is 'ead so 'aughtily, an' looked most
    dignified.

Not bad tempered, mind you, but kind of pained
    and vexed,
And 'e seemed to say, "Well, bli' me! Wot will
    they ask me next?
I've put up with some liberties, but this caps all
    by far,
To be assistant engine to a crocky motor car!"

Well, master 'e was in the car, a-fiddlin' with the
    gear,
An' the 'orse was meditatin', an' I was standin'
    near,
When master 'e touched somethin'—what it was
    we'll never know—
But it sort o' spurred the boiler up and made
    the engine go.

"'Old 'ard, old gal!" says master, and "Gently
    then!" says I,
But an engine wont 'eed coaxin' an' it ain't no
    use to try;
So first 'e pulled a lever, an' then 'e turned a
    screw,
But the thing kept crawlin' forrad spite of all
    that 'e could do.

And first he went quite slowly and the 'orse went
    also slow,
But 'e 'ad to buck up faster when the wheels
    began to go;
For the car kept crowdin' on 'im and battin' 'im
    along,
And in less than 'alf a minute, sir, that 'orse was
    goin' strong.

At first 'e walked quite dignified, an' then 'e 'ad
    to trot,
And then 'e tried a canter when the pace became
    too 'ot.

'E looked 'is very 'aughtiest, as if 'e didn't mind,
And all the time the motor car was pushin' 'im
    be'ind.

Now, master lost 'is 'ead when 'e found 'e
    couldn't stop,
And 'e pulled a valve or somethin' an' somethin'
    else went pop,
An' somethin' else went fizzywiz, and in a flash,
    or less,
The blessed car was goin' like a limited express.

Master 'eld the steerin' gear, an' kept the road
    all right,
And away they whizzed and clattered—my aunt!
    It was a sight.
'E seemed the finest draft 'orse as ever lived by
    far,
For all the country Juggins thought 't was 'im
    wot pulled the car.

'E was stretchin' like a grey'ound 'e was goin'
    all 'e knew;
But it bumped an' shoved be'ind 'im, for all that
    'e could do;
It butted 'im an' boosted 'im an' spanked 'im on
    a'ead,
Till 'e broke the ten-mile record, same as I al-
    ready said.

Ten mile in twenty minutes! 'E done it, sir.
    That's true.
The only time we ever found what that 'ere 'orse
    could do.
Some say it wasn't 'ardly fair, and the papers
    made a fuss,
But 'e broke the ten-mile record, and that's good
    enough for us.

You see that 'orse's tail, sir? You don't! No more
    do we.
Which really ain't surprisin', for 'e 'as no tail to
    see;
That engine wore it off 'im before master made
    it stop,
And all the road was littered like a bloomin'
    barber's shop.

And master? Well, it cured 'im. 'E altered from
    that day.
And come back to 'is 'orses in the good old-
    fashioned way.
And if you wants to git the sack, the quickest
    way by far
Is to 'int as 'ow you think 'e ought to keep a
    motor car.

Eneas Africanus

HARRY STILLWELL EDWARDS

Here is recommended reading for grouches. A lovable, laughable horse story, of which the author said: "Eneas would have been arrested in any other country than the South." He added: "Is the story true? Everybody says it is."

Personally, I think it's too good to be true.

Editor, *Telegraph and Messenger,*
Macon, Ga.

DEAR SIR:

I am writing to invoke your kind assistance in tracing an old family Negro of mine who disappeared in 1864, between my stock farm in Floyd County and my home place, locally known as Tommeysville, in Jefferson County. The Negro's name was Eneas, a small gray-haired old fellow and very talkative. The unexpected movement of our army after the battle of Resaca placed my stock farm in line of the Federal advance and exposed my family to capture. My command, Tommey's Legion, passing within five miles of the place, I was enabled to give them warning, and they hurriedly boarded the last southbound train. They reached Jefferson County safely but without any baggage, as they did not have time to move a trunk. An effort was made to save the family silver, much of it very old and highly prized, especially a silver cup known in the family as the Bride's Cup for some six or eight generations and bearing the inscription:

Ye bryde whose lippes kysse myne
And taste ye water an no wyne
Shall happy live an hersel see
A happy grandchile on each knee.

These lines were surrounded with a wreath and surmounted by a knight's head, visor down, and the motto: "SEMPER FIDELIS."

This cup was hurriedly packed with other silver in a hair trunk and entrusted to Eneas with verbal instructions as to travel. He drove an old-fashioned, flea-bitten, blooded mare to a one-horse wagon full of forage and carried all the Confederate money the family left, to pay his expenses. He was last seen, as I ascertained soon after the war from a wounded member of my command, about eight miles southeast of Atlanta, asleep in the wagon, the mare turning to the right instead of keeping the straight road to Macon. Eneas was a faithful Negro, born and raised in the Tommey family and our belief is he was murdered by army stragglers and robbed of the trunk. He had never been over the road he was traveling, as we always traveled to North Georgia by rail, shipping the horses likewise. His geographical knowledge consisted of a few names —places to which I had at different times taken him, and in the neighborhood of my home, such as Macon, Sparta, Louisville, and the counties of Washington and Jefferson. If given a chance to talk he would probably confine himself to Lady Chain, the mare he was driving; Lightning, the noted four-mile stallion temporarily in my possession; the Tommey family and our settlement, Tommeysville. On these topics he could talk eighteen hours a day.

I have no hope of ever seeing Eneas again, for if living he would have gotten back if he had to travel all over the South to do it, but there is a bare chance that the cup may be found, and I am writing to gratify my daughter, whose wedding day is approaching. All brides in the family, since 1670, have used this cup on their wedding days. If the cup was stolen, doubtless the thieves sold it, and if so, the holder may read these lines if they are given publicity. I am willing to waive any question of ownership and purchase the cup at the holder's valuation, if within my power; or, if unwilling to sell, he may loan the cup for a few days.

I shall be greatly obliged if you will publish this letter with a request that all southern papers, daily and weekly, copy the same. Thanking you in advance and with all good wishes for your happiness and prosperity, I am, most respectfully,

Your obed't servant,

GEORGE E. TOMMEY,
Late Major, Tommey's Legion, C. S. A.
P. O., LOUISVILLE, GA.

ALTHEA LODGE,
FAYETTE CO., GA.
October 15, 1872.

Maj. Geo. E. Tommey,
Louisville, Ga.

DEAR MAJOR TOMMEY:

I read with deep interest and sympathy your letter in the *Telegraph and Messenger* inquiring of a Negro named Eneas. This man, I am sure, came to my house about twenty miles south of Atlanta in 1864. I remember the occasion perfectly, because he mentioned your name and one of my boys was serving in your command. I gave him shelter for the night and food for himself and horse. He insisted on sleeping in his wagon. He told me that the mare was famous on the race track and very valuable and he was afraid to leave her. This struck me as singular, at the time, because she seemed old and broken down. I did not see any trunk, but his wagon was full of hay and fodder and he may have had one hidden under it. Eneas asked me to put him on the road to Thomasville—or so I understood him—and I gave him explicit directions as far as Newnan, advising him to get more at that point. He was gone when I arose next morning. I do hope you will find the old man, as well as the cup. I took quite a fancy to him. He gave me a very vivid description of yourself—whom I had long wished to meet—and of your home, the twelve-room house, lawn with its three foun-

tains, beautiful lake and your hundred Negroes in their painted cottages, etc.

Excuse this rambling letter. Your name has stirred an old woman's memories.

Sincerely your friend,

MARTHA HORTON

P.S.—My son, William, who served in your command, married a Connecticut girl. Think of it, Major! But she proved to be a noble-hearted woman and has influenced him to give up tobacco and stimulants in every form. He travels this territory for a New York house. His wife is well connected, and one of her ancestors came over in the Mayflower. She is with me now and sends you her regards. Billy has convinced her that next to General Joseph Johnston, you were the bravest man in the Georgia armies.

M. H.

TALBOTTON, GA.,
Oct. 18, 1872.

Major George Tommey,
Louisville, Ga.

SIR:

Read your letter in the *Columbus Enquirer*. I kept a livery stable here in '64 and saw the man you are hunting about that time. He drove a broken down old speckled gray mare he called Lady Chain, now that you mention it, and claimed she was in foal to Lightning, the great four-mile horse. I took this for a joke along with some of the fairy stories he gave me about the Tommeys, but he was so polite and humble that I let him stay over night in the stable. Offered to pay me next morning and seemed like he had about a bushel of Confedrit money; but I was long on Confed myself and didn't let him put any more on me. Don't remember seein any trunk. He was on his way to Thomasville, so he said, and I giv him as much directions as he could carry.

Very truly,

WILLIAM PETERS.

THOMAS COUNTY,
Oct. 19, 1872.

Major George Tommey,
Louisville, Ga.

DEAR SIR:

My wife remembered your old Nigger as soon as she read your letter in the Macon paper, and so did I when she called it to my mind. He was a big talker all right, and sat on our back steps half the night talking about the Tommeys, their race horse, twenty-room house, yard with six fountains, and a whole tribe of Niggers. We fed him, and he slept in his wagon. Next day he wanted to pay me in Confederate money; was using a corn sack for a pocketbook, and it was most full. He moved on to Thomasville, about six miles from here, but I don't think it was the place he was looking for. I reckon it must have been Tommeysville he was looking for. Major, I took a good look at Lady Chain and you ain't lost much if you never get her back, but if you don't find the Nigger, you've lost the champion liar of Georgia. I hope you get him back, but it's hardly possible a man talking like he did could last seven years on the public road.

Respectfully,

ABNER CUMMING.

THOMASVILLE, GA.,
Oct. 19, 1872.

HON. SIR AND MAJOR:

Your man, Eneas, came to my home in Thomasville, in the winter of '65 or the fall of '64, in great distress. He said he had traveled a thousand miles to get to Thomasville, but it wasn't the right Thomasville. He had no idea of states, geography or direction, claimed he had lived in Jefferson County, next to Washington County, and as this describes two counties across the line in Florida, several people at different times had sent him over there. I gave him a letter to a friend over in Jefferson County near Tallahassee. He had an old gray mare he said was a famous race horse, but she didn't look it. Claimed she was in foal to the celebrated Lightning, whose four-mile race in the mud at New Orleans I witnessed. I thought the old Nigger was loose in the upper story. He had no trunk when here.

Very truly,

ANDREW LOOMIS.

TALLAHASSEE, FLA.,
Oct. 20, 1872.

Major Geo. E. Tommey,
Tommeysville, via Louisville, Ga.

MY DEAR SIR:

Eneas, your old Negro, whose name I had forgotten until I read your letter in *The Atlanta Constitution,* was on my plantation near here in

'65. He came here, very blue and utterly discouraged from Thomasville, Ga. Said he was looking for a little Thomasville owned by Major George E. Tommey. He brought a letter from a friend of mine. There are no Tommeys in this country and no Thomasville, and not knowing what to do with him, I passed him along to Colonel Chairs, a friend in Washington County which is on the gulf coast. Chairs wrote me that he had had a great deal of fun out of Eneas. The gulf astonished him. He declared solemnly that he knew he was in the wrong Washington, because there were no oranges, or scrub palmettoes, or big, green spiders (crabs) in his, and the water had no salt in it. Eneas talked a good deal of Macon and Louisville, and there being a county and town so named, besides another Thomasville, to the north in Alabama, Chairs started him up that way. I am truly sorry the old man came to grief. He was a harmless old fellow, though a picturesque liar, as are many old Negroes when they talk of their white folks.

It is possible that Eneas had a trunk, but I have no recollection of seeing one in his possession.

Yours very truly,

RANDOLPH THOMAS.

LOUISVILLE, ALA.,
Oct. 28, 1872.

Major G. E. Tommey,
Louisville, Ga.

SIR:

A ole nigger name of enus come by hyar in the firs yer atter the war with er old mare and er colt he claim was by the lightnin. He was lokin for a tomusville and I tried to show him the way back to tomusville, in Georgia, but he got mad and wanted to fight me, and if he hadn't been er ole man I would have busted him open. Mr. tommy, you wont never see yo nigger no more less he mends his way of acktin when you are tryin to help him.

Respectfully, sir, yours,

POMPEY WILEY (Colored).

He lef hyar for Macon County.

BARTON, WASHINGTON COUNTY, ALA.

Major G. E. Tommey,
Louisville, Ga.

DEAR SIR:

Your Negro, Eneas, came to my place in this county in 1865, I think, from a little village named Thomasville to the northeast. He was very poor and his pathetic story appealed to my sympathies. I let him have some rations and a piece of land and he planted a cotton crop. He married a young mulatto woman on my place that year, and when he left here about Christmas, 1866, carried with him a young baby besides the old mare and her colt. The colt, by the way, was a beauty.

Eneas was a puzzle to me, though I have lived among Negroes all my life. His stories of you and your place were marvels. But for the fact that he held the mare and colt in your name, refusing dozens of offers for the latter when in dire need, I should have put him down a reckless romancer. He began preaching here among the Negroes and proved to be a most eloquent spiritual advocate. He claimed to be the pastor of a big congregation at home. I heard him on one occasion when he baptized forty converts and was thrilled by his imagery and power.

Eneas knew nothing of geography beyond the names of a few towns and counties. Hearing of a Macon and Louisville over in Mississippi, he gathered his household goods into his wagon in December, '66. I do hope you will yet find him. Suppose you make inquiries through the African Methodist Church—he ought to be a bishop by this time.

Very respectfully,

JAMES TALLEY,

Attorney at Law.

SUNSHINE PARSONAGE,
WASHINGTON COUNTY,
MISSISSIPPI.

Major Geo. E. Tommey,
Louisville, Ga.

MY DEAR SIR:

I was greatly interested in your letter copied into our county paper from the *Telegraph and Messenger,* concerning Eneas Tommey. He was here in 1868 or 1869 with a wife and several children. They came in a one-horse wagon drawn by an old gray mare he called Lady Chain and followed by a splendid young colt he declared was from celebrated racing stock. An almost worn-out pass from his mistress, Mrs. Tommey, though it bore no date or address, saved the old man from arrest. His story, that he was lost and on his way home, though remarkable, was possible, and he was not molested. The narrative of his wanderings interested me greatly. He came up the river—the Mississippi—from Jefferson County, trying to find a ford. He had heard of a Washington parish and a Thomasville in Louisiana, and was trying to reach them. He rented a piece of land near here and raised a crop, leaving in 1869 for Jefferson County, Alabama. I gave him a letter to a minister in that county.

Very truly,

(REV.) JOHN SIMMS.

P.S.—I regret to say that after leaving here, Eneas, though an active minister of the Gospel, suffered the young horse to be entered in a county race. I understand that he won about $75. Allowance, however, must be made for the old man's necessities and distress.   J. S.

IDLEWILDE,
JEFFERSON COUNTY, ALA.
October 26, 1872.

Major Geo. E. Tommey,
Louisville, Ga.

MY DEAR SIR:

A Birmingham paper today gave me the explanation of a mystery that has puzzled my family for several years, when it reproduced your letter to the *Telegraph and Messenger.* Eneas— or the Rev. Eneas Tommey, as he called himself—came here in 1869 with a gray mare and a splendid young horse, which he claimed was of marvelous speed, and a letter from a friend of mine in Mississippi. He also brought a wife and two children. To the latter he added a third before leaving. My daughter was greatly interested in the old man's remarkable story and made an effort to help him. She took down a letter to you, which he dictated, made seven copies of it and sent one to every Thomasville in the South. They all came back to her. By good luck she retained one for her scrap book, and I enclose it that you may see how the faithful old fellow was trying to reach you. He stayed around here farming and preaching until 1870 when, hearing from a horse trader of a Macon and a Sparta in Tennessee, he moved on. He had no trunk with him, and I am afraid your cup is gone.

Very truly,

(REV.) AMOS WELLS.

P.S.—I am informed that Eneas participated in a horse race in Birmingham after leaving here and won a great deal of money.   A. W.

The letter of Eneas enclosed in that of the Rev. Mr. Wells:

Marse George: I am loss in er distric called Yallerhama, by a town name o' Burningham.

Ef you knows whar Burningham is, fer God's sake come ter me fer I can't git ter you! Me and Lady Chain is plum wore out.

Marse George, I been ter firs one an' den ernuther Thomasville, year in an' year out, tell thar ain't no sense in hit. An' I ain't hit de right one yit. Ev'y yuther place is name Thomasville er Macon er Washington er Jefferson. Everybody knows whar I wanter go but me, an' shows me de road; but all I kin do is ter keep movin. De firs Thomasville I got to I got back to fo' times. Hit was harder ter loose it than hit was ter find it!

Marse George, I come ter one pond I couldn't see ercross an' de water warn't no count. The last Thomasville was out most ter sundown an' I was headin' fer ernuther when I struck er creek a mile wide an' Lady Chain couldn't wade hit, so we turn back.

Marse George, Lady Chain's colt come, back in the secon' Jefferson, an' he sholy is old Lightnin's colt; long-legged, big-footed an' iron gray. I been tryin' him out hyar an' thar an' thar ain't nothin' kin tech him.

Marse George, I got ernuther wife down in de third Washington an' am bringin' her erlong. She weighs one hundred and sixty, an' picks fo' hundred pounds er cotton er day. She b'longs ter you, same as me an' Lady Chain an' de colt.

Marse George, er horse trader goin' by told me erbout some more Macons an' Spartas an' Jeffersons an' Washingtons up de country fum hyar an' ef I don't get word fum you by nex' month, I'm gointer move erlong.

Marse George, ef you knows whar I is fum dis hyar letter an' can't come yo'self, sen' fer me. I'm sick o' de road an' wanter git home. Do somp'n an' do hit quick!

Yo' ole Nigger,

ENEAS.

MACON, TENN.,
Oct. 30, 1872.

Maj. George E. Tommey,
Louisville, Ga.

MY DEAR SIR:

Eneas was here in 1869 or 1870 and remained about a year preaching at Mt. Zion and other places in the county. I do not know when I ever met a more original and entertaining talker. His description of your colonial house with its forty rooms, white columns and splendid parks has aroused in me a strong desire to visit the place if I am ever able to come to Georgia. I know it must have suffered from the ravages of the war, but doubtless enough remains to show its former magnificence. I am especially anxious to see the great lake with its flock of swans, and the twelve fountains on your lawn. My mother is a Georgian and I have often heard her describe the natural beauties of the state. There is a feeling with us all that at last it is "home" and that some day we shall all assemble in dear old Monroe County where Grandpa was born.

Eneas brought with him to this place a gray mare that was, he said, a famous race horse, and that the father of her colt was the greatest horse in the world. I had forgotten their names until I read your letter. Eneas insisted that you live at Thomasville next to Washington and Jefferson Counties, and near a town named Louisville. There are towns and counties of the same names in this state and he left to visit them. He seemed to have plenty of money. I hope you will hear from him yet, but I am afraid the trunk is gone. He had none when here.

Sincerely yours,

MARY ADKINS.

LOUISVILLE, TENN.,
Oct. 27. 1872.

SIR:

Don't you worry about old Eneas. He came here in or about '70 with a gray mare, a long-legged race horse; a young wife and three children, and give out that he was a minister of the Gospel. They stayed on my place and there were four children when they left. He was a preacher all right, 'cause I heard him time and again, but all the same he was the biggest liar in Tennessee at that time, and that's a great record for any man. Major, if half he said about you and your place is true, you ought to be President. You must have owned all the Niggers in Georgia, and your home must be spread over all three of them counties he has been looking for ever since freedom. About that Lightning colt—he certainly looks it. Eneas slipped him into a free-for-all up here and him and a strange white man about busted the county. I offered him $500 for the colt, but he said your price was $20,000. Considering you had never seen him, I thought that a little high and him and me didn't trade. Next day he was gone. I was away from home when he left. He owed me twenty dollars I had advanced him, taking a lien note on the crop. He sent me word that if the crop didn't pay out to send you the bill. Said he had plenty of money to pay the note, but didn't have time to wait for it to come due. Oh, you Eneas! Say, Major, if he ever gets back, and he will for you can't lose that kind of man for good, better nail down everything movable—including them twelve fountains.

Yours,

TOM JOHNSON.

P.S.—I say; twelve fountains.
P.S.S.—Forty-four rooms! Gosh! Is the Legion still with you?

WASHINGTON
COUNTY, N.C.,
Oct. 20, 1872.

Maj. George E. Tommey,
Louisville, Ga.

MY DEAR MAJOR:

Your old Negro has been on my plantation for about a year farming and preaching and romancing. He came straight through Tennessee and North Carolina, touching Sparta, Louisville, Washington and Jefferson Counties in the former, and the towns of Jefferson, Sparta and Macon in this state before he found me. I am affectionately known all over this section of the state as "Major Tommy," and as the old Negro was looking for "Major Tommy," somebody put him on my trail. He soon had me treed, but was greatly disappointed when he saw me. However, that did not keep him from paying me a year's visit. Eneas is a queer character—wisdom of the serpent and simplicity of a child. His story, probably growing with age, like the stories of some of our veterans, has beguiled many a lonely hour for me, but not until I read your letter in the *Richmond Dispatch* did I give him credit for many facts in it. The young race horse is certainly a fine animal and should you decide to sell him I trust you will give me the refusal. Eneas won several purses up here in local races. It seems he has a new name for his horse everywhere he goes. He says it keeps him from getting "too common." When Eneas was not plowing or racing, his favorite occupation was preaching, his subject usually being the wandering of the Hebrews in the desert. He left here for Jefferson, S.C. I am sorry to say I heard no mention of your lost cup, and if he had any trunk I was not informed of it.

With regards for yourself and all good wishes for the young bride, I am,

Very sincerely yours,

THOMAS BAILEY.
(Late) Major, 13th N.C. Volunteers, C.S.A.

EXTRACT FROM *Columbia* (S.C.) *Register,* October 27, 1872:

One of the surprises of yesterday's races came in the free-for-all two-mile dash, which was won by Chainlightning, entered by an old Negro man calling himself Eneas Tommey, who claims the horse was sired by the celebrated stallion Lightning, and that the dam, which he drives to a one-horse wagon on his way to Georgia, is Lady Chain. She was certainly a tired looking old lady. Eneas arrived late and at once attracted attention by his unique appearance and his limitless faith in Chainlightning. His story and the splendid horse interested some stablemen and after a private demonstration they succeeded in getting him entered and a rider engaged. In the get-off Chainlightning took the lead and gave a marvelous exhibition of speed. He led the bunch by a hundred yards at the end of the first mile and by nearly three hundred at the end of the second. He was then going strong and the efforts of the rider to stop him resulted in a runaway. When he came around the third time the crowd blocked the track and brought him to a standstill, but his rider was thrown. Eneas won $200. It is not known how his backers fared, but it is supposed that they cleaned up a good pile on the side. Eneas left yesterday, going toward Augusta, Ga. It was suggested afterwards that this may have been the man advertised for in the *Telegraph and Messenger* by a Major Tommey, of Louisville, Ga., a few weeks ago. The matter will be brought to his attention. One reason for the sudden departure of the old Negro, who had become quite a hero among members of his race, is said to be a movement to elect him to the State Senate.

LOUISVILLE, GA.—(Correspondence *Macon Telegraph and Messenger,* Oct. 31, '72.)—Your correspondent on Thursday last was the favored guest of Major George E. Tommey, the famous commander of the Tommey Legion, which rendered conspicuous service to the Confederacy as a part of Johnston's—afterwards Hood's—army, in the Tennessee and North Georgia campaigns. The Major lives about twelve miles from this place at Tommeysville, as his plantation is called. His delightful residence is one of the old-fashioned, two-story houses with broad hall and verandas and two large wings, and is situated in a beautiful grove of oak and hickory. The broad lawn in front abounds with roses and among them is a tiny fountain with a spray. Beyond the house lie the barns and the Negro quarters and a small artificial lake where ducks abound. Sherman's army missed the charming spot and the only suggestion of the "late unpleasantness" is the Major's sword crossed with the colors of the Legion over the broad fireplace at the end of the hall.

The occasion of your correspondent's visit was

the marriage of the Major's only daughter, Beauregarde Forrest, to Mirabeau Lamar Temple, of Dallas, Texas. The bride, a petite brunette of great beauty, entered life eighteen years ago, inheriting her mother's name, but by the act of the Georgia Legislature this was changed in honor of the two heroes of the Confederacy, dear to the heart of her illustrious father. The groom bears the names of two Georgia families long ago transported to the Lone Star State and is an attorney of great promise.

The wedding supper was charming in its simplicity and homeliness, using the word in its original sense. The broad back porch between the two wings was closed in with smilax and the feast was spread on a great home-made table twenty feet in diameter. Seats were placed for forty. Such a display of delicacies and substantials has not been seen in this section since the good old days before the war. The low-growing ferns and cut flowers of the decorations—there by the hundreds—did not hide the guests' smiling faces. Wine, the famous scuppernong of the Major's own vintage, was the only stimulant visible, for the Major and his good lady are almost total abstainers. When the guests were seated a grace was pronounced by the Rev. Mr. Thigpen, and fun and merriment broke loose. Toast after toast was given and sentiment and the poets were interspersed with songs from the family Negroes assembled in the back yard by a gigantic bonfire. Some of the songs were of exquisite harmony and pathos. Freedom, so far, had brought but little of brightness into the lives of these humble people.

A dramatic situation that will one day enter into a story, came during the supper festivities. A sudden excitement among the Negroes was followed by cries, some of merriment and some of fear, and by a stampede of the juniors. In the red light of the bonfire an old Negro suddenly appeared, reining up a splendid gray horse. The old man was seated in a red-wheeled road cart, enveloped in a flapping linen duster and wore a silk hat. His "Whoa, Chainlightnin!" resounded all over the place. Then he stood up and began to shout about Moses and the Hebrew children being led out of Egypt into the promised land. Major Tommey listened for a brief instant and rushed out. The newcomer met him with an equal rush and their loud greetings floated back to us clear as the notes of a plantation bell: "Eneas, you black rascal, where have you been?"

"Oh, Lord! Marse George! Glory be ter God! Out o' de wilderness! De projekin son am back ergin!"

"It's Eneas!" screamed the little bride, gathering up her skirts and rushing out. In the strong light, as the wedding party hurriedly followed, we could see the old Negro hanging to his master

and filling the night with his weird cries. Catching the excitement, the Negroes around began to moan and chant, taking their text from the old man's words.

"Where have you been, sir?" The Major was trying to free himself and choking with tears and laughter.

"All over de blessed worl', Marse George! but I'm home ergin!—You hyar me, Niggers?—home ergin!—

"Stop, sir!"

But suddenly the old man grew rigid in the grasp of a momentous thought. His voice sank to a whisper audible to only a few of us:

"Marse George, wha's Nancy?"

"Nancy is dead, Eneas," said the Major, sadly.

"Thank God!" said the old man fervently.

"Where is my trunk, Eneas?" The old Negro was making a horn of his hands and giving the plantation halloo. With his eyes set on the banking shadows beyond the fire, he waited, an inscrutable smile on his wrinkled face. Presently into the circle of light came an old gray mare, drawing a wagon in which sat a yellow woman, hovering over a small colony of children.

"I done brought you a whole bunch o' new Yallerhama, Burningham Niggers, Marse George! Some folks tell me dey is free, but I know dey b'long ter Marse George Tommey, des like Lady Chain and her colt! Marse George, you oughter see dat horse—"

"Where is the trunk?" repeated the Major, laughing and wiping his eyes. "Where did you leave it, Eneas?"

"I ain't lef' hit," said Eneas indignantly. "Git out o' dat wagon, Niggers, fo' I bus' somer you wide open!" The little colony fell over the wheels like cooters from a log, and drawing aside the hay that had held them, Eneas brought forth a time- and weather-defying hair trunk. He heaved a mighty sigh of relief as he dropped it on the ground:

"Dar 'tis, Marse George, an' I sho is glad to git shut o' dat ol' bunch o' hide an' har!" The bride danced and clapped her tiny hands: "My cup! My cup! Get it! Quick! Oh, please somebody, open the trunk."

Major Tommey picked up an ax and with one blow sliced off the ancient lock. From its snug nest in cotton batting, the bride lifted a shining cup, the cup, Mr. Editor, advertised in your columns a few weeks ago. A bucket rattled down in a nearby well and the bridegroom came with a great gourd of water. Then he read aloud the quaint inscription:

Ye bryde whose lippes kysse myne
An taste ye water an no wyne
Shall happy live an hersel see
A happy grandchile on each knee.

The little woman accepted the challenge with the cup, and smiling up to the face of her husband sipped of the crystal draught and handed him the cup. He, too, drank, but the slight flush on the bride's face was nothing to the fiery scarlet of his own, when a storm of applause greeted the act.

Eneas had drawn the Major aside and produced an old scrap pocketbook, stuffed with bills.

"Marse George," he began, "de bag o' yaller war money what dey gimme warn't no good over yonner whar I been. Countin' de c'llections I tuck up in de church an' what I winned on de track wid Chainlightnin' an' ain't spent—"

"Keep it, Eneas," said the Major, almost exploding with laughter, and patting the old man on the shoulder, "that bunch of Burningham Yallerhama Niggers more than squares us."

"George, you darling! You ignored my warning not to play the horses again!"

DRAWING BY AL ROSS

The Look of Eagles

JOHN TAINTOR FOOTE

If you have read "The Look of Eagles" before you'll enjoy reading it again; it's that kind of story—which you'll find out reading it for the first time. A successful movie version of the story was made some years ago under the title of Kentucky.

I HAD waited ten minutes on that corner. At last I ventured out from the curb and peered down the street, hoping for the sight of a red and white sign that read: "This car for the races." Then a road horn bellowed, too close for comfort. I stepped back hastily in favor of the purring giant that bore it, and looked up into the smiling eyes of the master of Thistle Ridge. The big car slid its length and stopped. Its flanks were white with dust. Its little stint that morning had been to sweep away the miles between Lexington and Louisville.

"Early, aren't you?" asked Judge Dillon as I settled back contentedly at his side.

"Thought I'd spend a few hours with our mutual friend," I explained.

I felt an amused glance.

"Diverting and—er—profitable, eh? What does the victim say about it?"

"He never reads them," I confessed; and Judge Dillon chuckled.

"I've come over to see our Derby candidate in particular," he informed me. "I haven't heard from him for a month. Your friend is a poor correspondent."

The gateman at Churchill Downs shouted directions at us a few moments later and the car swung to the left, past a city of stables. As we wheeled through a gap in a line of whitewashed stalls we heard the raised voice of Blister Jones.

He was confronting the hapless Chick and a steaming bucket.

"Fur the brown stud, eh?" we heard. "Let's look at it."

Chick presented the bucket in silence. Blister peered at its contents.

"Soup!" he sniffed. "I thought so. Go rub it in your hair."

"You tells me to throw the wet feed into him, didn't you?" Chick inquired defensively.

"Last week—yes," said Blister—"not all summer. Some day a thought'll get in your nut 'n' bust it!" His eye caught the motor and his frown was instantly blotted out.

"Why, how-de-do, Judge!" he said. "I didn't see you."

"Don't mind us," Judge Dillon told him as we alighted. "How's the colt?"

Blister turned and glanced at a shining bay head protruding from an upper door.

"Well, I'll tell you," he said deliberately. "He ain't such a bad sort of a colt in some ways. Fur a while I liked him; but here lately I get to thinkin' he won't do. He's got a lot of step. He shows me a couple o' nice works; but if he makes a stake hoss I'm fooled bad."

"Huh!" grunted Judge Dillon. "What's the matter? Is he sluggish?"

"That wouldn't worry me so much if he was," said Blister. "They don't have to go speed crazy all at once." He hesitated for a moment, looking up into the owner's face. Then, as one breaking terrible news: "Judge," he said, "he ain't got the class."

There followed a silence. In it I became aware that the blue and gold of Thistle Ridge would not flash from the barrier on Derby Day.

"Well, ship him home," said Judge Dillon at last as he sat down rather heavily on a bale of hay. He glanced once at the slim bay head, then turned to us with a smile. "Better luck next year," he said.

I was tongue-tied before that smile; but Blister came to the rescue.

"You still like that Fire Fly cross, don't you?" he asked with a challenge in his voice.

"I do," asserted Judge Dillon firmly. "It gives 'em bone like nothing else."

"Yep," agreed Blister—" 'n' a lot of it goes to the head. None of that Fire Fly blood fur mine. Nine out of ten of 'em sprawl. They don't gather up like they meant it. Now you take old Torch Bearer—"

I found a chair and became busy with my own thoughts. I wondered if, after all, the breeding of speed horses was not too cruelly disappointing to those whose heart and soul were in it. The moments of triumph were wonderful, of course. The thrill of any other game was feeble in comparison; but oh, the many and bitter disappointments!

At last I became conscious of a little old man approaching down the line of stalls. His clothes were quite shabby; but he walked with crisp erectness, with something of an air. He carried his soft hat in his hand and his silky hair glistened like silver in the sunshine. As he stopped and addressed a stableboy, a dozen stalls from where we sat, the courteous tilt of his head was vaguely familiar.

"Who's that old man down there?" I asked. "I think I've seen him before."

Blister followed my eyes and sat up in his chair with a jerk. He looked about him as though contemplating flight.

"Oh, Lord!" he said. "Now I'll get mine!"

"Who is it?" I repeated.

"Ole Man Sanford," answered Blister. "I ain't seen him fur a year. I hopped a hoss fur him once. I guess I told you."

I nodded.

"What's he talking about?" asked Judge Dillon.

And I explained how Old Man Sanford, a big breeder in his day, was now in reduced circumstances; how he had, with a small legacy, purchased a horse and placed him in Blister's hands; how Blister had given the horse stimulants before a race, contrary to racing rules; and how Mr. Sanford had discovered it and had torn up his tickets when the horse won.

"Tore up his tickets!" exclaimed Judge Dillon. "How much?"

"Fifteen hundred dollars," I replied. "All he had in the world."

Judge Dillon whistled.

"I've met him," he said. "He won a Derby thirty years ago." He bent forward and examined the straight, white-haired little figure. "Tore up his tickets, eh?" he repeated. Then softly: "Blood will tell!"

"Here he comes," said Blister uneasily. "He'll give me the once over 'n' brush by, I guess."

But Old Man Sanford did nothing of the sort. A radiant smile and two extended hands greeted Blister's awkward advance.

"My deah young friend, how is the world treatin' you these days?"

"Pretty good, Mr. Sanford," answered Blister and hesitated. "I kinda thought you'd be sore at me," he confessed. "While I didn't mean it that way, I give you a raw deal, didn't I?"

A hand rested on Blister's sleeve for an instant.

"When yoh hair," said Old Man Sanford, "has taken its color from the many wintuhs whose stohms have bowed yoh head, you will have learned this: We act accohdin' to our lights. Some are brighter, some are dimmer, than others; but who shall be the judge?"

Whether or not Blister got the finer shadings of this, the sense of it was plain.

"I might have knowed you wouldn't be sore," he said relievedly. "Here's Chick. You remember Chick, Mr. Sanford."

Chick was greeted radiantly. Likewise "Petah."

"And the hawses? How are the hawses? Have you a nice string?" Blister turned and "made us acquainted" with Old Man Sanford.

"Chick," he called, "get a chair fur Mr. Sanford. Pete—you boys start in with the sorrel hoss 'n' bring 'em all out, one at a time!"

"Why, now," said Mr. Sanford, "I mustn't make a nuisance of myself. It would be a great pleasuh, suh, to see yoh hawses; but I do not wish to bothah you. Suppose I just walk from stall to stall?"

He tried to advance toward the stalls, but was confronted by Blister, who took him by the arms, smiled down into his face, and gave him a gentle shake.

"Now listen!" said Blister. "As long as we're here you treat this string like it's yours. They'll come out 'n' stand on their ears if you want to see it. You got me?"

I saw a dull red mount slowly to the wrinkled cheeks. The little figure became straighter, if possible, in its threadbare black suit. I saw an enormous silk handkerchief, embroidered and yellow with age, appear suddenly as Old Man Sanford blew his nose. He started to speak, faltered, and again was obliged to resort to the handkerchief.

"I thank you, suh," he said at last, and found a chair as Judge Dillon's eyes sought mine.

We left him out of our conversation for a time; but as the string was led before him one by one the horseman in Mr. Sanford triumphed. He passed loving judgment on one and all, his face keen and lighted. Of the colt I had just heard doomed he said:

"A well-made youngsteh, gentlemen; his blood speaks in every line of him. But as I look him oveh I have a feeling—it is, of cohse, no moh than that—that he lacks a certain quality essential to a great hawse."

"What quality?" asked Judge Dillon quickly.

"A racin' heart, suh," came the prompt reply.

"Oh, that's it, is it?" said Judge Dillon, and added dryly: "I own him."

Mr. Sanford gave one reproachful glance at Blister.

"I beg yoh pahdon, suh," he said earnestly to Judge Dillon. "A snap judgment in mattehs of this sawt is, of cohse, wo'thless. Do not give my words a thought, suh. They were spoken hastily, without due deliberation, with no real knowledge on which to base them. I sincerely hope I have not pained you, suh."

Judge Dillon's big hand swung over and covered one of the thin knees incased in shiny broadcloth.

"No sportsman," he said, "is hurt by the truth. That's just exactly what's the matter with him. But how did you know it?"

Mr. Sanford hesitated.

"I'm quite likely to be mistaken, suh," he said; "but if it would interest you I may say that I missed a certain look about his head, and moh pahticularly in his eyes, that is the hallmark— this is merely my opinion, suh—of a really great hawse."

"What kind of a look?" I asked.

Again Mr. Sanford hesitated.

"It is hard to define, suh," he explained. "It is not a matteh of skull structure—of confohmation. It is—" He sought for words. "Well, suh, about the head of a truly great hawse there is an air of freedom unconquerable. The eyes seem to look on heights beyond our gaze. It is the look of a spirit that can soar. It is not confined to hawses; even in his pictures you can see it in the eyes of the Bonaparte. It is the birthright of eagles. They all have it. . . . But I express myself badly." He turned to Judge Dillon. "Yoh great mayeh has it, suh, to a marked degree."

"Très Jolie?" inquired Judge Dillon, and Mr. Sanford nodded.

I had heard of a power—psychic, perhaps— which comes to a few, a very few, who give their lives and their hearts to horses. I looked curiously at the little old man beside me. Did those faded watery eyes see something hidden from the rest of us? I wondered.

Blister interrupted my thoughts.

"Say, Mr. Sanford," he asked suddenly, "what did you ever do with Trampfast?"

"I disposed of him, suh, foh nine hundred dollahs."

Blister considered this for a moment.

"Look-a-here!" he said. "You don't like the way I handled that hoss fur you, 'n' I'd like a chance to make good. I know where I can buy a right good plater fur nine hundred dollars. I'll make him pay his way or no charge. What do you say?"

Mr. Sanford shook his head. "As a matteh of fact," he stated, "I have only six hundred dollahs now in hand. Aside from having learned that my racing methods are not those of today, I would not care to see the pu'ple and white on a six-hundred-dollah hawse."

"Why, look-a-here!" urged Blister. "All the big stables race platers. There's good money in it when it's handled right. Let a goat chew dust a few times till you can drop him in soft somewheres, 'n' then put a piece of change on him at nice juicy odds. The boy kicks a win out of him, maybe; 'n' right there he don't owe you nothin'."

Once more I saw a dull red flare up in Mr. Sanford's face; but now he favored Blister with a bristling stare.

"I have difficulty in following you at times, suh," he said. "Am I justified in believing that the word 'goat' is applied to a Thoroughbred race hawse?"

"Why, yes, Mr. Sanford," said Blister, "that's what I mean, I expect."

The old gentleman seemed to spend a moment in dismissing his wrath. When he spoke at last no trace of it was in his voice.

"I am fond of you, my young friend," he said. "Under a cynical exterior I have found you courteous, loyal, tender-hearted; but I deplore in you the shallow flippancy of this age. It is the fashion to sneer at the finer things; and so you call a racin' Thoroughbred a goat. He is not of stake quality perhaps." Here the voice became quite gentle: "Are you?"

"I guess not, Mr. Sanford," admitted Blister.

"Never mind, my boy. If man breeds one genius to a decade it is enough. And so it goes with hawses. Foh thirty years, with love, with reverence, I tried to breed great hawses—hawses that would be a joy, an honoh to my state. In those days ninety colts were foaled each spring at Sanfo'd Hall. I have spent twenty thousand dollahs foh a single matron. How many hawses —truly great hawses—did such brood mayehs as that produce? How many do you think?"

Judge Dillon gave Mr. Sanford the warm look of a brother.

"Not many," he murmured.

"Why, I dunno, Mr. Sanford," said Blister. "You tells me about one—the filly that copped the Derby fur you."

"Yes; she was one. And one moh, suh. Two in all."

"I never hear you mention but the one," said Blister.

"The other never raced," explained Mr. Sanford. "I'll tell you why."

He lapsed into silence, into a sort of reverie, while we waited. When he spoke it was totally without emotion. His voice was dull. It seemed somehow as though speech had been given to the dead past.

"It has been a long time," he said, more to himself than to us. "A long time!" he repeated, nodding thoughtfully, and again became silent.

"In those days," he began at last, "it was the custom of their mistress to go to the no'th pastuh with sugah, and call to the weanlin's. In flytime the youngstehs preferred the willow trees by the creek, and there was a qua'tah of a mile of level blue grass from those willows to the pastuh gate. She would stand at the gate and call. As they heard her voice the colts would come oveh the creek bank as though it were a barrier—a fair start and no favohs asked. The rascals like sugah, to be sure; but an excuse to fight it out foh a qua'tah was the main point of the game.

"One year a blood bay colt, black to the hocks and knees, was foaled in January. In June he got his sugah fuhst by two open lengths. In August he made them hang their heads foh shame—five, six, seven lengths he beat them; and their siahs watchin' from the paddocks.

"In the spring of his two-year-old fohm he suffered with an attack of distempah. He had been galloped on the fahm track by then, and we knew just what he was. We nuhsed him through it, and by the following spring he was ready to go out and meet them all foh the honoh of the pu'ple and white.

"Then, one night, I was wakened to be told that a doctoh must be fetched and that each moment was precious. I sent my body sehvant to the bahns with the message that I wished a saddle on the best hawse in stable. When pahtially dressed I followed him, and was thrown up by a stable man. . . .

"There was a moon—a gracious moon, I remembah—the white road to Gawgetown, and a great fear at my heart. I did not know what was under me until I gave him his head on that white, straight road. . . . Then I knew, I cannot say in what time we did those four miles; but this I can tell you—the colt ran the last mile as stanchly as the first, and one hour later he could barely walk. His terrific pace oveh that flinty road destroyed his tendons and broke the small bones in his legs. He gave his racin' life foh his lady, like the honest gentleman he was. His sacri-fice, howeveh, was in vain. . . . Death had the heels of him that night. Death had the heels of him!"

In a tense silence I seemed to hear a bell tolling. "Death had the heels of him!" it boomed over and over again.

Blister's eyes were starting from their sockets, but he did not hear the bell. He wetted his parted lips.

"What become of him?" he breathed.

"When the place was sold he went with the rest. You have seen his descendants race on until his name has become a glory. The colt I rode that night was—Torch Bearer."

Blister drew in his breath with a whistling sound.

"Torch Bearer!" he gasped. "Did you own Torch Bearer?"

"I did, suh," came the quiet answer. "I bred and raised him. His blood flows in the veins of many—er—goats, I believe you call them."

"Man, oh, man!" said Blister, and became speechless.

I, too, was silent of necessity. There was something wrong with my throat.

And now Judge Dillon spoke, and it was apparent that he was afflicted like myself. Once more the big hand covered the thin knee.

"Mr. Sanford," I heard, "you can do me a favor if you will."

"My deah suh, name it!"

"Go to Lexington. Look over the colts at Thistle Ridge. If you find one good enough for the purple and white—bring him back here. . . . He's yours!"

II

I went along. Oh, yes; I went along. I should miss two days of racing; but I would have missed more than that quite willingly. I was to see Old Man Sanford pick out one from a hundred colts—and all "bred clear to the clouds," as Blister explained to us on the train. I wondered whether any one of them would have that look—"the birthright of eagles"—and I hoped, I almost prayed, that we should find it.

That the colt was to be a purchase, not a gift, had made our journey possible. Five hundred dollars cash and "my note, suh, foh a like amount."

Judge Dillon had broken the deadlock by accepting; then offered his car for the trip to Lexington. At this a grin had appeared on Blister's face.

"No chance, Judge," he said.

"I thank you, suh, foh yoh generosity," apologized Mr. Sanford. "It gives me the deepest pleasuh, the deepest gratification, suh; but, if you will pahdon me, I shall feel moh at home on the train."

"You couldn't get him in one of them things on a bet," Blister explained; and so a locomotive pulled us safely into Lexington.

We spent the night at the hotel and drove to Thistle Ridge early next morning behind a plodding pair. Even in Kentucky, livery horses are—livery horses.

A letter from Judge Dillon opened the big gates wide and placed us in charge of one Wesley Washington—as I live by bread, that was his name—suspicious by nature and black as a buzzard. I reminded him of my previous visit to Thistle Ridge. He acknowledged it with no sign of enthusiasm.

"What kinda colt you want?" he asked Blister.

"A good one!" answered Blister briefly.

Wesley rolled the whites of his eyes at him and sniffed.

"You ain' said nothin'," he stated. "Dat's all we got."

"You're lucky," Blister told him. "Well, trot 'em out."

Then Wesley waved his wand—it chanced to be a black paw with a pinkish palm—and they were trotted out; or, rather, they came rearing through the doorway of the biggest of the big stables. Bays, browns, blacks, sorrels, chestnuts, roans—they bubbled out at us in an endless stream. Attached precariously to each of them—this was especially true when they reared—was a colored boy. These Wesley addressed in sparkling and figurative speech. His remarks, as a rule, were prefaced by the word "Niggah."

At last Blister shouted through the dust.

"Say," he said, "this ain't gettin' us nowhere. Holy fright! How many you got?"

"Dat ain' half," said Wesley ominously.

"Cut it out!" directed Blister. "You'll have me pop-eyed in a minute. We'll go through the stalls 'n' pick out the live ones. This stuff's too young anyway. We want a two-year-old broke to the barrier. Have you got any?"

I turned to Mr. Sanford. He was standing hat in hand, as was his custom, his ·face ablaze.

"The grandest spectacle I have witnessed in thirty yeahs, suh!" he informed me.

"Has we got a two-yeah-old broke to de barrieh?" I heard from Wesley. "Hush! Jus' ambulate oveh disaway." He led us to a smaller stable. It contained two rows of box stalls with a wide alley down the middle. Through the iron gratings in each stall I could see a snakelike head. The door at the opposite end of the stable looked out on the tawny oval of the farm track, and suddenly something flashed across the doorway so quickly that I only guessed it to be a Thoroughbred with a boy crouching along his neck.

Wesley's eye swept up and down the two lines of box stalls. He looked at Blister with a prideful gleam.

"All two-yeah-olds," he said, "an' ready to race."

If this statement made any impression it was concealed. Blister yawned and sauntered to the first stall on the right.

"Well, there might be a plater among 'em," he said. "This all you got?"

"Ain' dat enough?" inquired Wesley with a snort.

"Not if they're the culls," said Blister. "You read that letter, didn't you? We're to see 'em all. Don't forget that."

"Hyar dey is," said Wesley. "Jus' use yoh eyes an' yoh han's."

"All right," said Blister as he opened the stall door—"but don't hold nothin' out on us. Mr. Sanford here is an old friend of the Judge."

Wesley rolled an inspecting eye over Mr. Sanford.

"I ain' neveh seen him roun' hyar," he stated, and honors were easy.

The battle was on in earnest a moment later. The colt in the first stall was haltered and led out into the runway. He was jet black with one white star, and wonderful to see.

"Nothin' finah on fo' laigs," said Wesley, and I mentally agreed with him; but Blister walked once round that glorious creature and waved him back into his stall.

"Yep," he said; "he's right good on four legs, but he'll be on three when that curb begins to talk to him."

"Shuh!" said Wesley in deep disgust. "You ain' goin' to call dat little fullness in de tendon a curb, is you? He'll die of ole aige an' never know he's got it."

"He dies of old age before I own him," said Blister, and walked to the second stall.

And so it went for an hour. Mr. Sanford was strangely silent. When he ventured an opinion at all it was to agree with Wesley, and I was disappointed. I had hoped for delightful dissertations, for superhuman judgments. I had expected to see a master at work with his chosen medium. Instead, he seemed a child in the hands of the skillful Wesley, and I felt that Blister was our only hope.

This opinion had become settled when the unexpected happened. After a more than careful inspection of a chestnut colt, Blister turned to Wesley.

"What's this colt done?" he asked.

"Half in fifty," Wesley stated. "Jus' play foh him."

"Put a boy on him 'n' let's see him move," said Blister.

Then Mr. Sanford spoke.

"It will be unnecessary," he said quietly. "I do not like him."

A puzzled expression spread itself over Blister's face.

"All right," he said with a shade of annoyance in his voice. "You're the doctor."

And then I noticed Wesley—Wesley, the adroit—and a look of amazement, almost of terror, was in his eyes as he stared at Mr. Sanford.

"Yessuh," he said with a gulp. "Yessuh." Then he pulled himself together. "Put him up, black boy," he directed magnificently, and moved to the next stall.

I stayed behind and displayed a quarter cautiously.

"Do you like this colt?" I asked, looking the boy straight in the face.

For a moment he hesitated. Then:

"No, suh," he whispered.

"Why not?" I inquired.

There was a flicker of contempt in the white eyeballs.

"He's a houn'," I barely heard as the quarter changed owners.

It was a well-spent quarter; it had purchased knowledge. I knew now that among our party was a pair of eyes that could look deep into the heart of things. Old they were and faded, those eyes; but I felt assured that a glistening flank could not deceive them.

We worked down one side of the stable and up the other. We had seen twenty colts when we arrived at the last stall. It contained a long-legged sorrel and Blister damned him with a grunt when he was led out.

"If he ever gets tangled up," was his comment, "you don't get his legs untied that year. This all you got?"

Wesley assured him it was. We seemed to have reached an impasse. Then, as Blister frowned absently at the sorrel colt, a voice began singing just outside the stable. It was a rich treble and it chanted in a minor key. I saw the absent look wiped slowly from Blister's face. It was supplanted by a dawning alertness as he listened intently.

Suddenly he disappeared through the doorway and there came to me a regular scuff-scuff on the gravel outside, in time to the words of the song, which were these:

> "Bay colt wuck in fo'ty-eight,
> Goin' to de races—goin' to de races;
> Bay colt wuck in fo'ty-eight,
> Goin' to de races now."

I felt my jaw begin to drop, for Blister's voice had joined the unknown singer's.

> "Bay colt wuck in fo'ty-eight,"

sang the voice; and then a bellow from Blister:

> "Goin' to the races—goin' to the races."

The voice repeated:

> "Bay colt wuck in fo'ty-eight,"

and resigned to Blister's:

> "Goin' to the races now!"

I went hastily through that doorway and arrived at the following phenomena:

Exhibit A—One chocolate-colored boy, not more than three feet high. His shoes—I mention them first because they constituted one-half of the whole exhibit—were—— But words are feeble—prodigious, Gargantuan, are only mildly suggestive of those shoes. His stockings—and now I cross my heart and hope to die—were of the variety described commercially as ladies' hose, and they were pink and they were silk. Somewhere beneath their many folds two licorice sticks performed the miracle of moving those unbelievable shoes through an intricate clog dance.

Exhibit B—One Blister Jones, patting with feet and hands an accompaniment to the wonders being performed by the marvelous shoes.

Both exhibits were entirely in earnest and completely absorbed. As has been already told, they were joined in song.

As I assured myself that the phenomena were real and not imaginary, the words of the song changed.

> "Bay colt wuck in fo'ty-eight,"

came steadfastly from the smaller singer; but Blister, instead of "Going to the races," sang:

> "Where's he at? Where's he at?"

> "Bay colt wuck in fo'ty-eight,"

insisted Exhibit A; and Exhibit B sang:

> "Where's that bay colt now?"

They learn early, in Kentucky, that track and farm secrets are sacred. A suspicion of all outsiders, though dulled by the excitement of white folks' appreciation, still flickered somewhere in the kinky dome of Exhibit A. The song was twice repeated without variation, and the "Where's he at?" became tragic in its pleading tone.

At last Exhibit A must have decided that his partner in song was a kindred spirit and worthy of trust. At any rate,

> "Oveh in de coolin' shed—oveh in de coolin' shed,"

I heard; and Blister brought the duet to a triumphant close with:

> "Oveh in the coolin' shed now!"

He swung round and grinned at Wesley, who was standing stupefied in the doorway.

"Why, Wes!" he said reproachfully. "I'm surprised at you!"

Wesley glowered at Exhibit A.

"You ramble!" he said, and the marvelous shoes bore their owner swiftly from our sight.

So, through song, was the wily Wesley brought to confusion. We found four two-year-olds in the long, squatty cooling shed, and Wesley admitted, under pressure, that they were the pick of their year, kept for special training.

Three of them stood in straw to their knees, confined in three tremendous box stalls. One was being led under blankets up and down the runway. His sides lifted their covering regularly. His clean-cut velvet nostrils widened and contracted as he took his breath. His eyes were blazing jewels. To him went Blister, like iron filings to a magnet.

"Peel him fur a minute," he said, and the still dazed and somewhat chastened Wesley nodded his permission.

Then appeared the most perfect living creature I had ever seen. He was a rich bay—now dark mahogany because of a recent bath—and the sheer beauty of him produced in me a feeling of awe, almost of worship. I was moved as though I listened to the Seventh Symphony or viewed the Winged Victory; and this was fit and proper, for my eyes were drinking in a piece by the greatest of all masters.

Blister was cursing softly, reverently, as though he were at prayer.

"If he's only half as good as he looks!" he sighed at last. "How about *him,* Mr. Sanford?"

I had forgotten Old Man Sanford. I now discovered him standing before a stall and gazing raptly at what was within. At Blister's words he turned and surveyed the bay colt.

"The most superb piece of hawse-flesh," he said, "I have eveh had the pleasuh of observing. I could not fault him with a microscope. He is nothing shawt of perfection, suh—nothing shawt of perfection." His eyes lingered for an instant on the wet flanks of the uncovered colt. "He's too wahm to be without his clothing," he suggested, and turned again to the stall before him.

Blister covered the colt with one dexterous swing. He glanced at the name embroidered on the blankets.

"Postman," he read aloud. "He'll be by Messenger, won't he?" The boy at the colt's head nodded. "Worked in forty-eight just now, eh?" said Blister to no one in particular. Again the boy nodded. "Well," decided Blister, "we'll take a chance on him. Train fur Looeyville at four o'clock—ain't they, Wes?"

Wesley gave a moan of anguish.

"My Gawd!" he said.

"What's bitin' you?" demanded Blister. "We're payin' fur him, ain't we?"

"Lemme have dat letter one moh time," said Wesley. He absorbed the letter's contents as though it were poison, and came at last to the fatal "John C. Dillon" at the end. This he read aloud and slowly shook his head. "He's los' his min'," he stated, and glared at Mr. Sanford. "What you payin' fo' dis hyar colt?" he demanded.

Mr. Sanford glanced in our direction. His eyes had a far-away look.

"Were you addressing me?" he asked.

"Yessuh," replied Wesley. "I was inquirin' de price you aim to pay foh dis colt."

"That is a matteh," said Old Man Sanford, "that concerns only yoh mas—employeh and myself. Howeveh, I am not going to pu'chase the colt to which you refeh." He glanced dreamily into the stall before which he seemed rooted. "I have taken a fancy to my little friend in hyar. . . . Could you oblige me with a piece of sugah?"

As one man, Blister and I made a rush for that stall. We peered through the bars for a moment and our amazed eyes met. In Blister's an angry despair was dawning. He turned savagely on Mr. Sanford.

"You goin' to buy that shrimp?" he demanded.

"Yes, suh," said Old Man Sanford mildly. "I expect to pu'chase him. . . . Ah, here's the sugah!" He took some lumps of sugar from the now beaming Wesley and opened the stall door.

Blister stepped inside the stall and devoted some moments to vain pleadings. Mr. Sanford was unmoved by them.

Then the storm broke. Blister became a madman who raved. He cursed not only the small black two-year old, standing knee-deep in golden straw, but the small, white-haired old gentleman who was placidly feeding him sugar. The storm raged on, but Mr. Sanford gave no sign.

At last I saw a hand that was extended to the colt's muzzle begin to tremble, and I took Blister by the arm and drew him forcefully away.

"Stop!" I said in an undertone. "You're doing no good and he's an old man."

Blister tore his arm from mine.

"He's an old fool!" he cried. "He's chuckin' away the chance of a lifetime!" Then his eye fell on the bay colt and his voice became a wail. "Ain't it hell?" he inquired of high heaven. "Ain't it just hell?"

At this point Wesley saw fit to emit a loud guffaw. Blister advanced on him like a tiger.

"Laugh, you black boob!" he shot out, and Wesley's joyous expression vanished.

I saw that I was doing no good and joined Mr. Sanford in the stall.

"Rather small, isn't he?" I suggested.

"He could be a little larger," Mr. Sanford admitted. "He could stand half a han' and fifty pounds moh at his aige; but then, he'll grow. He'll make a hawse some day."

And now came Blister, rather sheepish, and stood beside us.

"I got sore, Mr. Sanford," he said. "I oughta be kicked!"

Old Man Sanford proffered a lump of sugar to the slim black muzzle. It was accepted so eagerly that the sugar was knocked from the extended hand. Mr. Sanford pointed a reproving finger at the colt.

"Not quite so fast, young man!" he admonished. Then he turned to Blister with a gentle smile. "Youth is hasty," he said, "and sometimes —-mistaken."

III

I returned to Cincinnati and work that night, filled with speculations about a small black colt and his new owner. The latter, I felt, had reached a stubborn dotage.

Two months rolled by; they crawled for me. . . . The powers above decreed that the paper should fight the Bull Moose to the death. I trained the guns of the editorial page on a dauntless smile and adored its dynamic owner in secret.

Those were full days, but I found time somehow for a daily glance at the racing news. One morning I read the following:

Postman, a bay colt, bred and owned by John C. Dillon, captured the two-year-old event without apparent effort. It was the winner's first appearance under colors. He is a big, rangy youngster, as handsome as a picture. He appears to be a very high-class colt and should be heard from.

"Poor Blister!" I thought; and later, as I read again and again of smashing victories by a great and still greater Postman, I became quite venomous when I thought of Old Man Sanford. I referred to him mentally as "That old fool!" and imagined Blister in horrid depths of despair.

Then the bugle called for the last time that year at Lexington, and the Thoroughbreds came to my very door to listen for it.

For days thereafter, as luck would have it, I was forced to pound my typewriter viciously, everlastingly, and was too tired when night came to do more than stagger to bed. At last there came a lull, and I fled incontinently to Latonia and the world of horse.

I approached Blister's stalls as one draws near a sepulcher. I felt that my voice, when I addressed him, should be pitched as though in the presence of a casket. I was shocked, therefore, at his lightness of mien.

"Hello, Four Eyes!" he said cheerfully. "How's the ole scout?"

I assured him that my scouting days were not yet over. And then:

"I've been reading about Postman," I said.

"Some colt!" said Blister. "He's bowed 'em home five times now. They've made him favorite fur the Hammond against all them eastern babies."

There was genuine enthusiasm in his voice and I was filled with admiration for a spirit that could take a blow so jauntily. His attitude was undoubtedly the correct one, but I could not accomplish it. I thought of the five thousand dollars that went, with the floral horseshoe, to the winner of the Hammond stake. I thought of a gentle, fine, threadbare old man who needed that five thousand—Oh, so desperately—and I was filled with bitter regrets, with malice and bad words.

"Of course he'll win it!" I burst out spitefully.

"Why, I dunno," drawled Blister, and added: "I thought Judge Dillon was a friend of yours."

"Oh, damn!" I said.

"Why, Four Eyes!" said Blister. " 'N' Chick listenin' to you too!"

Chick grinned appreciatively.

"Don't let him kid ya," he advised. "He wasn't so gay hisself till—"

"Take a shot of grape juice," interrupted Blister, " 'n' hire a hall."

Chick's voice trailed off into unintelligible mutterings as he turned away.

"How about Mr. Sanford's colt?" I asked. "Have you still got him?"

To my astonishment Blister broke into one of his rare fits of laughter. He all but doubled up with unaccountable mirth.

"Say, Chick," he called when he could control his voice, "he wants to know if we still got the Sanford colt!"

Chick had turned a rather glum face our way; but at the words his expression became instantly joyous.

"Oh, say!" he said.

Then began a series of hilarious exchanges, entirely without meaning to me.

"He's hangin' round somewhere, ain't he, Chick?"

"Why, maybe he is," said Chick.

"You still throw a little rough feed into him occasionally, don't you, Chick?"

"When I got the time," said Chick; and the two imbeciles roared with laughter.

At last Blister began beating me between the shoulder blades.

"We got him, Four Eyes," he told me between thumps. "Yep—we got him."

"Stop!" I shouted. "What the devil's the matter with you?"

Blister became serious.

"Come here!" he said, and dragged me to a stall. He threw back the upper door and a shaft of sunlight streamed into the stall's interior, bathing a slim black head and neck until they glistened like a vein of coal. "Know him?" asked Blister.

"Yes," I said. "He's bigger though."

"Look at him good!" ordered Blister.

I peered at the relaxed inmate of the stall, who blinked sleepily at me through the shaft of sunlight. Blister pulled me back, closed the stall door, and tightened his grip on my arm.

"Now listen!" he said. "You just looked at the best two-year-old God ever put breath in!"

I took in this incredible information slowly. I exulted in it for a moment, and then came doubts.

"How do you know?" I demanded.

"How do I know!" exclaimed Blister. "It 'ud take me a week to tell you. Man, he can fly! He makes his first start tomorrow—in the Hammond. Old Man Sanford'll get in tonight. Come out 'n' see a real colt run."

My brain was whirling.

"In the Hammond?" I gasped. "Does Mr. Sanford know all this?"

Blister gave me a slow, a thoughtful look.

"It sounds nutty," he said, "but I can't figger it no other way. As sure as you 'n' me are standin' here—he knowed it from the very first!"

Until I closed my eyes that night I wondered whether Blister's words were true. If so, what sort of judgment, instinct, intuition, had been used that day at Thistle Ridge? I gave it up at last and slept, to dream of a colt that suddenly grew raven wings and soared over the grandstand while I nodded wisely and said: "Of course—the birthright of eagles!"

I got to Blister's stalls at one o'clock next day, and found Mr. Sanford clothed in a new dignity hard to describe. Perhaps he had donned it with the remarkable flowered waistcoat he wore—or was it due to his flowing double-breasted coat, a sprightly blue in color and suggesting inevitably a leather trunk, dusty, attic-bound, which had yawned and spat it forth?

"Welcome, suh; thrice welcome!" he said to me. "I take the liberty of presuming that the pu'ple and white is honored with yoh best wishes today."

I assured him that from the bottom of my heart this was so. He wrung my hand again and took out a gold watch the size of a bun.

"Three hours moh," he said, "before our hopes are realized or shattered."

"You think the colt will win?" I inquired.

Mr. Sanford turned to the southwest. I followed his eyes and saw a bank of evil-looking clouds creeping slowly up the sky.

"I like our chances, suh," he told me; "but it will depend on those clouds yondeh. We want a fast track foh the little chap. He is a swallow. Mud would break his heart."

"She's fast enough now," said Blister, who had joined us; and Mr. Sanford nodded.

So for three hours I watched the sky prayerfully and saw it become more and more ominous. When the bugle called for the Hammond at last, Latonia was shut off from the rest of the world by an inverted inky cup, its sides shot now and then with lightning flashes. We seemed to be in a great vacuum. I found my lungs snatching for each breath, while my racing card grew limp as I clutched it spasmodically in a sweating hand.

I had seen fit to take a vital interest in the next few moments; but I glanced at faces all about me in the grandstand and found them strained and unnatural. Perhaps in the gloom they seemed whiter than they really were; perhaps my own nerves pricked my imagination until this packed humanity became one beating heart.

I do not think that this was so. The dramatic moment goes straight to the soul of a crowd, and this crowd was to see the Hammond staged in a breathless dark, with the lightning's flicker for an uncertain spotlight.

No rain would spoil our chances that day, for now, across the center field at the half-mile post, a mass of colors boiled at the barrier. The purple and white was somewhere in the shifting, surging line, born by a swallow, so I had been told. Well, even so, the blue and gold was there likewise—and carried by what? Perhaps an eagle!

Suddenly a sigh—not the customary roar, but a deep, intaking of the grandstand's breath—told me they were on the wing. I strained my eyes at the blurred mass of them, which seemed to move slowly in the distance as it reached the far turn of the back stretch. Then a flash of lightning came and my heart skipped a beat and sank.

They were divided into two unequal parts. One was a crowded, indistinguishable mass. The other, far ahead in unassailable isolation, was a single spot of bay with a splash of color clinging above.

A roar of "Postman!" shattered the quiet like a bombshell, for that splash of color was blue and gold. The favorite was making a runaway race of it. He was coming home to twenty thousand joyful backers, who screamed and screamed his name.

Until that moment I had been the victim of a dream. I had come to believe that the little old man, standing silent at my side, possessed an insight more than human. Now I had wakened. He was an old fool in a preposterous coat and waistcoat, and I looked at him and laughed a mirthless laugh. He was squinting slightly as he peered with his washed-out eyes into the distance. His face was placid; and as I noticed that I told myself that he was positively witless. Then he spoke.

"The bay colt is better than I thought," he said.

"True," I agreed bitterly, and noted, as the lightning flashed again, that the blue and gold was an amazing distance ahead of those struggling mediocre others.

"A pretty race," murmured Old Man Sanford; and now I thought him more than doddering—he was insane.

Some seconds passed in darkness, while the grandstand gave off a contented murmur. Then suddenly the murmur rose to a new note. It held fear and consternation in it. My eyes leaped up the track. The bay colt had rounded the curve into the stretch. He was coming down the straight like a bullet; but—miracle of miracles!—it was plain that he was not alone. . . .

In a flash it came to me: stride for stride, on the far side of him, one other had maintained a flight equal to his own. And then I went mad; for this other, unsuspected in the darkness until now, commenced to creep slowly, surely, into the lead. Above his stretching neck his colors nestled proudly. He was bringing the purple and white safe home to gold and glory.

Nearer and nearer he came, this small demon whose coat matched the heavens, and so shot past us, with the great Postman—under the whip —two lengths behind him!

I remember executing a sort of bear dance, with Mr. Sanford enfolded in my embrace. I desisted when a smothered voice informed me that my conduct was "unseemly, suh—most unseemly!"

A rush to the track followed, where we found Blister, quite pale, waiting with a blanket. Suddenly the grandstand, which had groaned once and become silent, broke into a roar that grew and grew.

"What is it?" I asked.

Blister whirled and stared at the figures on the timing board. I saw a look of awe come into his face.

"What is it?" I repeated. "Why are they cheering? Is it the time?"

"Oh, no!" said Blister with scornful sarcasm and a look of pity at my ignorance. "It ain't the time!" He nodded at the figures. "That's only the world's record fur the age 'n' distance."

And now there came, mincing back to us on slender, nervous legs, something wet and black and wonderful. It pawed and danced wildly in a growing ring of curious eyes.

Then, just above the grandstand, the inky cup of the sky was broken and there appeared the light of an unseen sun. It turned the piled white clouds in the break to marvels of rose and gold. They seemed like the ramparts of heaven, set there to guard from earthly eyes the abode of the immortals.

"Whoa, man! Whoa, hon!" said Blister, and covered the heaving sides.

As he heard Blister's voice and felt the touch of the blanket the colt grew quiet.

His eyes became less fiery wild. He raised his head, with its dilated blood-red nostrils, and stared—not at the mortals standing reverently about him, but far beyond our gaze— through the lurid gap in the sky, straight into Valhalla.

I felt a hand on my arm.

"The look of eagles, suh!" said Old Man Sanford.

"We're starting somethin' new. It's called The-Bookie-of-the-Month Club."

DRAWING BY KETCHAM [© 1950 BY *Cosmopolitan* MAGAZINE]

Come On–My Horse!

PAUL GALLICO

Paul Gallico by his own admission knew less about horse racing than any other field of sport. For that one good reason the following excerpt from his Farewell To Sport, *written on his departure from the athletic arenas in 1941, is all the more interesting. The truth was, as proven by his writings since, he had better things to do. Nevertheless, Gallico put his finger on the lure of the turf as neatly as Eddie Arcaro slips through on the rail.*

ALL I know about the ancient and occasionally honorable sport of horse racing is the excitement of going down to the betting pits and watching money change hands. I probably knew and wrote less about horse racing than any other game. And I suspect that this may have been the case because the ponies always seemed to me inseparable from page upon page of tiny numerals in fine print, figures that smacked unpleasantly of mathematics, a subject that has been distasteful to me ever since I found out, in early youth, that it is true that it cannot and does not lie. I suppose if I set my mind to it I could read the chart of a race and gain a fairly comprehensive idea of how the race was won and the position of the horses throughout the trial. But the hieroglyphics of the sport have always repelled me and I could never bring myself to study a form chart or a clocker's tabulation or a solidly massed page of past performances.

Still, when I went to the races occasionally, I liked to bet and, above all, I liked to win, which I rarely did because I was always betting with scared and poor money, a trenchant race-track phrase. But I always recall vividly the thrill of taking my day's program to an expert, possibly some veteran turf writer, or a famous brother sports columnist whose specialty was the ponies, like Bill Corum, or Damon Runyon or Joe Wil-

liams, or perhaps one of the visiting millionaires or celebrities or politicians, who must surely be in contact with good information, and asking him to mark it for me with his choices. There are a great friendliness and generosity in racing people. They will always share tips, good things, information, hunches, etc., provided you are a gentleman about it and are not inclined to hold them personally if the tips do not mature. There is even an eagerness, almost, to pass these tips along as though they gained strength by having other supporters, or perhaps there is a propitiatory thought behind the kind deed. I do not recall ever having had any hesitancy or conscience about thus picking the brains of the experts—I was perfectly willing to swap hunches on the outcome of prize fights or football games—and I was always as happy as a child with my marked program, especially before the races were run. I always felt that I held a practical fortune in my hands. Those penciled check marks, or rings drawn around the exciting and intriguing names of horses, represented vast sums of money for which perhaps I should not have to do any work. Who could tell? A year in Europe and freedom and independence, time to travel and write a new book, a new car, a paying up of all debts, the feeling of having for the first time a lot of money that I could spend, if I liked, for new clothes, books, records for my collection, a lot of new dogs—perhaps a motorboat. . . .

There is no more thrilling place in the world than a race track unless it be the Mint, because there is so much money about. And in the Mint it lies in cold, austere, static, unapproachable piles. At the race track it is red hot, alive, pulsating, and constantly changing hands. You keep seeing it. Lucky bettors come away from paying windows with their fingers full of green- and yellow-backs which they stuff into their pockets without counting. Everyone in the long queues up to the betting grilles has money in his or her hands. The white numbers up on the great, black odds-and-results board mean money. Everyone is talking money, handling money, feeling money, making or losing money.

And the turnover is so rapid and satisfying. To anyone accustomed to earning money the hard way, through a week's work at an office or shop or factory in exchange for a predetermined amount in a pay envelope or a printed check, or three weeks' labor on a story or article and a month's delay until it is sold and turned into cash, the speed of the race track is utterly fascinating and sometimes completely demoraliz-ing. Everything is on a cash basis. Twenty minutes sees the whole transaction finished. You buy your pari-mutuel ticket or place your bet with the bookie and stroll out onto the lawn to see the ponies run, or, rather, to watch your investment mature—or fail.

The physical running of the race, once the seemingly interminable yet thrilling and nerve-tingling delays at the post are over, occupies from one to two and a half minutes. By the time you have wandered back to the betting ring, the pay-off is up on the boards, and the pay-off windows are open. The men serving them are crisp, pleasant and friendly. It is no money out of their pockets. They slap the pile of bills and loose breakage silver down on the counter and thrust it out at you, and there you have it. True, the action in the gambling house is even faster, where the spinning ball, the tumbling dice or the turned-up card can make your fortune in a few seconds. But anyone can go to the race track and very few can patronize gambling houses. The gambling rooms are too tense and solemn. They have an atmosphere all their own, but to me it lacks the thrill and the real money fever of the race track.

"George is pretty disgusted—he hasn't picked a winner in a month!"

Gallorette

JOE H. PALMER

Ben Jones, of Calumet Farm fame, once remarked that Edward Christmas' handling of Gallorette was a perfect example of being given a fine horse and doing everything right. The proof is in the story and the fact that the American Trainers' Association voted her at the top of the list of great race mares.

THERE are a good many ways of acquiring brood mares but most of them are expensive. One of the cheaper methods is just to let them follow you around. This was more or less the system which Preston M. Burch used in obtaining Gallette, the dam of Gallorette, winner of a little more than $100,000 under the red and yellow blocks of W. L. Brann. She was a daughter of Sir Gallahad III, and though in her racing years the fame of that stallion as a brood mare sire was not what it is now, it was still high enough that Gallette had reason to be valued for the stud. However, virtually every possible effort was made to throw her away.

She was bred by Belair Stud, out of the fine race mare and great producer Flambette. The mare had won the Latonia and Coaching Club American Oaks, and she was the grandam of the Triple Crown winner Omaha, as well as the Ascot Gold Cup winner Flares, and the stakes winners Fleam and Anaflame. Among her own stakes winners were Flambino, Flaming, and Cycle, and one of her daughters, La France, produced the stakes winners Johnstown and Jacola. This is a most productive family, but of course most of the horses mentioned above were still to come in 1930, when Gallette was a yearling, and she was weeded out and sent to Saratoga to be sold in the sales there.

William du Pont liked her well enough to pay $11,000 for her. This was not tremendously high, as some of the prices went that year, but it was enough to include her among the top 5 per cent of the offerings. She was turned over to Mr.

Burch to train, and he remembers her as being big, somewhat crooked, and with ankles inclined to be mushy. As a two-year-old not much could be made of her, and because of her size, Mr. Burch suggested laying her up for a season and trying to get her in shape at three. She was consequently sent back to the farm, fired, and turned out.

The next year she was schooled to jump and late in the season ran in a hurdle race, where she placed. Mr. du Pont did not like her, however, and put her in a sale in Virginia, where a man named C. M. Adams bought her for $250. She was taken up to the Genesee Valley in New York, where she became a lady's hack, and by all logic this should have been the end of her.

But in 1936, when she was seven, she was advertised for sale, along with another mare named Princess Athene, a four-year-old, in one of the racing dailies. Mr. Burch saw the advertisement and was not much interested, but after it ran for a week or so with no takers he began to consider buying her. Being busy himself, he sent his brother, the late Selby Burch, up to the Valley to see her. He reported that both were sound and able to win, and that the asking price was $3,500 for the two. A deal was finally made at $2,500. Mr. Burch sent them to Kentucky and put them in charge of Price Sallee, who got Gallette to the races at Louisville. She raced in claiming races and was once second, once third. Several people wanted to buy her, and Trainer Sallee notified Mr. Burch that if he ran her again to be claimed he would lose her. So she was taken out of training, and the next year Mr. Burch traded a mare to Adolphe Pons for a season to Ariel, to whom she foaled her first, and only, colt. As to the earlier deal, Mr. Burch got out when Princess Athene was claimed for $3,500.

At about this time W. L. Brann, having bred Challedon out of a Sir Gallahad III mare, was understandably looking for more daughters of that stallion to breed to Challenger II. By this time Sir Gallahad III mares were very much at a premium and he couldn't find any. Mr. Burch, who has never bred horses on a large scale, suggested that he use Gallette. Mr. Brann tried first to buy, then to lease her, but Mr. Burch would do neither, so ultimately an arrangement was worked out whereby she would be bred annually to Challenger II, with Mr. Brann taking the first foal, Mr. Burch the next, as long as the agreement remained suitable to both.

Mr. Brann got a good early return on the deal when Gallette foaled, on February 7, 1942 at his Glade Valley Farm near Frederick, Maryland, the chestnut filly which came to the races as Gallorette. The next foal, also a filly, was the 1945 two-year-old Galladare, which of course belonged to Mr. Burch but was leased to Brookmeade Stable for racing purposes. Mr. Brann has a yearling filly now, and the mare was barren for 1946. In 1947, Mr. Burch hopes for her first colt by Challenger II, this prize being a matter of amicable rivalry between the two men.

Gallorette was trained by Edward A. Christmas, and being a big, growthy sort of filly was not brought out until late, making her first start at Laurel Park on September 14, 1944. This was in a maiden race at six furlongs, and she was third to M. B. Goff's Director, a Pilate gelding with Glen Riddle Farm's War Trophy second.

About a week later she ran again, this time at 5½ furlongs, and won by two lengths over a slow track, ridden by Douglas Dodson. Chronoflite was second, Four Queens third, and there were eight unplaced. The filly opened up a formidable lead early and was under hand riding at the end. She was out again on September 28 and cantered to her field, winning by six lengths from Run Bud Run.

On October 4 she ran for the Maryland Futurity, in which every starter but two was by Challenger II. One of these was the winner, however, this being R. A. Johnson's Petee Dee, by Petee-Wrack. Gallorette moved up on the inside in the stretch and held the lead briefly, just failing to last.

Gallorette won her next start, an allowance race at a mile and seventy yards, beating Sweet Chimes and Price Level, the latter one of the leading two-year-old fillies of the year. Next she tried for the Selima Stakes, and was beaten to third behind Busher and Ace Card, with such

good ones as Subdued, Monsoon, and Recce behind her.

She started twice more at two, finishing second both times. The first of these was in the Johnny Podgajny Purse, a six-furlong race named aptly for a pitcher for the Baltimore Orioles, which that season occupied the almost undivided attention of Pimlico's president, Henry A. Parr III. Whether this name was put on a six-furlong race because Podgajny sometimes did not go much beyond six innings is perhaps neither here nor there. Gallorette at any rate was beaten a half-length by Monsoon, after holding a short lead in the stretch. In her last race of the year she caught Brookfield Farm's Brookfield at his best, and he beat her nearly four lengths, after she had caught him at the furlong pole.

At three she was a vastly improved filly. She spent the intervening winter at Aiken, and she was ready for action on May 22, when she ran in an allowance race at six furlongs. Hoop Jr., also making his first start of the year, was an odds-on favorite, and for nearly a half-mile he led the field. Then Eddie Arcaro let out a wrap on Gallorette, which had been in second place, and she went past the favorite in such a fashion that Bobby Permane was reported to have said later that the wind almost sucked him out of the saddle. She won by nearly two lengths from Hitem, with War Trophy third, Hoop Jr. fourth.

She ran next for the Wood Memorial and was drawn in the first division. She ran well, taking the lead in midstretch, but she could not hold off Col. C. V. Whitney's Jeep. The Mahmoud colt was at his best in the early season and he beat her two lengths, with Dockstader third, Flood Town, War Jeep, Greek Warrior, and others among the unplaced.

In the Acorn Stakes at Belmont on June 7 Gallorette was second choice to the Whitney entry of Monsoon and Recce. The latter cut out a fast pace, with Gallorette second, Monsoon lying third to come up if her stablemate tired. When Gallorette subdued Recce, however, Monsoon was not quite able to the task, and Arcaro brought the Brann filly in winner by a length and a half, Monsoon and Recce in the next two places.

On June 16 Arcaro was busy with Devil Diver in the Suburban and George Woolf rode Gallorette in the Pimlico Oaks, which she won by three-fourths of a length from Recce, after being carried a little wide in the stretch. Be Faithful was third.

The Delaware Oaks, on June 28, was the occasion of Gallorette's next start, and with Arcaro in the saddle again she was held at three to five. Monsoon was given the best chance at her, but the field also included William Helis' Elpis, winner of the Coaching Club American Oaks.

Gallorette took the lead after about three furlongs, held Elpis safe well into the stretch, and
then drew out steadily to win by three lengths,
with something in reserve. Elpis beat Monsoon
a half-length for second place, and the other two
starters were outrun.

Gallorette left her own division in her next
start, for the Dwyer at Aqueduct, meeting some
of the better colts. Arcaro took the mount on
Pavot in this race, and Arnold Kirkland rode
Gallorette. William Ziegler Jr.'s Esteem ran his
best race of the season in this event, taking the
lead early and holding it into the last furlong.
Gallorette, never very far away, gradually
brought him to bay, and as she took the lead
seemed to have the race won. Down on the outside, however, came Ted Atkinson on Wildlife,
and the Easton colt beat her a nose on the post.
Esteem was a half-length farther back and nothing else was close.

The filly met Pavot again a week later in the
Empire City Stakes at Jamaica, this being a
$50,000 race at 1 3⁄16 miles. With Atkinson now
the rider, she was a strong second choice to the
Jeffords entry of Pavot and Red Stick, with
Esteem given some chance. Pavot ran an excellent race, taking a long lead early, and holding
on well. Gallorette came up in the stretch to pass
him but Pavot was not yet through. He fought
back gamely and went back to the filly's throat—
for a stride or so he seemed on even terms. This
time Gallorette was not to be denied, and she
came again stoutly to beat him three-fourths of
a length and was ready to draw clear. The outsider, Post Graduate, was third, and the race was
run in the creditable time of 1:56⅕.

By this time Gallorette was regarded as the
best filly in the East, and she would have been
given a good chance at any of the colts as well.
The star of Busher was just beginning to rise,
and an attempt was made to arrange a special
race between the two in Chicago, for a $25,000
purse. Gallorette had, however, been eased in
training a little after her two hard races, and
her owner and trainer, after dallying with the
idea for a day or so, decided against the special,
feeling that it would be difficult to get her quite
tight in time for it.

This may perhaps have been as well, for Gallorette never got back to her form again at three.
She returned to action in the Jersey Handicap at
Garden State Park on August 25 and was odds-
on. However, after thrusting up to the lead in
midstretch she faltered badly and finished fifth,
though she was beaten only about three lengths
in all, the winner being Trymenow. She was giving actual weight to all the field except Bobanet,
and was giving him four pounds by the scale.

She ran much the same way in the Discovery
Handicap on September 8. This time her stretch
run took her to second place, but she weakened

again and in the last furlong dropped back to
finish seventh of eleven. Bobanet won this race
but was disqualified, moving War Jeep into first
place.

Something seemed obviously wrong with the
filly, though no one could tell what, and she was
given another rest of about a month and a half,
and was brought back at Pimlico in a 1 1⁄16-mile
overnight handicap on October 27. She stayed
within striking distance of the lead all the way,
but was unable to rally in the stretch, finishing
fifth under 124 pounds, back of Salvo (four,
120), Polynesian (three, 126), He Rolls (seven,
115), and Gypster (four, 115).

She returned to New York for the Westchester
Handicap on November 3 and ran well up all
the way, but when Olympic Zenith and Buzfuz
started fighting seriously for the lead she could
not keep up to them. Stymie came down with a
rush to win the race, and Gallorette was fourth,
beaten about four lengths.

Her principal remaining engagement was in
the Pimlico Special, and in preparation for this
she ran in an overnight handicap at 1 1⁄8 miles,
carrying 113 pounds. She ran down the pacemaking Rampart and took the lead at the head of
the stretch. She could not hold Armed (128) in
the last furlongs, however, and he drew away to
win easily. The filly weakened at the end and
Rampart came again to beat her a head for
second place. Good Blood and Milcave were the
only others.

This was indication enough she would have no
chance at Armed at scale weights, and she was
the utter outsider for the Pimlico Special. She
ran a little better than expectation, finishing
fourth behind Armed, First Fiddle, and Stymie,
but beating War Date, Polynesian, and Pot o'
Luck.

Her tabulated record:

Year	Age	Starts	First	Second	Third	Unpl.	Won
1944	2	8	3	3	2	0	$ 7,950
1945	3	13	5	2	1	5	94,300
		21	8	5	3	5	$102,250

Gallorette's 1945 season divides into two parts.
The first section, through her victory in the Empire City Stakes, shows seven starts, five wins,
and two hard-running seconds. The second, after
she had been out of action for a little over a
month, shows six starts and only one third in a
small field. There is no obvious way to reconcile
these two sections, except on the premise that
she never really regained her form. From a filly
of her breeding, her conformation, and her performances at two, one would have expected her
to be better in the fall than in the early season.

It is possible that her race in the Jersey Handicap knocked her out. The track at Garden State
Park was in bad condition then, because of

literally weeks of rain at the beginning of the meeting, and a hard race over it, after a month's idleness, may have taken too much out of her. This was, at least, a tentative theory on the part of her trainer, for the filly did not seem sore or lame in her later starts but simply failed to display the power or the stamina of her earlier ones.

Any estimate of Gallorette's class must necessarily be based on her first seven starts. Had she run merely one or two good races it might be possible to hold them in light esteem, for it is not exactly unusual for a horse to turn in an outstanding performance which he can never duplicate. But she ran consistently well over a period of two months. During that time she was easily master of the fillies which opposed her, and she held her own against the colts.

She was a rugged, strong filly, with big joints and a good frame, very much of the type usually associated with Challenger II. Her head was very good and her expression feminine, but otherwise she was a rather masculine type of filly. Some of the Challengers are reported to be a little headstrong but this did not seem to be true of Gallorette; she was easy enough to handle.

The record of Gallorette would be remarkable, standing alone, for she won $261,410 in three seasons, and among her sex was third to Busher and Top Flight in earnings. But Top Flight won the greater part of her total at two, when her sheer speed made her unbeatable, and even Busher, who on some occasions took on handicap horses, won a great proportion of her money in races for two- and three-year-olds, in which she was to some extent protected by the conditions.

Gallorette, however, built up considerably more than half of her earnings in 1946, when she was pitted against the top handicappers of her time—Stymie, Pavot, Lucky Draw, First Fiddle, and the like—and sometimes carried actual top weight. She was, in other words, set somewhat more difficult tasks than were given Busher or Top Flight, and there have been few mares to make such a success in the handicap ranks. She missed one $50,000 race, for instance, trying to give Lucky Draw eleven pounds, and even so hustled him into a new track record. She was one of the few horses of either sex to lose the lead to Stymie and regain it through the stretch.

Not many fillies have the build or the constitution to bear up under the 1946 campaign she had. Gallorette was big, standing a trifle over 16.1, and rugged to go with it. She was perfectly sound, and if she trained off a little toward the end of both seasons, why so do the best of the handicappers after a comparable campaign. . . .

Her first start in 1946 came at Jamaica April 27, in the 1 1/16-mile Excelsior Handicap. She had top weight except for Murlogg Farm's Fighting Step, which eventually outgamed King Dorsett

and won by a half-length. Gallorette, with Arnold Kirkland up, ran a fairly good race to be fourth, being unable to gain on the leaders in the stretch.

She was fourth again in the Grey Lag Handicap May 4, but gave a somewhat better showing. She led for six furlongs and then dropped back, with Stymie winning from Bounding Home in track record time, 1:49⅗.

As a result of these two defeats she got into the Metropolitan Handicap on May 11 with 110 pounds, and Job Dean Jessop did the riding. The favorite was the Sunshine Stable entry of Buzfuz and Lets Dance, which finished eleventh and thirteenth, with Gallorette at nearly ten to one. She was away slowly, and was given time to find her stride before working forward, and in the stretch she came willingly and just at the end was up to beat Sirde (124) a nose. First Fiddle (126) was third, and the field also included Fighting Step (123) and Polynesian (126).

On May 24 Gallorette was odds-on for the overnight Nimba Handicap, also at a mile, and she won quite easily from Mahmoudess, Darby Dunedin, and others, again with Jessop up. In the Top Flight Handicap May 29 she had top weight of 128 pounds and was apparently anchored under it, finishing fifth. Sicily, under 113 pounds, was winner by a neck from Surosa (113), with Recce (118) third and the three-year-old Earshot (110) fourth. Gallorette was bothered somewhat in the stretch when Surosa bore over.

She was shipped to Delaware Park for the Sussex Handicap, and by way of preparation for it ran in an allowance race June 11 at 1 1/16 miles, winning easily from War Trophy, which she was giving six pounds. She was in front all the way. In the Sussex, however, Pavot beat her two lengths, carrying 115 pounds to the filly's 113. Stymie (126) was third, a length behind her.

In the Brooklyn she had 118 pounds, against 128 on Stymie, a five-pound advantage when the sex allowance is counted off, and the other weights ranged from 102 to 110. Helioptic set the pace, but Gallorette was ready to take the running from him at the top of the stretch. At this point Stymie was circling the field, and he got up just as Gallorette took over. It did not look that way from the stand, but Jessop said afterward that Stymie was a half-length ahead at one stage. The filly fought desperately, regained the lead nearing the furlong-pole, and lasted under pressure to win by a neck. Stymie was nearly five lengths ahead of Burning Dream, with five others unplaced. The 1¼ mile course was run in 2:05.

Under 119 pounds in the Massachusetts Handicap July 4, Gallorette was giving Pavot (120) four by the scale, and actual weight to everything else except Sirde (121). It was Sirde which followed the early pace, moving to the lead in the

Gallorette, with J. D. Jessop up, scores a length-and-a-quarter victory over Hornbeam, Ted Atkinson in the saddle, to win the Wilson Stakes at Saratoga, August 4, 1947. King Dorsett, with Bobby Permane up, is third. Gallorette set a track record of 1:35⅗ for the mile to thrill a record crowd of 15,795. [UPI]

stretch, but Pavot, coming from a little farther back, won by more than two lengths. Dinner Party (113) was up to get second, with Gallorette third. She had gained in the last quarter, and one thrust had taken her to second but she tired a little near the end.

In the Butler, under 116 pounds, she seemed a certain winner seventy yards out, since Stymie was running too late to catch her. But it was in this race that Lucky Draw found himself, and he was down at the end under a feather of 105 pounds to beat the filly a head. Stymie was third, and Lucky Draw broke the 1 3/16-mile record at Jamaica, going the route in 1:55⅕.

Rated by the scale she was exactly even with Pavot (126) in the Wilson on August 5, Gallorette carrying 121. She was going faster at the end but just failed to catch him, losing by a neck. Larky Day (112) was third, and in the field were Stymie (120), Lucky Draw (126), and other good ones. On August 19 she tried to give two actual pounds to King Dorsett (119) and Stymie (119) in an allowance race and they both beat her, with no other starters. The track was sloppy, which was not to her liking, and when she was hopelessly beaten Jessop eased her.

For the Bay Shore Handicap at Aqueduct September 9 she had 124 pounds, came up from behind to catch King Dorsett (120) in the stretch and beat him a neck. Polynesian (130) was a length and a half away third, and the others were lightweights.

The Edgemere represented something of a peak as far as weights were concerned. She had 123 pounds, which was not the most she had carried, but she had to give two pounds to Stymie (121), and from nineteen to six to the others. Stymie moved up faster than usual and ran through the stretch in a fashion Gallorette could not quite match. She made one good run at him, failed, and dropped back. She was second, beaten nearly two lengths, with King Dorsett third.

The richest race since the Brooklyn came for her in Beldame Handicap at Aqueduct September 21. The race was run in two divisions, Bridal Flower winning the other, and Gallorette's was the fastest by four-fifths of a second. She had top weight of 126 pounds, moved up on the back stretch to take the lead, came in ridden out to win by a half-length from War Date (113), with Kay Gibson (three, 105) third. Her share of the purse was $39,300, and she ran the 1⅛ miles in 1:51⅖ through very deep slop. She was, in fact, running through two or three inches of water, since a small stream was running along the rail for eight or ten feet out.

This, however, was her last success, and she ran without showing her best form in her three closing races. She ran against Lucky Draw at level weight in the Sysonby Special at Belmont October 12, and the point was not that she was

beaten, but that she could make no sort of race of it. Lucky Draw ran off and hid from her, winning by twelve lengths.

She ran in the Trenton Handicap at Garden State Park October 26, and could keep in contention only for about five furlongs. Then she dropped back to finish eighth of twelve, Turbine winning the race from Polynesian.

She ran again November 9 in the Westchester Handicap and was last of six. She had shipped to Pimlico with the Special in prospect, but did not come up to it in good condition and missed the engagement. She had apparently recovered for the Westchester, but she ran only six furlongs and then dropped back, with Assault winning from Lucky Draw.

Shortly after the Westchester she was shipped, with the rest of the Brann Stable, to Aiken again for the winter. Her tabulated record:

Year	Age	Starts	First	Second	Third	Unpl.	Won
1944	2	8	3	3	2	0	$ 7,950
1945	3	13	5	2	1	5	94,300
1946	4	18	6	5	2	5	159,160
		39	14	10	5	10	$261,410

Top Flight's money-winning record in the filly and mare division was set in 1932, and her figure of $275,900 stayed unapproached until 1945. Had Twilight Tear trained in that year it might have been broken twice since she had $202,165 at the beginning of the season. Though Twilight Tear went out of action, Louis B. Mayer's brilliant Busher swept to a new mark of $334,035. In 1947 W. L. Brann's Gallorette pushed this up to $351,685. This is not necessarily the end, since Gallorette may be trained again, and even if she is not, Bewitch has more than $200,000, going into her three-year-old season.

There is a remarkable difference in the three latest title holders. Top Flight got her eminence largely through a brilliant undefeated two-year-old campaign, in which she won seven stakes in seven tries, including the Futurity and the Pimlico Futurity, and earned the $219,000 which still remains the record for a two-year-old. At three she always beat the fillies she met, winning the Acorn, Oaks, Arlington Oaks, Alabama Stakes, and the Ladies' Handicap, but she could not win any of her races against colts. The season yielded a comparatively small $56,900.

Busher had a successful two-year-old season, winning three stakes and two other races from seven starts, but she confined her stakes efforts to the filly division, and earned only $60,300. Her three-year-old season was the brilliant one, since she won ten of thirteen starts and ran her total to $334,035, getting most of it by going into the handicap division and beating such as Armed and others.

Gallorette had a most moderate two-year-old

season, a good but not sensational three-year-old career, at the end of which she had won only slightly more than $100,000. She got the rest of her total by slugging it out, over a two-year period, with Assault and Stymie, Lucky Draw, Pavot and others.

Top Flight was a marvelously precocious two-year-old. Busher was one of the most brilliant three-year-old fillies of the last decade, at least. Gallorette was primarily a handicapper, a campaigner, tough, hardy, sound, and combative. It is virtually certain she could have done nothing with Top Flight at two, and doubtful she could have handled Busher at three. But one suspects she could have taken them both apart at four. What Gallorette did has hardly been attempted by any mare since Esposa. . . .

After her third winter at Aiken, where she prospered hugely, she came back to the races at Jamaica on April 19, in the six-furlong Fighting Fox Handicap. There were five starters, and bettors picked them just as they came. Polynesian, at odds-on, won nicely from the second choice Buzfuz, and Tidy Bid was third choice and third. Gallorette, with Jessop up, finished fourth and worked out a mile in 1:42⅗. Larky Day was the other.

If this was a conditioner for the Excelsior Handicap on April 26 it failed in its purpose, for Gallorette, this time with H. B. Wilson, ran indifferently and finished fifth, behind Coincidence, Polynesian, Lets Dance, and Calvados. She was never in the hunt, as far as the leaders went. But this was the last time, until November, that she ran without getting part of the purse.

Charley Givens was the rider in the Metropolitan, which she had won in 1946. She had 116 pounds, and ran rather well to be third. She had a little bad luck and passed it on. As she moved in the stretch she was bumped by Buzfuz, which was beginning to fail, and as she swerved out she bumped Stymie in the middle of his run. He went on to win by a length from Brown Mogul (112), and Gallorette saved third from Buzfuz. Back in the field were such as Pavot and Lets Dance.

On June 2 she won her first stakes of the year, the Queens County Handicap at a mile and a sixteenth. She had 119 pounds, which was topped by the scale only by Stymie, which had 128. Jessop kept her close to the pace, sent her to the lead in the stretch. Stymie was at her head in the last furlong, but Gallorette fought hard and increased her advantage a little, beating him a neck. The purse was $14,950, and it was a milestone for Gallorette. It ran her all-time earnings to $279,185, and thus took her past Top Flight's old mark. Among the fillies, only Busher, with $334,035, lay ahead. Gallorette crept up by inches, but she crept.

The Carter Handicap, a seven-furlong dash at Aqueduct on June 7, found her top weight at 123 pounds. Basil James was the rider and she was a slight favorite. She began slowly, then came fast through the stretch, but Rippey (112), suited by the distance and his weight, won by a neck from Inroc (118), with Gallorette third. Behind her were Tidy Bid, Pellicle, and others, and the race was run, in slop, in 1:23.

Her next race was the overnight Capra Handicap, where she had 128 pounds. The others were Kay Gibson (108), Elpis (114), and Rytina (109). Gallorette was ridden by Eric Guerin, who kept her behind Rytina's early pace and brought her on around the last turn. Gallorette came willingly, and won without much trouble from Kay Gibson, with Elpis third.

In the Butler Handicap of 1946 Gallorette had just about settled the issue with Stymie when along came Lucky Draw under a feather to beat her a nose. In the 1947 running she had 117 pounds, and had Assault (135) as well as Stymie (126) to beat. She was just ready to take Risolater when Stymie and Assault ranged up outside her. Assault was pinched in between the other two, and if Gallorette could have held on to the finish he could hardly have won. But as he started coming through a very tight hole, Gallorette came to the end of her strength. This left Assault room, and he went on to beat Stymie a head, with Gallorette third, about two lengths farther back.

In her next start, Gallorette left New York for the only time during the season there. She went down to Monmouth Park to try for the Monmouth Handicap, in which she was the starting highweight with 119 pounds except for Polynesian (127). The latter had bad racing luck and Gallorette, which seemed about to run over horses in midstretch, flattened near the end and was third, behind Round View (112), and Talon (112). The time, 2:01⅕, was a new track record, but Gallorette was beaten about eight lengths. She got $2,500 in second place, and this ran her winnings to $294,085, putting her hard on Busher's trail. One big one would do it.

Gallorette cut the gap materially with the Wilson Stakes, at Saratoga August 4. She did not have a particularly good field to beat, the others being Hornbeam, King Dorsett, Bridal Flower, and Brown Mogul. Except that the latter was two pounds overweight, all starters would have had 112 pounds. Jessop rode Gallorette, and he let her run a while before asking her to level. When he did the mare came brilliantly, cut down the leaders, and won by a length and a half from Hornbeam. Her time was excellent, being 1:35⅗ for the mile, but it must be added that Saratoga had made its racing surface even largely by taking most of the cushion off. The purse was $16,350, and it pushed Gallorette past the $300,000 mark, the exact total being $310,435. Now even a middle-sized one would do it.

But Gallorette consistently failed to win any middle-sized ones. She ran a good, hard courageous race in the Whitney Stakes, at a mile and a quarter, dueling with Rico Monte all through the last quarter-mile. She was getting a pound, or four less than her sex would have entitled her to in a weight for age race. To the last forty yards either could have won, but in the last few strides Rico Monte pushed out to win by a head. But there was still $5,000 for Gallorette, and her old rival, Stymie, was two lengths behind her.

She had another try at Rico Monte in the Saratoga Handicap, this time getting two pounds from him, with Boss the only other starter. The race was run almost exactly as the Whitney had been, Gallorette leading into the stretch, fighting hard with Rico Monte up to the very end, and going under to him by a neck. Guerin, who rode her, lodged a claim of foul against the winner, but the stewards saw no interference and the result stood. Rico Monte had wedged inside her through the stretch, but Gallorette, on the outside, had had room to run.

Gallorette had 122 pounds in the Aqueduct Handicap, on September 1, getting ten from Stymie, which was about what she had needed to beat him in 1946, and she was giving weight to all the others. She ran well from the beginning, and was best of the others, but she could not quite contain Stymie's stretch run, and was beaten a half-length. Elpis (114) was third, Bridal Flower (114) fourth. Second money was $5,000, and this brought her total to $326,475. Just a little one would do it.

But Gallorette could not manage a little one. She had 122 pounds again for the Edgemere Handicap September 13, at a mile and a furlong, and this time was getting twelve pounds from Stymie. That she got anything at all was largely because there were only four horses in the race. Stymie's stretch run failed by a length and a half to catch Elpis, and Bridal Flower, which had headed Gallorette after a long struggle and had caught Elpis once in the stretch, was third. Gallorette was fourth and last, for $1,250.

Busher was now almost certainly in reach, and when Gallorette started for the Beldame Handicap on September 20 she needed no more than second place. She was drawn in the top division, and had the high weight, 126, which was the same situation Miss Grillo had in the other division. Each of them finished second. Gallorette, with Jessop up, followed the pace closely, closed in on the leading Risolater in the stretch. Snow Goose, a three-year-old under 106 pounds, was running through the stretch like a gray wraith, and she overwhelmed Gallorette by nearly three lengths. But the latter, second by more than two lengths from Camargo, was the new money-winning leader of her sex. The $10,000 in second

money had lifted her at last past Busher, to a new total of $337,685.

Try as she would, Gallorette could not improve on this race. In the Ladies' Handicap, on October 7, she ran well again, but not well enough to be better than third, behind Snow Goose and But Why Not, but ahead of Elpis, Miss Grillo, Cosmic Missile, and others.

In the Scarsdale, November 1, she handled Stymie well enough, but she could never catch nor seriously threaten With Pleasure, which gave her seven pounds by the scale and beat her two lengths. She was a half-length ahead of Double Jay at the finish, and the field included little else except Stymie, which was in one of his moody spells.

She started again on the last Saturday of the New York season, in the $50,000 Westchester, and here ran one of her worst races. She had 118 pounds, and chased With Pleasure into the stretch, and with a furlong to go was only a half length behind him. But here she tired and horses went past. She finished fifth, as Bridal Flower got up to beat With Pleasure, and Donor and Lets Dance also were ahead of Gallorette. She did, however, beat Cosmic Bomb, which apparently did not like the sloppy track and put in one of his poor efforts.

Gallorette closed her season—it might very well have been her final start—in the Byran and O'Hara Memorial Handicap on Bowie's closing day, November 29. She had 124 pounds, got two by the scale from the three-year-old Double Jay, and gave heavy concessions to the five others. With Arnold Kirkland up, she was slightly favored, but for the first six furlongs she was kept in tight quarters. Leaving the back stretch she bulled her way through between horses and set out for the pacemaking Double Jay. She caught him in the upper stretch, and though she could not shake him off she held him to the end. But outside this struggle came Double Jay's running mate Incline, under 107 pounds, and he was along to beat them both three-fourths of a length. Considering her early trouble, she was probably best, even at the weights.

It will of course be noted that though Gallorette was the new leading money-winner of her sex, she backed into the honor with second, third, and fourth monies, earned in eight of her last nine starts. However, one suspects that Gallorette was well past her peak in 1947, and the fact remains that she was one of the gamest mares of her time and perhaps the toughest.

Her tabulated record:

Year	Age	Starts	1st	2nd	3rd	Unpl.	Won
1944	2	8	3	3	2	0	$ 7,950
1945	3	13	5	2	1	5	94,300
1946	4	18	6	5	2	5	159,160
1947	5	18	3	6	5	4	90,275
		57	17	16	10	14	$351,685

ART AND THE HORSE
a Portfolio of Artists' Impressions

RAOUL DUFY, *Le Paddock à Deauville*

ABOVE

Sketch of a horse. Limestone. EGYPTIAN, XXVI
  DYNASTY

RIGHT

Greek vase, VI CENTURY, B.C. *Horse Race,*
  ATHENIAN

[BOTH, COURTESY OF THE METROPOLITAN MUSEUM OF ART]

Broadside, North Carolina, 1817

EDGAR DEGAS, *Race Horses* [COURTESY MUSEUM OF FINE ARTS, BOSTON]

EDGAR DEGAS, *Head of a Horse. Pencil*
[COURTESY METROPOLITAN MUSEUM OF ART]

A SET OF CURRIER & IVES PRINTS
OF AMERICAN RACE HORSES

THE GRAND RACER KINGSTON, BY SPENDTHRIFT

A CLOSE LAP ON THE RUN IN.

GRAND ISLAND JOCKEY CLUB
THE FUTURITY RACE AT SHEEPSHEAD BAY.

READY FOR THE SIGNAL.
THE CELEBRATED RUNNING HORSE HARRY BASSETT, BY LEXINGTON, DAM CANARY BIRD.

PAINTINGS BY VAUGHN FLANNERY

—noted artist and observer of the American racing scene.

The Marquee, Belmont [FROM THE COLLECTION OF THE HONORABLE AND MRS. JOHN HAY WHITNEY]

The Seven Furlong Chute, Saratoga [COURTESY KRAUSHAAR GALLERIES, NEW YORK]

Repainting the Weathervane, Pimlico
[FROM THE COLLECTION OF THE MARYLAND JOCKEY CLUB]

Two studies of Steeplechasers at Fair Hills, Md. [COURTESY KRAUSHAAR GALLERIES, NEW YORK]

EDWARD TROYE (*1808–74*), *the outstanding painter of the horse in America during the 19th century, was born in Switzerland of French parentage, and came to the United States as a young man. Some three hundred of Troye's officially commissioned portraits survive; two are shown here.* TRANBY (*top picture*) *was a famous English race horse, foaled in 1826 and imported to America in 1835.* REEL (*bottom picture*) *was the snow-white dam of Glencoe, another English import of the 1830s and one of the most influential progenitors of American racing stock* [FROM THE COLLECTION OF THE JOCKEY CLUB, NEW YORK CITY]

Racing for the Rubles

JOHN GODLEY, LORD KILBRACKEN

If it hadn't been for John D. Schapiro and the Washington, D.C., International Handicap run over his Laurel Race Course, the American idea of Russian horses would be that they are good for pulling sleighs. Although they haven't proved otherwise in international competition so far, the following article gives us an insight on mutuel action on the steppes.

WHEN I was in Moscow recently on a journalistic assignment, I took a day off from sputniks and Khrushchev to go to the trotting races at the Hippodrome. These races are different in Russia from the ones we know—curiously enough, they are not all sulky races, the horses being sometimes ridden just like our flat races. This lends them a little extra excitement. With me I took Valia, the young and pretty girl interpreter who had been placed at my disposal by Intourist. I could have gone alone if I wished, but I felt her services would be indispensable, even though she'd never been to the races before and didn't know a furlong from a fetlock.

The Hippodrome is little more than a mile from Red Square, at the far end of Gorky Street. The first race was at one o'clock, but I couldn't leave till 1:30, and our taxi then made slow progress through the holidaying crowds in the streets. It was the day after the anniversary of the Bolshevik revolution and the whole city was still celebrating. Four races had been decided by the time we reached the course, but there were 12 on the program—one every 15 or 20 minutes —so I had lots of time to lose my money.

It was a brilliantly clear day. The long grandstand with its peeling yellow paint and crumbling ornamented decorations seemed to belong to the 19th century, as though it hadn't been painted or changed in any way since before the revolu-tion. And very likely it hadn't been. There weren't many spectators, and almost all were men, most of them, it seemed, in black hats and black overcoats. In front of this peeling grandstand was the oval dirt track and, beyond it, a looming backdrop, rose the gray skyscrapers of Moscow.

Admission to the most expensive enclosure was only eight rubles—the equivalent of 80¢ at the effective rate of exchange. Cheaper stands, I had noticed, cost four rubles and two rubles. Valia and I, however, got into the best enclosure for nothing, by presenting two of the sightseeing coupons provided by Intourist before I left London.

The race cards informed me that I was attending the Bolshie Races, in honor of the "Fortieth Anniversary of the Great October Socialist Revolution." I turned without delay to look at the list of horses for the next race. It's difficult enough, God knows, to pick a winner at the best of times, and I now found myself faced with choosing from the following:

1. Игла
2. Бравый
3. Ветряк
4. Нагиб
5. Избалованный
6. Лирик

Seeking some kind of guidance, I asked Valia the meaning of the three lines of print at the top of the page. She had to ask for help to get an exact, knowledgeable translation, and she then wrote it down for me as follows: "Fifth run. 2:10 P.M. For foal and mare of eldest age. Distance 1,600 m., 900 points (540–270–90)." It wasn't any good my complaining that the foal-and-mare-of-eldest-age part didn't mean a thing; she insisted that was what it said. (I found out later that it was a race for colts and fillies over four years old.) The distance, 1,600 meters, would be once around the track, 11 yards short of a mile.

I asked about the points.

"That is prize money," Valia said. "Each point is worth 80 kopecks. The winning jockey receives 540 points, so he gets 432 rubles. The second and third jockeys get 270 points and 90 points respectively."

I didn't understand why they couldn't just put down the prize money in rubles, but instead I asked, tactlessly: "And how about the owners? How much prize money do they receive?"

"Gospodin Kilbracken!" said Valia indignantly. "All horses belong to the state!"

All horses, anyway, were now lined up for the start; I relinquished the struggle for the moment and let the race go by without a bet. Игла went out into a long lead, but Лирик, who seemed to have a great many supporters, was always well placed, and swept to the front at the distance. The phlegmatic Russians didn't show much excitement, but there was scattered cheering as he neared the winning post. His supporters were counting their winnings when Нагиб came from nowhere and won by a neck in a very thrilling finish. There were the usual complaints all round, such as I have heard on race tracks all over the world when a favorite is narrowly beaten, and I turned my attention immediately to the vital problem of finding the next winner.

We had watched the race from the rails, amongst a group of young men who had all backed Нагиб. Valia now asked them for some information on the next race, which was one of the two biggest of the day, worth 1,500 points to the winning jockey. They were all very helpful when they heard I came from Ireland, with the intense curiosity about the West which I had generally found in Russia. Like true racegoers, however, they realized that the only thing which mattered right then was the next winner. My personal inclination was for Ловкач, which means Clever Boy—or that's how Valia translated it, anyway. Clever Boy's rider, Master Jockey Tarasov, had a son riding in the same race, and with only seven runners I thought the Tarasovs would share the spoils. My friends on the rails, however, scouted the idea, especially a short little man in a white cap, who refused to tell me his name but who seemed extremely confident. He said it would be a pushover for Контакт, which is pronounced "contact" and means contact. The others agreed so confidently that I asked Valia to back Contact for me: ten rubles on the nose.

Valia, I could tell, disapproved of betting on principle, though I could see the idea fascinated her all the same. She joined the line at the parimutuel window rather as though she were lining up for opium. Ten rubles ($1) is the minimum stake, and I saw no signs of anything approaching heavy betting; 100 rubles would be considered a very big wager. The tote, Valia told me, keeps only 2 per cent; needless to say, there are no bookies. I really wasn't surprised when Tarasov and son took the lead together with half a mile to go, from which point they had the verdict in safekeeping. The race went to father on Clever Boy by a comfortable two lengths from his son. The Tarasovs thus scooped 1,800 rubles ($180) between them. Contact was soon out of contact and without much difficulty finished last.

The man in the white cap was disappointed but not despondent, and informed me that the next result, at least, was completely a foregone conclusion. There were only four runners, and the winner would be Прнятель, which is pronounced "priyatel" and means Good Friend. Despite my experience with Contact, I felt I needed a good friend, and there was a regular gleam in Valia's eye when I gave her all of 20 rubles to stake. The issue was never in doubt; Priyatel won by 20 lengths or more.

I had backed my first Russian winner, which called for a celebration, and we all went to the bar, where Valia had a mineral water and the rest of us had vodkas, and there was a good deal of backslapping and toast drinking. When the dividend was announced, I learned that I had won a grand total of six rubles. This would not even pay for the drinks. Valia said it didn't matter, however, because in the next race, according to Mr. Whitecap, there was an even greater certainty: a gray mare named Вышка, which is pronounced "vyshka" and means watchtower. "She is champion of Moscow Hippodrome," Valia informed me.

This time she suggested that I put on the money, perhaps because she was afraid that she might herself be tempted to bet. I did so, by holding up the appropriate number of fingers and tendering 20 rubles. Watchtower was left at least 30 lengths at the start, and was still ten lengths behind every other runner when they passed the stands the first time around. (The race was over 2,400 meters, a circuit and a half.) However, all my friends were still perfectly certain she would win. And so, in fact, she did: Watchtower seemed suddenly to start moving twice as fast as any other horse in the race, went straight through her field, and was soon five or ten lengths clear. From this point there was no holding her; she went farther and farther ahead, and won by 30 or 40 lengths.

Having learned my lesson over Priyatel, I didn't suggest drinks this time. It was just as well. My winnings amounted to precisely four rubles, odds of one to five, which wouldn't have paid for Valia's mineral water.

My big thrill of the day came in the next race when Jockey Second Class Olga Burdova, a buxom wench on whose talents I risked 20 rubles, drove her horse from behind to win me 127 rubles. Valia at this stage suggested we call it a day, perhaps because her desire to gamble was now becoming irresistible. I agreed; it was getting chilly and I'd only lose all my winnings.

Later I totted up my profit-and-loss account as we drove back to the gray city.

"I've won 87 rubles," I told Valia finally. This was not quite $9, but it seemed a major triumph.

She gave me one of her sidelong looks.

"Capitalist," she said.

"I have a feeling this race is fixed!"

DRAWING BY LYONS

[REPRINTED FROM *Argosy* © 1957 BY POPULAR PUBLICATIONS, INC.]

Morning at Saratoga:
The Vanderbilt Barn

FRANK GRAHAM

Probably no journeyman newspaperman is more admired and respected by his own associates than Frank Graham. This column is a fine example of his rare talent for reporting from a fabulous memory. Graham never takes a note and has never been accused of misquoting. He is the gentle bystander who puts his punch on the typewriter.

SARATOGA SPRINGS, AUG. 6.—They were saddling a gray filly in the stable yard.

"She's a refugee," Dave Woods said. "That's Bukhara II that Alfred bought from the Aga Khan and brought over from France."

"She's a refugee from the winner's circle," Alfred Vanderbilt said. "I'm beginning to think she never will win a race."

It was very early in the morning. One set of the Vanderbilt horses had been on the main track and the boys were getting another set ready.

"The coffee is in the office," Mike McGrath said.

Mike is Alfred's chauffeur. In one way or another he has been around horses most of his life. He once had a trainer's license in Maryland and says that when he was a kid he wanted to be a jockey but grew too big.

"The only riding I ever did," he said, "was when I was eight years old. We had a Saint Bernard and I used to ride him and I taught him to jump hedges with me on his back."

"Don't mind him," Alfred said. "Let's go in and have some coffee."

There were a pot of coffee and a half-dozen heavy china cups on a table in the office. Lee McCoy, the trainer, and Bill Reedy, the stable and farm agent, came in and Alfred poured the coffee and everybody sat around drinking it.

"Mike is a wonderful man," Alfred said. "He probably is the best open-road driver in the country. He put me on The Chief in Los Angeles and when I got to New York he was waiting for me."

"How long has he been with you?" Dave asked.

"About seven years. He came out to the farm one day and asked me for a job. I asked him what he could do and he said he could do anything. I asked him if he could drive and he said he could. So I said:

" 'Well, I'll try you. Maybe I won't like you and maybe you won't like me. But we'll see.'

"A few days later I had him drive me to Baltimore to get the train to New York. At the station he said:

" 'What will I do now?'

"I said: 'I don't know. What would you like to do?'

"He said he might run up to New York so I said:

" 'All right. Go ahead.'

"When I got to my house he was there."

They finished the coffee and went out in the

stable yard. Mike was standing in front of Pathfinder's stall. The colt was restless and Mike said:

"That horse needs racing."

"He'll get it," Alfred said.

Mike shrugged.

"About time," he said.

New World, the "big horse" of the Vanderbilt stable, bowed a tendon in his left foreleg the other day. The swelling has gone down and while the colt will not be able to race for a while it is all right to gallop him and he had been in the first set on the track. Now Jimmy Varner, the boy who works him, was holding him and Specs, a Negro groom, was rubbing him. Alfred ran his hand along the bowed tendon. The colt stood still.

"Seems to be coming along all right," Alfred said.

"Yes, sir, Mr. Vanderbilt," Specs said. "It's coming good."

"Did it seem to hurt him this morning?"

"No, sir," Jimmy said. "The only time it ever seemed to hurt him was right when it happened."

"I hear you knew he bowed it even before you saw it."

"Yes, sir. He just kind of went this way and I knew what had happened and I pulled him up."

"Were you ever a race rider, Jimmy?" Dave asked.

"No, sir."

"Where did you come from, Maryland?"

"No, sir. Pennsylvania. Johnstown, Pennsylvania."

"How did you get out of the flood?" Specs asked. "Take to the hills?"

"Say, how old do you think I am, anyway?"

"Looking at you," Specs said, "I would say about eighty."

"I'm thirty-seven," Jimmy said.

The stable blacksmith came by. His name is Duke Montura and he owns a couple of horses that he campaigns on the half-mile tracks.

"What's the matter, Duke?" Alfred asked. "Why the big frown?"

"I just got a wire from my trainer," Duke said. "He says he needs dough."

"You'd better send it to him. If you don't he might sell one of your horses."

"That wouldn't be a bad idea," Duke said.

"Duke bought a horse in a sale in Maryland last year," Dave said. "One of the papers said the horse was sold to the Duke of Montura and everybody thought the turf had recruited a new owner from the Italian nobility."

Milton Woodward, one of the exercise boys, brought Pathfinder out of his stall and lined him up with the others that were going out in the second set.

"Ever see Stagehand run?" he asked.

"Yes," Dave said.

"This one runs just like him."

"You mean he starts slowly?"

"Yes."

"But is he as fast?"

"He's as fast as Stagehand was when he was a two-year-old," Milton said. "Stagehand wasn't no good as a two-year-old, neither."

"If you mean what I think you mean," Alfred said, "that's a hell of a way to describe one of my horses."

The boy laughed as he was boosted into the saddle. The set started for the track and they followed the horses. On the way they met Roy Waldron, who trains for the Milky Way Stable.

"You're selling your yearlings tonight, eh, Alfred?" Waldron asked.

"Yes," Alfred said. "Come over and bring some money with you."

"I'll be there. Are they any good?"

"What do you expect me to say, at least until the sale is over?"

"Are you going to the sale, Alfred?" Dave asked.

"I don't know yet. I don't know what to do. If you don't go they say you are not interested and if you do and your horses don't bring any money, your friends are embarrassed and think they ought to bid."

They watched the horses work, then went back to the stable and saw them cooled out.

"Well," Alfred said, looking at his watch, "let's eat. Where's Mike?"

"I'll get him," one of the boys said.

When the boy came back with Mike, Alfred was at the wheel.

"Get in back," Alfred said.

"Come now, Mr. Vanderbilt," Mike said. "Fun is fun, but I wouldn't see the car smashed just for a joke."

"Get in back," Alfred said again. "I can drive as well as you can."

"I know it," Mike said.

"That's the old oil," Alfred said.

"That," Mike said, "is the old, old oil."

He got in the back seat and Alfred drove around to the clubhouse, where Harry Stevens had breakfast ready for them at a table on the veranda.

My Big $61,908 Ordeal

ERNEST HAVEMANN

I admire Ernest Havemann, the compulsive horse player, and I certainly admire $61,908.80, even before taxes. As far as this book is concerned, however, I particularly admire the way this account is written. The reader knows right from the beginning that the miracle is going to come off, but that doesn't lessen the sustained excitement of the story one bit.

WHEN people ask me these days, "What's new?" I reply, as calmly as I can, "Well, a funny thing happened to me at the race track."

It all started, you might say, a couple of Wednesdays ago in a New York restaurant where, as writers often do, I was having lunch with a magazine editor. For reasons which will become clear later, he shall be nameless. No, he shan't be nameless at all. He hurt my feelings; this is my chance to get even, and, as it happens, I don't especially care just now what magazine editors think of me. He was Jack Tibby of *Sports Illustrated*. Our conversation got around to horse racing and I said, "Jack, I'm leaving for California tomorrow, which means I'll surely be going to the track at Caliente. You better send along a couple of dollars for the five-ten."

The Caliente track is just across the Mexican border south of Los Angeles. The five-ten pool there is a long-shot horse player's delight—a wonderful get-rich-quick scheme where you try to pick as many winners as you can in the fifth, sixth, seventh, eighth, ninth and tenth races— six races in all. It costs only $2 to try, and so many people do try, from all over southern California and northern Mexico, that the pool runs into tens of thousands of dollars. If you pick all six winners—or even if you pick only five but nobody else does any better—you can win yourself a small fortune. One man once won $98,000;

I wrote a story about him, and I've tried at every opportunity to win the pool myself ever since.

"So you're still dreaming," Jack said.

Like any self-respecting, compulsive horse player, I replied with some indignation, "I'm not dreaming at all. I know—I *know*—that sooner or later I'm bound to hit it."

Jack, who is a conservative man with a savings account and a house in the suburbs, looked at me pityingly and said, "You should live so long."

"The last time I was there," I told him, "I lost it in two photo finishes. All I needed was one head and one nose difference, maybe six inches in all, and I would have had the whole pot."

"That's what they all say," Jack said.

But horse players love company; it gives them courage; so I tried once more. "Just buy a dollar of my action," I begged him. "What's one measly dollar?"

"No, thanks," said Jack. "I prefer to spend it on something more sensible. I may buy some buggy-whip stock."

That's the way it's been all my life. My father was a jockey briefly before he attained his full growth; I lived in a house with photographs of race horses and my dad in his silks all over the walls, and I began reading the *Daily Racing Form* at the age of 12. I've been picking the horses for 38 years. I've been to 43 race tracks on the North American continent and several more in London, Paris and Moscow. Wherever I happen to be, if I have an afternoon off you can find me at the track.

It isn't an easy life. Conservative friends like Jack Tibby look down their noses at me. Even people who are themselves addicted to the most outrageous hobbies scorn you: I have a wealthy friend who spends about $5,000 a year on new cameras and darkroom supplies, yet he stoutly maintains that anybody who would blow $10 on a horse race must be a madman. He may be right at that. The psychiatry books all say that the compulsive gambler is a masochist who doesn't really want to win but in fact takes a perverse pleasure in losing.

Once I was interviewing Paul Henning, the television writer, and he told me his hobby was attending foreign language courses; he and his wife were working their way through Spanish, French and German and when they retired they were going around the world, chattering like natives wherever they went. Then, to be polite, he asked me what my hobby was, and I felt not only silly but uncouth.

Worst of all is the inevitable wise guy who always seems to be around when I mention the horses. "Yeah?" he says, with a self-satisfied and superior air. "Picking them for 38 years, you say? Tell me this. Are you ahead? Or shouldn't I ask, ha ha?"

A fellow like that would never understand that you don't play the horses to win. Anybody who has enough sense to read the *Racing Form* knows you can't beat a game where state taxes and the track commission eat up about 15¢ out of each $1 bet. You buy your mutuel tickets at the race track for the same reason other people buy tickets to the movies or football games. Or for the same reason some people climb mountains.

Driving home to Jersey from the lunch with Jack Tibby, I almost decided that if I had my life to live over I would do it differently. All I have to show for 38 years of horse-playing, I told myself, is my own firm but strictly unverified conviction that I am the world's greatest handicapper. And, as Jack implied, every compulsive horse player considers himself the world's greatest handicapper. Once at Hollywood Park I nearly came to blows with Marty Ritt, the movie director, because he kept insisting that *he* was the greatest and I kept insisting that *I* was. The sad and funny thing was that neither of us cashed a single ticket that day.

As for the misses, Jack was right about that, too. My wife has been telling me for years that she didn't so much mind the money I kept losing in the five-ten; it was listening to all those tales of photo finishes and what might have been.

A man who spends his money on golf at least has his muscles. The man whose hobby is boats can take his friends for a ride. The amateur painter can use his canvases for Christmas presents. All a compulsive horse player has is his dreams, which he knows in his heart are tinsel.

Yet this is how compulsive a horse player can get: on the following Saturday night, after a hard week's work, after a flight from New York to Los Angeles and the misery of adjusting to the three-hour time difference and after a party with some friends that lasted a lot longer than it should have, I sat up in my hotel room and read the *Daily Racing Form,* special Caliente edition, until 3 A.M. Studying the *Form* is perhaps the happiest part of the horse player's life. The past performances which appear there in such marvelously condensed detail are more fascinating than any crossword puzzle or mystery novel. Each line of type stirs visions of luscious long shots, as yet untested by harsh reality.

I put check marks next to the names of a few horses I thought might win and question marks next to a few that seemed to deserve further consideration, and ran great X's through a considerable number that seemed to have very little chance.

I slept fitfully, bothered by a recurrent dream that my horse in the fifth race fell going into the first turn. I got up at 7 A.M., feeling awful. The hotel coffee shop was still closed and I had to settle for two undercooked eggs at the counter of a diner, while the meter of my cab kept grinding away outside. (As you know if you have ever been in L.A., it's almost impossible to hail a cab in the street and the fares there are murder.) I was at the airport a half hour early and found that a dozen other compulsive horse players were there ahead of me. Our tribe may risk being late to the office, late to the theater, late for our own weddings—but never late to the track.

Sitting in the waiting room, I tried to study the form sheet some more. Handicapping the horses, I should explain for the benefit of those who have never tried it, is hard work. You have to examine each horse's record from at least a half dozen angles. You look for consistency: a horse that has been winning or running close in all his recent starts figures to do it again. You look for what handicappers call "class": every horse has his own level and will beat the cheaper horses and lose to the better ones. You ask yourself whether the horse seems to be improving or tailing off.

You study the time figures: a horse that has been running six furlongs consistently in $1:10\frac{3}{5}$ —that's one minute, 10 and $\frac{3}{5}$ seconds—figures to win by at least three lengths from a horse that has never run faster than $1:11$. You look for early speed and late speed: sometimes a horse that breaks away from the starting gate fast will get so far ahead that nothing can catch him, but sometimes horses with early foot will wear one another out fighting for the lead, and a slower horse with more endurance will pass them in the stretch.

Different handicappers have different methods. Myself, I'm what's called a "speed man," partial to early foot. I figure that once a horse gets out in front nothing can get in his way, and the others can't win unless they catch him.

As I say, it's hard work. Picking one winner is difficult enough. Trying to pick six calls for the head of a mathematician and the endurance of a channel swimmer.

The type of the *Racing Form* danced before my eyes. I looked again at the horses I had checked as likely winners and was moved to wonder, in the colder light of day, what I had ever seen in them. Or had my brain been more alert when I made the check marks than it was now? (If there is anything that horrifies a horse player, it is changing his mind and then watching his original selections win.)

I began thinking of the long day ahead. The special plane to Caliente takes off from Los Angeles at 9:30 A.M. and deposits you at a little airfield near the Mexican border an hour later. Then you climb into a chartered bus, ride to the border, climb out, walk across the boundary line and get into a rattledy-bang old taxicab whose driver regards the final four-mile road to the track as his own private race course, to be negotiated as a point of honor without delay for bumps, curves, right-angle turns, pedestrians or any trucks that happen to get in the way.

You arrive at the track, already exhausted and with nerves ajangle, just in time to find a seat and make a bet on the first race, which starts at 11:30 A.M. Ten races and five hours later, just as the sun is beginning to set—that same sun that was just rising when you got up to begin your long day's journey—you sprint for a cab and repeat the whole process in reverse.

I went to the airport washroom and examined my face in the mirror. My eyelids drooped. I already looked dead tired. I told myself that anybody who would do what I was doing was a plain damn fool.

I need hardly add that if somebody had offered me $50 to turn back, I would have refused it.

The plane ride only made things worse. The air was a little bumpy over the coast line, just enough to jolt my *Racing Form* every time I had the type in focus. In the seat ahead of me a woman kept reading the *Form* aloud to her husband. Each time I managed to figure, between jolts, that Horse A had once run a 1¹⁄₁₆ mile race in 1:44⅖, she was saying about Horse B, "You see? They ran it in 1:45⅕ that day and he was beaten a length and a half." The dope on her

horses and mine got inextricably intertwined in my weary head.

All I had been able to do by the time I got to the track was narrow down the day's racing to this:

Race	No. of Starters	No. of Horses I Liked
5	11	8
6	8	3
7	12	6
8	11	2
9	8	2
10	7	3

I did a little mathematics on the back of my program and got a shock. A $2 ticket in the five-ten entitles you to one horse in each race, six horses in all. If you want to try to increase your chances by picking more than one horse per race, you have to pay $2 for each possible combination of your selections. To find how much a ticket on all the horses I liked would cost, I had to figure how many combinations it took to couple all eight of my horses in the fifth race with all three in the sixth, these with all six in the seventh, and so on. In other words, I had to multiply 8x3x6x2x2x3, then multiply the whole thing again by $2. It came out—try it yourself—to $3,456.

I'm not that compulsive. It was back to work on the form sheet.

I finally wound up with the ticket shown on page 177. It cost, as you can see, $96. That's a lot of money to invest on your chances of picking six winners. Despite being the world's greatest handicapper, I have never picked six straight winners in my life. The professionals on the *Racing Form,* who pick all the races every day, are lucky to come up with six in a row every year or two. As often as not, the five-ten is won by somebody who takes a $2 flyer on a couple of solid favorites, hooked up with horses whose numbers correspond to the ages of his kids. But it was my first visit to Caliente in months; it might be my last for several more months, and you're young and compulsive only once.

The ticket was bought at 11:58 A.M. This was about two hours before the deadline, which is post time for the fifth race. I could have spent the two hours in further study, and probably could have narrowed down my choices and saved some money. But I'd had it. The *Racing Form* had lost its charm. All in the world I wanted to do, at 11:58 A.M., was forget about five-ten, eat some lunch and settle back in the sunshine to enjoy some nice quiet $2 bets on the early races. I wondered: do mountain climbers work this hard?

In the first four races of the day I had nothing but losers. Only one of the horses I bet on was even in the money. I was delighted. A man can pick only so many winners in his lifetime, and I didn't want to waste any of them before the five-ten. (This is a line of reasoning which I doubt you will be able to follow unless you too are a compulsive horse player or worry about black cats; but it is an accurate account of what I was thinking.)

In the fifth race my No. 5 horse—his name was Dipalot—won and paid $30.20. I was gratified but hardly elated; I hate to think how often I've started the five-ten with a pretty good long shot and then run out of luck. In the sixth race my No. 7, Stymie's Hour, came from ten lengths back to run away from the others and pay $11.60. Still I wasn't about to buy any champagne: the trick of lasting a lifetime as a compulsive horse player is to permit yourself to dream just a little bit, not so much that you get ulcers whenever your hopes are dashed. I indulged myself in a little doodling on the back of my program, nothing more. The money in the five-ten pool, the figures on the tote board showed, amounted to $97,112. Allowing for the track's 15% commission, there would be $82,545 left over for the winners. A quarter of that came to $20,636.20; this amount would be the consolation money to be split among the holders of the second-best tickets of the day. I stopped right there. Any horse player would be happy to have a share of $20,636.20 any day of the week.

In the seventh race I had six horses going for me; you would have thought that I might feel pretty confident as the field of 12 horses went into the starting gate. The trouble is that when you have been playing the horses as long as I have, you can never be confident; you've been tantalized and disappointed far too often. Once in a seven-horse race I had six horses going for me on my five-ten ticket and the seventh horse won.

But this was another day. Down the stretch the race was between my No. 8 and my No. 10, both long shots. No. 8—Emancipation—got it and paid $22.80. Now I really began to have dreams of glory. On the back of my program I subtracted $20,636.20 from $82,545 and found that first money in the five-ten would be—holy smoke!—$61,908.80.

The best part was that my horse in the next race, No. 7, Blossom Time, was what I call a BBBB. Usually, after I finish studying all the day's races in the form sheet, I put down a BB next to one horse, meaning that he's my day's Best Bet. BBBB means Best Best Best Bet, an honor I don't pass out lightly or often. But Blossom Time had just run two great races in a row, including 1⅟₁₆ miles in 1:44⅖. Nothing else in the race figured to run it faster than about 1:45⅜. That's a difference of seven lengths, and seven lengths is a runaway.

I seldom go to the paddock to watch the horses being saddled. In fact I have no respect whatever for horse players who claim that they can look at the horses in the paddock and pick a winner. Maybe a trainer who lives with a horse day after day can tell how it feels by looking at it, but I can't, and I never saw any other horse player who could. So I usually stay in the stands between races and study the *Form,* or, if I've finished my handicapping and am alone at the track, I read. (I finished the three-volume Ernest Jones biography of Freud in the course of a meet at Belmont Park and reread *Crime and Punishment* one year at Laurel.) But this time you couldn't have kept me away from the paddock. I wanted to make sure Blossom Time didn't look sick or lame. She turned out to be a nice little bay filly, just turned four. She looked great and I felt great.

Well, it was just one of those things. There's an old saying around the track that there are 50 ways to lose a horse race and only one way to win it, and Blossom Time ran into one of the 50. She was in the middle of a line of horses stretched across the track as they went to the first turn; the horses on the inside of her bore out; the horses on the outside of her bore in, and her jockey had to ease her back. Way back. No horse, not even a BBBB, can make up for that kind of racing luck.

Blossom Time tried gamely and closed a lot of ground, but the best she could do was third.

So long, old dreams of glory. You were great while you lasted.

Was I sad, angry, maybe wildly suicidal? No. It's only the amateurs who gnash their teeth and tear up their tickets. My tribe shrugs it off. We've been through it all before. We halfway expect it.

But then I took another look at the result board and saw that the winner, the No. 1 horse, Serado, was a long shot of long shots, 30-to-1, paying $63.60. Nobody but a handicapper gifted with a sixth sense—or possibly someone playing his own telephone number—was very likely to have had Serado on a five-ten ticket. And if he had Serado, how likely was he to have had the previous three winners?

Dreams of glory, welcome back. You're a little tarnished now, but I still cherish you.

Some men to my left were marveling at the day's steady procession of long shots. "There ain't anybody going to have six winners today," declared one of them. "Four ought to do it," said another. I blurted out that I already had three winners on my ticket—a violation of the compulsive horse player's credo of minding your own business—and immediately wished I hadn't. I heard them whispering, and could see them staring at me from time to time. Eventually one of them tapped me on the arm and asked, "Would you take a hundred dollars for your ticket, right now?"

He said it with the expression of a cherub, but of course there was larceny in his soul. I made him a counteroffer. I said I would take $10,000, and naturally he gave up. I have often wondered since what I would have done if he had turned out to be a big gambler with a thick bankroll and had said okay. I'm sure I would have refused the $10,000—when you get that close to the five-ten it isn't just the money, it's the principle of the thing—but I would have had to think about it.

For one thing, the next race, the ninth, had me scared. There were two horses that any handicapper in the world would have given a good chance: Maxine Welch and Navy King. No matter how you looked at their past performances, they were hard to separate, as handicappers say. I had decided at the last minute, after a lot of soul-searching and perhaps a little mental coin-tossing, to take Maxine Welch, No. 2. The crowd was making Navy King an even-money favorite. Maxine Welch was five to one. Had I picked the right one? Why hadn't I had enough courage to invest some more money and pick them both?

Maxine had to do it for me, and the crowd thought she wouldn't.

For the first half of the race Maxine was running nicely in second place, behind a horse named Elsie's Bull. Going around the stretch turn, she passed Elsie's Bull and went into the lead. Fine—but there came Navy King. He had once been three lengths behind her; now he was a length behind; as they came into the stretch he was a half-length behind. When they passed me, a sixteenth of a mile from the finish, Navy King was only a head behind—and when a horse is gaining like that, he usually goes on to win.

Navy King looked my Maxine in the eye and she looked right back. That surge had exhausted him. Maxine pulled away again. The finish was too close for comfort, but a big No. 2 went up on the result board.

One more to go. I quit thinking and started walking. I walked to the ground floor of the grandstand and up to the top floor. Then I explored the clubhouse. I must have put in a good mile and a sixteenth myself in the half hour between races, which was the longest half hour I have ever spent.

I had two solid horses in the race: No. 6, Locris, which the crowd was making a three-to-two favorite, and No. 2, Jeff's Fury, the second choice at two to one. But as I glanced at my form sheet from time to time I began noticing a horse named José Hardrock, whose record kept looking better and better. Again the regrets. Why hadn't I given more thought to José when I was making out my five-ten ticket? Not to be superstitious, but how can you bet against a horse named José Hardrock in Mexico?

The tenth was a 5½-furlong race, a short sprint in which the horses have to go full tilt from start to finish; if you fall too far behind at 5½ furlongs you can't possibly make up the distance to win. After the horses had gone a quarter of a mile, my No. 2 had fallen out of it. The race was strictly between my Locris and—oh, the pity of it—José Hardrock.

Around the turn it was Locris on the outside, leading by a half-length, a miserable, insignificant little half-length, with José Hardrock lapped against him on the inside. They were both flying—and José, saving ground, had less far to fly. The half-length gap closed an inch at a time. When they straightened out in the stretch it had closed completely. In fact José had his head in front.

I shuddered and turned away. All I could think of—you can see how slap-happy I must have been—was that old race track story about the man who went to the track every day with two dollars, bet it on the first race and, if he won, started trying to pyramid his winnings into an eight-horse parlay. One day he had the first seven winners and was ahead $25,000—which he then bet on the last race and lost. When he got home his wife asked, "Well, how did it go?" and he replied, "Same old thing. I lost two dollars." That was me. Same old thing. Close but no cigar.

When I finally brought myself to look back at

the horses they were just going under the wire. Miracle of miracles, Locris was in front again.

I did what any sensible horse player would have done: I walked as fast as I could to the nearest bar. I had five winners. I was bound to be at least among the runners-up. Had anybody had six—or were five winners good enough for the first money? And if five did turn out to be good enough, how many other people also had five and would share the $61,908 pot?

Caliente, sitting there in all that sunshine, draws happy crowds. The people at the clubhouse bar, having lost a little or won a little, knowing they were beaten in the five-ten and thus without a worry in the world, were talking and cracking jokes and laughing and having the time of their lives. In the mirror above the bar I saw that I myself looked as if I was ready to walk into a hospital for major surgery.

From where I stood, I couldn't see the five-ten result board. I stepped closer, stood on tiptoe and looked over the heads of the crowd. The lights had not yet come on. The board said NO. OF WINNERS—blank, NO. OF WINNING TICKETS—blank, and PAY—blank. Naturally I went back for another drink. The next time I looked, the blanks began to light up. They said 5, 1 and $61,908.80.

A man next to me whistled and said, "Now, how do you suppose anybody could have come up with five of those long shots?" All I could do was shake my head dumbly as if I marveled myself, as indeed I did at that moment. Then I suddenly remembered: if I didn't dash for a cab to catch the special bus that met my special plane, I was about to be stranded in Mexico without even a toothbrush. I dashed.

All the way back to Los Angeles my fellow passengers were moaning—but good-naturedly, of course, because they were the kind of horse-players who don't really expect to win—that it had been a rough day at the track. I sat in numb silence, wondering if I had read the board right, wondering if I had actually put the numbers on my ticket that I thought I had, afraid to take the ticket out of my pocket to look at it. The others must have figured that I had lost more than anybody.

As a matter of fact (and again I don't expect anybody but my fellow horse players to comprehend this) I was actually a little bit sorry I had won. If you're a mountain climber, what do you do after Everest? What does a horse player do for an encore after winning the five-ten? How could I ever again expect any thrill from betting $2 on an even-money favorite, an act which has given me pleasure for 38 years?

I thought about income taxes, and they made my stomach sink. I had just written an article on taxation and if my memory served me right, I would owe the government at least $25,000 even if I quit working and never earned another cent this year, a sort of enforced vacation I would hardly relish. Anything I did earn from now on would be taxed starting at about 65¢ out of every dollar, and going on up from there.

It isn't fair, of course. When a horse player has a bad year and drops a couple of thousand, thus seriously jeopardizing the mortgage payments and the family diet, the Bureau of Internal Revenue won't let him deduct his losses. If he wins, the Bureau says he has to count the money as income and pay the tax. This is a heads-I-win-tails-you-lose proposition and I would lay eight to five it's unconstitutional. Unfortunately there is no National Association for the Advancement of Compulsive Horse Players to go to bat for us in the Supreme Court.

Did I think of the possibility of trying to cheat? Yes, of course I did. It occurred to me that I was probably a fool not to have somebody in Mexico collect the money for me, in cold cash, keep 10% for himself and slip me the rest in a dark alley. But I come from a long line of compulsively honest folks. Besides, if I did try to cheat, I would never be able to talk about my victory—and what good is winning the five-ten if you can't brag about it?

It was the next day before the worrisome thoughts disappeared and elation set in. I checked my ticket against the results in the papers. I had five winners all right. A headline in the Los Angeles *Herald-Examiner* said: UNKNOWN FAN WINS $61,908. Hallelujah! I was that "unknown fan."

I called up my wife and toyed with her a little while, complaining about all the long shots and photo finishes, then casually broke the news as if it were something that happened every day. I could just imagine how her face looked at the other end of the line. I imagined Jack Tibby's face when he heard about it and realized that a dollar's worth of confidence in me would have brought him $645; five dollars would have brought him $3,225.

Best of all, I thought about the next wise guy who will surely ask me some day, "Picking them for 38 years, you say? Are you ahead of them?" There is only one answer to that question, and being able to say it is more precious than gold. I am now.

A Stableboy's Day

THOMAS HOLCROFT

I like this piece for several reasons; written in the late 18th century, it depicts a way of life remarkably similar to the same workaday endeavor of today. Also, it demonstrates that the miniature muscle-men of the stable area are sometimes inordinately literate. Thomas Holcroft later became an actor and successful playwright.

ALL the boys in the stable rise at the same hour, from half-past two in spring, to between four and five in the depth of winter. The horses hear them when they awaken each other, and neigh, to denote their eagerness to be fed. Being dressed, the boy begins with carefully clearing out the manger, and giving a feed of oats, which he is obliged no less carefully to sift. He then proceeds to dress the litter; that is, to shake the bed on which the horse has been lying, remove whatever is wet or unclean, and keep the remaining straw in the stable for another time. The whole stables are then thoroughly swept, the few places for fresh air are kept open, the great heat of the stable gradually cooled, and the horse, having ended his first feed, is roughly cleaned and dressed. In about half an hour after they begin, or a little better, the horses have been rubbed down, and reclothed, saddled, each turned in his stall, then bridled, mounted, and the whole string goes out to morning exercise; he that leads being the first: for each boy knows his place.

Except by accident, the race horse never trots. He must either walk or gallop; and in exercise, even when it is the hardest, the gallop begins slowly and gradually, and increases till the horse is nearly at full speed. When he has galloped half a mile, the boy begins to push him forward, without relaxation, for another half-mile. This is at the period when the horses are in full exercise, to which they come by degrees. The boy that can best regulate these degrees among those of light weight is generally chosen to lead the gallop; he goes first out of the stable, and first returns.

The morning's exercise often extends to four hours, and the evening's to much about the same time. Being once in the stable, each lad begins his labor. He leads the horse into his stall, ties him up, rubs down his legs with straw, takes off his saddle and body clothes; curries him carefully, then with both currycomb and brush, never leaves him till he has thoroughly cleaned his skin, so that neither spot nor wet, nor any appearance of neglect may be seen about him. The horse is then reclothed, and suffered to repose for some time, which is first employed in gratifying his hunger, and recovering from his weariness. All this is performed, and the stables are once more shut up, about nine o'clock.

Accustomed to this life, the boys are very little overcome by fatigue, except that early in the morning they may be drowsy. I have sometimes fallen slightly asleep at the beginning of the first brushing gallop. But if they are not weary, they are hungry, and they make themselves ample amends for all they have done. Nothing perhaps can exceed the enjoyment of a stableboy's breakfast: what then may not be said of mine, who had so long been used to suffer hunger, and so seldom found the means of satisfying it? Our breakfast consisted of new milk, or milk porridge, then the cold meat of the preceding day, most exquisite Gloucester cheese, fine white bread, and concluded with plentiful draughts of table beer. All this did not overload the stomach, or in the least deprive me of my youthful activity, except that like others I might sometimes take a nap for an hour, after so small a portion of sleep.

"Look, dear, I only go to the races in the hope of bringing home a little something extra for you and children."

DRAWING BY GEORGE PRICE   [© 1956 BY THE NEW YORKER MAGAZINE, INC.]

How the Old Horse Won the Bet

OLIVER WENDELL HOLMES

Somewhere along the line this compiler of the literature of the turf had to break down. I do so gracefully and with a deep bow to Dr. Holmes, whose literary attainments would adorn any collection. Please note, by way of explanation, that the author of this poetry is the father of the late noted Justice of the Supreme Court and his subject is trotting, a sport encountered only once before in this volume, and not hereafter.

'T was on the famous trotting-ground,
The betting men were gathered round
From far and near; the "cracks" were there
Whose deeds the sporting prints declare:
The swift g.m., Old Hiram's nag,
The fleet s.h., Dan Pfeiffer's brag,
With these a third—and who is he
That stands beside his fast b.g.?
Budd Doble, whose catarrhal name
So fills the nasal trump of fame.
There too stood many a noted steed
Of Messenger and Morgan breed;
Green horses also, not a few;
Unknown as yet what they could do;
And all the hacks that know so well
The scourgings of the Sunday swell.

Blue are the skies of opening day;
The bordering turf is green with May;
The sunshine's golden gleam is thrown
On sorrel, chestnut, bay, and roan;
The horses paw and prance and neigh,
Fillies and colts like kittens play,
And dance and toss their rippled manes
Shining and soft as silken skeins;
Wagons and gigs are ranged about,
And fashion flaunts her gay turn-out;
Here stands—each youthful Jehu's dream—
The jointed tandem, ticklish team!
And there in ampler breadth expand

The splendors of the four-in-hand;
On faultless ties and glossy tiles
The lovely bonnets beam their smiles;
(The style's the man, so books avow;
The style's the woman, anyhow);
From flounces frothed with creamy lace
Peeps out the pug-dog's smutty face,
Or spaniel rolls his liquid eye,
Or stares the wiry pet of Skye,—
O woman, in your hours of ease
So shy with us, so free with these!

"Come on! I'll bet you two to one
I'll make him do it!" "Will you? Done!"

What was it who was bound to do?
I did not hear and can't tell you,—
Pray listen till my story's through.
Scarce noticed, back behind the rest,
By cart and wagon rudely prest,
The parson's lean and bony bay
Stood harnessed in his one-horse shay—
Lent to his sexton for the day;
(A funeral—so the sexton said;
His mother's uncle's wife was dead.)

Like Lazarus bid to Dives' feast,
So looked the poor forlorn old beast;
His coat was rough, his tail was bare,
The gray was sprinkled in his hair;

Sportsmen and jockeys knew him not,
And yet they say he once could trot
Among the fleetest of the town,
Till something cracked and broke him down,—
The steed's, the statesman's, common lot!
"And are we then so soon forgot?"
Ah me! I doubt if one of you
Has ever heard the name "Old Blue,"
Whose fame through all this region rung
In those old days when I was young!

"Bring forth the horse!" Alas! he showed
Not like the one Mazeppa rode;
Scant-maned, sharp-backed, and shaky-kneed,
The wreck of what was once a steed,
Lips thin, eyes hollow, stiff in joints;
Yet not without his knowing points.
The sexton laughing in his sleeve,
As if 't were all a make-believe,
Led forth the horse, and as he laughed
Unhitched the breeching from a shaft,
Unclasped the rusty belt beneath,
Drew forth the snaffle from his teeth,
Slipped off his head-stall, set him free
From strap and rein,—a sight to see!

So worn, so lean in every limb,
It can't be they are saddling him!
It is! His back the pigskin strides
And flaps his lank, rheumatic sides;
With look of mingled scorn and mirth
They buckle round the saddle-girth;
With horsy wink and saucy toss
A youngster throws his leg across,
And so, his rider on his back,
They lead him, limping, to the track,
Far up behind the starting point,
To limber out each stiffened joint.

As through the jeering crowd he past,
One pitying look Old Hiram cast;
"Go it, ye cripple, while ye can!"
Cried out unsentimental Dan;
"A Fast-Day dinner for the crows!"
Budd Doble's scoffing shout arose.

Slowly, as when the walking-beam
First feels the gathering head of steam,
With warning cough and threatening wheeze
The stiff old charger crooks his knees;
At first with cautious step sedate,
As if he dragged a coach of state;
He's not a colt; he knows full well
That time is weight and sure to tell;
No horse so sturdy but he fears
The handicap of twenty years.

As through the throng on either hand
The old horse nears the judges' stand,
Beneath his jockey's feather-weight

He warms a little to his gait,
And now and then a step is tried
That hints of something like a stride.

"Go!"—Through his ear the summons stung
As if a battle-trump had rung;
The slumbering instincts long unstirred
Start at the old familiar word;
It thrills like flame through every limb,—
What mean his twenty years to him?
The savage blow his rider dealt
Fell on his hollow flanks unfelt;
The spur that pricked his staring hide
Unheeded tore his bleeding side;
Alike to him are spur and rein,—
He steps a five-year-old again!

Before the quarter pole was past,
Old Hiram said, "He's going fast."
Long ere the quarter was a half,
The chuckling crowd had ceased to laugh;
Tighter his frightened jockey clung
As in a mighty stride he swung,
The gravel flying in his track,
His neck stretched out, his ears laid back,
His tail extended all the while
Behind him like a rat-tail file!
Off went a shoe,—away it spun,
Shot like a bullet from a gun;
The quaking jockey shapes a prayer
From scraps of oaths he used to swear;
He drops his whip, he drops his rein,
He clutches fiercely for a mane;
He'll lose his hold—he sways and reels—
He'll slide beneath those trampling heels!
The knees of many a horseman quake,
The flowers on many a bonnet shake,
And shouts arise from left and right,
"Stick on! Stick on!" "Hould tight! Hould tight!"
"Cling round his neck and don't let go—
That pace can't hold—there! Steady! Whoa!"

But like the sable steed that bore
The spectral lover of Lenore,
His nostrils snorting foam and fire,
No stretch his bony limbs can tire;
And now the stand he rushes by,
And "Stop him!—Stop him" is the cry.
Stand back! he's only just begun—
He's having our three heats in one!

"Don't rush in front! He'll smash your brains;
But follow up and grab the reins!"
Old Hiram spoke. Dan Pfeiffer heard,
And sprang impatient at the word;
Budd Doble started on his bay,
Old Hiram followed on his gray,
And off they spring, and round they go,
The fast ones doing "all they know."
Look! Twice they follow at his heels,

As round the circling course he wheels,
And whirls with him that clinging boy
Like Hector round the walls of Troy;
Still on, and on, the third time round!
They're tailing off! They're losing ground!
Budd Doble's nag begins to fail!
Dan Pfeiffer's sorrel whisks his tail!
And see! In spite of whip and shout,
Old Hiram's mare is given out!
Now for the finish! At the turn,
The old horse—all the rest astern—
Comes swinging in, with easy trot;
By Jove! he's distanced all the lot!

That trot no mortal could explain;
Some said, "Old Dutchman come again!"
Some took his time,—at least they tried,
But what it was could none decide;
One said he couldn't understand
What happened to his second hand;
One said 2:10; *that* couldn't be—

More like two twenty-two or three;
Old Hiram settled it at last;
"The time was two—too dee-vel-ish fast!"

The parson's horse had won the bet;
It cost him something of a sweat;
Back in the one-horse shay he went;
The parson wondered what it meant,
And murmured, with a mild surprise
And pleasant twinkle of the eyes,
"That funeral must have been a trick,
Or corpses drive at double-quick;
I shouldn't wonder, I declare,
If brother—Jehu—made the prayer!"

And this is all I have to say
About that tough old trotting bay,
Huddup! Huddup! G'lang! Good day!

Moral for which this tale is told:
A horse *can* trot, for all he's old.

OPPOSITE

ANATOMY AND THE HORSE: GEORGE STUBBS

George Stubbs (1724–1806) combined extraordinary skills as an artist and an anatomist to establish new standards of realism and pictorial authority in horse portraiture. The six drawings on the following pages are from his great work The Anatomy of the Horse, *published in England in 1766. The drawings are from a group of eighteen in the possession of the Royal Academy of Arts, London, and are reproduced by permission of the Academy.*

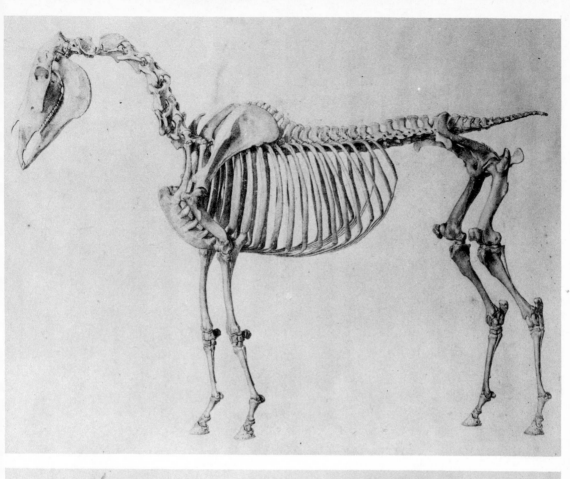

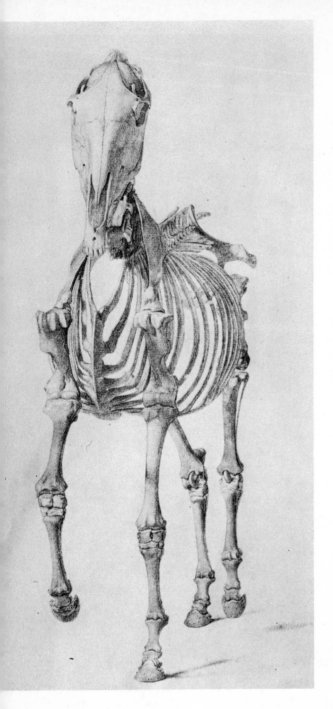

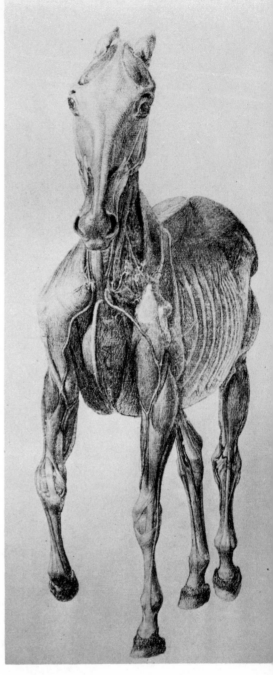

Stubbs was born in Liverpool, England, the son of a currier. At fifteen he was apprenticed to a painter, but he received only a few weeks' instruction. An early interest in anatomy led him to teach the subject in York, at the same time working as a painter of portraits, farm life and animals. His students encouraged him to make a study of horse anatomy, but "the young surgeons altogether failed to share the labour and expense

with him," his biographer, the painter Ozias Humphry, writes. Stubbs spent two years completing the huge enterprise on his own. The following is a graphic account of his procedure.

"The first subject that he prepared was a horse which was bled to death by the jugular vein: after which the arteries and veins were injected. A Bar of Iron was then suspended from the ceiling of the room by a Teagle to which Iron Hooks of

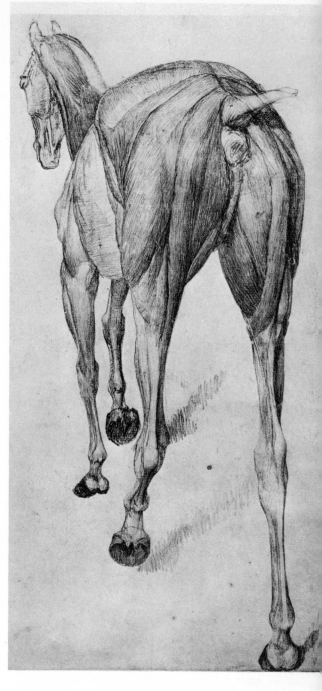

various sizes and lengths were fixed. Under the bar a plank was swung about 18 inches wide for the horse's feet to rest upon and the animal was suspended to the iron bar by the above mentioned hooks. . . . He first began by dissecting and designing the muscles of the abdomen proceeding thro five different layers of muscles. . . . Then he proceeded to dissect the head . . . he made careful designs . . . and wrote the explana-

tion, which usually employed him a whole day. He then took off another layer of muscles . . . and so he proceeded until he came to the skeleton. . . ."

Stubbs went on from his anatomical research to paint horse portraits of outstanding beauty and dynamic pictorial organizations, which are to be found in museums and private collections on both sides of the Atlantic.

The Rocking-Horse Winner

D. H. LAWRENCE

This moving story about a juvenile horse player is one of the most famous in the literature.

THERE was a woman who was beautiful, who started with all the advantages, yet she had no luck. She married for love, and the love turned to dust. She had bonny children, yet she felt they had been thrust upon her, and she could not love them. They looked at her coldly, as if they were finding fault with her. And hurriedly she felt she must cover up some fault in herself. Yet what it was that she must cover up she never knew. Nevertheless, when her children were present, she always felt the center of her heart go hard. This troubled her, and in her manner she was all the more gentle and anxious for her children, as if she loved them very much. Only she herself knew that at the center of her heart was a hard little place that could not feel love, no, not for anybody. Everybody else said of her: "She is such a good mother. She adores her children." Only she herself, and her children themselves, knew it was not so. They read it in each other's eyes.

There were a boy and two little girls. They lived in a pleasant house, with a garden, and they had discreet servants, and felt themselves superior to anyone in the neighborhood.

Although they lived in style, they felt always an anxiety in the house. There was never enough money. The mother had a small income, and the father had a small income, but not nearly enough for the social position which they had to keep up. The father went in to town to some office. But though he had good prospects, these prospects never materialized. There was always the grinding sense of the shortage of money, though the style was always kept up.

At last the mother said, "I will see if *I* can't make something." But she did not know where to begin. She racked her brains, and tried this thing and the other, but could not find anything successful. The failure made deep lines come into her face. Her children were growing up, they would have to go to school. There must be more money, there must be more money. The father, who was always very handsome and expensive in his tastes, seemed as if he never *would* be able to do anything worth doing. And the mother, who had a great belief in herself, did not succeed any better, and her tastes were just as expensive.

And so the house came to be haunted by the unspoken phrase: *There must be more money! There must be more money!* The children could hear it all the time, though nobody said it aloud. They heard it at Christmas, when the expensive and splendid toys filled the nursery. Behind the shining modern rocking horse, behind the smart doll's-house, a voice would start whispering: "There *must* be more money! There *must* be more money!" And the children would stop playing, to listen for a moment. They would look into each other's eyes, to see if they had all heard. And each one saw in the eyes of the other two that they too had heard. "There *must* be more money! There *must* be more money!"

It came whispering from the springs of the still-swaying rocking horse, and even the horse, bending his wooden, champing head, heard it. The big doll, sitting so pink and smirking in her new pram, could hear it quite plainly, and seemed to be smirking all the more self-consciously because of it. The foolish puppy, too, that took the place of the teddy-bear, he was looking so extraordinarily foolish for no other reason but that he heard the secret whisper all over the house. "There *must* be more money!"

Yet nobody ever said it aloud. The whisper was everywhere, and therefore no one spoke it. Just as no one ever says: "We are breathing!" in spite of the fact that breath is coming and going all the time.

"Mother," said the boy Paul one day, "why don't we keep a car of our own? Why do we always use Uncle's, or else a taxi?"

"Because we're the poor members of the family," said the mother.

"But why *are* we, Mother?"

"Well—I suppose," she said slowly and bitterly, "it's because your father has no luck."

The boy was silent for some time.

"Is luck money, Mother?" he asked, rather timidly.

"No, Paul. Not quite. It's what causes you to have money."

"Oh!" said Paul vaguely. "I thought when Uncle Oscar said *filthy lucker,* it meant money."

"*Filthy lucre* does mean money," said the mother. "But it's lucre, not luck."

"Oh!" said the boy. "Then what *is* luck, Mother?"

"It's what causes you to have money. If you're lucky you have money. That's why it's better to be born lucky than rich. If you're rich, you may lose your money. But if you're lucky, you will always get more money."

"Oh! Will you? And is Father not lucky?"

"Very unlucky, I should say," she said bitterly.

The boy watched her with unsure eyes.

"Why?" he asked.

"I don't know. Nobody ever knows why one person is lucky and another unlucky."

"Don't they? Nobody at all? Does *nobody* know?"

"Perhaps God. But He never tells."

"He ought to, then. And aren't you lucky either, Mother?"

"I can't be, if I married an unlucky husband."

"But by yourself, aren't you?"

"I used to think I was, before I married. Now I think I am very unlucky indeed."

"Why?"

"Well—never mind! Perhaps I'm not really," she said.

The child looked at her, to see if she meant it. But he saw, by the lines of her mouth, that she was only trying to hide something from him.

"Well, anyhow," he said stoutly, "I'm a lucky person."

"Why?" said his mother, with a sudden laugh.

He stared at her. He didn't even know why he had said it.

"God told me," he asserted, brazening it out.

"I hope He did, dear!" she said, again with a laugh, but rather bitter.

"He did, Mother!"

"Excellent!" said the mother, using one of her husband's exclamations.

The boy saw she did not believe him; or rather, that she paid no attention to his assertion. This angered him somewhere, and made him want to compel her attention.

He went off by himself, vaguely, in a childish way, seeking for the clue to "luck." Absorbed, taking no heed of other people, he went about with a sort of stealth, seeking inwardly for luck. He wanted luck, he wanted it, he wanted it. When the two girls were playing dolls in the nursery, he would sit on his big rocking horse, charging madly into space, with a frenzy that made the little girls peer at him uneasily. Wildly the horse careered, the waving dark hair of the boy tossed, his eyes had a strange glare in them. The little girls dared not speak to him.

When he had ridden to the end of his mad little journey, he climbed down and stood in front of his rocking horse, staring fixedly into its lowered face. Its red mouth was slightly open, its big eye was wide and glassy-bright.

"Now!" he would silently command the snorting steed. "Now, take me to where there is luck! Now take me!"

And he would slash the horse on the neck with the little whip he had asked Uncle Oscar for. He *knew* the horse could take him to where there was luck, if only he forced it. So he would mount again, and start on his furious ride, hoping at last to get there. He knew he could get there.

"You'll break your horse, Paul!" said the nurse.

"He's always riding like that! I wish he'd leave off!" said his sister Joan.

But he only glared down on them in silence. Nurse gave him up. She could make nothing of him. Anyhow he was growing beyond her.

One day his mother and his Uncle Oscar came in when he was on one of his furious rides. He did not speak to them.

"Hallo, you young jockey! Riding a winner?" said his uncle.

"Aren't you growing too big for a rocking horse? You're not a very little boy any longer, you know," said his mother.

But Paul only gave a blue glare from his big, rather close-set eyes. He would speak to nobody when he was in full tilt.

His mother watched him with an anxious expression on her face.

At last he suddenly stopped forcing his horse into the mechanical gallop, and slid down.

"Well, I got there!" he announced fiercely, his blue eyes still flaring, and his sturdy long legs straddling apart.

"Where did you get to?" asked his mother.

"Where I wanted to go," he flared back at her.

"That's right, son!" said Uncle Oscar. "Don't you stop till you get there. What's the horse's name?"

"He doesn't have a name," said the boy.

"Gets on without all right?" asked the uncle.

"Well, he has different names. He was called Sansovino last week."

"Sansovino, eh? Won the Ascot. How did you know his name?"

"He always talks about horse races with Bassett," said Joan.

The uncle was delighted to find that his small nephew was posted with all the racing news. Bassett, the young gardener, who had been wounded in the left foot in the war and had got his present job through Oscar Cresswell, whose batman he had been, was a perfect blade of the turf. He lived in the racing events, and the small boy lived with him.

Oscar Cresswell got it all from Bassett.

"Master Paul comes and asks me, so I can't do more than tell him, sir," said Bassett, his face terribly serious, as if he were speaking of religious matters.

"And does he ever put anything on a horse he fancies?"

"Well—I don't want to give him away—he's a young sport, a fine sport, sir. Would you mind asking him himself? He sort of takes a pleasure in it, and perhaps he'd feel I was giving him away, sir, if you don't mind."

Bassett was serious as a church.

The uncle went back to his nephew, and took him off for a ride in the car.

"Say, Paul, old man, do you ever put anything on a horse?" the uncle asked.

The boy watched the handsome face closely.

"Why, do you think I oughtn't to?" he parried.

"Not a bit of it! I thought perhaps you might give me a tip for the Lincoln."

The car sped on into the country, going down to Uncle Oscar's place in Hampshire.

"Honor bright?" said the nephew.

"Honor bright, son!" said the uncle.

"Well, then, Daffodil."

"Daffodil! I doubt it, sonny. What about Mirza?"

"I only know the winner," said the boy. "That's Daffodil."

"Daffodil, eh?"

There was a pause. Daffodil was an obscure horse, comparatively.

"Uncle!"

"Yes, son?"

"You won't let it go any further, will you? I promised Bassett."

"Bassett be damned, old man! What's he got to do with it?"

"We're partners. We've been partners from the first. Uncle, he lent me my first five shillings, which I lost. I promised him, honor bright, it was only between me and him; only you gave me that ten-shilling note I started winning with, so I thought you were lucky. You won't let it go any further, will you?"

The boy gazed at his uncle from those big, hot, blue eyes, set rather close together. The uncle stirred and laughed uneasily.

"Right you are, son! I'll keep your tip private. Daffodil, eh? How much are you putting on him?"

"All except twenty pounds," said the boy. "I keep that in reserve."

The uncle thought it a good joke.

"You keep twenty pounds in reserve, do you, you young romancer? What are you betting, then?"

"I'm betting three hundred," said the boy gravely. "But it's between you and me, Uncle Oscar! Honor bright?"

The uncle burst into a roar of laughter.

"It's between you and me all right, you young Nat Gould," he said, laughing. "But where's your three hundred?"

"Bassett keeps it for me. We're partners."

"You are, are you! And what is Bassett putting on Daffodil?"

"He won't go quite as high as I do, I expect. Perhaps he'll go a hundred and fifty."

"What, pennies?" laughed the uncle.

"Pounds," said the child, with a surprised look at his uncle. "Bassett keeps a bigger reserve than I do."

Between wonder and amazement Uncle Oscar was silent. He pursued the matter no further, but he determined to take his nephew with him to the Lincoln races.

"Now, son," he said, "I'm putting twenty on Mirza, and I'll put five for you on any horse you fancy. What's your pick?"

"Daffodil, Uncle."

"No, not the fiver on Daffodil!"

"I should if it was my own fiver," said the child.

"Good! Good! Right you are! A fiver for me and a fiver for you on Daffodil."

The child had never been to a race meeting before, and his eyes were blue fire. He pursed his mouth tight, and watched. A Frenchman just in front had put his money on Lancelot. Wild with excitement, he flayed his arms up and down, yelling *Lancelot! Lancelot!* in his French accent.

Daffodil came in first, Lancelot second, Mirza third. The child, flushed and with eyes blazing, was curiously serene. His uncle brought him four five-pound notes, four to one.

"What am I to do with these?" he cried, waving them before the boy's eyes.

"I suppose we'll talk to Bassett," said the boy. "I expect I have fifteen hundred now; and twenty in reserve; and this twenty."

His uncle studied him for some moments.

"Look here, son!" he said. "You're not serious about Bassett and that fifteen hundred, are you?"

"Yes, I am. But it's between you and me, Uncle. Honor bright!"

"Honor bright all right, son! But I must talk to Bassett."

"If you'd like to be a partner, Uncle, with Bassett and me, we could all be partners. Only, you'd have to promise, honor bright, Uncle, not to let it go beyond us three. Bassett and I are lucky, and you must be lucky, because it was your ten shillings I started winning with. . . ."

Uncle Oscar took both Bassett and Paul into Richmond Park for an afternoon, and there they talked.

"It's like this, you see, sir," Bassett said. "Master Paul would get me talking about racing events, spinning yarns, you know, sir. And he was always keen on knowing if I'd made or if I'd lost. It's about a year since, now, that I put five shillings on Blush of Dawn for him; and we lost. Then the luck turned, with that ten shillings he had from you: that we put on Singhalese. And since that time, it's been pretty steady, all things considering. What do you say, Master Paul?"

"We're all right when we're sure," said Paul. "It's when we're not quite sure that we go down."

"Oh, but we're careful then," said Bassett.

"But when are you *sure?*" smiled Uncle Oscar.

"It's Master Paul, sir," said Bassett, in a secret, religious voice. "It's as if he had it from heaven. Like Daffodil, now, for the Lincoln. That was as sure as eggs."

"Did you put anything on Daffodil?" asked Oscar Cresswell.

"Yes, sir. I made my bit."

"And my nephew?"

Bassett was obstinately silent, looking at Paul.

"I made twelve hundred, didn't I, Bassett? I told Uncle I was putting three hundred on Daffodil."

"That's right," said Bassett, nodding.

"But where's the money?" asked the uncle.

"I keep it safe locked up, sir. Master Paul he can have it any minute he likes to ask for it."

"What, fifteen hundred pounds?"

"And twenty! And *forty,* that is, with the twenty he made on the course."

"It's amazing!" said the uncle.

"If Master Paul offers you to be partners, sir, I would, if I were you—if you'll excuse me," said Bassett.

Oscar Cresswell thought about it.

"I'll see the money," he said.

They drove home again, and, sure enough, Bassett came round to the garden house with fifteen hundred pounds in notes. The twenty pounds' reserve was left with Joe Glee, in the Turf Commission deposit.

"You see, it's all right, Uncle, when I'm *sure!* Then we go strong, for all we're worth. Don't we, Bassett?"

"We do that, Master Paul."

"And when are you sure?" said the uncle, laughing.

"Oh, well, sometimes I'm *absolutely* sure, like about Daffodil," said the boy; "and sometimes I have an idea; and sometimes I haven't even an idea, have I, Bassett? Then we're careful, because we mostly go down."

"You do, do you! And when you're sure, like about Daffodil, what makes you sure, sonny?"

"Oh, well, I don't know," said the boy uneasily. "I'm sure, you know, Uncle; that's all."

"It's as if he had it from heaven, sir," Bassett reiterated.

"I should say so!" said the uncle.

But he became a partner. And when the Leger was coming on Paul was "sure" about Lively Spark, which was a quite inconsiderable horse. The boy insisted on putting a thousand on the horse, Bassett went for five hundred, and Oscar Cresswell two hundred. Lively Spark came in first, and the betting had been ten to one against him. Paul had made ten thousand.

"You see," he said, "I was absolutely sure of him."

Even Oscar Cresswell had cleared two thousand.

"Look here, son," he said, "this sort of thing makes me nervous."

"It needn't, Uncle! Perhaps I shan't be sure again for a long time."

"But what are you going to do with your money?" asked the uncle.

"Of course," said the boy, "I started it for Mother. She said she had no luck, because father is unlucky, so I thought if *I* was lucky, it might stop whispering."

"What might stop whispering?"

"Our house. I *hate* our house for whispering."

"What does it whisper?"

"Why—why"—the boy fidgeted—"why, I don't know. But it's always short of money, you know, Uncle."

"I know it, son, I know it."

"You know people send mother writs, don't you, Uncle?"

"I'm afraid I do," said the uncle.

"And then the house whispers, like people

laughing at you behind your back. It's awful, that is! I thought if I was lucky—"

"You might stop it," added the uncle.

The boy watched him with big blue eyes, that had an uncanny cold fire in them, and he said never a word.

"Well, then!" said the uncle. "What are we doing?"

"I shouldn't like Mother to know I was lucky," said the boy.

"Why not, son?"

"She'd stop me."

"I don't think she would."

"Oh!"—and the boy writhed in an odd way—"I *don't* want her to know, Uncle."

"All right, son! We'll manage it without her knowing."

They managed it very easily. Paul, at the other's suggestion, handed over five thousand pounds to his uncle, who deposited it with the family lawyer, who was then to inform Paul's mother that a relative had put five thousand pounds into his hands, which sum was to be paid out a thousand pounds at a time, on the mother's birthday, for the next five years.

"So she'll have a birthday present of a thousand pounds for five successive years," said Uncle Oscar. "I hope it won't make it all the harder for her later."

Paul's mother had her birthday in November. The house had been "whispering" worse than ever lately, and, even in spite of his luck, Paul could not bear up against it. He was very anxious to see the effect of the birthday letter, telling his mother about the thousand pounds.

When there were no visitors, Paul now took his meals with his parents, as he was beyond the nursery control. His mother went into town nearly every day. She had discovered that she had an odd knack of sketching furs and dress materials, so she worked secretly in the studio of a friend who was the chief artist for the leading drapers. She drew the figures of ladies in furs and ladies in silk and sequins for the newspaper advertisements. This young woman artist earned several thousand pounds a year, but Paul's mother only made several hundreds, and she was again dissatisfied. She so wanted to be first in something, and she did not succeed, even in making sketches for drapery advertisements.

She was down to breakfast on the morning of her birthday. Paul watched her face as she read her letters. He knew the lawyer's letter. As his mother read it, her face hardened and became more expressionless. Then a cold, determined look came on her mouth. She hid the letter under the pile of others, and said not a word about it.

"Didn't you have anything nice in the post for your birthday, Mother?" said Paul.

"Quite moderately nice," she said, her voice cold and absent.

She went away to town without saying more.

But in the afternoon Uncle Oscar appeared. He said Paul's mother had had a long interview with the lawyer, asking if the whole five thousand could not be advanced at once, as she was in debt.

"What do you think, Uncle?" said the boy.

"I leave it to you, son."

"Oh, let her have it, then! We can get some more with the other," said the boy.

"A bird in the hand is worth two in the bush, laddie!" said Uncle Oscar.

"But I'm sure to *know* for the Grand National; or the Lincolnshire; or else the Derby. I'm sure to know for *one* of them," said Paul.

So Uncle Oscar signed the agreement, and Paul's mother touched the whole five thousand. Then something very curious happened. The voices in the house suddenly went mad, like a chorus of frogs on a spring evening. There were certain new furnishings, and Paul had a tutor. He was *really* going to Eton, his father's school, in the following autumn. There were flowers in the winter, and blossoming of the luxury Paul's mother had been used to. And yet the voices in the house, behind the sprays of mimosa and almond-blossom, and from under the piles of iridescent cushions, simply trilled and screamed in a sort of ecstasy: "There *must* be more money! Oh-h-h; there *must* be more money. Oh, now, now-w! Now-w-w—there *must* be more money!—More than ever! More than ever!"

It frightened Paul terribly. He studied away at his Latin and Greek with his tutors. But his intense hours were spent with Bassett. The Grand National had gone by: he had not "known," and had lost a hundred pounds. Summer was at hand. He was in agony for the Lincoln. But even for the Lincoln he didn't "know," and he lost fifty pounds. He became wild-eyed and strange, as if something were going to explode in him.

"Let it alone, son! Don't you bother about it!" urged Uncle Oscar. But it was as if the boy couldn't really hear what his uncle was saying.

"I've got to know for the Derby! I've got to know for the Derby!" the child reiterated, his big blue eyes blazing with a sort of madness.

His mother noticed how overwrought he was.

"You'd better go to the seaside. Wouldn't you like to go now to the seaside, instead of waiting? I think you'd better," she said, looking down at him anxiously, her heart curiously heavy because of him.

But the child lifted his uncanny blue eyes.

"I couldn't possibly go before the Derby, Mother!" he said. "I couldn't possibly!"

"Why not?" she said, her voice becoming heavy when she was opposed. "Why not? You can still go from the seaside to see the Derby with your Uncle Oscar, if that's what you wish. No need for you to wait here. Besides, I think you care too much about these races. It's a bad sign. My family has been a gambling family, and you won't know till you grow up how much damage it has done. But it has done damage. I shall have to send Bassett away, and ask Uncle Oscar not to talk racing to you, unless you promise to be reasonable about it: go away to the seaside and forget it. You're all nerves."

"I'll do what you like, Mother, so long as you don't send me away till after the Derby," the boy said.

"Send you away from where? Just from this house?"

"Yes," he said, gazing at her.

"Why, you curious child, what makes you care about this house so much, suddenly? I never knew you loved it."

He gazed at her without speaking. He had a secret within a secret, something he had not divulged, even to Bassett or to his Uncle Oscar.

But his mother, after standing undecided and a little bit sullen for some moments, said:

"Very well, then! Don't go to the seaside till after the Derby, if you don't wish it. But promise me you won't let your nerves go to pieces. Promise you won't think so much about horse racing and *events,* as you call them!"

"Oh, no," said the boy casually. "I won't think much about them, Mother. You needn't worry. I wouldn't worry, Mother, if I were you."

"If you were me and I were you," said his mother, "I wonder what we *should* do!"

"But you know you needn't worry, Mother, don't you?" the boy repeated.

"I should be awfully glad to know it," she said wearily.

"Oh, well, you *can,* you know. I mean, you *ought* to know you needn't worry," he insisted.

"Ought I? Then I'll see about it," she said.

Paul's secret of secrets was his wooden horse, that which had no name. Since he was emancipated from a nurse and a nursery governess, he had had his rocking horse removed to his own bedroom at the top of the house.

"Surely, you're too big for a rocking horse!" his mother had remonstrated.

"Well, you see, Mother, till I can have a *real* horse, I like to have *some* sort of animal about," had been his quaint answer.

"Do you feel he keeps you company?" she laughed.

"Oh, yes! He's very good, he always keeps me company, when I'm there," said Paul.

So the horse, rather shabby, stood in an arrested prance in the boy's bedroom.

The Derby was drawing near, and the boy grew more and more tense. He hardly heard what was spoken to him, he was very frail, and his eyes were really uncanny. His mother had sudden strange seizures of uneasiness about him. Sometimes, for half an hour, she would feel a sudden anxiety about him that was almost anguish. She wanted to rush to him at once, and know he was safe.

Two nights before the Derby, she was at a big party in town, when one of her rushes of anxiety about her boy, her first-born, gripped her heart till she could hardly speak. She fought with the feeling, might and main, for she believed in common sense. But it was too strong. She had to leave the dance and go downstairs to telephone to the country. The nursery governess was terribly surprised and startled at being rung up in the night.

"Are the children all right, Miss Wilmot?"

"Oh, yes, they are quite all right."

"Master Paul? Is he all right?"

"He went to bed as right as a trivet. Shall I run up and look at him?"

"No," said Paul's mother reluctantly. "No! Don't trouble. It's all right. Don't sit up. We shall be home fairly soon." She did not want her son's privacy intruded upon.

"Very good," said the governess.

It was about one o'clock when Paul's mother and father drove up to their house. All was still. Paul's mother went to her room and slipped off her white fur cloak. She had told her maid not to wait up for her. She heard her husband downstairs, mixing a whisky and soda.

And then, because of the strange anxiety in her heart, she stole upstairs to her son's room. Noiselessly she went along the upper corridor. Was there a faint noise? What was it?

She stood, with arrested muscles, outside his door listening. There was a strange, heavy, and yet not loud noise. Her heart stood still. It was a soundless noise, yet rushing and powerful. Something huge, in violent, hushed motion. What was it? What in God's name was it? She ought to know. She felt that she knew the noise. She knew what it was.

Yet she could not place it. She couldn't say what it was. And on and on it went, like a madness.

Softly, frozen with anxiety and fear, she turned the door handle.

The room was dark. Yet in the space near the window, she heard and saw something plunging to and fro. She gazed in fear and amazement.

Then suddenly she switched on the light, and saw her son, in his green pajamas, madly surging on the rocking horse. The blaze of light suddenly lit him up, as he urged the wooden horse, and lit her up, as she stood, blond, in her dress of pale green and crystal, in the doorway.

"Paul!" she cried. "Whatever are you doing?"

"It's Malabar!" he screamed, in a powerful, strange voice. "It's Malabar!"

His eyes blazed at her for one strange and senseless second, as he ceased urging his wooden horse. Then he fell with a crash to the ground, and she, all her tormented motherhood flooding upon her, rushed to gather him up.

But he was unconscious, and unconscious he remained, with some brain fever. He talked and tossed, and his mother sat stonily by his side.

"Malabar! It's Malabar! Bassett, Bassett, I *know!* It's Malabar!"

So the child cried, trying to get up and urge the rocking horse that gave him his inspiration.

"What does he mean by Malabar?" asked the heart-frozen mother.

"I don't know," said the father stonily.

"What does he mean by Malabar?" she asked her brother Oscar.

"It's one of the horses running for the Derby," was the answer.

And, in spite of himself, Oscar Cresswell spoke to Bassett, and himself put a thousand on Malabar: at fourteen to one.

The third day of the illness was critical: they were waiting for a change. The boy, with his rather long, curly hair, was tossing ceaselessly on the pillow. He neither slept nor regained consciousness, and his eyes were like blue stones. His mother sat, feeling her heart had gone, turned actually into a stone.

In the evening, Oscar Cresswell did not come, but Bassett sent a message, saying could he come up for one moment, just one moment? Paul's mother was very angry at the intrusion, but on second thoughts she agreed. The boy was the same. Perhaps Bassett might bring him to consciousness.

The gardener, a shortish fellow with a little brown mustache, and sharp little brown eyes, tiptoed into the room, touched his imaginary cap to Paul's mother, and stole to the bedside, staring with glittering, smallish eyes at the tossing, dying child.

"Master Paul!" he whispered. "Master Paul! Malabar came in first all right, a clean win. I did as you told me. You've made over seventy thousand pounds, you have; you've over eighty thousand. Malabar came in all right, Master Paul."

"Malabar! Malabar! Did I say Malabar, Mother? Did I say Malabar? Do you think I'm lucky, Mother? I knew Malabar, didn't I? Over eighty thousand pounds! I call that lucky, don't you, Mother? Over eighty thousand pounds! I knew, didn't I know I knew? Malabar came in all right. If I ride my horse till I'm sure, then I tell you, Bassett, you can go as high as you like. Did you go for all you were worth, Bassett?"

"I went a thousand on it, Master Paul."

"I never told you, Mother, that if I can ride my horse, and *get there,* then I'm absolutely sure—oh, absolutely! Mother did I ever tell you? I *am* lucky!"

"No, you never did," said the mother.

But the boy died in the night.

And even as he lay dead, his mother heard her brother's voice saying to her: "My God, Hester, you're eighty-odd thousand to the good, and a poor devil of a son to the bad. But, poor devil, poor devil, he's best gone out of a life where he rides his rocking horse to find a winner."

AROUND THE TRACK
A PORTFOLIO OF PHOTOGRAPHS BY ROBERT RIGER

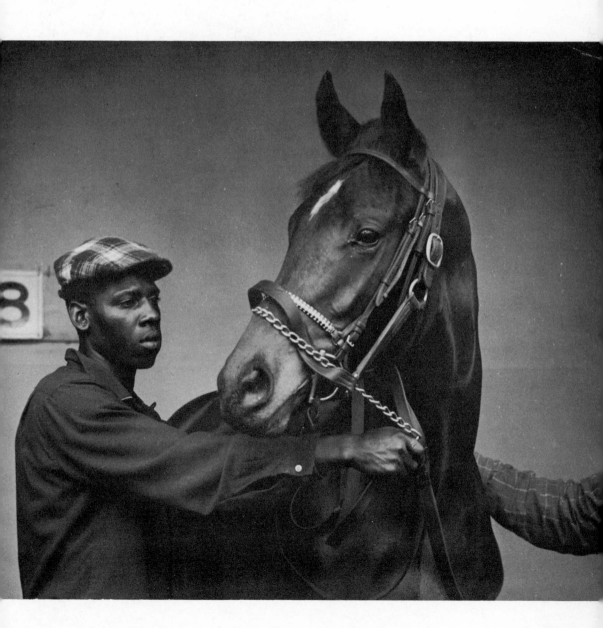

What's It Get You?

J. P. MARQUAND

I once asked Joe Palmer, a competent judge of literature as well as of horses and horse races, his favorite in racing fiction. "What's It Get You" was his reply, and at the time I wasn't certain whether it was a comment or an opinion. Now I know.

THE day had been a hard one at the Seven Oaks track. Following a custom which was invariable with him when he possessed the capital, Jack White had been betting on a series of long shots. He had not been betting blindly; instead, he had drawn upon his encyclopedic knowledge of past performances, and of sires and dams through the equine generations. For Jack White lived from an accurate digest of facts and from the reservoir of his own personal experience derived from thirty years at the track. In speaking of the financial difficulties besetting the nation, Jack White often said that if the bankers and the brokers had known as much about their securities as he did about four-legged prospects, there would have been no need for a New Deal.

"Furthermore," he said, "they don't take distress like gentlemen, and distress is good for the soul. That's why I've got a beautiful nature, and I have got a beautiful, even, tolerant, forgiving disposition, haven't I, boys? All because I know distress."

He was right, in a way. He was a magnificent object of fortitude in his bedroom in the Hotel Dixie that evening, tilted back in his chair, his shoes off, his vest unbuttoned. He had played five of his selections to win that afternoon and had watched them good-naturedly through his nickel-rimmed spectacles as they had faded; and now he seemed oblivious of nervous strain, only gently, hospitably weary.

"It was a nice day, boys," he said. "It always is, with sun and seven good honest races. Set down on the bed, boys, and help yourselves to cigars and whisky; it's all on me." His partner, Henry Bledsoe, stirred a spoonful of bicarbonate of soda into a glass of water. It was evident that Mr. Bledsoe did not agree with Mr. White.

"Honest, hell!" he said. "This track is packed with operators who ought to be in stripes. The stewards and the paddock judges are blind, and what's more—" Mr. Bledsoe groaned—"the sport is gone," he said; "there ain't no gentlemen any more."

Jack White looked at him in mild rebuke. "Henry," he said, "don't get passionate. Henry, you've been saying the same thing for thirty years."

Mr. Bledsoe's lean jaws clamped together and he slapped a bony hand on his knee. "Well, it's true," he said, "ain't it?"

Jack White answered with another question: "You and I've been honest, haven't we? And yet we've made a living."

"Well, it ain't your fault we have," snapped Henry.

Jack White blew a cloud of cigar smoke before him. "No, not anybody's fault," he answered. "I may be romantic, but I like to have ideals. I like to think that the average race is straight, and I believe it is. Maybe a race is straight because a horse is straight if he has a proper family tree. He's there to run because his kind have run. He's there to run because he's honest. If he has the heart to go, he goes; and no ninety-pound boy on him is going to stop him much and no electric shocks and dope will make him go much faster. If he has the heart, he goes; if he hasn't, he fades out. No, sir, it's the horse who wins the race."

"Gentlemen," said Henry Bledsoe, "ain't it amazing that he never learns a thing?"

Jack White stared into another cloud of smoke without giving any sign of having heard. His mind was clearly back at the track again, moving pleasantly through a gallery of memories. "Henry," he said, "Honeyboy in the fifth race, did he remind you of anything? He did me, Henry."

Mr. Bledsoe scratched his chin, and the room was silent as he thought, respectfully silent.

At any moment, in such company, a piece of information might be dropped that was as sound as a Coolidge dollar. Henry Bledsoe's slightly haggard face had brightened with understanding. "You can't fool me on horses, Jack," he said. "I seen it in the paddock. He was like Mr. Cavanaugh's Fighting Bob, but I could tell the difference in the dark." Mr. Bledsoe glanced around the room and smiled bitterly. "And what's more, gentlemen," he said, "I can tell you just what's coming. My dear old friend, Mr. White, who would lose his shirt each meeting if it weren't for me, is going to tell you a story to back up his own convictions. He's going to tell you about Daisy Cavanaugh, who handled horses down in the state of Maryland last year; and he's going to tell you about Mr. Cavanaugh's Fighting Bob, an unlikely three-year-old, if there ever was one, in order to prove that there are still gentlemen on the track; and when he's finished, it won't mean a damn thing, that's all. . . . Jack, do I have to listen? If I do, I want more soda."

Jack White blew another cloud of smoke. "Give him some more soda, boys," he said. "But there's one thing, Henry: the old man was a gentleman."

Henry Bledsoe seemed refreshed by his second spoonful of bicarbonate. "Yes," he said, "old Mr. Cavanaugh, he certainly was a gentleman, and what did it get him, White?"

Gentlemen [said Jack White], I don't need to tell you about the track at Langleyville, that Mecca where sportsmen have gathered each spring and autumn to follow the vicissitudes of the running horse for over a generation. Losing or winning, I can be happy at Langleyville. The officials, right down to the gate keepers, are capital fellows, and the restaurant proprietor is very apt to trust you, if you look him in the eye. I love to look across that fine oval of green out to the rolling country beyond it. It all speaks to

me of horseflesh. Yes, and educated money, and best of all I like the air, the spring air of the Chesapeake that is half rich land and half salt water. . . . All right, Henry, I won't go on, but I love artistic places.

That is why I always stop at Mrs. Griscom's boarding house when I am down at Langleyville. The exterior of that boarding house, two miles out of town, may not be superficially attractive, but, believe me, it has ever been a sanctuary of the harassed racing men. Mrs. Griscom, you may recall, is the widow of Sam Griscom, one of the most passionate plungers in the history of the track, who shot himself at New Orleans the day when Lightning Joe ran fourth in the Creole Handicap. Though I do not approve personally of such heights of feeling, that accident of Sam's, who was essentially a capital fellow, did much for Mrs. Griscom's charity. Yes, gentlemen, you can take it from me, go to Mrs. Griscom when you are in distress. Her features may be stern, but in her heart she knows the accidents of chance.

Accurately speaking, Henry and I were not in great throes of distress when a kindly motorist set us down at Langleyville one early April morning three days before the meet opened. Personally, I should have preferred taking the train, but Henry was holding the toll, and Henry is kind of mean with money. Henry's got a Yankee streak that way. It was a beautiful, early April morning, and the sun was shining on the dewy streets of Langleyville. As we stood on the sidewalk with our suitcases, near the courthouse, it was like coming home. We hadn't been in front of the courthouse half a minute before a party I had seen near the paddock in Miami came up to us.

"Hey, Mr. White," he said, "hey, Mr. Bledsoe, will you join me at breakfast at the Langley House?"

I did not like his looks. He was the kind who wouldn't do something for nothing; he was youngish—which wasn't against him—and well dressed—and that wasn't against him, either. It was his face—a pinky face with sandy eyebrows and a round button of a nose and rosebud lips. I did not like his face.

"That's kind of you, mister," I began.

"Greenway," he said—"Joe Greenway, to you, Mr. White. You're here early, aren't you? So am I."

Then Henry spoke up. "Thank you, Mr. Greenway," he said. "Mr. White and I have had a very hearty breakfast. We're waiting for a bus. Good morning, Mr. Greenway."

I don't know what it is about Henry, but he has no sentiment and gentle manners. "Henry," I said, "I was hungry and you took away my breakfast."

Henry only snapped his jaws together. "I'd rather go hungry," he said, "and keep my reputation. Won't you never learn to be careful who you're seen with? That boy is one of the Maxey crowd."

Now, everybody at the track has heard of Maxey. Personally, I have found him a capital fellow within limits, but everybody didn't. Jake Maxey had got into trouble at Miami, and there was a little shooting trouble in Hamilton last summer where his name was mentioned. I could see Henry's point in not wanting to be seen with one of Maxey's boys.

"What's he doing here?" I asked.

Henry clicked his teeth again. "We'll find out soon enough," he said. "You keep away from Maxey, White. Thank God I've got the roll."

"If you won't eat with Maxey's boy," I said, "let's you and me go to the hotel ourselves."

"I said," said Henry, "thank God I've got the roll. You and me are conserving capital, White, and we'll keep on conserving until we find an investment. We'll get breakfast at Mrs. Griscom's."

"Then let's hire a cab. I'm getting faint," I said.

"Hire a cab, nothing," said Henry. "We'll wait here till we get a free ride. We've only got three hundred dollars, and we don't break it until we get an investment."

It took us two hours to get to Mrs. Griscom's, but Henry was right, for we finally got set down there in front of her place for nothing. It was like being at home, once we got to Mrs. Griscom's. She took us into the parlor right away.

"You're early, boys," she said. "You wouldn't be here early if you wasn't in distress. Well, all the rooms are taken."

"Mrs. Griscom," I said, "you come out on the front porch with me. . . . Henry, you stay here." I knew that Mrs. Griscom would be all right when we were alone. "Did you take a good look at Henry?" I asked her. "He looks just the way Sam did at New Orleans, Mrs. Griscom. You don't want Henry on your conscience, do you?"

"He's got money, and he's holding out," she said. "I know Henry."

"Yes, Mrs. Griscom, you're right," I told her. "But you know how Henry is when he gets moods. Just now he wants to feel he's getting something for nothing. When he gets it, Henry will pay for it all right."

"All right," said Mrs. Griscom, "you can have the two back rooms, and you better go into the dining room. They're having a late breakfast."

"Who," I asked.

"The Cavanaughs," she told me. "Old Mr. Cavanaugh and his daughter Daisy."

"Not old Hendrick Cavanaugh, the owner?" I asked her. "I thought old Cavanaugh was through."

"Well, he's here," she said. "They've brought down six horses they've been boarding at Oak Hill, and the girl, she's conditioning them. She's a dear, sweet girl, too, even if she dresses like a jockey. She's going to turn the horses over to Shiny Denny."

The name made me remember Mr. Greenway by the courthouse. You have to be quick in my business in putting facts together. "I want to know," I said. "Shiny Denny was Maxey's trainer, wasn't he, back in '32?"

Mrs. Griscom understood me, and we exchanged a meaning glance. Life on the track moves as fast as the horses. I could recall the time just as well as she could when the Cavanaugh stables were known up and down the coast and when you could see the Cavanaugh colors—maroon and white and yellow—on almost any track.

"Mr. Cavanaugh needs money," she said.

"Does he own anything?" I asked.

And Mrs. Griscom sighed. "One three-year-old," she said, "that Fighting Bob. Out of his old Daisy Dimple by Bob Bender. Maxey's trainer will saddle him in part payment for conditioning his string."

Names, as everyone must know, have a way of bobbing up and down. Horse breeding and horse sense don't often go hand in hand. In the minute, as I stood up on the front porch, I was fitting together in my mind everything I had heard about old man Cavanaugh. The word was that the depression had cleaned him out. His place, Oak Hill, with its five hundred acres, its thirty-room house, its stables and its private track, had been on sale for the past five years, while the paint was peeling off it and the roofs were beginning to leak. His racing string had been sold off five years back, with the exception of two colts and his old mare, Daisy Dimple. Then he had gone in for boarding for friends and others. It was none of my business, but just the same it hurt me to think of an operator like Maxey, whose money was made from half a dozen rackets, boarding horses at Oak Hill. As I say, I was piecing the facts together, even down to this three-year-old, Fighting Bob, that was Cavanaugh's own property. Fighing Bob had performed once the previous year on the track in one of the maiden races. He had been so wild then that they couldn't get him in the starting stall. The Daisy Dimple colts were either brilliant or very wild. I looked at Mrs. Griscom and asked her a single question, purely out of curiosity:

"How does it happen Cavanaugh's staying with you?"

"Same reason as you," she said. "He was a friend of my husband's. He was awful kind to Sam." Then she looked me up and down and made a remark which I do not care to interpret:

"Mr. Cavanaugh's a real gentleman."

I sighed. "I don't like it," I said; "it don't fit right."

"What don't fit right?" she asked.

"Maxey's trainer boarding horses with a gentleman!"

I had never met Mr. Cavanaugh socially until that morning in Mrs. Griscom's dining room. He was the kind who had the same manners for everyone—elegant, fine manners. He stood up when Mrs. Griscom introduced us, a thin old man, slightly sprung in the knees. He wore a suit with small black-and-white checks that might have been smart fifteen years ago, and a pearl-gray Ascot tie. His face was lean and clean-bred like his hands. He had a snow-white mustache, waxed at the ends, and white curly hair.

"Gentlemen," he said, "I'm very greatly honored. Though our paths have, unfortunately, never met, reputation travels far. Everyone who knows the sport of kings has seen Mr. Bledsoe at the track in the mists of early morning, and, Mr. White, I have heard you highly spoken of in many, many places. It is an honor to have you both complete our company. I look forward to happy evenings during the meeting, gentlemen. . . . Daisy, my dear, may I present Mr. Bledsoe and Mr. White?"

At first I thought it was all make-believe, but it wasn't. It was only the way he talked. His eyes were kind and steady, like his voice. He was bowing to a girl in boots and breeches standing beside him, his daughter, Daisy. Ready to ride, she would not have tipped the scales at ninety pounds. She had a figure like a boy's in the paddock; she even had that jockey slouch. She had short, yellow, curly hair and her face was as pretty as a movie queen's. Her eyes were steady like the old man's and she had a rider's mouth, firm, but not hard enough to be cruel. Daisy Cavanaugh was a lady, pants and boots and all.

"You've got nice hands, miss," I said. "I can always tell a rider as soon as I shake hands."

"Thank you," she said, "I have to have them. We've brought down Mr. Denny's horses from the farm, six of them—they're quite a handful—and one of our own, Fighting Bob."

Henry didn't say anything. Henry is never much at talking.

"Perhaps Mr. Bledsoe is surprised," Daisy Cavanaugh said. "I suppose I'm about the only girl in this business."

"Daisy," said Mr. Cavanaugh, "now, Daisy!"

"I'm sure that Shiny Denny will be very pleased when he gets here," I said. "May I ask when he arrives?"

"Sometime tomorrow morning," she told me. "He has Stable No. 2. He's tucking down Mr. Maxey's Lighthouse. Lighthouse is entered in the South Cove Handicap next week."

"Yes," I said. "And he will be the favorite. It's kind of hard on Mr. Maxey to run a favorite, even for a big purse." She looked at me for a second before she answered, and I looked back.

"Well," she said, "what of it?"

"Nothing of it," I said, "nothing, miss. I'm acquainted with Mr. Maxey. Lighthouse is very fast."

"And may I venture to add," Mr. Cavanaugh broke in, "that I, for one, have found Mr. Maxey strictly honorable in all his dealings."

"I'm glad, sir," I said.

Daisy was still looking at me. "You know a great deal, don't you, Mr. White?" she remarked. "You follow the races, don't you?"

"Daisy," said Mr. Cavanaugh, "Daisy."

"Yes, miss," I told her. "Racing is all I know. I'm just an ordinary gambler, miss."

The hard look left her eyes. "Call me 'Daisy'; don't call me 'miss.' I'm just a common horse conditioner myself."

"Call me 'Jack,'" I said. "Every morning I'm at the track to see the exercising. I'll look forward to seeing you."

"Thanks, Jack," she said. "I'm going to breeze Fighting Bob tomorrow. We're entering him in the third race, Monday—an allowance race for three-year-olds. Will you clock him for me? I think he's ready."

"And believe me, sir," said Mr. Cavanaugh, "I should be delighted to receive your opinion as a friend and an expert."

Then Henry Bledsoe spoke up. "Mrs. Griscom," he called, "I'll trouble you for a glass of water and a spoon. I'm taking my bicarbonate now."

I liked Daisy and Mr. Cavanaugh. We had a capital time all day. We spent a long while together, running over old races and talking of this and that, and to hear him was like the fresh air from the bay. There was no hard word from Mr. Cavanaugh about anything or anybody.

"If I wager on an animal of mine, sir," he said, "I wager on him to win, and so I will do with Fighting Bob. He has the makings of a great horse, sir, and his dam's courage to run a fine race. I hope you'll agree with me, sir, when we work him out tomorrow."

Toward evening, after supper, Henry and I walked down the road a piece alone. "Old fool," Henry kept saying beneath his breath, "old fool and a tenth-rate horse."

"But, Henry," I told him, "Mr. Cavanaugh's a gentleman."

"Yes," said Henry, "and that's why he's a fool, ain't it? There's something isn't right, White; there's something isn't right."

It disturbed me to hear Henry say it, because Henry is quick that way. I knew myself that something wasn't right, but I would have bet my bottom dollar that neither Mr. Cavanaugh nor Daisy was in it.

It has been my custom for many years to rise at dawn and to proceed to the track to see the horses train. At such times, Henry would hold the watch, while I would simply sit and look and maybe walk around the stables and talk to friends. That is the time, in those early morning sessions, when one can learn all sorts of useful things, if one has ears and eyes. It is always a beautiful sight to me to see the horses jogging around the track, past the deserted grandstand, more beautiful than any picture.

"Believe me, sir," said Mr. Cavanaugh, "there is no Turner in the National Gallery to equal it. May I tempt you with a touch of my flask, sir? The world may change, but good horseflesh is the same, thank God."

He said it as we stood leaning on the rail of the deserted judges' stand at the Langleyville track that next morning. Mr. Cavanaugh was wrapped in an old coaching coat that made him look like a faded sporting print on some tack-room wall. He was peering through an antiquated pair of field glasses. The sun was coming up, driving away the mist.

"Ah!" he said. "Daisy is bringing out Fighting Bob!"

Now, what I'm trying to tell you is right dramatic in its way. Take people alone, and they may have no interest, but take them in their relations to others and you can have anything from tragedy to comedy. Down by the stable then, I saw Daisy, with the sun streaking that gold hair of hers, riding a rangy bay out to the track. He was stepping soft, as though he had eggs under him.

"You like him, sir?" asked Cavanaugh, and he twisted the corner of his mustache. He was pleased to see his own horse on the track. Before I had time to think of a truthful answer—the horse's looks were good enough, but I didn't like his action—a young fellow in a leather wind-break jacket came bounding up the steps.

"Good morning, Mr. Cavanaugh," he said. "I'm glad to see you here." Mr. Cavanaugh twisted the end of his mustache again. I had known the boy since he was a kid exercising for the Whitlers. His name was Tommy Cole. As long as I had known him, he had been sober and well-behaved, and now he was training for the Huntley stables and worth all the money that they paid him.

"Morning, Mr. Bledsoe," Tom Cole said. "Miss Cavanaugh asked will you please clock Fighting Bob? She's going to turn him loose out of the six-furlong chute."

I was pleased to see that Fighting Bob had improved. He went into the stall like he was used to it, and then he came out a-roaring to a clean, fast start. Daisy Cavanaugh was riding him like a man. She was saving him till she got around the turn, and then I saw her hands move, and Fighting Bob moved with them, and then I forgot about Daisy's riding.

Tom Cole nudged me with his elbow. "Did you ever see anything so beautiful?" he asked. He

was thinking of Daisy, but I was thinking of the horse. There was something in Fighting Bob's conformation that reminded me of an animal that had paid me money once. Daisy gave him his head, and he went across the line in style. Daisy eased him up and came walking back, rubbing her eyes on her sleeve, but I hardly looked at her, I was looking at the horse.

"What's the time?" she called, and Henry Bledsoe called it back.

"Mr. White, sir," said Mr. Cavanaugh, "I trust you agree with me that Fighting Bob is a credit to the Oak Hill stock."

"He'll have mighty fine odds Monday, sir," I said. I might have added, it is one thing for a horse running by himself and another as to how he behaves in a crowd.

"Pa," called Daisy, "come on down to the stables! Shiny Denny's here. . . . And won't you gentlemen come too?"

We walked behind them slowly toward Stable No. 2, and Henry and I exchanged a glance. Henry and I may be different in some ways, but we understand each other.

"Henry," I said, "I'd kind of like to get up close to Fighting Bob. Does he remind you of anything?" There isn't much that Henry doesn't remember. He has the clocker's gift for spotting a horse in the twilight under wraps, if he has seen him as much as once.

"White," he said in my ear, "you're a born fool with money, but you're not a fool about everything. As far as my facts go, Fighting Bob might as well be Maxey's Lighthouse. Comical, ain't it, that Fighting Bob and Maxey's Lighthouse should be in the same stable? White stocking on the near foreleg, star the size of a half dollar on the forehead."

"That's the difference," I said. "Fighting Bob's forehead is plain."

"Yes," said Henry Bledsoe softly, "the difference of a white half dollar."

Then I mentioned another thought to Henry which was running in my mind: "The odds are going to be almighty heavy on Fighting Bob, third race, Monday, Henry. If ever there was a rank outsider who might start at sixty to one, it's Fighting Bob." Henry coughed behind his hand.

"White," he asked me, "do you reckon Maxey's thought of that?"

The door to Stable No. 2 was closed. Mr. Cavanaugh and Daisy and Tom Cole were out in front of it, and with them was that button-nosed Greenway and Shiny Denny. Shiny Denny was in his store clothes, polishing his nails. He was a little, leather-faced, black-eyed man, who had been a jockey when I had known him first.

"How's Lighthouse, Shiny?" I asked him. "Did he van down nice?" Shiny laughed, showing a set of yellow teeth, and jerked his thumb toward the closed door.

"Lighthouse is resting comfortably inside," he said. "Honest, boys, I wish I could take you in to see him, but now that Miss Cavanaugh's turned over to me, the stable is closed. No offense intended. Mr. Maxey's orders."

"Why, Shiny," I told him, "I always believed in quiet stables. How is Maxey? When's he coming down?"

"Mr. Maxey's coming down on Monday," Shiny said; "not that he's got anything running, you understand." Then he polished his nails again and turned to Daisy Cavanaugh. "You done a swell job on those horses, miss," he added, "and I've got a piece of news for you that makes me kind of sick. I've got to leave for New York tonight. My dear old mother's dying up in the Bronx. It hurts me, because I know you're counting on me for Monday. I can't be here, I simply can't, to saddle Fighting Bob."

I saw Mr. Cavanaugh twitch at his mustache and I saw Daisy's lips come tight together, and I knew the only thing they cared about was seeing Fighting Bob in that Monday's race. Furthermore, in all the years I'd known him, I'd never heard Shiny speak of his mother in the Bronx. I knew one thing just as sure as shooting. There was something going to happen that Monday, and Maxey was getting out from under.

"I'm very sorry, sir," I heard Mr. Cavanaugh saying, "This is a very bitter blow to me, but we'll forget it. Fighting Bob can't start without a trainer."

Then I saw Daisy and young Tom Cole looking at each other, and then Tom Cole cleared his throat. "If you'll let me, Mr. Cavanaugh," he said, "I'll be proud to saddle Fighting Bob the third race Monday, and Mr. Huntley will be proud to have me. None of our own are entered. You know and I know that no horse can enter a race unless a licensed trainer saddles him."

"Why," Mr. Cavanaugh began, "that's a great kindness, Mr. Cole." And they looked at each other for a second or two, and then Tom Cole said: "I'd do a sight more than that, you know."

Then I looked at Denny, because he interested me more than anybody else just then. It seemed to me that he was pleased—too pleased.

"That's fine," he said. "Then everything's all right. You've got a great horse, Mr. Cavanaugh."

Henry Bledsoe did not have much to say that day. There wasn't much need to talk, because Henry and I understood each other. About an hour before supper, he spoke to Mrs. Griscom.

"Jack and I won't be in to supper," he said; "we're walking up to town."

It was the first time I had heard that we were going into town, but I understood what Henry meant. Henry was thinking of the roll. Henry was onto something, and I knew what.

There is only one drugstore in Langleyville, and Henry and I walked in. First Henry bought a package of cigarettes and some matches. This surprised me, because Henry thinks cigarette smoking is a sin, and he doesn't spend money without reason. Then Henry began to talk to the clerk, and talking is not in Henry's line. On the back counter of the store was a row of patent medicines, sarsaparilla, and Indian remedies. Henry is good on patent medicines, he's tried them all, and right away the clerk knew he was talking to a master.

"Are you a salesman, mister?" the clerk said.

"No," said Henry. "Bless you, no, I've never sold the stuff. It's only I'm interested in my own insides. How's your line of hair dye?" said Henry. "Do you move much hair dye, friend?"

"Well, no, sir," the clerk said. "Hair dye goes mighty slow hereabouts."

"I want to know," Henry said. "You'd think somebody would buy it."

"Well," the clerk said, "now you speak of it, I did sell a bottle this afternoon."

"I want to know," said Henry. "Who bought it? An oldish man?"

The boy in the white coat grinned. "Why, no," he said. "That's why I remember it. The party didn't look as though he needed hair dye for himself. He was a youngish fellow with a round button nose and a kind of a rosebud mouth. One of the racing crowd, a stranger here like you, sir."

"Well," said Henry, "would you give me a glass of water and a spoonful of bicarbonate? They tell me soda puts color in the hair."

Once we were outside the store, Henry tapped my arm. He did not need to comment on what we had heard, because I had ears. Greenway had bought a bottle of brown hair dye, and Maxey's horse named Lighthouse had a white star on his forehead. "Come on," said Henry. "We're going to the track."

It was pitch dark at the track by then. A light wind was blowing, sighing through the emptiness of the grandstand, and you could swear that horses' ghosts were running on the wind. There were lights in the superintendent's house; and lights in the stable tack rooms were just small dots of light in a bare black carpet. Henry tapped my arm again.

"White," he whispered, "I'm going into Stable 2. I want to look at them two horses close. Take these cigarettes. There's a pile of straw outside of Stable 3. You walk by it, light a cigarette and drop a match in the straw. And when it takes, you holler 'Fire!' That'll fetch 'em out, and all I want is half a minute."

Now, everybody knows there's nothing more serious around a track than fire. I wanted to argue with Henry, but he is hard to argue with, and I did exactly what he said. I walked over to the rubbish pile and dropped three matches in it. The straw took fire like tinder, and then I started running, shouting:

"Fire in Stable No. 3!"

The sight of the blaze brought the boys out of the stables like bees out of hives. Even when it was out, a crowd still stood around the straw pile, talking, and then Henry was back, tapping on my arm.

"All right, let's blow," he said. "Them two are alike as two peas. You go back to Griscom's, White. I want to watch that Greenway party. He'll be calling in the bank tomorrow morning, or else I miss my bet."

I was tired when I got back to Griscom's, but somehow I couldn't sleep, and maybe you can't blame me, now that you see the picture as I saw it. In a sense, we were onto something good, but I was troubled by conscience just the same. The trouble was that Mr. Cavanaugh was a gentleman.

Next morning was Saturday, a bright, clear day. Around noon Henry came back and we walked down the road a piece. Henry was looking pretty pleased.

"Greenway cashed a telegraph order for seventy-five hundred dollars," he said. "I guess we know where it's going, White—on Fighting Bob, third race, Monday afternoon—and our roll is going with it."

But somehow I couldn't do it quite like that.

"No, Henry," I said, "no we don't. I'm going to tell Mr. Cavanaugh about this, Henry."

Henry's mouth fell open. Sometimes Henry is mighty ugly when he is mad. "You mind your own business," he snapped. "What are these Cavanaughs and these crooks to you and me?" I could see his point; but still, I have a conscience.

"No," I said, "Mr. Cavanaugh's a friend of mine. Mr. Cavanaugh must decide for himself." Then Henry began to swear. He turned the air sky-blue, but I knew that I was right.

"The trouble is, Henry," I said, "Mr. Cavanaugh's a gentleman."

"Well, we ain't, are we?" Henry shouted.

"No," I said, "but we've got instincts. No, Henry, you leave this to me. We ought to tell Mr. Cavanaugh on Monday. It's up to him, not us."

Maybe I was a fool. I'm never wholly sure. It isn't easy, in my position, to see a sure thing tossed away, but when I think of the race track at Langleyville that Monday, maybe I was right.

We had a touch of bourbon whisky before we left for the track.

"I admire your abstemiousness, Mr. White," Mr. Cavanaugh told me, "and I honor it, but I must beg of you for once to break your invariable rule. It isn't often these days that a horse of mine is running. Maybe this will be the last time I see my colors on a track. I must beg of you, sir, to touch glasses with me. To my three-year-old, sir, Fighting Bob!"

"To Fighting Bob, sir," I said.

"Daisy," he said, "fill up my flask in case these gentlemen or I should need encouragement. . . .

And, gentlemen, we take our places in the clubhouse today. The admission is on me. . . . No, sir, I insist. You must gratify an old man's whim."

Once he was inside the club, Mr. Cavanaugh was bowing, smiling, talking. He knew everybody who was worth while there at the club. He went into one of the upper rooms and ordered a round of drinks, though I took lemonade.

"Yes, gentlemen," he kept saying, "keep your eyes on my Fighting Bob in the third race. His dam was Daisy Dimple—you remember Daisy Dimple, gentlemen."

When the horses were going to the post for the first race, Henry and I got up. "If you'll excuse us," I said, "we're going down to the stands." And then I lowered my voice and added, "Mr. Cavanaugh, I admire you very greatly; that's why I have a request to make. There's a man I want you to see in private. Could you arrange to see us in this room, alone? I want you to see him before the horses are led out to the paddock for the third."

Mr. Cavanaugh's head went back. "This is most unusual," he said. "Are you insinuating that there is something wrong? If there is, I'll ask for you to kindly tell me now."

"You'll know why when I get back," I told him. "I can only say right now, I think you'll thank me, sir."

Money was going down on Fighting Bob—so much that he had dropped from 50 to 1 to 20 on the probable-odds board.

"Jack," said Henry, "there's still time. Will you be a born fool all your life?" I knew by the odds that Maxey had placed his money, and Henry knew it too.

"No," I said, "after Mr. Cavanaugh's seen Maxey, maybe we'll bet then."

When Maxey is at the track, he always stands between races at the hot-dog stand near Entrance No. 6, in case anyone should want to see him. Maxey was standing there smoking a cigarette, a broad-shouldered little man with smooth black hair and a face the color of unbaked clay. It was the sort of face that would not change at anything. When I came up, he turned a pair of eyes on me, icy cold.

"Howdy, Jack," he said. "What's on your mind."

And I put my arm through his and whispered in his ear:

"Maxey, you and I are walking over to the clubhouse to see Mr. Cavanaugh, unless you want for me to holler for the track detective."

I felt Maxey's arm grow stiff.

"What's your game, pal?" he asked.

"It's not my game," I said. "It's yours. We're going up to the clubhouse to talk about Fighting Bob." Maxey's eyelids fluttered, but that was the only sign he gave.

Daisy and Mr. Cavanaugh were waiting for us in the room upstairs, alone, when Henry and Maxey and I came in. I closed the door and put my back against it.

"Mr. Cavanaugh," I said, "there's something I think you ought to know. And what you do is your business, not mine. I'll never say a word, and Mr. Maxey here will tell you whether I'm right or wrong. It's my opinion that Mr. Maxey has been making use of you, Mr. Cavanaugh. Right this minute Lighthouse is in Fighting Bob's stall, with the star on his forehead painted out. He's ready to run for Fighting Bob in the third race, and I thought you ought to know."

Maxey smiled and lighted a cigarette.

"That's baloney," he said.

I looked at Daisy and Mr. Cavanaugh. Both their faces had grown white. Mr. Cavanaugh started to speak, and stopped. "Now wait, Mr. Cavanaugh," I went on. "I'm not blaming this on you, and generally I don't go in for reform. Maxey is betting seventy-five hundred on Fighting Bob, because Lighthouse is ringing for him. If you want my opinion, Maxey has done a first-rate job. It's my honest belief that if Lighthouse runs, no one will know it. I believe that Lighthouse is a sure winner if he runs. Henry, here, is ready to go down and bet. I thought I ought to tell you first, that's all."

"Hey," said Maxey, and his voice was no longer cool, "if you know so damn much, why didn't you play along and keep your mouth shut?"

"Because I've got a conscience, Maxey," I told him. "And Mr. Cavanaugh's a gentleman. I suggest we walk down to the stable right now, quick, before they lead 'em out, and see if I'm right or wrong; or maybe, Maxey, you'd like me to call for the detective. You can take your choice."

Mr. Cavanaugh stood up very straight and spoke very slowly. There was no great change in his voice, but somehow his voice was terrible.

"We'll go to the stables," he said.

Maxey licked his lips.

"Now wait a minute," he said, "wait a minute. Let's talk sense. We're all sensible here, ain't we? Sure, I had the thought two weeks ago. Lighthouse is a ringer for that dog, Fighting Bob. Listen, folks, I know when I'm licked, and now I got a business proposition. We all sit down and take it easy. We don't say a word until this race is over. I've got seventy-five hundred up on Bob and we ought to get twenty to one. Now, come, you don't want to bust up a sure thing. Seventy-five hundred, and fifteen minutes from now it's a hundred and fifty grand." Maxey licked his lips again. "I'm being straight. I'm telling you clean truth, and here's my proposition, folks: A fifty-fifty cut, just as soon as we cash in. I'm no piker; I've never been a piker. Fifty grand for you and the little lady, Mr. Cavanaugh, and twenty-five grand split between White and Bledsoe, and that's

more money than any of you folks'll see again. What do you say? Let's sit down and be sociable."

Maxey's voice stopped, and when it did you could hear the noise from the crowd outside, a restless sound like the ocean against the rocks. It was a good quarter of a minute before anyone said a word. Mr. Cavanaugh took a cigar from his pocket, cut off the end and lighted it, but his fingers were trembling when he held the match.

"Mr. White," he said, "this is very shocking, both to me and to my daughter. I hope sincerely you feel we are in no wise connected with this, and I am very deeply grateful to you, sir. Neither my daughter nor I would have permitted a friend of hers to saddle a horse which we did not own. As for me, I want you to know that I've always raced clean. My money's down on Fighting Bob and I owe it to the public to put him on the track."

He bowed to me and turned toward Maxey. It was like a show to see it. "And as for you, you rascal," said the colonel, "I could hand you to the law, but I'm going to be the law. We're going to the stables now and my eye will be on you, Mr. Maxey. You've put your money on Fighting Bob, and if I were you, Mr. Maxey, I'd yell for Fighting Bob to win. We'll start walking to the stables now. Mr. Maxey, you'll walk between Mr. White and me, please."

I was proud to be walking with Mr. Cavanaugh. There are not so many things that I can be proud of, but I was proud of that. We walked to Stable No. 2 not too fast, and not too slow, just as the horses were moving out from the paddock for the second race. Mr. Cavanaugh chatted to us just as though nothing were wrong. "It's a very fine day for racing, Mr. White," he said, "and the crowd is in a betting mood. Do you remember the old days at Saratoga? This is like a Saratoga day. . . . Mr. Maxey, tell your men to get outside; we shall want the stable to ourselves." We blinked, once the stable door was closed behind us, and then we were used to the fainter light. A horse was standing in the third stall on the right. His bridle was on already. I could have sworn he was Fighting Bob. Mr. Cavanaugh stood in front of him.

"White," he said, "I declare, I think you're wrong."

"Take the flask out of your pocket, Mr. Cavanaugh," I said; "wash his face for him. Whisky will take out the dye."

Mr. Cavanaugh's motions were deliberate. He drew out his flask and sopped his handkerchief with the whisky.

"Steady, boy," he said, and rubbed hard between the horse's eyes. There was a small white star between the eyes when he took his handkerchief away. Holding the handkerchief between his thumb and forefinger, he offered it to Mr. Maxey. "Take it as a souvenir," he said, "and I should keep it carefully if I were you. Where's Fighting Bob?"

"There," Daisy said, "down there on the left."

"Daisy," said Mr. Cavanaugh, "lead him out. . . . Help me to shift those horses, Maxey, if you don't want to go to prison. Then call a boy to lead my entry to the paddock."

Then, just as though nothing had happened, we walked back to the clubhouse again and stood on the terrace waiting for the start. "Yes," said Mr. Cavanaugh, "it's a nice day for a race." Maxey did not say a word.

"If you'll excuse me," said Henry, "I think I'll place a bet."

"By all means," said Mr. Cavanaugh, "and if you'll take a tip from me, I'd bet on Fighting Bob."

Then a voice shouted from the loudspeakers like a voice of doom: "The horses are now going to the post."

Maxey cleared his throat. "The betting windows are closed now," he said; "if you'll excuse me, this company is too holy. I never seen fifty grand tossed away like that. Maybe you're a gentleman, but what's it get you, Cavanaugh?"

"My dear fellow," said Mr. Cavanaugh, "it's never got me anything. It's always been a minus quantity. Must you be going, really? Then don't come back again." Maxey drew a deep breath that was almost like a sigh.

"Mister," he said, "you're damn well right, I won't."

Then Daisy took my hand. "Thank you," she whispered, "thank you, Mr. White."

Mr. Cavanaugh was looking through his battered glasses. "He's standing nicely, my dear," he said; "he'll start this time." And then there was a sound like waves, that sound that will make me roll over when I'm dead, a soft sound, too hushed to be a shout, and our own voices joined in it as we said, "They're off!"

Now, believe me, that first second when they're off is always just pure gold. The color and the motion is like the sun through a stained-glass window, I sometimes think. It's a brave sight, a fine sight.

"Daisy," said Mr. Cavanaugh, "we've got a good boy up. Take the glasses, my dear. He's fourth; he's on the rail."

Then Daisy's voice was shaking. "Yes," she said, "he's going well! He's coming up! He's coming up!" I did not like to be there to see it. The boy was Jerry Hoberg, a good rider. There was a black from the Nixon stables that I had always fancied; at the halfway mark this black came out of the bunch easily. At the last turn he took second place and then he moved out ahead. Mr. Cavanaugh looked away from the track.

"A very pretty race. The Nixon black wins," he said.

"Wait a minute," I said to him—"wait a minute. Bob is coming up." The crowd saw it a second later. Fighting Bob was moving as though he were pushed upon a wave. He was in third, he was in second before the boy on the black horse looked behind him. Just for an instant I thought the rush might pull him through, but the boy in front looked soon enough. Down came his whip, and the black drew off. Fighting Bob was gaining, but not enough, not enough. Daisy was holding my hand, and I saw that she was crying, and then Mr. Cavanaugh saw it too.

"Don't cry, my dear," he said. "That was a pretty challenge. He hasn't got his dam's courage, but how could we tell that?"

"Father," Daisy was sobbing, "it's my fault. I thought he was better. It was my fault to make you put up your bottom dollar." Mr. Cavanaugh patted her shoulder very gently. "My dear," he said, "others have lost with us. After all, what's racing for? It was a very pretty race."

"Yes, sir," I said, and then I saw that Henry Bledsoe was back. Henry was beckoning to me. "White," he said, "come over here. I don't want the old man to know."

"Know what?" I asked him, and Henry looked embarrassed. "White," said Henry, "he ain't our kind. We got to keep away from sports like him. I kind of got to liking him, White, down there in the stable, and you know what I found myself doing? I found myself putting our roll on Fighting Bob to win." I felt a little cold inside, but Henry and I have been broke before. "We're in good company," I said.

"No, we ain't," said Henry, "and that's why I'm ashamed. I been a piker, White. The last minute I put down on Fighting Bob to run second, and now he's paying 12 to 1, but don't tell the old man, will you, please? Just tell him we bet on Fighting Bob."

Right Royal

JOHN MASEFIELD

This classic account of a steeplechase is a sort of Cinerama—every hoof-beat, every tactic of the race, every emotion of the jockey is experienced by the reader—much as the roller-coaster effects of the new screen techniques are conveyed to an audience. There is a wonderful rhythm to the lines of John Masefield's poem. If you feel cheated here by being served only the start of the race and the finish you are entitled to claim foul, and I am certain the stewards will sustain your objection.

The Start:

Then a gray-haired man with a hawklike face
Read from a list each rider's place.
Sitting astride his pommely hack,
He ordered them up or sent them back;
He bade them heed that they jump their nags
Over every jump between the flags.
Here Kubbadar, who was pulling double,
Went sideways, kicking and raising trouble,
Monkery seconded, kicking and biting,
Thunderbolt followed by starting fighting.

The starter eyed them and gave the order
That the three wild horses keep the border,
With men to hold them to keep them quiet.
Boys from the stables stopped their riot.
Out of the line to the edge of the field
The three wild biters and kickers wheeled;
Then the rest edged up and pawed and bickered,
Reached at their reins and snatched and snick-
  ered,
Flung white foam as they stamped their hate
Of passionate blood compelled to wait.

Then the starter shouted to Charles, "Good
  heaven,
This isn't a circus, you on Seven."
For Royal squirmed like a box of tricks
And Coranto's rider, the number six,
Cursed at Charles for a green young fool

Who ought to be at a riding school.
After a minute of swerves and shoving,
A line like a half-moon started moving;
Then Rocket and Soyland leaped to stride,
To be pulled up short and wheeled to side.
Then the trickier riders started thrusting,
Judging the starter's mind too trusting;
But the starter said, "You know quite clearly
That isn't allowed; though you'd like it dearly."

Then Cannonade made a sideways bolt
That gave Exception an ugly jolt.
Then the line, reformed, broke all to pieces.

Then the line reforms, and the tumult ceases.
Each man sits tense though his racer dances;
In a slow, jerked walk the line advances.

And then in a flash, more felt than seen,
The flag shot down and the course showed green,
And the line surged forwards and all that glory
Of speed was sweeping to make a story.

One second before, Charles Cothill's mind
Had been filled with fear to be left behind,
But now with a rush, as when hounds leave cover,
The line broke up and his fear was over.
A glimmer of bay behind The Ghost
Showed Dear Adonis still there at post.

Out to the left, a joy to his backer,
Kubbadar led the field a cracker,
The thunder of horses, all fit and foaming,
Made the blood not care whether death were
    coming.
A glimmer of silks, blue, white, green, red,
Flashed into his eye and went ahead;
Then hoof-casts scattered, then rushing horses
Passed at his side with all their forces.
His blood leapt up, but his mind said "No,
Steady, my darling, slow, go slow.
In the first time round this ride's a hunt."

The Turk's Grave Fence made a line in front.
Long years before, when the race began,
That first of the jumps had maimed a man;
His horse, the Turk, had been killed and buried
There in the ditch by horse-hoofs herried;
And over the poor Turk's bones at pace
Now, every year, there goes the race,
And many a man makes doctor's work
At the thorn-bound ditch that hides the Turk,
And every man as he rides that course
Thinks, there, of the Turk, that good old horse.

The thick thorn-fence stands five feet high,
With a ditch beyond unseen by eye,
Which a horse must guess from his urgent rider
Pressing him there to jump it wider.
And being so near both Stand and Post,
Out of all the jumps men haunt it most,
And there, with the crowd, and the undulled
    nerves,
The old horse balks and the young horse swerves,
And the good horse falls with the bad on top
And beautiful boldness comes to stop.

Charles saw the rush of the leading black,
And the forehands lift and the men sway back:
He steadies his horse, then with crash and crying
The top of the Turk's Grave Fence went flying.
Round in a flash, refusing danger,
Came the Lucky Shot right into Ranger;
Ranger swerving knocked Bitter Dick,
Who blundered at it and leaped too quick;
Then crash went blackthorn as Bitter Dick fell,
Meringue jumped on him and rolled as well.
As Charles got over he splashed the dirt
Of the poor Turk's grave on two men hurt.

Right Royal landed. With cheers and laughter
Some horses passed him and some came after;
A fine brown horse strode up beside him,
It was Thankful running with none to ride him;
Thankful's rider, dizzy and sick,
Lay in the mud by Bitter Dick.

In front was the curving street of Course,
Barred black by the leaps unsmashed by horse.
A cloud blew by and the sun shone bright,

Showing the guard-rails gleaming white.
Little red flags, that gusts blew tense,
Streamed to the wind at each black fence.
And smiting the turf to clods that scattered
Was the rush of the race, the thing that mattered,
A tide of horses in fury flowing,
Beauty of speed in glory going,
Kubbadar pulling, romping first,
Like a big black fox that had made his burst.

And away and away and away they went,
A visible song of what life meant.
Living in houses, sleeping in bed,
Going to business, all seemed dead,
Dead as death to that rush in strife,
Pulse for pulse with the heart of life.

"For to all," Charles thought, "when the blood
    beats high
Comes the glimpse of that which may not die;
When the world is stilled, when the wanting
    dwindles,
When the mind takes light and the spirit kindles,
One stands on a peak of this old earth."

Charles eyed his horses and sang with mirth.
What of this world that spins through space?
With red blood running he rode a race,
The beast's red spirit was one with his,
Emulous and in ecstasies;
Joy that from heart to wild heart passes
In the wild things going through the grasses;
In the hares in the corn, in shy gazelles
Running the sand where no man dwells;
In horses scared at the prairie spring;
In the dun deer noiseless, hurrying;
In fish in the dimness scarcely seen,
Save as shadows shooting in a shaking green;
In birds in the air, neck-straining, swift,
Wing touching wing while no wings shift,
Seen by none, but when stars appear
A reaper wandering home may hear
A sigh aloft where the stars are dim,
Then a great rush going over him:
This was his; it had linked him close
To the force by which the comet goes,
With the rein none sees, with the lash none feels,
But with fire-mane tossing and flashing heels.

The roar of the race course died behind them,
In front were their Fates, they rode to find them,
With the wills of men, with the strengths of
    horses,
They dared the minute with all their forces.

The Finish:
Now they charged the last hurdle that led to the
    Straight,
Charles longing to ride, though his spirit said
    "Wait."

He came to his horses as they came to the leap,
Eight hard-driven horses, eight men breathing
deep.

On the left, as he leaped it, a flashing of brown
Kicking white on the grass, showed that Thank-
ful was down;
Then a glance, right and left, showed that, bar-
ring all flukes,
It was Soyland's, Sir Lopez', or Peterkinooks'.

For Stormalong blundered and dwelt as he landed,
Counter Vair's man was beaten and Monkery
stranded.
As he reached to Red Ember the man on the red
Cried, "Lord, Charlie Cothill, I thought you were
dead!"

He passed the Red Ember, he came to the flank
Of Peterkinooks, whom he reached and then
sank.
There were only two others, going level alone,
First the spotted cream jacket, then the blue,
white and roan.

Up the street of green race course they strained
for the prize,
While the stands blurred with waving and the air
shook with cries:
"Now, Sir Lopez!" "Come, Soyland!" "Now, Sir
Lopez! Now, now!"
Then Charles judged his second, but he could not
tell how.

But a glory of sureness leaped from horse into
man,
And the man said, "Now, beauty," and the horse
said, "I can."
And the long-weary Royal made an effort the
more,
Though his heart thumped like drum-beats as he
went to the fore.

Neck and neck went Sir Lopez and Soyland together,
Soyland first, a short head, with his neck all in
lather;
Both were ridden their hardest, both were doing
their best,
Right Royal reached Soyland and came to his
chest.

There Soyland's man saw him with the heel of
his eye,
A horse with an effort that could beat him or
tie;
Then he glanced at Sir Lopez, and he bit through
his lip,
And he drove in his spurs and he took up his
whip.

There he lashed the game Soyland who had given
his all,
And he gave three strides more, and then failed
at the call,
And he dropped behind Royal like a leaf in a
tide:
Then Sir Lopez and Royal ran on side by side.

There they looked at each other, and they rode,
and were grim;
Charles thought, "That's Sir Lopez. I shall never
beat him."
All the yells for Sir Lopez seemed to darken the
air,
They were rushing past Emmy and the White
Post was there.

He drew to Sir Lopez; but Sir Lopez drew clear;
Right Royal clung to him and crept to his ear.
Then the man on Sir Lopez judged the moment
had come
For the last ounce of effort that would bring his
horse home.

So he picked up his whip for three swift slashing
blows,
And Sir Lopez drew clear, but Right Royal stuck
close.
Charles sat still as stone, for he dared not to stir,
There was that in Right Royal that needed no
spur.

In the trembling of an instant power leaped up
within,
Royal's pride of high spirit not to let the bay win.
Up he went, past his withers, past his neck, to
his head.
With Sir Lopez' man lashing, Charles still, seeing
red.

So they rushed for one second, then Sir Lopez
shot out:
Charles thought, "There, he's done me, without
any doubt.
Oh, come now, Right Royal!"
                     And Sir Lopez changed feet
And his ears went back level; Sir Lopez was beat.

Right Royal went past him, half an inch, half a
head,
Half a neck, he was leading, for an instant he led;
Then a hooped black and coral flew up like a
shot,
With a lightninglike effort from little Gavotte.

The little bright mare, made of nerves and steel
springs,
Shot level beside him, shot ahead as with wings.

Charles felt his horse quicken, felt the desperate
beat
Of the blood in his body from his knees to his
feet.

Three terrible strides brought him up to the mare,
Then they rushed to wild shouting through a
whirl of blown air;
Then Gavotte died to nothing; Soyland came
once again
Till his muzzle just reached to the knot on his
rein.

Then a whirl of urged horses thundered up,
whipped and blown,
Soyland, Peterkinooks, and Red Ember the roan.

For an instant they challenged, then they drooped
and were done;
Then the White Post shot backwards, Right
Royal had won.

Won a half length from Soyland, Red Ember
close third;
Fourth, Peterkinooks; fifth, Gavotte harshly
spurred;
Sixth, Sir Lopez, whose rider said, "Just at the
Straight
He swerved at the hurdle and twisted a plate."

Then the numbers went up; then John Harding
appeared
To lead in the Winner while the bookmakers
cheered.

A Room at the Barn

JOHN McNULTY

One of the pleasures of my own experience with newspapermen is to have been with them on a story and to have been completely unaware at the time of the fact that they were mentally composing the story—never taking a note, just observing and listening. Then later I would read in black and white of things seen, things said, and more often of the overall significance of a slight incident. John McNulty was a master of this, along with such fine writers and reporters as Red Smith, Joe Palmer, Frank Graham and others.

ONCE in a great while, a man all of a sudden finds himself completely happy and content. His stomach feels good; he's breathing fine and easy; there's nothing whatever bothering him in his mind; the sun is shining, perhaps, but it doesn't have to be; a breeze is blowing gently, perhaps, but it doesn't need to be; and nearby there is something or somebody he has a deep fondness for. What he's fond of can be a boat, or a woman, or a horse—anything at all. About eleven o'clock in the morning on Tuesday, April 14, I was silently grateful to find myself in that pleasant fix. At that hour, I was sitting alone in a warm and comfortable room no more than thirty yards away from the stall in which stood the race horse Native Dancer. I have a deep fondness for Native Dancer.

Because of my feeling about the horse, I had long wanted to know him better—pay him a visit and stay with him for a day or so. That's not an altogether easy thing to do; my idea, in its way, was like having the notion that it would be nice to drop in at the White House for a weekend to see how things go around there. Nevertheless, through the intercession of friends, I had got permission to go and stay awhile with Native Dancer, who was then stabled in Alfred Gwynne Vanderbilt's barn at Belmont Park.

That Tuesday morning, I left my house in Manhattan about seven o'clock and, in a car driven by a friend, went out to the track, at Elmont, Long Island. It was a gray, chill morning, brightening slowly, with a fairly sharp wind nosing about. The gates at Belmont are closely guarded at all hours, and we were stopped there by uniformed attendants, who examined our credentials and then waved us inside, to the stable area of the vast racing plant.

A sign on the road that wound between the dozens of long barns said:

> SLOW
> PLEASE CONSIDER
> THE HORSES

So we went slowly, and here and there, as a group, or "set," of horses hove into view on the way to or from early-morning exercise at the track, we stopped until they had passed. My friend pulled up at Barn 20, where two men were standing near two automobiles and chatting. The license of one car was AG-2; the other's was ND 46-46. "That AG one is Mr. Vanderbilt's, for Alfred Gwynne Vanderbilt," said my companion, who is well versed in such matters. "The one with ND on it belongs to Bill Winfrey, Mr. Vanderbilt's trainer, and the ND, of course, is for Native Dancer. That's them, talking." In a few moments, I was introduced to Mr. Vanderbilt and to Mr. Winfrey. When I said, "Pleased to meet you, Mr. Winfrey," he corrected me. "I'm Bill Winfrey," he said. "Mr. Winfrey is a trainer over at Jamaica. He's my father."

"Make yourself at home," Mr. Vanderbilt said to me cordially. "I got to be going along."

There is a well-made two-story brick dormitory a few yards from Barn 20, for the use of trainers, stable foremen, and some of the help. It contains two offices and twenty-two rooms and four baths; half of it is occupied by the Vanderbilt people, and half by the Woodvale Farm people, whose barn is nearby. Bill Winfrey took me to a ground-floor room he had been using and told me it would be mine during my visit. He and his wife live in an apartment house about ten minutes away from the track.

That morning, the sports pages of the newspapers had announced that if conditions were right, Native Dancer would have a public trial between the fifth and sixth races at the Jamaica track, which is currently holding its spring meeting. (Racing doesn't start at Belmont until May 6.) Native Dancer had been scheduled to run in the fifth race the previous day, but only two owners had expressed a willingness to put their horses up against him, and the race had been canceled. Mr. Vanderbilt requested that the public trial be substituted, and the Jamaica authorities had agreed, in order to satisfy the thousands of race-goers who wanted a look at Native Dancer. In the trial, Native Dancer was to take the track with two stablemates from Barn 20, break from the starting gate, as in a regular race, and run six furlongs, or three-quarters of a mile. It would be a make-believe race, without betting, but—or so it was hoped—it would give Native Dancer the feeling of having been in a real race, and this was desirable because, as Bill Winfrey explained while I unpacked, the horse had not raced since October 22. "He needs racing to tighten him up for what's ahead of him," he said.

Bill told me that he was going to drive over to Jamaica and see what shape the track was in, and that I could go along if I liked. "It's been raining a lot," he said as we got into ND 46-46, "and the track's still pretty wet. We'll go walk on it—see exactly how it feels." Driving along, he explained that he'd like to run the horse with his forelegs bandaged, and for that reason he didn't want a wet track. "It isn't that anything's the matter with the forelegs," he went on. "But sometimes a horse will rap himself running fairly fast. That is, he will clip the back of a foreleg with one of his hind hoofs and make a cut. Bandages on the forelegs tend to prevent that from happening. But if the track is wet, the bandages naturally get wet and shrink up, and

they're apt to squeeze too tight on the tendons, harmfully. Well, we'll look at the track and see."

At Jamaica, we stopped alongside the track at a point opposite the clubhouse and offices, and clambered between the rails onto the track itself. Bill took eight or ten analytical steps on the sandy, loamy, and still wet surface. The wind was now blowing hard. "Oh, this is O.K.," he said happily. "This wind will do the trick more than the sunshine. They'll harrow this up after every race and the wind will get at it. Then the horses in the early races will toss it up and the wind will get at it some more. So by the time we go on, it'll be all right. So far, O.K.; we'll go ahead and run him."

We climbed back through the rails and drove around the track to the offices, so Bill could notify the officials that he was willing to proceed with the public trial. As we walked through the office corridors, I noticed that horsemen who were gathered there greeted Bill with a cordiality tinged with friendly envy, which I attributed, no doubt correctly, to his being the trainer in whose hands fate had placed Native Dancer. An odd thing, though, was that they never mentioned that name. "How's the big horse?" some would ask, and others, "How's your gray horse doing?" To all of them Bill answered, "First-rate, so far." The touch of envy was certainly understandable. Last year, as a two-year-old, Native Dancer ran in nine races and won them all.

On the way back to Belmont, I asked Bill to tell me a little about himself—where he was born and all that. He said that he was born in Detroit in 1916, but that his family had moved here soon afterward and he'd gone to grammar school at P.S. 108, in Queens. "It's right across from Aqueduct," he said. "You can see its roof from the stands there. Later, for three or four months, I went to high school at John Adams, down the boulevard from Aqueduct. Then, my father being a horseman and all, we went down to Florida, where there was a big fuss about letting me into high school without papers from up in New York, and we didn't have the papers with us. Anyway, that gave me a chance to convince my folks that I wanted race track more than high school, and they let me do it. I went to helping my father. Walking hots and things like that." The phrase "walking hots" denotes one of the lowly and yet one of the necessary jobs at a race track. It means slowly walking a horse around and around, leading him by a shank, for an hour or more, until he cools off from a race or a workout.

When Bill was a little over sixteen, he got a license as a jockey; sixteen is as young as a jockey can be, by law. But his jockeyship was short-lived, Bill said. "When I got my license in Florida, in January, I weighed ninety-one pounds, and by Saratoga, in August, I was a hundred and ten. I was long on weight and short on ability—that's what it amounted to. I just plain wasn't any good as a jockey, but I turned out to be pretty good as an exercise boy, and I went along for a while at that." An exercise boy is a fellow, sometimes a former or a future jockey but not always so, who rides race horses during their practice spins in the early mornings. I asked Bill what qualities he thought made a good exercise boy. He didn't answer right away. He has, I noticed soon after I met him, a mannerism that he indulges in whenever he's thinking something out, big or small. He holds his left hand up to his face, palm outward, and nibbles the second joint of his little finger. He nibbled it now. "Well, after at least ordinary skill at riding, of course, I think it's confidence that makes a good boy," he said finally. "A boy lacks confidence, he's apt to communicate that lack to the horse, I believe, which makes everybody nervous—horse, boy, trainer, everybody. A boy has confidence, he sits there feeling good, and the horse feels good because the boy's confidence imparts itself to the horse, and there you are. Confidence is probably the main thing. Bernie Everson, our boy for the gray horse, has it. Good boy. We trust him."

I then said something that has been said many times about the gray horse—that, conceivably, he might turn out to be one of the great race horses of all time. "He's got a lot yet to prove— got most of it yet to prove," Bill said, and after a pause, he went on, still nibbling and driving one-hand. "Tell the truth, a man my age doesn't deserve a horse like him," he said. "I'm only thirty-seven—not quite that yet. My father, training horses all his life, is sixty-eight, and he never had the luck to handle a horse like him. And I know so many trainers—some seventy, seventy-five years old, training horses fifty years and more, working hard, knowing their business much more than I know it—who never had the luck to get anybody like this gray horse. Tell the truth, a man of thirty-seven doesn't deserve it, that's all. I've had good luck, and all I can do is hope it holds. Still, I don't want to get greedy for luck. I've had more than my share already. For instance, I came on with Mr. Vanderbilt at just the right time. I don't want to get technical with you, but for a long while Mr. Vanderbilt bred his horses according to one system, or method, or whatever you want to call it. Then he changed to another system. I wasn't with him when he changed; my luck was in the fact that I stepped into this job just when the fruits of the new system were ready to be harvested, and that's what's happening. Whether the gray horse would have done as well, or perhaps better, with some other trainer, I don't know. Nobody else knows, either."

I said that training a horse with such a record and such potentialities must give rise to a lot of worry. "I try to worry as little as I can," Bill said. "I think of it like this: Say we take every precaution we can think of against something happening to him; say we feed him as right as we know how; say we have the best men we can get to take care of him, the best to ride him in workouts, the best to ride him in his races— that way we give him every opportunity to do the great things. That's all we can do. From then on, it's out of our hands—turned over to luck, Providence, or whatever. That's all we can do, and we're trying to do it."

By then, we were back at Barn 20, and it was still only about ten o'clock in the morning. "Now let's go in and see him," Bill said.

Bill conducted me into the long barn and to Stall No. 6, where Native Dancer lives. We looked in at him standing cater-cornered across the boxlike stall, in deep straw. Kneeling beneath him and adjusting the comfort-and-protection bandages he wears while resting was a large colored man, who glanced up at us and smiled a greeting. "This is Lester Murray, who takes care of him," Bill said to me, and Murray, while still going on with his work, kneeling calmly beneath the horse's belly, acknowledged the introduction. "I got some small chores to do," Bill went on, "so I'll leave you here with Murray."

I asked Murray how much Native Dancer weighs, and he told me about eleven hundred and twenty-five pounds, or about ninety pounds more than he weighed at the end of his two-year-old year.

"How high is he?" I asked. "How tall, I mean?"

"He'll go a little more than sixteen hands," Murray answered. That means Native Dancer is a fairly big horse—five feet four and more from the ground to the withers, which is that hump on a horse's back just above the shoulder.

"Would you like to have a good look at him, sir?" Murray asked me. "What did Mr. Winfrey say your name was, sir?"

"McNulty," I said.

"I mean your first name, sir."

"John."

"I'll turn him round, Mr. John, so you get a good look at him."

Murray got up and slapped the horse loudly on his massively muscular rump. "Turn round, now, you big bum!" he said to him. It was the rough tone of endearment some men use when they greet a crony. Obediently, the horse swung around as far as he could, considering that his halter was chained, loosely, to two walls of the stall at one corner.

I believe that Native Dancer is handsome, majestic, fit to be looked at for a long, long while and looked at often, just for the pleasure of seeing a living creature so marvelously contrived by the millions of years that have passed since a horse was a creature about eleven inches high. I thought he looked just wonderful, though I have to confess that once race horses move off the pages of the *Morning Telegraph* they are reasonably unfamiliar to me. He is not a light gray, which is what most people think of when someone mentions a gray horse. He is dark gray—almost black here and there. Iron gray, some might say, but *iron* is too prosaic a word. His face is quite light; sometimes, when seen from a certain angle, it appears to be a silvery mask. On his left side, just below and just behind where his saddlecloth sits during a race, there is a very light-gray design—something like a free-hand map of France. His tail is dark, with a shimmer of gray toward the end. There in the stall, he looked much bigger than he ever looks on the track. He was very calm as Murray knelt down again and went back to work on the bandages.

While Murray worked, he talked to the horse banteringly, in a kind of reassuring monotone with music in it. "Don't you lift up that old leg at me, you big old horse, you," he'd say. "Stand still there now, you big bum, stand still now, while I get this here bandage fixed up pretty and nice, stand still. You got work to do today, horse, and I going to fix you up so you can do it right, like you always do."

A plump black cat strolled along, stood beside me for a minute, and then impudently, superciliously, stepped into the stall. Around her neck was a beautiful collar woven of two strands of leather—one cerise and one white—in a diamond pattern. Cerise and white are the Vanderbilt racing colors. Later, I learned that the harnessmaker for the stable outfits all the stable cats with these collars, which he fashions from old browbands once worn by the Vanderbilt racers as part of their full-dress regalia.

Murray finished his bandaging, stood up and stretched, and slapped a happy slap on the horse's rump. "Hello, you old cat!" he said, looking down. "Mr. John, let me tell you something about that old cat. When we was coming back here all the way across the country from Santa Anita, out in California, that old cat—we call her Mom—she come along with us. She had a little box in the car, not far from this horse. Once in a while, he'd lean over and nuzzle her in the back of the neck with his nose. That old cat's not afraid of him, and he don't mind her. Well, Mr. John, that Mom never in her life had anything but black kittens in her whole life. Then we get back here, and in a week that Mom have five kittens. And every single, solitary one of them gray! Gray like him! He's a powerful horse, he is."

Murray came out of the stall and said he was going to feed the gray horse about half an hour early because of the doings that afternoon. Ordinarily, he explained, Native Dancer, along with the twenty-six other horses in the Vanderbilt barn, is fed at eleven in the morning, four in the afternoon, and one in the morning. This is a routine more or less peculiar to the stable. "Feeding him at one o'clock in the morning like that lets him get his food digested up some before his workout time," Murray said. "I'm going to cut him a little short on this feeding. Usual, he gets two quarts of oats at eleven o'clock, but this time I'll give him about a quart and a half. Then, usual, he gets four quarts at four o'clock, and four quarts more at one o'clock. That makes ten quarts altogether. Night watchman give him that one-o'clock stuff." He told me that the gray horse is a "good doer," which means a horse with a fine appetite. He would eat more than ten quarts a day if he could get it. Then, of course, there's his hay. The hayrack in his stall is filled twice a day, and he munches at it when he isn't resting—sort of a between-meals snack, the hay is. Later, Bill Winfrey told me that his hay is mixed clover until about four days before a race, when he's switched to plain timothy. "Timothy doesn't have any of those nice sweet buds in it," he said. "With the clover hay, he's like a child with Tootsie Rolls or something; he stuffs himself with it. The timothy is just straight food, and he's more sensible about that."

Murray got the quart and a half of oats ready, poured it into the feedbox, and then unfastened the halter chains so the horse could turn around and eat, which he did avidly. We both watched while he ground away the oats. Pretty soon, Murray said he was going to get some lunch and let Harold Walker, his second-in-command, carry on.

Walker, another big colored man, came in and took a look at the gray horse eating. "He doing good, like always," he said. Then he and I went into an office at the end of the line of stalls and sat down in two chairs there, leaving the door open. "I set here and I can see every one of them stall doors," Walker said. "That's a rule—got to be somebody here every minute, keep an eye on everything. Tom Drysdale, he the night watchman, he's here all night." There was hardly a sound in that great big place, except us talking and a few barn swallows or sparrows chirping or making a swift flutter of wings as they swooped toward nests in the eaves with bits of loot—wisps of hay, or some oats, or pieces of string they got Lord knows where. There was a television set by our side, but neither one of us thought of turning it on—not interested. It was enough sitting there, looking down past the gray horse, past all the others, smelling the clean, unforgettable smell of grain and hay and liniment and ammonia and faint old aromatic race-horse sweat. "I think I'll just walk down past all those horses and look at them," I said. "Then I guess I'll go to my room for a little rest," I said to Walker.

"That's good," he answered. "Just walk along and see 'em. Them two-year-olds, they'll want to know who you are. But them others, they won't care." I walked along past the stalls and peeked in at First Glance and Young Buck and Whence and Whither and Half Caste and Lap of Luxury and the others. The two-year-olds turned around and stared and the others didn't care. I went back to my room for a while.

Back in the room, that was when the time came that I felt so good that Tuesday morning. Very quiet it was in the room, just as in the barn. I thought how Native Dancer looked, over in his stall, thirty yards or so away. He was tuned so exquisitely he almost thrummed standing still. I wondered how many people knew about the gray horse. Millions, certainly, have heard of him, and thousands, like me, read all they can about him. They know that his sire was Polynesian and his dam Geisha; that's where he gets the gray, from Geisha. They know about the nine races he ran last year and won, and a few of them know to the dot his share of those purses, which was $230,495. Thinking about that figure led me to speculate on how much the gray horse is worth, which, in turn, led me to the conclusion that such speculation is foolish, because there were so many things about him that had no price. So I gave up this train of thought and went back and sat down with Harold Walker again.

It was getting to be time to take the gray horse and the others over to Jamaica for the public trial. Pretty soon, Bill Winfrey came along and outlined his plans for the run. He said that the two horses he would race against the big horse were Beachcomber and First Glance. Beachcomber is a three-year-old gelding who had never raced. "Sometimes he runs pretty fast for a short distance in the morning, though," Bill said. First Glance is a well-known handicap horse who has won some big races. He is six years old—twice as old as Native Dancer. He is cleverly named, being by Discovery out of Bride Elect. "The plan is this," Bill said. "We'll start from the gate, of course. The regular rider, Eric Guerin, will ride the gray horse, Bernie Everson will ride First Glance, and Albert Bao —that's one of our exercise boys—will ride Beachcomber. What I figure to do is have Beachcomber get away from the gate fast and grab a lead on the gray horse and the other. Beachcomber won't go fast very far, and when the gray horse catches him, I'd like to have First Glance kind of take over and give the gray horse a run. That way, there'll be some sort of competition for the gray horse all through the thing. That is, if everything works out as planned, which it may not."

The van that was to take the horses to Jamaica hadn't come yet, so we strolled down to Stall No. 6. As we looked in, Murray was just turning a bucket upside down and climbing onto it, on the off side of the gray horse. Standing on the bucket and talking to the horse, Murray began to braid his mane. "Now I'm going to fix you up pretty, you big bum, before all those people look at you," he was saying. He worked away patiently, the horse hardly moving at all. Every once in a while, he'd wet his fingers in his mouth and then moisten the braid. It took him about half an hour to fix the braid just right.

As Murray finished, the van pulled up outside the barn door. Big yellow van. A ramp was put against the side door of the van, and a heavy mat was laid down on the ramp. Wooden side railings, more than waist-high on a man, were affixed to the ramp. John C. Mergler, the stable foreman, supervised operations, and Winfrey also stood by. Altogether, eight men took places in or near the van, as if they were taking battle stations. A horse could get hurt at a time like this. Native Dancer was the first to go into the van. He went up the ramp willingly, and as he went Murray slapped him goodbye on the rump. The two other horses also went in easily, and the van door was closed and locked. The driver invited me to climb up in front with him, and we started off, taking Native Dancer to the races. Oh, well, to a make-believe race, anyway.

The two other horses didn't quite do their jobs in the public trial. But after it was over, Bill Winfrey said it was all right, things hadn't worked out badly at all.

When Fred L. Capossela, the race announcer, said over the loudspeaker that Native Dancer was coming onto the track, hundreds of horse players ran to the trackside from near the mutuel windows, where they had been engaged in the engrossing business of betting on the sixth race. Running out to see him close to, they looked like hundreds of water bugs skating on the surface of a brook. The gray horse and the two others walked up the track, then back around to the three-quarter pole, where the gate was. On a track, the three-quarter pole means a pole on the rail three-quarters of a mile from the finish—not from the start, as a nonracing person might, and often does, think.

What happened was that when the three horses got off, Native Dancer jumped out of the gate ahead of the two others. Beachcomber never did head him. Jockey Guerin had to hold the gray horse tightly in order to let First Glance catch up. That way—Native Dancer on the outside, First Glance inside and a little behind, and

Beachcomber straggling—they went past the crowd and past the finish wire.

After we got back to Barn 20 without mishap, Bill and Murray and Walker and Mergler all felt the legs of the gray horse and found them O.K. The other men drifted away then, leaving Murray and me standing by Stall No. 6. "He keyed up," Murray said. "He a little mixed up in his mind, but he all right, Mr. John. He don't know was that a race he was in or wasn't it a race. They had the gate, they had them other two horses, and I guess they had the crowd yelling. Just the same, he don't know. He like a race, but he mixed up about *was* it a race."

Unconsciously, as he talked, Murray was cleaning a fleck of dirt off a bridle strap hanging by the stall door. I was looking down at his overalls. On his left pants leg, between the knee and the ankle, was fastened a row of shiny safety pins. They looked like some odd military decoration. They were, in reality, the badge of the man who "rubs horses." With the safety pins thus arranged, Murray, while on his right knee beneath a horse, could handily reach one to fasten a bandage with. "You know what I think is missing in his mind, what got him mixed up in his mind, Mr. John?" he asked.

"No," I said.

"It all look like a race to him except one thing," Murray said. "They never brought him back to no winner's circle. Mr. John, this horse never been no place else but in that winner's circle. Every single, solitary time he run a race. He don't know what to make out of it, no winner's circle this time. It got him mixed up in his mind."

When I awoke the next morning, it was not yet fully daybreak. I turned on the bed light to look at my watch and saw it was ten minutes to five. Race-trackers go to bed early and get up early. When I went to close the window against the morning chill, I heard three voices.

"Get an extry ring!" one voice said loudly, as if to someone a long distance away.

"What kind of ring for what?" another voice said, far away.

"Extry coffee ring!" the first voice said.

"Oh, coffee bun!" the faraway one hollered back.

"Yuh, yuh, coffee bun—get an extry one!" the first voice said.

Then there was a third voice, this one singing. Five o'clock in the morning, the sun coming up, and the voice singing a blues—"Got no-body to call my own!"

After breakfast, I walked over toward the training track, which is adjacent to the Vanderbilt barn. A couple of stable lads were there beside the rail. On the far side of the track, in the gray morning, two horses were moving. In the grayness and chill, one of the far-off horses was gray, too. Nobody mentioned his name. As the two horses came around the bend and into the stretch, the gray horse became grayer to the eye. The sound of hoofs hit sweetly on the ears. Although it is made by four hoofs, the gallop has a triple beat—"Tump-a-tum! Tump-a-tum! Tump-a-tum!" I watched and listened for a moment and then returned to the stable area.

Even before the big horse came back to the barn after the workout, his imminent approach was felt. It was in the air. "He coming back," I heard Murray say. Some of the men around the barn gathered outside to see if "he" was in sight yet. He was. He came down the road, between the barns, back to his home.

As Native Dancer passed each stall where a Vanderbilt horse was being groomed, work stopped for a few moments. "There he go," one groom said, pausing to watch, holding his currycomb in his right hand. Then he went back to work on his horse, and it was nice to hear him say, "You a good horse, too."

Command Performance

ROGER MORTIMER

This is one of the more interesting chapters from a most interesting volume, The Jockey Club
*(Great Britain), from the pen of Roger Mortimer. It provides an entertaining picture of sport-
ing life in the latter half of the 18th century in England, with central circumstances not too
unfamiliar on the contemporary 20th-century sporting scene.*

IN MANY RESPECTS the Prince of Wales, subsequently George IV, was an odious individual.
It can be counted in his favor, though, that he
was genuinely fond of racing, and beyond extravagance, there is little in his career on the
turf deserving of censure. His membership of
the Jockey Club was proved by his horse Anvil
running second in a Jockey Club Plate in 1786.
The probability is that he was elected a member
of the club when he came of age three years
previously.

From the very start, as was only to be expected
of a person of his character, he raced on a scale
that was not only ostentatiously lavish but thoroughly extravagant as well. If he wanted a horse
he bought it, and the price he paid was imma-
terial. He had over twenty horses in training
and his stable was said to cost him over £ 30,000
a year. In 1786 this state of affairs was brought
to a somewhat undignified conclusion, at any
rate for the time being, by the fact that he was
hopelessly in debt. From this predicament he was
temporarily rescued by Parliament, his debts
being paid and his income increased. Whereupon
his stable, which had shrunk to half a dozen
animals, was promptly expanded to forty.

On the whole he was a successful owner, particularly between 1800 and 1807, when he won
over a hundred races. His greatest single success
came in 1788 when he won the Derby with Sir

Thomas, a horse he had bought on his own
judgment for 2,000 guineas, a big sum in those
days, from his breeder, Mr. Francis Taylor of
Newmarket. His racing career ended suddenly in
1791, at least as far as Newmarket was concerned, with what was known as the Escape
Affair, perhaps the greatest and most contro-
versial scandal in the history of a sport in which
controversy and scandal are anything but uncommon.

Escape, by Highflyer, was bred by the prince
and was bought by a Mr. Franco when the
prince's debts compelled him to reduce his establishment. While the horse was a yearling in Mr.
Franco's possession, there occurred the incident
which gave him his name of Escape. One night
he managed to kick through the woodwork of
his loose box, and in so doing got one of his legs
caught between the boards. Fortunately he did
not break his fetlock, and it was found possible
to release him without frightening him into doing
himself an injury. When Mr. Franco heard of
this misadventure, he decided to commemorate
the incident in the horse's name.

Two years after he had sold him, the prince,
in funds once again, was able to buy Escape
back for 1,500 guineas. This price was not considered excessive, as some people reckoned
Escape the best colt in training at that time.

The bare outline of "the affair" is as follows.

On October 20, 1791, Escape, ridden by Sam Chifney, ran against three very inferior animals. Naturally Escape was a heavily backed and short-priced favorite, but to the dismay and bewilderment of his backers, he finished last, the result being:

Mr. Dawson's *Coriander*	1
Lord Grosvenor's *Skylark*	2
Lord Clermont's *Pipator*	3
H.R.H. The Prince of Wales's *Escape*	4

Now, it is well known that horses are not machines, a biological fact that enables so many bookmakers to pass the dreary winter months sunning themselves in South Africa. The mere defeat of a hot favorite, therefore, would be regarded as regrettable, possibly as mysterious, but part of the game. Escape, however, turned out again the following day, with Chifney again his rider. His opponents included Skylark and Pipator, who had beaten him the day before, as well as a very useful horse in Chanticleer, and in view of his mediocre performance the previous day, his price on this occasion was five to one against. The result was as follows:

H.R.H. The Prince of Wales's *Escape*	1
Lord Barrymore's *Chanticleer*	2
Lord Grosvenor's *Skylark*	3
Duke of Bedford's *Grey Diomed*	4
Lord Clermont's *Pipator*	5
Mr. Barton's *Alderman*	6

Thus Escape defeated not only the well-backed favorite Chanticleer, but also reversed the previous day's form completely with Skylark and Pipator.

Inevitably there were allegations of foul play, and it was freely stated that Chifney, whose reputation was no better than that of many leading jockeys since, had, with or without the connivance of the prince, stopped Escape the first day and backed him on the second. Such was the outcry that the matter was brought up for investigation by the stewards of the Jockey Club, Sir Charles Bunbury, Mr. Thomas Panton and Mr. Ralph Dutton. Chifney's explanation was not deemed satisfactory, particularly by Bunbury, who made that quite clear to the prince, saying that "if Chifney were suffered to ride the prince's horses, no gentleman would start against him."

It is a creditable episode in a discreditable life that the prince, without hesitation, stood by the servant whom he trusted and believed to have served him well. Despite the pressure that was being put upon him, he refused to take any action that would imply condemnation of Chifney. Instead, he disposed of his stud, shook the dust of Newmarket off his heels, and gave up the sport that had afforded him so much pleasure.

The central figure in the Escape affair is not really the prince but the jockey Sam Chifney. Born in Norfolk in 1753, Chifney was five feet five inches high, and right up to the end of his career he had no difficulty in going to scale at seven stone twelve. He began to ride in races when attached to Foxe's stable at Newmarket in 1770, and from the start he showed remarkable aptitude. In his own modest words:

In 1773 I could ride horses in a better manner in a race than any other person ever known in my time, and in 1775 I could train horses for running better than any person I ever yet saw. Riding I learnt myself and training I learnt from Mr. Richard Prince, training groom to Lord Foley.

The basic principle of Chifney's theory of race riding was to keep a slack rein early on and then come with a tremendous rush at the finish. He was in fact the first man to perfect the art of riding a waiting race. Here is his own description of his method:

The first fine part in riding a race is to command your horse to run light in his mouth; it is done with manner; it keeps him the better together, his legs are the more under him, his sinews the less extended, less exertion, his wind less locked; the horse running thus to order, feeling light for his rider's wants; his parts are more at ease and ready; and can run considerably faster when called upon than when he has been running in the fretting, sprawling attitude, with part of his rider's weights in his mouth.

And as the horse comes to his last extremity, finishing the race, he is the better forced and kept straight with manner, and fine touching to his mouth. In this situation the horse's mouth should be eased of the weight of the rein, if not it stops him little or much. If a horse is shy, he should be forced with a manner up to this order of running, and particularly so if he has to make play, or he will run the slower, and jade the sooner for the want of it.

The phrase at Newmarket is, that you should pull your horse to ease him in his running. When horses are in their great distress in running, they cannot bear that visible manner of pulling as looked for by many of the sportsmen; he should be enticed to ease himself an inch at a time, as his situation will allow.

This should be done as if you had a silken rein as fine as a hair, and you were afraid of breaking it.

This is the true way a horse should be held fast in his running.

N.B. If the Jockey Club will be pleased to give me two hundred guineas, I will make them a bridle as I believe never was, and I believe never can be excelled, for their light weights to hold their horses from running away.

Conceited Chifney may have been, but there is no doubt that he possessed a most wonderfully light pair of hands. On one occasion he went to ride a horse called Knowsley in a King's Plate at Guilford. Now, Knowsley was a tremendous puller and had run away with every jockey who had ridden him. Accordingly Chifney was handed for inspection and approval in the weighing room a great heavy curb-bridle, with the aid of which it was hoped that he might keep Knowsley in check. "Take that silly gimcrack away and bring me a plain snaffle," said Chifney, who then proceeded to win the race with ease, passing the post on a slack rein, a feat which he repeated at Winchester soon after. He was just as effective on a sluggish horse as on a hard puller, and what is more, he induced a lazy horse to run freely without using either the whip or the spur.

Famous as Samuel Chifney was as rider and trainer, his reputation was equaled, if not eclipsed, by those of his two sons, William, born in 1784, and Samuel, born in 1786. William became a highly skilled and successful trainer; young Sam one of the greatest riders in racing history.

Both boys owed almost everything to the judgment of their father and the very thorough manner in which he schooled them. William, the quicker and more intelligent, was brought up to learn training and stable management. Young Sam, phlegmatic but resolute, was coached in riding. From the time he could sit on a pony young Sam was taught every aspect of the art of race riding by a great master of that art, and right through his boyhood he virtually lived in the saddle. Like his father, young Sam came to specialize in the waiting game, and it was he rather than old Sam who perfected the famous "Chifney Rush."

For a good many years fortune as well as fame smiled on the two brothers and they enjoyed a tremendous win when Priam, trained by William, won the Derby in 1830. Unfortunately a few years later William thought he had a second Priam in Shillelagh and they both backed him as if defeat was out of the question. Shillelagh was beaten by inches by Plenipotentiary. The brothers, good spenders but poor savers, had to sell their stud and their fine houses. As regards the houses, they were adjoining ones, and young Sam's had been greatly enlarged and improved by the Duke of Cleveland, one of his patrons. This caused jealousy and ill-feeling between the two wives, and to spite her sister-in-law Mrs. William Chifney induced her husband to have built a magnificent new house in which not a single old brick was to be used. Hardly had this edifice been completed when the losses incurred over Shillelagh compelled its sale at a great loss to Mr. J. F. Clarke, who subsequently resold it to Prince Batthyany.

From then on the sun never shone quite so benignly on the Chifney brothers again. They had to abandon the luxurious and extravagant manner in which they had long been living and revert to the style and demeanor of servants rather than masters. Young Sam continued to ride till 1843, but gradually his phlegmatic nature degenerated into idleness and sloth. His weight increased because he could not be bothered to take exercise, and as he refused to waste unless he particularly wanted the ride, he missed hundreds of winning opportunities. Even when Lord Chesterfield offered him a retainer—merely asking him to take the best mounts in the stable and leave the rest to Conolly—he refused, and so missed winning the Oaks and the St. Leger in 1838. *Pipe and Peace* had always been his motto and he was at his happiest when he could stroll over a couple of stubble fields with a gun and his lemon and white pointer Banker; or better still, just sit quietly for hours and watch his pet foxes playing in their enclosure. In the year of his retirement he had the luck to be left a house and some stables by his old patron, Squire Thornhill, and there he lived till the closing years of his life when he moved to Hove. His last visit to a race course was to see his nephew Frank Butler win the Derby on West Australian, and a few months later he died peacefully in his seventieth year. His brother William survived him by eight years. William's old age, like the old age of so many who have gambled heavily on the turf, was spent in dire poverty, and it was seldom that he could raise sufficient money for a third-class ticket to Newmarket to visit the scene of so many of his former triumphs. Even in his shabby old blue cloak, though, and with a broad-brimmed hat secured by a bandanna handkerchief, he managed to preserve a certain air of distinction. He was nearly eighty when he died in lodgings off the St. Pancras Road.

Four years after the Escape affair, old Sam Chifney was very hard up and in the hope of easing the situation he wrote a book called *Genius Genuine* in which, amongst other subjects, he gave his own version of Escape's running on those two October afternoons. The price of the book, which ran to only a hundred and seventy pages, was £5, and it says much for Chifney's fame and for public interest in the Escape affair that the demand for it was considerable. A second edition, also costing £5 a copy, was produced some years later.

This is the story as told by Chifney [paraphrased by Roger Mortimer]:

On July 14, 1790, he was retained for life by the prince at wages of 200 guineas a year to ride his horses. Almost immediately it came to his ears that Mr. Lake, the prince's racing manager, and Neal, the prince's training groom, were both opposed to his appointment and were intent on making it as short as possible.

He was told quite clearly by the prince when he took up the appointment that his final riding orders were to be given by Mr. Lake: "Sam Chifney, if at any time it should happen that I give you orders to ride, you will always go to Mr. Lake for your final orders; and Mr. Lake and you will make any alteration you like and where you please."

No doubt that ought to have been a sensible and satisfactory arrangement, but Chifney gives several instances to show that Lake's riding orders were sometimes totally unsuited to the horse concerned and were in fact deliberately given to ensure defeat so that he could lay the horse while the prince and his friends were backing it. Furthermore, in Chifney's opinion, Neal was a singularly incompetent trainer and in consequence the prince's horses were often very unfit when they ran. Lake was perfectly well aware of this, but used his knowledge of the horses' condition for his personal advantage.

With regard to Escape, Chifney had had his eye on him for a long time. In April 1789 he had seen him beaten over four miles by Harpator. Later that year he watched him beat Nimbler, "a fast runner," and from what he saw he concluded that Escape was a good horse with a fine turn of speed.

At Ascot in June 1790 Escape was beaten in the Oatlands Stakes, because, Chifney thought, too much use had been made of him. Soon afterwards his personal connection with the horse began. In August 1790 he went to York to ride Escape, who had been heavily backed by the prince to win both the Great Subscriptions. Escape won the first race but was given a tough battle by a horse whose public form was extremely moderate; on the second day he had better horses against him and finshed well down the course. Chifney considered that Escape had not been fit to run and, as on other occasions, he had advised the prince to that effect before the race. The prince had sensibly taken his advice and had hedged the greater part of his bet.

Escape was evidently a fit horse at the beginning of October as he won a couple of races on one day. After that success the prince shook Chifney's hand and said: "Sam Chifney, no person but you shall ride for me."

Escape's next outing was on the fatal October 20. As Chifney was riding down to the course that day on his cob with his saddle tied round his waist, he passed the prince with a party of friends, and the prince called out to him: "Sam Chifney, Escape is sure of winning today, is he not?"

Chifney reined in his cob, touched his cap and replied, "Your Highness, I do not think Escape is sure to win today."

"Yes," replied the prince, "Escape is sure of winning today."

"I then," says Chifney, "took the liberty of advising His Royal Highness not to bet upon him, as the odds, from his previous performances, were likely to be high upon him, and much might be lost, though little could be won."

Chifney says that at this point he was under a peculiar embarrassment as he wanted to tell the prince that Escape was not quite fit to run. It is difficult to understand why he did not impart that information as, according to his own story, he had done under similar circumstances in the past. He could have trotted off straight away after the prince's party and spoken to his master then, while a second opportunity occurred later on when the prince, seated in Lord Barrymore's carriage by the rails, called him over to receive his riding orders. But he never said a word about Escape's condition.

The prince's orders to Chifney were to make strong play on Escape. He emphasized that point and Chifney said he understood his instructions perfectly. The prince then drove off with Lord Barrymore to the betting post and Chifney did not see him again till after the race.

Immediately afterwards Chifney met Lake and they both agreed that it would be madness to make strong play with Escape. Finally Lake said, "I think, as you do, that Escape had better wait at all events; and as I see the prince's carriage, I will go up at once and make everything perfectly pleasant."

Up at the saddling stable Chifney inquired if Escape had had a sweat since last he ran, and the lad with Escape replied that he had not.

There is little to be said about the race. Chifney waited with Escape but was well beaten. When he returned to scale he was met by the prince, who said, "Chifney, you have lost this race by not making strong play as I desired you." Chifney excused himself and said he hoped the prince had not lost any money.

"No, I have not lost a stiver," the prince replied, "but that don't argue. Escape would have won if you had made play. I am a better jockey than you and Mr. Lake together. You have lost the race by not obeying my orders."

Later in the afternoon the prince asked Chifney how it was that Escape came to be beaten, as Chifney had told him that Escape was the best horse in the world.

"I did tell Your Royal Highness," Chifney replied, "that Escape was the best horse in England, and I think the same of him now. It is a fortnight since he last ran. He has not had a sweat since, and, though he looks straight and handsome to the eye, he is unfit to run; and I believe that was the cause of his being beaten today."

The prince then told Lake that he intended to run Escape the following day. Chifney expressed his pleasure at this decision and strongly advised the prince to back Escape, who would be very much the fitter for the race he had just had.

The next day the prince gave Chifney his orders and told him to make play on Escape and Chifney repeated his advice to the prince to back his horse on this occasion. Having given this recommendation to the prince, Chifney apparently thought it advisable to have a little on the horse himself (there was no rule against jockeys betting in those days). Accordingly he went to Mr. Lake "and told him I would thank him to lose twenty guineas for me upon Escape." Lake is then said to have made the curious and ungrammatical reply: "No, I will have nothing to do with it, there are so many unpleasant things happen." Chifney then approached Mr. Vauxhall Clark, who laid him the odds to 20 guineas.

There is little to be said about the race itself. Skylark made the running; Chifney waited with Escape and won comfortably. As soon as the horses had passed the post harsh things were being said about Chifney and his royal master. "As I came from scale," Chifney wrote, "I was told Mr. Lake had been saying something severe to His Royal Highness concerning Escape's running."

The next day Chifney was summoned to the prince in his dressing room. "Sam Chifney," said the prince, "I have sent for you upon very unpleasant business. I am told that you won six or seven hundred pounds the day before yesterday when you rode Escape and were beat on him."

Chifney replied that he believed His Royal Highness had not such an opinion of him.

The prince then said he had also heard that Chifney had won a similar sum over Escape's second race. Chifney emphatically denied both stories. The prince appeared to believe him implicitly but strongly advised him to make an affidavit specifying just what bets he had made and this he agreed to do. "Your doing it," said the prince, "will give yourself satisfaction, it will give the public satisfaction, and it will give me satisfaction."

The prince then asked Chifney whether he had any objection to being examined by the Jockey Club, and Chifney replied that he had not. The prince added that he had heard that Chifney had been arrested at Ascot Heath for a debt of £300 and that the debt had been paid for him by Mr. Vauxhall Clark. When Chifney said it was the first he had heard about it, the prince requested him to add his denial to the affidavit.

That concluded the interview, but on the Heath later in the day the prince called out to Chifney to come over and join him and Sir Charles Bunbury. The three then rode off together, the prince in the middle in between Chifney and Sir Charles. The prince again asked Chifney if he was willing to be examined by the Jockey Club, and Chifney replied that he was proud to meet any man upon the subject. The prince then turned to Bunbury: "There, Charles, you hear him say he is proud to meet any man upon the subject. Now, Sir Charles, I beg of you to take every pains you possibly can so as to make yourselves perfectly satisfied; then inclose me Sam Chifney's affidavits and apprise me how the business ends, as I am going to Brighton tonight."

The prince then left Sir Charles and his final remark to Chifney was: "Sam Chifney, this business should be explained"; to which Chifney replied, "Your Highness, I do not know how to explain it."

Later that day Chifney was summoned to appear before the stewards of the Jockey Club. Sir Charles asked him a number of questions; what bets he had had on Escape in the first race; what bets the second day; and who made the bets for him. Chifney gave the same replies that he had given to the prince. Chifney was then asked what his motive was for waiting with Escape the first day, to which he merely replied, somewhat foolishly, by telling Sir Charles that he was a wrong judge of his man. Sir Charles, not surprisingly, looked dissatisfied with that answer, but according to Chifney, Mr. Dutton said, "I think Chifney spoke very fairly," and Mr. Panton apparently agreed with him. At all events, Sir Charles asked no more questions and shortly afterwards the examination ended.

Some days later Chifney was summoned by a letter from Sir John Lade to attend on the prince at once at Carlton House. There the prince told him of Bunbury's words, "if he suffered Chifney to ride his horses, no gentleman would start against him." The prince said he had told Sir Charles that if he or any person could make it appear that Sam Chifney had done wrong, that he would never speak to him again; and without that, he would not sacrifice him for any person. Rather than do so, he would leave the turf. He would always be glad to see Chifney, and if he ever kept horses again, he would ask Chifney to train and manage them. Shortly after this interview the prince and Chifney went to Sir John Lade's house, where the prince put his hand on his heart, said he sincerely believed Chifney to be an honest man, and settled on him the sum of 200 guineas a year. "I cannot give it to you for your life, Sam Chifney, I can only give it for my own," and with those words the Escape affair to all intents and purposes came to an end.

After this long lapse of time, it would be unwise to pass any judgment on the affair, particularly as the only detailed evidence that remains comes from a leading participant who would hardly be willing to show himself in an unfavorable light. No suspicion, however, is attached to the prince, whose conduct throughout seems to have been beyond reproach.

Whether Chifney is as innocent as he would have his readers believe is perhaps open to question. The nature of racing, and of some of those who take a leading part in it, is such that jockeys are continually exposed to temptation, and the resistance of some is conspicuously weaker than that of others. Moreover, Chifney's riding had come under suspicion more than once before this incident occurred.

On the other hand, Escape was a horse that had never numbered consistency among his virtues. He needed a lot of work to get him fit, and if, as Chifney says, he was short of a gallop the first day, it is possible that the first race brought him on considerably. Moreover, the two races were over different distances, the first being over two miles, the second one over four. Certainly, on the evidence now available, it looks as if Chifney should have been given the benefit of the doubt that so clearly existed.

Opinion among members of the Jockey Club was by no means unanimous, and Lord Malmesbury's diary records that Colonel St. Leger told him that Lake was the real cause of the trouble. A more widely held opinion was that certain members of the Club were bitterly jealous of the prince, resenting both his popularity and his racing successes.

"What were you going to be if you grew up?"

DRAWING BY BOB SCHROETER

The Iron Men

TOM O'REILEY

The story of the "Tote," a romance in electronics, can and has been told in highly technical terms. The importance of this machine to the growth and acceptance of racing with pari-mutuel wagering is tremendous. Tom O'Reiley's inimitable light touch is the least tedious way of telling what part the Iron Men play in a day's fun at the races.

Not even William Saroyan's celebrated pinball machine, which lit up, waved flags and played "The Star-Spangled Banner," in his Broadway smash hit, *The Time of Your Life,* could create more excitement than the twinkling, golden lights of a Totalisator odds board flashing the photo-finish results and pay-off prices at a race track. No horse from Bold Ruler to the Godolphin Arabian could cause a more astonished roar than an odds board heralding a four-figure pay-off. The resultant shouts of "Oh!" "Ah!" and "No!" greeting those figures would have brightened the eyes of Egypt's Sphinx. If money makes the mare go, it also makes the crowd roar.

The Totalisator is much more than a mere machine. It is an implacable electronic giant that compresses all the hopes, fears, prejudices and sentiments of a great racing crowd into relentless numbers flashed on the infield board. A mammoth kibitzer at the greatest game in sport, it is also a calculating tease silently winking out hints on which way the betting weather blows. Horse No. 10's opening odds are 20 to 1. Five minutes later, the board lights twinkle and the odds drop to 3 to 1. A restless murmur goes through the crowd. People turn studiously to their forms.

Which horse is No. 10? Who owns him? Who trains him? Who is betting? What did he do last time out? Those falling figures on the odds board

are worthy of investigation. Here it is! No. 10 is a filly owned by a famed Texas oil millionaire. She is making her first start on any track. A lot of money must have been bet on her to cause that change in the odds. The stable must be confident.

There is a certain breed of bettor, familiar to all racing patrons, who would never dream of purchasing a mutuel ticket until the Totalisator board had winked out its very last signal before the start of a race. This type waits until the last horse has entered the starting gate and the field is lined up ready to go. Then, with a final frantic peek at the board, he makes a dash for the betting windows. There are no figures to prove it, but track physicians assert that over half the accidents they treat in their infirmaries are caused by last-minute odds-board watchers who don't look where they are going. With their heads full of figures, they turn from the board to bump into posts, fall down steps and trip over fellow-players while rushing toward the betting windows. Quite often they study too long and fail to get their bets down on time, even if they arrive safely. This simply proves the well known fact that horses can move faster than humans.

It should be noted here that buttons are as important to a Totalisator as zippers to Gypsy Rose Lee. Any attempt to describe, fully, what happens when a mutuels clerk presses a button issuing a betting ticket may sound dangerously close to a cross between an M.I.T. electronics lecture and the tenor part of Gracie Fields' great war song, "She's the Girl That Makes the Thing That Spins the Thing That Cuts the Thing That Works the Thing That's to Win the Bloomin' War."

Of course, sellers, cashiers, lightning calculators (a rare breed) and other personnel are employed by the track. They handle the cash. The Totalisator acts as an independent auditing agency that guarantees accuracy while it affords great savings in time, materials, efforts and, incidentally, money.

Just about the only thing the Tote doesn't do is to make selections.

You do that. Betcha!

The Good, the True and Mr. Leach

JOE H. PALMER

To quote Red Smith on Joe Palmer: ". . . there never was another in his time or before to compare with him." Even without that, in which Red has the support of all who knew and read Joe Palmer, I would have every justification, for the edification of the readers of this collection, to include more than a sampling of the Palmer prose. These chapters I have chosen from his book This Was Racing *are those that pleased me the most because they sounded like Joe just "kicking it around." He was a rarely gifted person and I will always be grateful for the gift of having been his friend.*

M IAMI, FLORIDA—The tropical serenity of this winter fairyland was brusquely disturbed last week by the arrival from Kentucky of a Mr. George Browne (Brownie) Leach. Mr. Leach directs the public relations of Churchill Downs, and a part of his mission was to advise one and all that the Kentucky Derby will be run on the first Saturday of next May, and to give turf writers preliminary training for it. The date of the Derby is correct, but no one should be misled by this. Mr. Leach has a great respect for the truth, and uses it sparingly.

There was a time, for instance, away before Pearl Harbor, when his family was dozing contentedly through Beethoven's Sixth, or Pastoral, Symphony on a Sunday afternoon, when the music was interrupted by the announcement that fighting had broken out on the streets of Washington. The Army and Navy forces, and such Marines as were available were fighting from behind barricades, but were slowly being pressed back to a scant perimeter around the White House. A little later a breathless announcement was made that a train bearing reinforcements from Fort Dix had been derailed by insurgents at Philadelphia.

There was a considerable to-do and calling in of neighbors and telephoning to the newspapers before it was discovered that Mr. Leach had hooked a microphone in to the loudspeaker of the radio and was in the basement, drawing on an imagination which has never yet been caught overdrawn, though great demands have been made on it.

There was another occasion when Mr. Leach was walking peacefully down the street with an acquaintance. A merchant who was normally restrained suddenly opened the door of his establishment, stuck out his head, and addressed Mr. Leach as follows: "You lying ———." He then closed the door and went about his business.

This was because Mr. Leach had been invited, the day before, to speak to the Lions Club. He had explained that Keeneland, having pioneered the Totalisator in Kentucky and made the first experiment with a nonprofit racing organization, had now embarked on another "first" in racing. It had set steam pipes about five inches below the top level of the racing strip, and was prepared to make a wet track into a fast one within two hours of the falling of the last raindrop.

There was some skepticism abroad at first, but

Mr. Leach began to smother the company under figures about the amount of pipe used, the number of elbow joints and T-joints used, and incredulity began to die. The amount of steam necessary to dry the track, he said, would pull a ten-car train from Cincinnati to New Orleans and back as far as Chattanooga. Some of the Lions were as much as three days realizing they had been sold a pup.

But Mr. Leach's most skillful triumph over veracity was on a trip from Lexington to New York on a train called the George Washington, named for a man who could not tell a lie but frequently ridden by people who can.

While Mr. Leach's attention was engaged elsewhere, the train went surreptitiously out of Kentucky into West Virginia, a state inhabited by the Kenawaha Valley and Prohibitionists, where no liquor can be sold on trains, unless you count beer, as who would? Not our hero, at any rate. He chose his weapon, which was a dull magazine, and went into the club car.

He seated himself next to two couples who were trying to see what was at the bottom of a pair of bottles, and began to read industriously about bird life in the Aleutians. The company became increasingly convivial, so much so that one of the gentlemen was moved to ask Mr. Leach if they were disturbing him. He said no, that aside from losing his place a couple of times, he had not been bothered at all.

There was some further conversation, and this elicited the information that Mr. Leach had been newly graduated from the College of the Bible at Transylvania, had been ordained, and was on his way to his first parsonage at Charlottesville.

The celebrants were somewhat abashed, as most people are when they discover a member of the third sex among them, and hoped they had not given any offense to the cloth.

It turned out that Mr. Leach was a broad-minded clergyman. He said that as far as he could see the group had merely been laughing and having fun, that the conversation, while occasionally tart, had been within proper bounds and that he could see nothing reprehensible about the occasion. This was appreciated, and activities, on a more moderate scale, were resumed.

With somewhat longer acquaintance Mr. Leach confessed to a long-standing curiosity about alcohol. It had always been banned, if not actually abhorred, in his family, and of course all of his ministerial training set him against it. Many of his colleagues, he said, were fanatic about it, and yet he had known people who drank who were very pleasant people. The attraction it had for its devotees had always baffled him a little.

"In fact," he admitted shamefacedly, "I've sometimes been tempted to try it, just to see what effect it has."

There's nothing brightens a long train journey like getting a preacher drunk, so one of the party shoved the bottle over. "Go ahead, help yourself," he said. Mr. Leach shied from it like a colt from a flapping paper on the track. "I guess I couldn't," he said doubtfully.

The bottle continued to fascinate him, as a snake is supposed to do with a dove. He put forth a hand and then withdrew it. Finally he steeled himself.

"After all," he said, "we don't know each other. Tomorrow you'll be in New York and I'll be in Charlottesville, and the chances are we'll never see each other again. If I'm ever going to try it, now is the time."

With what seemed inexperience, he filled a tumbler half full, amid covert smiles and nudgings from the four. I need not detain you with the rest of the story. Picture to yourself four persons journeying liquorless through West Viriginia, happy in the belief they had done something naughty, and Mr. Leach retiring contentedly to his roomette, secure in the knowledge that the job had been done.

People Named Stevens

JOE H. PALMER

MIAMI, FLORIDA—This tourist was peacefully eating lunch in the clubhouse at Hialeah, while visions of daily-double tickets danced in his head. There entered upon the scene the Lord of the Manse, one Harry Stevens, of H. M. Stevens, Inc., which has parlayed the hot dog into a catering business which, among other originally unforeseen results, has added inches to the deponent's girth.

"You're late," he said, accusingly.

It was admitted, but the blame was placed on the Miami Transit Company, which had added a touch of southern leisure to the morning's bus schedule.

"I wanted to tout you on the crabmeat," Mr. Stevens continued. "We just flew in a fresh lot. Big chunks, like that."

My companion beat his hands on the table in impotent frustration. He was already committed to a cross-section of man's best friend, the western steer. Being in the midst of an admirable and highly edible assemblage of curried shrimp, I was able to bear the news with more composure. The shrimp, it developed, had been Mr. Stevens's sleeper play in case the crabmeat was at too short a price.

This brought to mind an incident which illustrates the intimacy which exists between H.M.S., Inc., and racing in the East, the two having each grown fat in the other's presence. This observer, who eats frequently, was having breakfast with the Greentree trainer, John Gaver, at the stable cottage at Belmont Park. It was in the late summer, and the baseball pennant races were drawing to a close. The remark was flung out that it would be nice if the World Series would be between Cleveland and St. Louis, because then it would be

out West where it wouldn't bother anybody and where the people didn't have much fun anyway.

"What?" thundered Mr. Gaver, putting down his newspaper. This was a sign that matters of grave import were to be considered, and while the remark was shrinkingly repeated, it was in a more subdued tone.

"Don't you like Frank Stevens?" demanded Mr. Gaver with what seemed a deceptive mildness.

Sure I liked Frank Stevens. A man among men. An upholder of the best traditions of racing and gastronomy. A bulwark and reliance of the press. A man who had seen the elephant and heard the owl. Who didn't like him?

"Don't you like Joe Stevens?" asked Mr. Gaver, obviously bent on a catechism of considerable extent.

To save Mr. Gaver's time, which was valuable, though perhaps not very at that time of the morning, it was freely admitted that there were no bounds to this department's admiration for Joe Stevens, and there aren't, either. It was also stated that I thought well of Hal, Bill, Harry and Young Joe Stevens, who were the only other members of the clan I knew personally. Furthermore, a warm and pleasant understanding existed with the Stevens headwaiters in New York, Maryland and New Jersey, to wit, Peppy Heuchler, Frank Jirack and Jerry Bastianse, as well as with a man named Jimmy Smith who worked at the counter outside the press room at Hialeah and was wine steward at Churchill Downs.

Since Mr. Gaver appeared still unmollified, it was added that there was a deep debt owed to a young lady in the New York Stevens office who came up with tickets to things that had been sold out, even though our meetings had been entirely over a device credited to the late Alexander Graham Bell.

"All right," said Mr. Gaver grimly. "Now, do you know that Stevens has the concessions at the Polo Grounds, Yankee Stadium, Ebbets Field, Braves Field and Fenway Park?"

It was humbly admitted that this circumstance had escaped notice, because (a) there was no list of the Stevens concessions easily available, and (b) there had been no firsthand observations of these ball parks.

"Well," said Mr. Gaver, "you know it now. And if the World Series isn't in any of those parks the Stevenses don't make any money out

of it. Cleveland! St. Louis! Bah!" ("Bah" is a synopsis, rather than an exact rendition of Mr. Gaver's final remark.)

He picked up the paper again, with the air of a man who has successfully explained the bees and flowers to an overly inquisitive child, and began to investigate whether the Giants were mathematically out of it, which they were. This indicated that the incident was closed. This abashed listener immediately became a confirmed rooter for the Giants, Dodgers and Braves in the National League and for the Yankees and Red Sox in the American. Mr. Gaver was in no mood for any brooking.

DRAWING BY O. SOGLOW   [© 1956 BY THE NEW YORKER MAGAZINE, INC.]

Saratoga, or The Horse at Home

JOE H. PALMER

AMERICAN racing was seriously disrupted about ninety years ago by a dispute over states' rights. The war which accompanied this ended calamitously through the hasty action of a General R. E. Lee at Appomattox, presumably because he did not then envision Paul Robeson, but racing gained here, as it does in most wars. It got Saratoga.

In 1863, with the southern tracks such as Metarie and Lexington slightly unavailable because of the growth of paternalism in the Federal government, a group of racing men staged a meeting at Saratoga, which had long been a health resort in the days before you could keep your health by buying pills or choosing the proper brand of cigarettes. If my information is correct, there was corn growing in the infield, foreshadowing the corn which is still connected with Saratoga. But a lot of people, including this typist, like corn.

The meeting was so surprisingly successful that a somewhat better site was picked out and a grandstand constructed for a meeting in 1864. There still exists, in the spidery handwriting of one of the long-dead Alexanders of Woodburn, a list of the nominations which that nursery made to the first running of the Travers Stakes of 1864. One of them, a three-year-old named Kentucky, won it, running a mile and three-quarters in 3:18¾, because this was before stop watches caught time in fifths of a second.

There is a temptation here to write about Kentucky, but it will be resisted. But the notation has to be made that in 1861 the stallion Lexington, referred to in the somewhat sentimental periodicals of the day as the "Blind Hero of Woodburn," got three foals—Kentucky, Norfolk, and Asteroid —which left the races as "the Great Trium-

virate." None of the three was ever beaten, except on the one occasion that two of them met in the same race.

If you will look through the records of yesteryear, you will find that the Travers Stakes was run in 1897 and was not run again until 1901, and that there is an even longer lacuna in the history of the Saratoga Cup at about the same time. The reason is that in the late '90s Saratoga fell flat on its face, and that before the 1901 meeting a group of prominent racing owners headed by W. C. Whitney (grandfather of C. V. Whitney and Greentree Stable) picked it up and set it to running again. The Grand Union Hotel Stakes, the Saratoga Special, the Saratoga Handicap and the Albany Handicap date from that year, the latter race being so named before it was realized that this was feeding the hand that bites you. The Hopeful was instituted then, although, being a futurity, it was not run until 1903.

What W. C. Whitney and his friends understood in 1901 is still apparent to the more serious minds in racing. A fresh deck has been substituted since. Even when this tourist first went to Saratoga there were six races a day, starting at two-thirty or three (memory wavers a little), and people were out of the track at five o'clock to begin tanking up against the yearling sales which followed after dinner. Now it's eight races and the daily double and the damned public-address system. But Saratoga is still the focal point of racing in New York, at least, and if it goes, something dies.

It used to be that a New York stable could race in Saratoga in August or it could go to hell. Now it can race in Saratoga or it can go to New Jersey or Chicago. This circumstance supplies an

234]

excellent touchstone for picking out sheep from goats. The big stables, and the little ones which are honestly interested in the perpetuation of racing, go to Saratoga. They meet, deliberately, tougher competition for a smaller amount of money.

This is because Saratoga, in our time, has become a symbol. It doesn't draw as many people as Jamaica or Aqueduct. It doesn't contribute as much to the state treasury because the handle is lower than at the least of the metropolitan tracks. It has a somewhat antiquated clubhouse from which you cannot see very well unless you have a box or a friend who has one. It doesn't make any money for the stockholders.

Even so, any time you want to know whether racing in New York can still consider itself a sport or whether it is a highly elaborate pin-ball machine, just look to see if Saratoga has dates. There is no objection here to people who try to make money—I try it myself, with rather indifferent success. But there should be, in racing or baseball or business, an occasional gesture which is not made solely toward the cashier.

Now, local horse players are divided, like Gaul, into three parts. Those suffering from severe wounds or extreme battle fatigue will stay at home, get their business in order again, catch up on their correspondence, and note with pleasure how much little Lucy has grown since April 1. Those who have been only slightly scratched will adventure into New Jersey to face the lighter weapons of Atlantic City, a locality which has always beckoned insistently to strong men and weak women. But the Palace Guard goes to Saratoga, where there is grass on the turf.

When this department was first learning that two and two can be made to equal $9.60 and $4.20, it was felt in the area drained by Elkhorn Creek that Saratoga was quite a promising youngster, considering that it was a parvenu of 1863, with no ante-bellum tradition at all. But the ancient Lexington track was dismantled years ago, for a slum-clearance project, and the dust which had felt the beat of more than a century of racing hooves is now periodically washed from the faces of slightly underprivileged children.

With that dismantling, Saratoga became the oldest of American race tracks, and succeeded legitimately to title of Queen Mother of Racing in these states. She is, as the aged frequently are, somewhat dependent on the loyalty of her children, but this has not ever failed. As yet there are, to be sure, some who deny her authority, now that the old lady has gone into trade to sustain her social position. These may be distinguished in battle by a solid black bar on the left side of their shields.

It is admitted that age and tradition, so becoming to a race track, can be overdone in a hotel, and these remarks are to be applied to Saratoga, the race track, and not without reservation to Saratoga, the village in the foothills of the Adirondacks. There are areas in which the possibilities of indoor plumbing have not been fully explored, and a man may easily feel his enthusiasm vanish when there is a battered washbowl on the bedroom wall and the bathroom's down the corridor and turn to the left.

As to the native fauna of the place, no August visitor can very well testify because there are none at that time. There are, of course, persons who, having made fortunes elsewhere, have made their homes in Saratoga to spend their declining years standing off the natives. But your true Saratogian rents his house, often for less than half the purchase price, in August and goes to live with relatives.

The casinos and roadhouses are operated by outside talent, as is the race track. The reason for this is that, though it is against probability, a man can in theory win either at horse playing or roulette, and the native Saratogian looks upon such a situation as wasteful. A cut of the gross, he reasons, is five times better business.

And yet, one comes to believe on slow, serene, cool mornings that Saratoga does give full value received. If the visitor gets banged about a little, he must remember that for eleven months of the year someone has to work to keep the place in order, to keep the lawns in a level green glow which apparently does not exist anywhere else, and to hold the shrubbery in some sort of order, and for such services, of course, one pays.

I suspect that if all the things one criticizes were promptly remedied, Saratoga would become a modern humdrum town with a race track on the outskirts. Perhaps nothing is as hard to do, or as expensive, as to keep time from passing, and Saratoga has mastered at least the illusion of this, with the result that racing in August is a jewel.

So this summer visitor seems to have argued himself out of any complaints at all. It is to be hoped that Saratogians will keep to their ways, and that the local paper will, as it did two years ago, see no inconsistency in hoping, editorially, that prices would not be raised against August residents. At the same time it was increasing its street price from five cents to ten.

This is the month in which New York horse players are turned out on grass. After five months of concrete and asphalt and gravel, they may have the lawns of Saratoga to play with. They may even take off their shoes and wriggle their toes in the grass, though the Saratoga Association, which is conservative, will not approve.

Actually, of course, the bite is on at Saratoga just as severely as at Aqueduct, and the art of sucker-trimming has been raised to a level which will thrill the connoisseur. Some of this is in the hands of imported organizations but the natives are adept at it, too, and you begin to wonder if Burgoyne lost the Battle of Saratoga by military maladroitness or if the local taverns and hostelries just sapped his resources.

But being deluded, and even being frisked by the citizenry at Saratoga, is a good deal like eating honey. You will notice that the gentry who kick and bawl about prices and practices at Louisville around Derby time seldom have much to say about fleecing in Saratoga, yet I can assure you that over a distance of ground Louisville couldn't give Saratoga a pound.

This is because Saratoga applies an anesthetic, of tranquil shaded lawns, of big white quiet houses, of a leafy and mellowed antiquity, and morning after morning of golden serenity. By the time the subject revives and discovers what has been done to him, time has slipped past and it isn't news any more. Nothing's as dead as yesterday's newspaper expense account.

For the casual race-goer, Saratoga is about the only place in the East where he can see racing. Elsewhere he merely sees races, which isn't the same thing at all. At Saratoga the mornings are almost as much a part of the show as the afternoons, and since some of the stable area is as open to view as the Pennsylvania Station, a visitor doesn't have to know a man or have a badge to get a pretty fair idea of the entire show.

This department cannot conscientiously indorse any uncivilized nonsense like getting up and watching horses work with the morning mists swirling behind them, and while the wood smoke from under the hot water kettles may be stimulating to brighter-eyed people it always reminds me that it hasn't been long enough since last night. Still, it's worth doing once. You will remember it a long time, and that saves having to do it again.

But for persons less avid for experience, I give you Saratoga at the third set, or the second-cup-of-coffee stage when you can begin to see a little, out of one eye. Breakfast on the clubhouse porch is particularly recommended, if only for that sublime sense of siting at ease and watching other people work.

Though Saratoga avails itself of a squalling public-address system and an unornamental but quite handy Totalisator in the afternoons, it has nevertheless contrived to stand fairly still while racing became "modern." It is the only track this side of Keeneland where horses are saddled in the open, and where the ordinary racing customer can see enough of a horse to recognize him next time. A little outmoded, a little low on verve, and nearly always faintly patronizing toward the slap-dash ways of its contemporaries, Saratoga has kept on with its quiet ways, and its reward is that a little of the old time yet lingers.

A man who would change it would stir champagne.

The Old Kentucky Association track at Lexington was constructed strictly as an affront to whatever muse presides over architecture. Latonia was set in a depression quite properly known as "Death Valley," because it could get more fiendishly hot there in July than anywhere else in the world. You may love Pimlico to your heart's content but you cannot, on oath, call it pretty, and to get around the plant on a Saturday would make an eel take second thought. And some day I may discover why I like Bowie in late November. Careful thought has thus far failed to adduce any reasons.

It is therefore a relief to feel the attraction of a racing plant which demonstrably deserves it. For four wonderful, sleepy weeks—a small voice, calling itself experience, here says, "You mean sleepless weeks"—racing makes at least a partial return to the unhurried, graceful and leisurely atmosphere in which it was born. This flavor lingers in but a few places and is consequently the more precious.

Saratoga has its critics, of course, but it is customarily shelled from long range. Let a man hang around the place for a while and drink his breakfast from the clubhouse porch and you have no more trouble with him. Saratoga is slightly contagious, though you can't catch it at Jamaica.

There is a story that Lily Langtry once upset Saratoga's slow decorum by appearing publicly in red slippers. She would have to go a little deeper than that now, for I suppose a man can see more curious things going up and down Saratoga's Broadway in the morning than he could see in the same time at the Bronx Zoo. But a man has no business on Broadway in the morning. He ought to be either at the race track or sensibly in bed.

The themes at Saratoga are old friends and young horses, and most of the important racing is devoted to finding out what sort of two-year-olds are about. There are excellent and venerable races for horses above that age, notably the Travers and the Saratoga Cup, but from the Flash Stakes on the opening program to the Hopeful on closing day, the youngsters hold the major portion of the stage. Middleground, to refresh your memory, made most of his reputation there. And, not to go too far back, Bimelech, Whirlaway, Devil Diver and Pavot came to their full stature in the Hopeful.

And, of course, there's the biggest gamble of the horse business in the evenings when the Fasig-Tipton Company offers (as of the preliminary catalog) 437 Thoroughbred yearlings gathered from Kentucky, Virginia, Maryland, New Jersey and elsewhere.

You should be warned, perhaps, that horse auctions are hypnotic. Couple of years ago a friend of mine, who had no more idea of buying a horse than a steam calliope, and not much more use for one, suddenly heard himself make the successful bid on a brood mare with a foal at foot. He seemed somewhat dazed afterward but his wife was well ahead of him in that respect.

"What will we do with them?" she asked me, with the accumulated sadness of all the daughters of Eve. "We just have a three-room apartment."

There is, in the Saratoga infield, a lake. On this lake floats, and has floated since 1620, a small blue canoe. For some years I have tried to find out why it is there, though being lazy naturally and by personal inclination as well, I have not been very persistent about it. Ask one of the older veterans of Saratoga and he smiles mysteriously and shakes his head silently. This is intended to mean he isn't telling. Actually it means he doesn't know.

One reason I haven't worked more on this is that I've had a hint that there's an Indian legend connected with it. If I could be sure of this I'd give up at once, because the noble savage, whatever his merits, was notably deficient in imagination. When I was in the fourth grade I could tell a better lie than any Indian legend I ever heard.

In my own territory, for instance, every limestone jutting which pushes itself out of the river palisades with a drop as much as fifty feet under it is known as "Lovers' Leap." Grub around and you'll find that an Indian maiden, barred by her family or friends or circumstance from meeting up with a good buck, is supposed to have climbed up on it and hopped off on her head. If half the stories had any foundation, the Indian in Kentucky would have become extinct without waiting for Dan'l Boone. So this canoe thing has to be handled carefully.

Stymie–Common Folks

JOE H. PALMER

ON the cold blustery afternoon of January 28, 1921, several hundred persons huddled in the wind-swept stands of the old Kentucky Association track at Lexington to see one horse gallop past them. Down he came, a great red chestnut with a copper mane and a high head, flying the black and yellow silks of Samuel D. Riddle. This was Man o' War, leaving the race tracks forever.

Fourteen years passed before Lexington considered another horse worth a turnout. Then, on March 11, 1935, some 500 citizens assembled, on a foul, wet afternoon, to see Equipoise take his last public gallop. This was at the private track of the C. V. Whitney farm, because it was in that unbelievable two-year period when Lexington had no public race track.

The next performance, and as far as I know the last one, came on August 8, 1943, when Calumet Farm celebrated "Whirlaway Day." By this time the Chamber of Commerce had got into the act, and there was a remarkable spate of Congressmen, southern oratory, news cameras and radio announcers. This is not a complete list.

It is unlikely (though you can never tell about a chamber of commerce) that there will be any such doings over Stymie, when he arrives to enter the stud at Dr. Charles Hagyard's Green Ridge Farm. It isn't that the other three were Kentuckians coming home, and that Stymie's an outlander from Texas. It was thoroughly appropriate that Stymie should have his final public appearance at Jamaica, because he's a Jamaica kind of horse. Though I have no doubt he will do well in the stud, his kinship is with the race track, not the breeding farm.

Man o' War, Equipoise and Whirlaway all were equine royalty from the day they were foaled. Stymie was common folks. It is true that

he carries the blood of both Equipoise and Man o' War, but all pedigrees are purple if you go back a little. He was the son of a horse that had won two common races, out of a mare that couldn't win any. Nobody ever thought the first three were anything but good. Stymie began as a $1,500 plater that couldn't get out of his own way.

Stymie wasn't, of course, as good as any of the three. But he was immeasurably tougher. Could he have got to the races one more time, he would have started as many times as all three of the others together. If you want to clutter your mind with a perfectly useless bit of information, Man o' War made his reputation by blazing 19 miles and five furlongs; Equipoise, stopping now then to grow a new hoof, ran just a trifle over 50 miles in competition. Whirlaway lasted a little longer, and lacked half a furlong of running 66 miles. But Stymie's journey to leadership among the world's money winners took him 142 miles, plus a furlong and 60 yards. That's more than the other three together.

Man o' War and Equipoise and Whirlaway each won the first time out, at short odds, as they were expected to do. Stymie was 31 to 1 in a $2,500 claiming race and he ran as he was expected to do, too, finishing seventh. He was out 14 times before he could win, and that was a $3,300 claimer.

You are not to imagine that Stymie was accidentally and mistakenly dropped into a claiming race before anyone appreciated his quality. He ran 12 times in claiming races and got beat in 11 of them. He was, until the fall of his two-year-old season, right where he belonged. Then, from this beginning, he went on to win $918,485.

This is, you will see, basically the story of the

ugly duckling, of Cinderella among the ashes, of Dick Whittington and his cat, and of all the world's stories none has ever been preferred to that which leads to the public and very glorious triumph of the oppressed and the downtrodden. Jamaica's horse players are to some extent oppressed and downtrodden, and perhaps in Stymie they find a vicarious success.

The horse envisioned by a breeder, in Kentucky or elsewhere, is the son of a Derby winner out of an Oaks mare, which can sweep the futurities at two and the classics at three, and then come back to the stud to send other great racers to the wars. These are, roughly, the specifications which fit such horses as Citation and Count Fleet and War Admiral, and the like.

But the race trackers, I think, save most of their affection for the Exterminators and the Stymies and the Seabiscuits, who do it the hard way in the handicaps, pounding out mile after bitter mile, giving weight and taking their tracks wet or dry, running for any jockey, and trying with what they've got, even when they haven't got enough. That's why Stymie fitted a farewell at Jamaica better than a welcome in Kentucky.

He's a curious horse, this obscurely bred Texas product. This tourist leaned on Jack Skinner's back fence at Middleburg one December for maybe a half hour, just studying Stymie, which did not return the compliment, but went on picking at the scanty winter grass. Except for the crooked blaze which gives him a devil-may-care expression, he's the most average horse you ever saw. Not tall, not short, not long, not close-coupled. Good bone, good muscle, good chest— nothing outstanding, nothing poor. As a result, of course, he is almost perfectly balanced, and maybe this is what makes him tick.

However, there is another matter. When Stymie comes to the peak of condition, he exudes vitality so you expect to hear it crackle. He comes to a hard, lean fitness that you seldom see in domestic animals, unless in a hunting dog that has been working steadily, or perhaps a hunter that has been having his ten miles a day over the fields. This is when, as Hirsch Jacobs says, he gets "rough." It isn't temper or meanness. He just gets so full of himself that he wants things to happen.

The faster he goes the higher he carries his head, which is all wrong according to the book, but is a characteristic of the tribe of Man o' War, to which he is inbred. This tourist, who doesn't scare easily in print, will long remember the way Stymie came around the turn in the Pimlico Cup Handicap with his copper mane flying in the wind, making pretty good horses look as if they had just remembered a pressing engagement with the quarter pole.

He is not a great horse, in the sense that Man o' War and Equipoise were great. He isn't versatile. There are dozens of horses around that can beat him at a mile, and even at a mile and a quarter he would have trouble with Armed or Lucky Draw, just as he had trouble with Devil Diver. He can't make his own pace and he can't win slow races. He needs something up ahead to draw the speed from the field, to soften it up for his long, sweeping rush at the end.

But give him a field with speed in it, at a mile and a half or more, and horses had better get out of his way, even Whirlaway.

Anyway, another fine and ardent and satisfactory story of the turf was brought to a close at Jamaica. And it was happy to note that, for all the long campaign, it was no battered and limping warrior which left us. Stymie never looked better with his bronze coat in great bloom, and the high head carried as proudly as ever.

As he stood for the last time before the stands, people around the winner's inclosure were shouting to his groom, "Bring him in here, for just one more time."

The groom didn't obey, and probably he was right. Stymie never got in a winner's circle without working for it.

It was no time to begin.

Chase Me

DON REED

The radio broadcast of the Metropolitan Mile at Belmont Park, the race which marked the sudden end of Chase Me, had the same sort of dramatic and tragic impact on its listeners as the famous broadcast of the dirigible Hindenburg disaster at Lakehurst, N.J. Here is the succinct account of the storybook horse's career, written by my old friend and associate, Don Reed.

W HEN Chase Me, Maryland's "Broadway Bill," died a year ago today, a throng of 25,000 dazed turf fans stood in silence. A moment before these same fans had been cheering wildly as nine of the country's leading Thoroughbreds, including Equipoise, thundered over the Metropolitan Mile at Belmont Park.

But Chase Me's career was a storybook rather than a real-life drama. It was the tale of an unwanted colt, confounding expert judges of horseflesh, of success where success was least expected.

Back in 1929 Rigan McKinney, then a prominent amateur jockey and now owner of a string of steeplechasers, together with John Bosley Jr., of Monkton, Maryland, bought a mare at the disposal sale of Harry Sinclair's Rancocas Stud.

That mare, Mayanel, was in foal to Purchase, often rated among the true greats of the turf. Mayanel was taken to Monkton and it was there that Chase Me was born.

As a yearling, Chase Me was treated with little consideration. Not that he lacked all the attention that a good horseman gives all his charges, but the matter of his ownership never seemed to give anyone much thought.

McKinney had a horse called Huon Pine to which Bosley took a fancy. So a deal was made whereby the latter would gain title to Huon Pine. Part of that deal called for Bosley to pay a bill against the yearling Chase Me, which then became his property.

Chase Me, as a two-year-old, was found to be suffering from bad knees and Bosley immediately dropped all plans for racing him. The colt was permitted to live a life of ease around the Bosley place.

Then chance stepped into the picture once more. Bayard Warren, known in fox-hunting and steeplechase circles as an enthusiast of the first order, made Mrs. Bosley a present of a horse called Young Prince. Young Prince looked like a possible winner to Mr. Bosley, who was leaving for Canada with a string. A little family persuasion and a trade had been made by which Chase Me became the property of Mrs. Bosley.

Good horsewoman that she is, Mrs. Bosley took another look at Chase Me's bad knees and promptly gave the "unwanted" horse to her daughter Sarah. Sarah had come to like Chase Me for his gentle nature and after some deliberation decided to make a jumper of him.

It was a wise decision. Chase Me proved an apt pupil and within a comparatively short time was being entered in horse shows as an open jumper. Miss Bosley's faith in the animal began to be rewarded. Chase Me began to win in the classes in which he was entered. His behavior was perfect and Maryland horse-show and hunt followers soon came to know him as one of the more useful members of the hunt and show strings.

Throughout this period, while Chase Me on

many occasions proved his courage, he never gave any indication of the hidden speed which later was to bring him fame on the flat. All this was discovered quite by accident.

Mrs. Bosley, anxious to give a horse called Lord Johnson a morning workout, sent Chase Me on the track to work alongside her flat racer. She ordered a sprint at the close of the workout. What she saw brought about an eventful chapter in the history of the turf.

Chase Me, the two-year-old with bad legs, the hunter and jumper, suddenly cut loose with a burst of speed and outran Lord Johnson by a considerable margin.

Knowing full well that this performance might have been just a freak, Mrs. Bosley put Chase Me into training on the flat and sent him to one of the large eastern stables with a view to making a sale if the horse showed anything. The trainer of that eastern stable refused to run Chase Me because of his knees. Probably he has regretted that decision ever since.

They tell a little story of Chase Me during his training period which is indicative of the horse's appeal to the members of the Bosley family. A workout boy rode the horse to the starting gate, where an assistant starter walked out to lead Chase Me into a stall. Chase Me, used to the antics of the Bosley children and friend of all those who had come to see him in the horse shows, stopped in his tracks and calmly held out his right forepaw to shake hands with the starter.

Unable to make a deal for the horse, Mrs. Bosley took a chance and started him under her own colors at Havre de Grace in September of 1933. It was a race for horses of ordinary class. Chase Me got away from the barrier in good style. He ran up with the leaders until entering the stretch. Then as Mrs. Bosley watched with her heart in her throat, Chase Me flashed to the front and stayed there—to win by nearly twenty lengths.

Veteran turfmen gasped. Mrs. Bosley didn't know whether to laugh or cry. Still unconvinced, she entered Chase Me in another race a few days later against slightly better horses. He won again.

Moving down to historic Pimlico, Chase Me continued his career as a flat runner by grabbing off first honors in two more races. By this time all Maryland and most of the other racing centers of the country talked more about Chase Me than any other horse running.

As the 1933 fall season drew near its close, Chase Me went to Bowie. He made it five straight and turf writers were beginning to ask, "Just how good is this Bosley horse?"

Came the $5,000 Bryan and O'Hara Memorial Handicap with a field that included A. C. Bostwick's Mate, 1931 winner of the Preakness; W. R. Coe's Pomposity, winner of the $25,000 Latonia

Championship, Mad Frump, Watch Him, Kerry Patch, Osculator and Inlander.

Could Chase Me perform against these top-notchers as he had previously in his lesser engagements? Twelve thousand fans who crowded Bowie on November 25, 1933, can furnish the answer.

Chase Me rang up his sixth straight to win the handicap. He came into the stretch trailing Mate, caught the former Preakness victor and, with a thrilling drive, beat the Bostwick horse to the wire by more than a length. As Johnny Gilbert brought Chase Me back to the judges' stand and to receive the plaudits of the multitude, there was no happier family in the United States than the Bosleys.

An accident almost prevented Sarah Bosley from witnessing the triumph of her pet. Her hand lacerated by a saw a couple of days before the race, she had been taken to a Baltimore hospital. Mrs. Bosley, however, called for her daughter, took her to the track for the race and returned her to the hospital immediately afterward. Both were on hand to greet Chase Me with lumps of sugar as he stood in the winner's circle. John Bosley III, intensely interested in the proceedings, did not wait for the presentation of the cup which goes to the victor but accompanied the family pet to the stable.

Chase Me retired for the winter. As the spring racing season rolled around in 1934, speculation on Chase Me's chances of extending his string was the one topic of turfdom.

He came back to the races on May 2 at Pimlico to take his seventh straight over a mile-and-70-yard route. His performance was far from his best and apparently he was in need of the race as a conditioner.

Then came one of the few disappointing chapters in his career. He was entered in the Dixie Handicap, a race in which Equipoise also was to run. Few believed he was ready to challenge "Ekky," but Chase Me's name remained on the list of entries until shortly before post time, when Mrs. Bosley declared him out of the race. Nervousness was given as the reason and a huge turnout of Maryland fans missed an opportunity of comparing their pride with the great Equipoise.

But the two were to meet. Only a short time later Mrs. Bosley shipped Chase Me to Belmont Park for the Metropolitan Mile. Equipoise also was entered. Both went to the post, along with seven other Thoroughbreds.

Chase Me and Equipoise broke seventh and eighth in the field of nine. Good Advice jumped into the lead. At the halfway mark Chase Me was running a length in front of C. V. Whitney's great champion as they made their bids to overhaul the leaders. Equipoise, with the great stride for which he is noted, was pulling even with

Chase Me at the three-quarter pole.

Into the stretch for the final drive they pounded. The crowd was wild. Suddenly Jockey Freddie Slate, riding Chase Me, went catapulting through the air and the horse, stumbling and then turning a somersault, landed near the outside fence.

Despite the fact that the finish of a stake race was near, a hush fell over those 25,000 fans. Slate and Chase Me lay motionless on the track as Equipoise came on to finish first. But what matter that Equipoise was disqualified for fouling Mr. Khayyam in the stretch and the latter awarded the race?

Chase Me lay there in the dust. Slate struggles to his feet and walks slowly over to his mount. Willing hands of spectators who have jumped the fence help Chase Me arise. There is a loud groan through the stands as it is seen that Chase Me stands on only three legs.

Mrs. Bosley, the only member of her family present, runs down the track to her pet. Tears streaming down her face, she realizes that Chase Me has broken his left shoulder. The bone protrudes through the flesh. Like a true sportswoman, Mrs. Bosley accompanies Chase Me to a clump of trees nearby, where a shot ends his agony and cuts short a career full of romance.

Nobody will ever know just what happened to Chase Me. Jockey Slate says as far as he knows none of the other horses in the race bumped the Bosley star. Mrs. Bosley thinks Chase Me had all four feet in the air when something threw him off balance.

Chase Me, technically, had been beaten. A horse which starts and does not finish is a beaten horse according to racing rules. Those who knew and loved Chase Me will remember him as unbeaten in his seven starts. And it is just as well to remember him that way. What are the rules and regulations when a horse like Chase Me is involved?

The Goddess of Good Fortune, who had smiled on Chase Me long enough to have Mrs. Bosley discover his running qualities and who had followed him through seven straight victories, apparently was supplanted that day by the Evil Spirit of Misfortune.

Knowing that Chase Me faced the greatest battle of his career in meeting Equipoise, Mrs. Bosley had contracted for the services of Mack Garner as jockey for that day. Garner, veteran of the turf and winner of the Kentucky Derby on Cavalcade, was believed to be the best possible bet to get the most out of the horse.

But Garner did not ride. Just a few days before the running of the Metropolitan, little Duke Bellizi, rider for the Brookmeade Stable of Mrs. Isabel Dodge Sloane, had died of injuries received in a fall during a race. The Brookmeade outfit was in mourning for Duke, and Garner, also one of Mrs. Sloane's jockeys, canceled his mount on Chase Me for that reason.

Unable to secure another noted flat rider at such short notice, Mrs. Bosley turned to Slate. He had a fine record as a steeplechase jockey and had ridden some on the flat. There was some criticism of Mrs. Bosley's choice, but she still avers her faith in the boy she chose. But who knows what might have happened in that race had Garner been on Chase Me? No two boys would have had Chase Me at that spot at the moment of the accident. But fate decided otherwise and so ended an illustrious turf record.

Chase Me was buried on the beautiful Long Island estate of A. C. Bostwick. Unlike Broadway Bill in the motion picture, Chase Me did not win his last race. But like Mark Hellinger's famed filmed Thoroughbred, Chase Me died giving his best for a loving owner.

Seabiscuit vs. War Admiral

GRANTLAND RICE

It was rather fitting that the greatest race he "ever saw" was run on Granny Rice's 60th birthday. It was my own first important sport-publicity promotion and was the occasion of my meeting, for the first time, practically all the great sports writers of the past three decades. Of all the many fine accounts of the 'Race of the Century" no one will begrudge the selection given here, for Rice was the acknowledged dean of sports writers.

A LITTLE horse with the heart of a lion and the flying feet of a gazelle yesterday proved his place as the gamest Thoroughbred that ever raced over an American track.

In one of the greatest match races ever run in the ancient history of the turf, the valiant Seabiscuit not only conquered the great War Admiral but, beyond this, he ran the beaten son of Man o' War into the dirt and dust of Pimlico.

Head and head around the last far turn, Seabiscuit, ably ridden by George Woolf, beat War Admiral by a full three lengths down the last furlong with a dazzling burst of speed that not only cracked the heart of the Admiral but, in addition, broke the track record, set by Pompoon. Seabiscuit took a fifth of a second from the track record, which he now holds at 1:56⅘.

The drama and the melodrama of this match race, held before a record crowd keyed to the highest tension I have ever seen in sport, set an all-time mark.

You must get the picture from the start to absorb the thrill of this perfect autumn day over a perfect track. As the two Thoroughbreds paraded to the post there was no emotional outburst. The big crowd was too full of tension, the type of tension that locks the human throat.

You looked at the odds flashed upon the mutuel board—War Admiral one to four, Seabiscuit two to one. Even those backing War Admiral, the great majority of the crowd, felt their pity for the son of Hard Tack and Swing On, who had come along the hard way and had churned up the dust of almost every track from the Great Lakes to the Gulf, from the Atlantic to the Pacific.

After two false walking starts, they were off. But it wasn't the fast-flying War Admiral who took the lead. It was Seabiscuit, taking the whip from Woolf, who got the jump. It was Seabiscuit who had a full-length lead as they passed the first furlong. The Admiral's supporters were dazed as the 'Biscuit not only held this lead, but increased it to two lengths before they passed the first quarter.

The 'Biscuit was moving along as smoothly as a southern breeze. And then the first roar of the big crowd swept over Maryland. The Admiral was moving up. Stride by stride, Man o' War's favorite offspring was closing up the open gap. You could hear the roar from thousands of throats—"Here he comes—here he comes!"

And the Admiral was under full steam. He cut away a length. He cut away another length as they came to the half-mile post—and now they were running head and head. The Admiral looked Seabiscuit in the eye at the three-quarters—but Seabiscuit never got the look. He was too busy running with his shorter, faster stride.

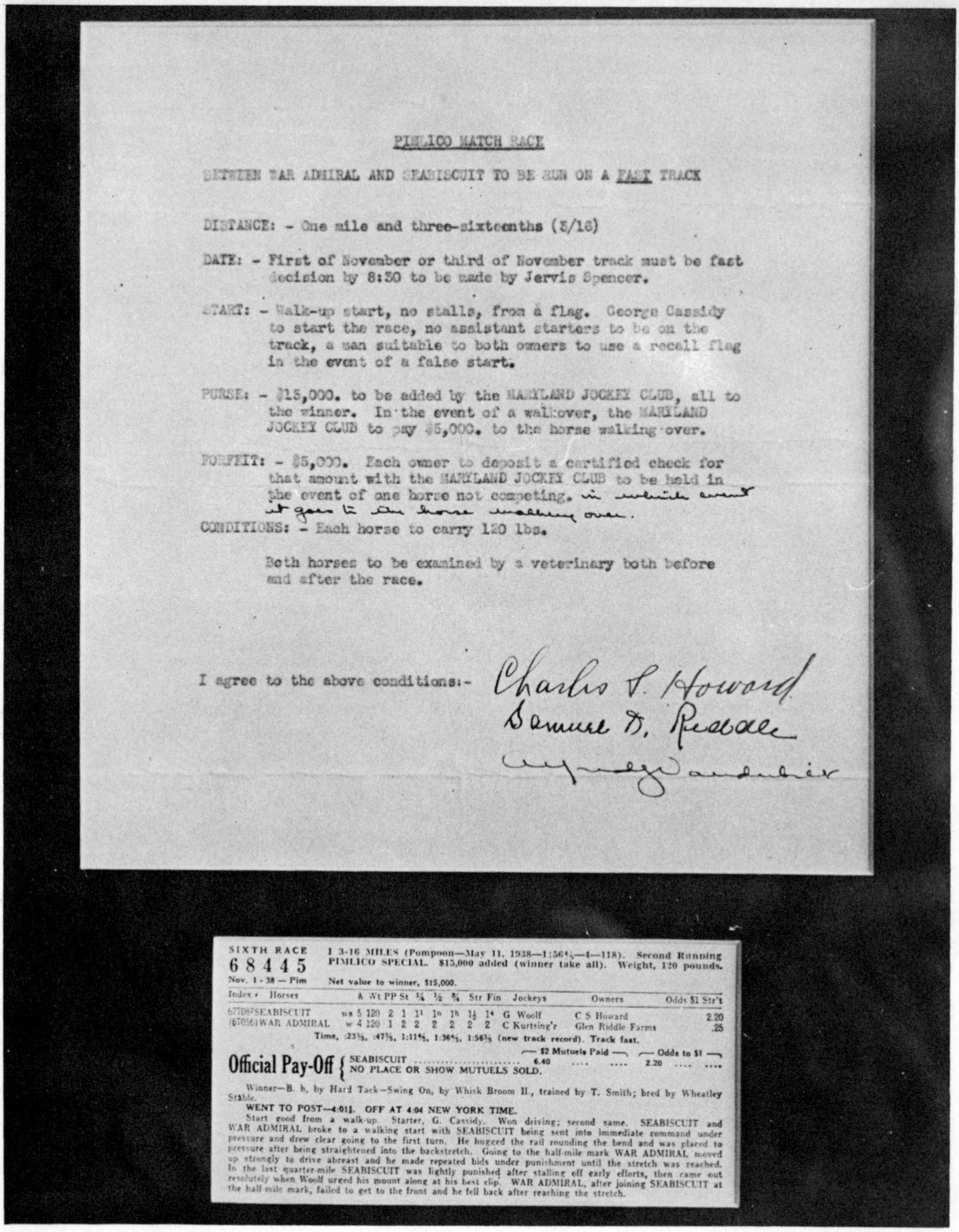

PIMLICO MATCH RACE

BETWEEN WAR ADMIRAL AND SEABISCUIT TO BE RUN ON A FAST TRACK

DISTANCE: - One mile and three-sixteenths (3/16)

DATE: - First of November or third of November track must be fast decision by 8:30 to be made by Jervis Spencer.

START: - Walk-up start, no stalls, from a flag. George Cassidy to start the race, no assistant starters to be on the track, a man suitable to both owners to use a recall flag in the event of a false start.

PURSE: - $15,000. to be added by the MARYLAND JOCKEY CLUB, all to the winner. In the event of a walkover, the MARYLAND JOCKEY CLUB to pay $5,000. to the horse walking over.

FORFEIT: - $5,000. Each owner to deposit a certified check for that amount with the MARYLAND JOCKEY CLUB to be held in the event of one horse not competing. in which event it goes to the horse walking over.

CONDITIONS: - Each horse to carry 120 lbs.

Both horses to be examined by a veterinary both before and after the race.

I agree to the above conditions:- Charles S. Howard
Samuel D. Riddle
Alfred G. Vanderbilt

SIXTH RACE
68445
Nov. 1 - 38 — Pim

1 3-16 MILES (Pompoon—May 11, 1938—1:56 4/5—4—118). Second Running PIMLICO SPECIAL. $15,000 added (winner take all). Weight, 120 pounds.

Net value to winner, $15,000.

Index	Horses		A	Wt	PP	St	$\frac{1}{4}$	$\frac{1}{2}$	$\frac{3}{4}$	Str	Fin	Jockeys	Owners	Odds $1 Str't
67706^2	SEABISCUIT	wa	5	120	2	1	1^1	1^n	1^h	$1\frac{1}{2}$	1^4	G Woolf	C S Howard	2.20
(67056)	WAR ADMIRAL	w	4	120	1	2	2	2	2	2	2	C Kurtsing'r	Glen Riddle Farms	.25

Time, :23 1/5, :47 3/5, 1:11 4/5, 1:36 4/5, 1:56 3/5 (new track record). Track fast.

Official Pay-Off { SEABISCUIT .... $2 Mutuels Paid: 6.40 .... Odds to $1: 2.20 ....
NO PLACE OR SHOW MUTUELS SOLD.

Winner—B. h, by Hard Tack—Swing On, by Whisk Broom II., trained by T. Smith; bred by Wheatley Stable.

WENT TO POST—4:01½. OFF AT 4:04 NEW YORK TIME.

Start good from a walk-up. Starter, G. Cassidy. Won driving; second same. SEABISCUIT and WAR ADMIRAL broke to a walking start with SEABISCUIT being sent into immediate command under pressure and drew clear going to the first turn. He hugged the rail rounding the bend and was placed to pressure after being straightened into the backstretch. Going to the half-mile mark WAR ADMIRAL moved up strongly to drive abreast and he made repeated bids under punishment until the stretch was reached. In the last quarter-mile SEABISCUIT was lightly punished after stalling off early efforts, then came out resolutely when Woolf urged his mount along at his best clip. WAR ADMIRAL, after joining SEABISCUIT at the half-mile mark, failed to get to the front and he fell back after reaching the stretch.

The signed agreement (above) which culminated in the famous War Admiral-Seabiscuit race at Pimlico on November 1, 1938, is a remarkable document. It is undated but was signed about mid-September of 1938, by Charles S. Howard at Belmont Park and by Samuel D. Riddle at the Information Desk in Pennsylvania Station, New York City, where Alfred Vanderbilt waited to waylay the Philadelphia sportsman.

Riddle, it was generally felt, would have preferred not to have his colt meet Seabiscuit at that particular time. A similar match—for a $100,000 purse—scheduled for Belmont Park in May, had fallen through. Vanderbilt got the race for Pimlico, of which he was president, for a mere $15,000, and racing people today still shake their heads and wonder how he persuaded the two owners to agree. What combination of guile and psychology Vanderbilt used on Howard and Riddle isn't known, but he had one thing going for him. He knew his men, and he himself had been through the experience of owning a great horse and having to meet the pressures that go with it. His Discovery had faced similar challenges. In any case, Vanderbilt arranged what is still considered "the match of the century." [PHOTO BY LAWRENCE MCNALLY, BALTIMORE *News-Post*]

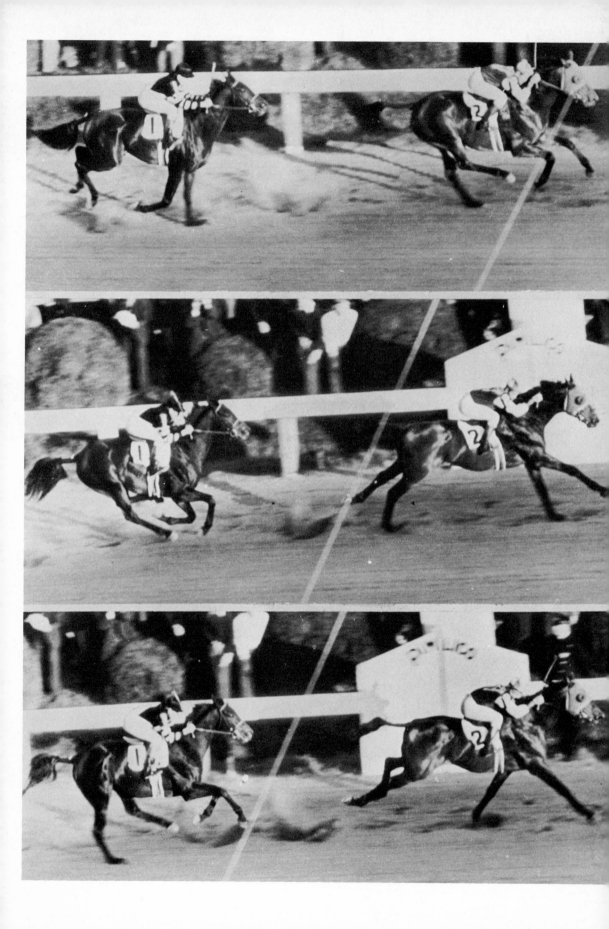

For almost a half mile they ran as one horse, painted against the green, red and orange foliage of a Maryland countryside. They were neck and neck—head and head—nose and nose.

The great Admiral had thrown his challenge. You could see that he expected Seabiscuit to quit and curl up. But Seabiscuit has never been that brand of horse. I had seen him before in two $100,000 races at Santa Anita, boxed out, knocked to his knees, taking the worst of all the racing luck—almost everything except facing a firing squad or a machine-gun nest—and yet, through all this barrage of trouble, Seabiscuit was always there, challenging at the wire. I saw him run the fastest half-mile ever run at Santa Anita last March, when he had to do it in his pursuit of Stagehand.

So, when War Admiral moved up on even terms and 40,000 throats poured out their tribute to the Admiral, I still knew that the 'Biscuit would be alongside at the finish. The 'Biscuit had come up the hard way. That happens to be the only way worth while. The Admiral had known only the softer years—the softer type of competition. He had never before met a combination of a grizzly bear and a running fool.

Head and head they came to the mile. There wasn't a short conceded putt between them. It was a question now of the horse that had the heart. Seabiscuit had lost his two-length margin. His velvet had been shot away. He was on his own where all races are won—down the stretch.

He had come to the great kingdom of all sport —the kingdom of the heart.

The Admiral had shown his reserve speed. From two lengths away he was now on even terms. But, as they passed the mile post with three-sixteenths left—the vital test—the stretch that always tells the story—where 40,000 looked for the fleet War Admiral to move away—there was another story. Seabiscuit was still hanging on. Seabiscuit hadn't quit. With barely more than a final furlong left, the hard-way son of Hard Tack must have said to the Admiral—"Now let's start running. Let's see who is the better horse."

Foot by foot and yard by yard, Woolf and Seabiscuit started moving away. Charlie Kurtzinger gave the Admiral the whip. But you could see from the stands that Admiral suddenly knew he had nothing left in heart or feet to match this wild, crazy five-year-old who all his life had known only the uphill, knockdown devil-take-the-loser route, any track—any distance—any weight —any time. And who the hell are you?

War Admiral had no answer. Down the final furlong the great-hearted 'Biscuit put on extra speed. He moved on by. Then he opened a small gap. Forty thousand expected the Admiral to move up, close the gap again. But the Admiral was through. He had run against too many plow horses and platers in his soft, easy life. He had never tackled a Seabiscuit before.

He had never met a horse who could look him in the eye down the stretch and say to him, in horse language, "Now let's start traveling, kid. How do you feel? I feel great. This is down my alley."

Yard by yard Seabiscuit moved on ahead. Then it was length by length. Seabiscuit left the Admiral so far behind that it wasn't even a contest down the stretch. War Admiral might just as well have been chasing a will o' the wisp in a midnight swamp. He might just as well have been a fat poodle chasing a meat wagon. He had been outrun and outgamed—he had been run off the track by a battered five-year-old who had more speed and heart.

The race, they say, isn't to the swift. But it is always to the swift and the game. It so happened that Seabiscuit had these two important qualities in deep abundance. War Admiral could match neither flying feet nor fighting heart. Man o' War's brilliant son hung on with all he had until it came to the big showdown—to the point when the hard-way Thoroughbred, the horse from the wrong side of the track, began really to run.

As a result of this race, Seabiscuit moves up into second place for total lifetime winnings with $340,000—just back of Sun Beau with $376,244. But there is only one Seabiscuit—the next one to him is Exterminator. These have been the two great horses, year by year, of the American turf.

I nominate Seabiscuit for heart and speed, for all it takes at the top for one of the greatest competitive efforts I have ever seen in a matter of forty years.

Quite a horse, this Seabiscuit. None was a better, gamer, or faster one over the route.

Maxims from Methuselah

GRANTLAND RICE

Much of Granny Rice's reporting was sheer poetry and much of his poetry was philosophical. He was as fast with a piece of original verse as Don Meade was out of the gate on a two-year-old.

Take your pick from the tipsters, who give you
    the winning horse.
But kindly remember the answer in the heart of
    your black remorse.

Horse racing's an opium dream beyond all dreams
    ever spun,
Where every sad bloke in the mob should have
    won every race that was run.

Did you ever notice, my friend, in the race
    track's grotto of tears,
How many go to the seller's maw—how few to
    the lone cashier?

Did you ever notice, old pal, in the race track's
    dizzy spin
There are ninety ways that a horse can lose—
    with only one way to win?

Gentleman from Sheepshead Bay

JAMES ROACH

Change the word "was" to "is" in the last sentence of this column and you'll get the correct title for Jim Roach's capsule portrait of Mr. Fitz—"He is a fine man." It's characteristic of the dean of American trainers if he has to say something about a man or an animal to say something nice. Oh, yes, for future biographers of "Sunny Jim"—and they will be myriad—take note that he is fond of crab cakes and an occasional Manhattan cocktail—that is, if there is room remaining after recounting his amazing record on the American turf.

NEW YORK, July 17, 1949

SUNNY JIM FITZSIMMONS, taking his ease in the shade of a tree on the clubhouse turn at Jamaica, was asked if he could provide any details about his first day of work at a race track.

"I certainly can, son," said Mr. Fitz. "It was March 4, 1885, when I went to work for the Brannon Brothers at Sheepshead Bay. I was a little less than eleven. I remember the date because it was the day Grover Cleveland was inaugurated for his first term. I guess they were all Democrats around that barn, because they were having a celebration and were serving up egg-nogs.

"They asked me to have one. It tasted even better than sarsaparilla to me. Funny thing—when I walked home I discovered that there were more trees around than there usually were."

Mr. Fitz has been a race tracker ever since. As a matter of fact, he was a race tracker long before the day he had that eggnog. For the great trainer, who will be seventy-five next Saturday, was born on the site of the old Sheepshead Bay track.

"They built that race track right around me," said Mr. Fitz. "My father's house was located close to where the judges' stand was put up. They finished the track in 1880, six years after I was born. Mr. Clare, father of Tom Clare, who later was the Saratoga superintendent, had the job of grading the site. He used to take me up behind him on his horse and ride me around the place. I guess I was the first jockey ever to ride down the Sheepshead Bay stretch."

Mr. Fitz has traveled a far piece along the racing trail since those days. He was a jockey in his teens, and he has been a trainer since about 1893. There's no trainer in the land with a record to match his. For confirmation of that statement, pick up a copy of *The American Racing Manual* and turn to the section on stakes records. In it will be found the names of more than 200 Fitz-simmons-trained stakes winners. They're listed under the names of more than ninety stakes.

Some of the highlights; two winners of the triple crown, three in the Kentucky Derby, five in the Belmont Stakes, six in the Dwyer, six in the Wood Memorial, seven in the Empire City, eight in the Saratoga Cup, and eight in the Lawrence Realization.

What's the secret of success as a trainer?

"Good horses and good bosses," said Mr. Fitz. "A trainer needs a boss who will stick with him. When a man runs into bad luck, he needs support. And anybody who couldn't train for the people I train for just can't train."

At the present time Mr. Fitz has about fifty

horses in his Aqueduct barns. They fly the silks of the Belair Stud, Mrs. Whitney Stone, Ogden Phipps and the Wheatley Stable. In 1948 he started his twenty-fifth year with Belair—owned by William Woodward, the chairman of The Jockey Club—and this year he started his twenty-fifth campaign with Wheatley, owned by Mr. and Mrs. Henry Carnegie Phipps.

If he had to pick one horse out of all those he has trained, which one would it be?

"I guess that would have to be Gallant Fox, son," said Mr. Fitz. "He would always battle for you. There never were any excuses with him. The other horse just had to be the best horse if he was to beat him."

The Fox of Belair won the triple crown series of Preakness, Derby and Belmont Stakes in 1930 and sired Omaha, Belair's triple-crowner of 1935. Gallant Fox was the only triple-crowner to sire a triple-crowner. The Fox was Belair's first Derby starter and Omaha was its second. Its sixth was Johnstown, the 1939 winner at Churchill Downs.

What race gave Mr. Fitz his biggest thrill as a trainer?

"Well, I suppose I'd have to say that first Derby," said Mr. Fitz, "though I didn't see the race. I was in the crush in the infield and I just got glimpses of the horses as they went by. I didn't know who had won till the crowd set up a holler for Gallant Fox. Then I tried to get to my horse. I ran into half a dozen cops on horseback who were pushing the crowd back. They pushed me up to about the eighth pole.

"I did see Omaha's race. I was in Mr. Hancock's box. But when I went to get down on the track, I couldn't get near my horse.

"In Johnstown's Derby, Colonel Matt Winn and Tom Young, the track superintendent, made sure that I got a seat in a box on the rail right at the finish. But I didn't take a seat in the front row. When the field went by the first time the others jumped up on the seats in front of me and I couldn't see much. I did catch a glimpse of Johnstown going by. Then I saw him go by again. I saw maybe a sixteenth of the race each time through the stretch."

Maybe his experiences at the Derby provide the reason why Mr. Fitz never is seen in the stands at the New York horse parks. At Jamaica his battle station is behind the hedge at about the seven-eighths pole. At Aqueduct he does his race watching from the back stretch. At Belmont he sits in a little stand on the outside rail up beyond the finish.

What's his daily routine?

"I get up at five-thirty," said Mr. Fitz, "and go to the barns at about six-thirty. The previous night we've made out the slips for the morning works, and we do what has to be done. I get through with that anywhere from nine-thirty to eleven, then take a little nap, have lunch and go to the track, if I have horses running. I get ready to go to bed at six-thirty, and then I start looking at the movies. I mean the television set. I think I'd better get rid of it. It keeps me up too late."

He's known as Mr. Fitz around the tracks and he's often called Sunny Jim in print. Who gave him that Sunny Jim tag?

"That was George Daley of *The World*," said Mr. Fitz. "He and Vince Treanor were fine men. All the newspaper men have been fine to me."

Mention was made to Mr. Fitz of what W. O. McGeehan said about him some twenty years ago. It went something like this: "To horses as well as humans, he's Sunny Jim."

"That was nice of McGeehan, son," said Mr. Fitz. "He was a fine man."

Little Miss Marker

DAMON RUNYON

This is Runyon at his most popular, if not at his best. Runyon had a knack of using the plausible character with the implausible situation and serving up a highly entertaining and satisfactory fiction piece. "Little Miss Marker" is one of his better-known stories, made into a first-rate movie with the young Shirley Temple in the title role, and has been done several times on television.

ONE evening along toward seven o'clock, many citizens are standing out on Broadway in front of Mindy's restaurant, speaking of one thing and another, and particularly about the tough luck they have playing the races in the afternoon, when who comes up the street with a little doll hanging onto his right thumb but a guy by the name of Sorrowful.

This guy is called Sorrowful because this is the way he always is about no matter what, and especially about the way things are with him when anybody tries to put the bite on him. In fact, if anybody who tries to put the bite on Sorrowful can listen to him for two minutes about how things are with him and not bust into tears, they must be very hard-hearted, indeed.

Regret, the horse player, is telling me that he once tries to put the bite on Sorrowful for a sawbuck, and by the time Sorrowful gets through explaining how things are with him, Regret feels so sorry for him that he goes out and puts the bite on somebody else for the saw and gives it to Sorrowful, although it is well known to one and all that Sorrowful has plenty of potatoes hid away somewhere.

He is a tall, skinny guy with a long, sad, mean-looking kisser, and a mournful voice. He is maybe sixty years old, give or take a couple of years, and for as long as I can remember he is running a handbook over in Forty-ninth Street

next door to a chop-suey joint. In fact, Sorrowful is one of the largest handbook makers in this town.

Any time you see him he is generally by himself, because being by himself is not apt to cost him anything, and it is therefore a most surprising scene when he comes along Broadway with a little doll.

And there is much speculation among the citizens as to how this comes about, for no one ever hears of Sorrowful having any family, or relations of any kind, or even any friends.

The little doll is a very little doll indeed, the top of her noggin only coming up to Sorrowful's knee, although of course Sorrowful has very high knees, at that. Moreover, she is a very pretty little doll, with big blue eyes and fat pink cheeks, and a lot of yellow curls hanging down her back, and she has fat little legs and quite a large smile, although Sorrowful is lugging her along the street so fast that half the time her feet are dragging the sidewalk and she has a license to be bawling instead of smiling.

Sorrowful is looking sadder than somewhat, which makes his face practically heart-rending as he pulls up in front of Mindy's and motions us to follow him in. Anybody can see that he is worried about something very serious, and many citizens are figuring that maybe he suddenly discovers all his potatoes are counterfeit, because nobody can think of anything that will worry Sorrowful except money.

Anyway, four or five of us gather around the table where Sorrowful sits down with the little doll beside him, and he states a most surprising situation to us.

It seems that early in the afternoon a young guy who is playing the races with Sorrowful for several days pops into his place of business next door to the chop-suey joint, leading the little doll, and this guy wishes to know how much time he has before post in the first race at Empire.

Well, he only has about twenty-five minutes, and he seems very down-hearted about this, because he explains to Sorrowful that he has a sure thing in this race, which he gets the night before off a guy who is a pal of a close friend of Jockey Workman's valet.

The young guy says he is figuring to bet himself about a deuce on this sure thing, but he does not have such a sum as a deuce on him when he goes to bed, so he plans to get up bright and early in the morning and hop down to a spot on Fourteenth Street where he knows a guy who will let him have the deuce.

But it seems he oversleeps, and here it is almost post time, and it is too late for him to get to Fourteenth Street and back before the race is run off, and it is all quite a sad story indeed, although of course it does not make much impression on Sorrowful, as he is already sadder than somewhat himself just from thinking that somebody may beat him for a bet during the day, even though the races do not start anywhere as yet.

Well, the young guy tells Sorrowful he is going to try to get to Fourteenth Street and back in time to bet on the sure thing, because he says it will be nothing short of a crime if he has to miss such a wonderful opportunity.

"But," he says to Sorrowful, "to make sure I do not miss, you take my marker for a deuce, and I will leave the kid here with you as security until I get back."

Now, ordinarily, asking Sorrowful to take a marker will be considered great foolishness, as it is well known to one and all that Sorrowful will not take a marker from Andrew Mellon. In fact, Sorrowful can almost break your heart telling you about the poorhouses that are full of bookmakers who take markers in their time.

But it happens that business is just opening up for the day, and Sorrowful is pretty busy, and besides the young guy is a steady customer for several days, and has an honest pan, and Sorrowful figures a guy is bound to take a little doll out of hock for a deuce. Furthermore, while Sorrowful does not know much about kids, he can see the little doll must be worth a deuce, at least, and maybe more.

So he nods his head, and the young guy puts the little doll on a chair and goes tearing out of the joint to get the dough, while Sorrowful marks down a deuce bet on Cold Cuts, which is the name of the sure thing. Then he forgets all about the proposition for a while, and all the time the little doll is sitting on a chair as quiet as a mouse, smiling at Sorrowful's customers, including the Chinks from the chop-suey joint who come in now and then to play the races.

Well, Cold Cuts blows, and in fact is not even fifth, and along late in the afternoon Sorrowful suddenly realizes that the young guy never shows up again, and that the little doll is still sitting in the chair, although she is now playing with a butcher knife which one of the Chinks from the chop-suey joint gives her to keep her amused.

Finally it comes on Sorrowful's closing time, and the little doll is still there, so he can think of nothing else to do in this situation but to bring her around to Mindy's and get a little advice from different citizens, as he does not care to leave her in his place of business alone, as Sorrowful will not trust anybody in there alone, not even himself.

"Now," Sorrowful says, after giving us this long spiel, "what are we to do about this proposition?"

Well, of course, up to this minute none of the rest of us know we are being cut in on any proposition, and personally I do not care for any part of it, but Big Nig, the craps shooter, speaks up as follows:

"If this little doll is sitting in your joint all afternoon," Nig says, "the best thing to do right now is to throw a feed into her, as the chances are her stomach thinks her throat is cut."

Now, this seems to be a fair sort of an idea, so Sorrowful orders up a couple of portions of ham hocks and sauerkraut, which is a very tasty dish in Mindy's at all times, and the little doll tears into it very enthusiastically, using both hands, although a fat old doll who is sitting at the next table speaks up and says this is terrible fodder to be tossing into a child at such an hour and where is her mamma?

"Well," Big Nig says to the old doll, "I hear of many people getting a bust in the snoot for not minding their own business in this town, but you give off an idea, at that. Listen," Big Nig says to the little doll, "where is your mamma?"

But the little doll does not seem to know, or maybe she does not wish to make this information public, because she only shakes her head and smiles at Big Nig, as her mouth is too full of ham hocks and sauerkraut for her to talk.

"What is your name?" Big Nig asks, and she says something that Big Nig claims sounds like Marky, although personally I think she is trying to say Martha. Anyway, it is from this that she gets the name we always call her afterward, which is Marky.

"It is a good monicker," Big Nig says. "It is short for marker, and she is certainly a marker unless Sorrowful is telling us a large lie. Why," Big Nig says, "this is a very cute little doll, at that, and pretty smart. How old are you, Marky?"

She only shakes her head again, so Regret, the horse player, who claims he can tell how old a horse is by its teeth, reaches over and sticks his finger in her mouth to get a peek at her crockery, but she seems to think Regret's finger is a hunk of ham hock and shuts down on it so hard Regret lets out an awful squawk. But he says that before she tries to cripple him for life he sees enough of her teeth to convince him she is maybe three, rising four, and this seems reasonable, at that. Anyway, she cannot be much older.

Well, about this time a guinea with a hand organ stops out in front of Mindy's and begins grinding out a tune while his ever-loving wife is passing a tambourine around among the citizens on the sidewalk and, on hearing this music, Marky slides off of her chair with her mouth still full of ham hock and sauerkraut, which she swallows so fast she almost chokes, and then she speaks as follows:

"Marky dance," she says.

Then she begins hopping and skipping around among the tables, holding her little short skirt up in her hands and showing a pair of white panties underneath. Pretty soon Mindy himself comes along and starts putting up a beef about making a dance hall of his joint, but a guy by the name of Sleep-out, who is watching Marky with much interest, offers to bounce a sugar bowl off of Mindy's sconce if he does not mind his own business.

So Mindy goes away, but he keeps muttering about the white panties being a most immodest spectacle, which of course is great nonsense, as many dolls older than Marky are known to do dances in Mindy's especially on the late watch, when they stop by for a snack on their way home from the night clubs and the speaks, and I hear some of them do not always wear white panties, either.

Personally, I like Marky's dancing very much, although of course she is no Pavlowa, and finally she trips over her own feet and falls on her snoot. But she gets up smiling and climbs back on her chair and pretty soon she is sound asleep with her head against Sorrowful.

Well, now there is much discussion about what Sorrowful ought to do with her. Some claim he ought to take her to a police station, and others say the best thing to do is to put an ad in the Lost and Found columns of the morning bladders, the same as people do when they find Angora cats, and Pekes, and other animals which they do not

wish to keep, but none of these ideas seems to appeal to Sorrowful.

Finally he says he will take her to his own home and let her sleep there while he is deciding what is to be done about her, so Sorrowful takes Marky in his arms and lugs her over to a fleabag in West Forty-ninth Street where he has a room for many years, and afterward a bell hop tells me Sorrowful sits up all night watching her while she is sleeping.

Now, what happens but Sorrowful takes on a great fondness for the little doll, which is most surprising, as Sorrowful is never before fond of anybody or anything, and after he has her overnight he cannot bear the idea of giving her up.

Personally, I will just as soon have a three-year-old baby wolf around me as a little doll such as this, but Sorrowful thinks she is the greatest thing that ever happens. He has a few inquiries made around and about to see if he can find out who she belongs to, and he is tickled silly when nothing comes of these inquiries, although nobody else figures anything will come of them anyway, as it is by no means uncommon in this town for little kids to be left sitting in chairs, or on doorsteps, to be chucked into orphan asylums by whoever finds them.

Anyway, Sorrowful says he is going to keep Marky, and his attitude causes great surprise, as keeping Marky is bound to be an expense, and it does not seem reasonable that Sorrowful will go to any expense for anything. When it commences to look as if he means what he says, many citizens naturally figure there must be an angle, and soon there are a great many rumors on the subject.

Of course one of these rumors is that the chances are Marky is Sorrowful's own offspring which is tossed back on him by the wronged mamma, but this rumor is started by a guy who does not know Sorrowful, and after he gets a gander at Sorrowful, the guy apologizes, saying he realizes that no wronged mamma will be daffy enough to permit herself to be wronged by Sorrowful. Personally, I always say that if Sorrowful wishes to keep Marky it is his own business, and most of the citizens around Mindy's agree with me.

But the trouble is Sorrowful at once cuts everybody else in on the management of Marky, and the way he talks to the citizens around Mindy's about her, you will think we are all personally responsible for her. As most of the citizens around Mindy's are bachelors, or are wishing they are bachelors, it is most inconvenient to them to suddenly find themselves with a family.

Some of us try to explain to Sorrowful that if he is going to keep Marky it is up to him to handle all her play, but right away Sorrowful starts talking so sad about all his pals deserting him and Marky just when they need them most that it softens all hearts, although up to this time we are about as pally with Sorrowful as a burglar with a copper. Finally every night in Mindy's is meeting night for a committee to decide something or other about Marky.

The first thing we decide is that the fleabag where Sorrowful lives is no place for Marky, so Sorrowful hires a big apartment in one of the swellest joints on West Fifty-ninth Street, over-looking Central Park, and spends plenty of pota-toes furnishing it, although up to this time Sor-rowful never sets himself back more than about ten bobs per week for a place to live and con-siders it extravagance, at that. I hear it costs him five G's to fix up Marky's bedroom alone, not counting the solid gold toilet set that he buys for her.

Then he gets her an automobile and he has to hire a guy to drive it for her, and finally when we explain to Sorrowful that it does not look right for Marky to be living with nobody but him and a chauffeur, Sorrowful hires a French doll with bobbed hair and red cheeks by the name of Mam'selle Fifi as a nurse for Marky, and this seems to be quite a sensible move, as it insures Marky plenty of company.

In fact, up to the time that Sorrowful hires Mam'selle Fifi, many citizens are commencing to consider Marky something of a nuisance and are playing the duck for her and Sorrowful, but after Mam'selle Fifi comes along you can scarcely get in Sorrowful's joint on Fifty-ninth Street, or around his table in Mindy's when he brings Marky and Mam'selle Fifi in to eat. But one night Sorrowful goes home early and catches Sleep-out guzzling Mam'selle Fifi and Sorrowful makes Mam'selle Fifi take plenty of breeze, claiming she will set a bad example to Marky.

Then he gets an old tomato by the name of Mrs. Clancy to be Marky's nurse, and while there is no doubt Mrs. Clancy is a better nurse than Mam'selle Fifi and there is practically no danger of her setting Marky a bad example, the play at Sorrowful's joint is by no means as brisk as formerly.

You can see that from being closer than a dead heat with his potatoes, Sorrowful becomes as loose as ashes. He not only spends plenty on Marky, but he starts picking up checks in Mindy's and other spots, although up to this time picking up checks is something that is most repulsive to Sorrowful.

He gets so he will hold still for a bite, if the bite is not too savage and, what is more, a great change comes over his kisser. It is no longer so sad and mean-looking, and in fact it is almost a pleasant sight at times, especially as Sorrowful gets so he smiles now and then, and has a big hello for one and all, and everybody says the Mayor ought to give Marky a medal for bringing about such a wonderful change.

Now Sorrowful is so fond of Marky that he wants her with him all the time, and by and by there is much criticism of him for having her around his handbook joint among the Chinks and the horse players, and especially the horse players, and for taking her around night clubs and keep-ing her out at all hours, as some people do not consider this a proper bringing-up for a little doll.

We hold a meeting in Mindy's on this proposi-tion one night, and we get Sorrowful to agree to keep Marky out of his joint, but we know Marky is so fond of night clubs, especially where there is music, that it seems a sin and a shame to deprive her of this pleasure altogether, so we finally com-promise by letting Sorrowful take her out one night a week to the Hot Box in Fifty-fourth Street, which is only a few blocks from where Marky lives, and Sorrowful can get her home fairly early. In fact, after this Sorrowful seldom keeps her out any later than 2 A.M.

The reason Marky likes night clubs where there is music is because she can do her dance there, as Marky is practically daffy on the sub-ject of dancing, especially by herself, even though she never seems to be able to get over winding up by falling on her snoot, which many citizens con-sider a very artistic finish, at that.

The Choo-Choo Boys' band in the Hot Box always play a special number for Marky in be-tween the regular dances, and she gets plenty of applause, especially from the Broadway citizens who know her, although Henri, the manager of the Hot Box, once tells me he will just as soon Marky does not do her dancing there, because one night several of his best customers from Park Avenue, including two millionaires and two old dolls, who do not understand Marky's danc-ing, bust out laughing when she falls on her snoot, and Big Nig puts the slug on the guys, and is trying to put the slug on the old dolls, too, when he is finally headed off.

Now, one cold, snowy night, many citizens are sitting around the tables in the Hot Box, speaking of one thing and another and having a few drams, when Sorrowful drops in on his way home, for Sorrowful has now become a guy who is around and about, and in and out. He does not have Marky with him, as it is not her night out and she is home with Mrs. Clancy.

A few minutes after Sorrowful arrives, a party by the name of Milk Ear Willie from the West Side comes in, this Milk Ear Willie being a party who is once a prize fighter and who has a milk ear, which is the reason he is called Milk Ear Willie, and who is known to carry a John Roscoe in his pants pocket. Furthermore, it is well known that he knocks off several guys in his time, so he is considered rather a suspicious character.

It seems that the reason he comes into the Hot Box is to shoot Sorrowful full of little holes, be-cause he has a dispute with Sorrowful about a parlay on the races the day before, and the chances are Sorrowful will now be very dead if it does not happen that, just as Milk Ear outs with the old equalizer and starts taking dead aim at Sorrowful from a table across the room, who pops into the joint but Marky.

She is in a long nightgown that keeps getting tangled up in her bare feet as she runs across the dance floor and jumps into Sorrowful's arms, so if Milk Ear Willie lets go at this time he is apt to put a slug in Marky, and this is by no means Willie's intention. So Willie puts his rod back in his kick, but he is greatly disgusted and stops as he is going out and makes a large complaint to Henri about allowing children in a night club.

Well, Sorrowful does not learn until afterward how Marky saves his life, as he is too much horrified over her coming four or five blocks through the snow barefooted to think of anything else, and everybody present is also horrified and wondering how Marky finds her way there. But Marky does not seem to have any good explanation for her conduct, except that she wakes up and discovers Mrs. Clancy asleep and gets to feeling lonesome for Sorrowful.

About this time, the Choo-Choo Boys start playing Marky's tune, and she slips out of Sorrowful's arms and runs out on the dance floor.

"Marky dance," she says.

Then she lifts her nightgown in her hands and starts hopping and skipping about the floor until Sorrowful collects her in his arms again, and wraps her in an overcoat and takes her home.

Now, what happens but the next day Marky is sick from being out in the snow barefooted and with nothing on but her nightgown, and by night she is very sick indeed, and it seems that she has pneumonia, so Sorrowful takes her to the Clinic hospital, and hires two nurses and two croakers, and wishes to hire more, only they tell him these will do for the present.

The next day Marky is no better, and the next night she is worse, and the management of the Clinic is very much upset because it has no place to put the baskets of fruit and candy and floral horseshoes and crates of dolls and toys that keep arriving every few minutes. Furthermore, the management by no means approves of the citizens who are tiptoeing along the hall on the floor where Marky has her room, especially such as Big Nig, and Sleep-out, and Wop Joey, and the Pale Face Kid and Guinea Mike and many other prominent characters, especially as these characters keep trying to date up the nurses.

Of course I can see the management's point of view, but I wish to say that no visitor to the Clinic ever brings more joy and cheer to the patients than Sleep-out, as he goes calling in all the private rooms and wards to say a pleasant word or two to the inmates, and I never take any stock in the rumor that he is looking around to see if there is anything worth picking up. In fact, an old doll from Rockville Centre, who is suffering with yellow jaundice, puts up an awful holler when Sleep-out is heaved from her room, because she says he is right in the middle of a story about a traveling salesman and she wishes to learn what happens.

There are so many prominent characters in and around the Clinic that the morning bladders finally get the idea that some well-known mob guy must be in the hospital full of slugs, and by and by the reporters come buzzing around to see what is what. Naturally they find out that all this interest is in nothing but a little doll, and while you will naturally think that such a little doll as Marky can scarcely be worth the attention of the reporters, it seems they get more heated up over her when they hear the story than if she is Jack Diamond.

In fact, the next day all the bladders have large stories about Marky, and also about Sorrowful and about how all these prominent characters of Broadway are hanging around the Clinic on her account. Moreover, one story tells about Sleep-out entertaining the other patients in the hospital, and it makes Sleep-out sound like a very large-hearted guy.

It is maybe three o'clock in the morning of the fourth day Marky is in the hospital that Sorrowful comes into Mindy's looking very sad, indeed. He orders a sturgeon sandwich on pumpernickel, and then he explains that Marky seems to be getting worse by the minute and that he does not think his doctors are doing her any good, and at this Big Nig, the craps shooter, speaks up and states as follows:

"Well," Big Nig says, "if we are only able to get Doc Beerfeldt, the great pneumonia specialist, the chances are he will cure Marky like breaking sticks. But of course," Nig says, "it is impossible to get Doc Beerfeldt unless you are somebody like John D. Rockefeller, or maybe the President."

Naturally, everybody knows that what Big Nig says is very true, for Doc Beerfeldt is the biggest croaker in this town, but no ordinary guy can get close enough to Doc Beerfeldt to hand him a ripe peach, let alone get him to go out on a case. He is an old guy, and he does not practice much any more, and then only among a few very rich and influential people. Furthermore, he has plenty of potatoes himself, so money does not interest him whatever, and anyway it is great foolishness to be talking of getting Doc Beerfeldt out at such an hour as this.

"Who do we know who knows Doc Beerfeldt?" Sorrowful says. "Who can we call up who may have influence enough with him to get him to just look at Marky? I will pay any price," he says. "Think of somebody," he says.

Well, while we are all trying to think, who

comes in but Milk Ear Willie, and he comes in to toss a few slugs at Sorrowful, but before Milk Ear can start blasting Sleep-out sees him and jumps up and takes him off to a corner table, and starts whispering in Milk Ear's good ear.

As Sleep-out talks to him Milk Ear looks at Sorrowful in great surprise, and finally he begins nodding his head, and by and by he gets up and goes out of the joint in a hurry, while Sleep-out comes back to our table and says like this:

"Well," Sleep-out says, "let us stroll over to the Clinic. I just send Milk Ear Willie up to Doc Beerfeldt's house on Park Avenue to get the old Doc and bring him to the hospital. But, Sorrowful," Sleep-out says, "if he gets him, you must pay Willie the parlay you dispute with him, whatever it is. The chances are," Sleep-out says, "Willie is right. I remember once you out-argue me on a parlay when I know I am right."

Personally, I consider Sleep-out's talk about sending Milk Ear Willie after Doc Beerfeldt just so much nonsense, and so does everybody else, but we figure maybe Sleep-out is trying to raise Sorrowful's hopes, and anyway he keeps Milk Ear from tossing these slugs at Sorrowful, which everybody considers very thoughtful of Sleep-out, at least, especially as Sorrowful is under too great a strain to be dodging slugs just now.

About a dozen of us walk over to the Clinic, and most of us stand around the lobby on the ground floor, although Sorrowful goes up to Marky's floor to wait outside her door. He is waiting there from the time she is first taken to the hospital, never leaving except to go over to Mindy's once in a while to get something to eat, and occasionally they open the door a little to let him get a peek at Marky.

Well, it is maybe six o'clock when we hear a taxi stop outside the hospital and pretty soon in comes Milk Ear Willie with another character from the West Side by the name of Fats Finstein, who is well known to one and all as a great friend of Willie's, and in between them they have a little old guy with a Vandyke beard, who does not seem to have on anything much but a silk dressing gown and who seems somewhat agitated, especially as Milk Ear Willie and Fats Finstein keep prodding him from behind.

Now it comes out that this little old guy is nobody but Doc Beerfeldt, the great pneumonia specialist, and personally I never see a madder guy, although I wish to say I never blame him much for being mad when I learn how Milk Ear Willie and Fats Finstein boff his butler over the noggin when he answers their ring, and how they walk right into old Doc Beerfeldt's bedroom and haul him out of the hay at the point of their Roscoes and make him go with them.

In fact, I consider such treatment most discourteous to a prominent croaker, and if I am Doc Beerfeldt I will start hollering copper as soon as I hit the hospital, and for all I know maybe Doc Beerfeldt has just such an idea, but as Milk Ear Willie and Fats Finstein haul him into the lobby who comes downstairs but Sorrowful. And the minute Sorrowful sees Doc Beerfeldt he rushes up to him and says like this:

"Oh, Doc," Sorrowful says, "do something for my little girl. She is dying, Doc," Sorrowful says. "Just a little bit of a girl, Doc. Her name is Marky. I am only a gambler, Doc, and I do not mean anything to you or to anybody else, but please save the little girl."

Well, old Doc Beerfeldt sticks out his Vandyke beard and looks at Sorrowful a minute, and he can see there are large tears in old Sorrowful's eyes, and for all I know maybe the doc knows it has been many and many a year since there are tears in these eyes, at that. Then the doc looks at Milk Ear Willie and Fats Finstein and the rest of us, and at the nurses and internes who are commencing to come running up from every which way. Finally he speaks as follows:

"What is this?" he says. "A child? A little child? Why," he says, "I am under the impression that these gorillas are kidnapping me to attend to some other sick or wounded gorilla. A child? This is quite different. Why do you not say so in the first place? Where is the child?" Doc Beerfeldt says. "And," he says, "somebody get me some pants."

We all follow him upstairs to the door of Marky's room and we wait outside when he goes in, and we wait there for hours, because it seems that even old Doc Beerfeldt cannot think of anything to do in this situation no matter how he tries. And along toward ten-thirty in the morning he opens the door very quietly and motions Sorrowful to come in, and then he motions all the rest of us to follow, shaking his head very sad.

There are so many of us that we fill the room around a little high narrow bed on which Marky is lying like a flower against a white wall, her yellow curls spread out over her pillow. Old Sorrowful drops on his knees beside the bed and his shoulders heave quite some as he kneels there, and I hear Sleep-out sniffing as if he has a cold in his head. Marky seems to be asleep when we go in, but while we are standing around the bed looking down at her, she opens her eyes and seems to see us and, what is more, she seems to know us, because she smiles at each guy in turn and then tries to hold out one of her little hands to Sorrowful.

Now very faint, like from far away, comes a sound of music through a half-open window in the room, from a jazz band that is rehearsing in a hall just up the street from the hospital, and Marky hears this music because she holds her head in such a way that anybody can see she is listening, and then she smiles again at us and whispers very plain, as follows:

"Marky dance."

And she tries to reach down as if to pick up her skirt as she always does when she dances, but her hands fall across her breast as soft and white and light as snowflakes, and Marky never again dances in this world.

Well, old Doc Beerfeldt and the nurses make us go outside at once, and while we are standing there in the hall outside the door, saying nothing whatever, a young guy and two dolls, one of them old, and the other not so old, come along the hall much excited. The young guy seems to know Sorrowful, who is sitting down again in his chair just outside the door, because he rushes up to Sorrowful and says to him like this:

"Where is she?" he says. "Where is my darling child? You remember me?" he says. "I leave my little girl with you one day while I go on an errand, and while I am on this errand everything goes blank, and I wind up back in my home in Indianapolis with my mother and sister here, and recall nothing about where I leave my child, or anything else."

"The poor boy has amnesia," the old doll says. "The stories that he deliberately abandons his wife in Paris and his child in New York are untrue."

"Yes," the doll who is not old puts in. "If we do not see the stories in the newspapers about how you have the child in this hospital we may never learn where she is. But everything is all right now. Of course we never approve of

Harold's marriage to a person of the stage, and we only recently learn of her death in Paris soon after their separation there and are very sorry. But everything is all right now. We will take full charge of the child."

Now, while all this gab is going on, Sorrowful never glances at them. He is just sitting there looking at Marky's door. And now as he is looking at the door a very strange thing seems to happen to his kisser, for all of a sudden it becomes the sad, mean-looking kisser that it is in the days before he ever sees Marky, and furthermore it is never again anything else.

"We will be rich," the young guy says. "We just learn that my darling child will be sole heiress to her maternal grandpapa's fortune, and the old guy is only a hop ahead of the undertaker right now. I suppose," he says, "I owe you something?"

And then Sorrowful gets up off his chair, and looks at the young guy and at the two dolls, and speaks as follows:

"Yes," he says, "you owe me a two-dollar marker for the bet you blow on Cold Cuts, and," he says, "I will trouble you to send it to me at once, so I can wipe you off my books."

Now he walks down the hall and out of the hospital, never looking back again, and there is a very great silence behind him that is broken only by the sniffing of Sleep-out, and by some first-class sobbing from some of the rest of us, and I remember now that the guy who is doing the best job of sobbing of all is nobody but Milk Ear Willie.

"Daddy took me to the zoo. One of the animals came in and paid $33.80 across the board."

DRAWING BY SALO   [© 1960 BY THE CURTIS PUBLISHING COMPANY]

A Guy like Sande

DAMON RUNYON

Meeting a deadline is one thing, but the double-feature trick pulled by Damon Runyon in his coverage of Gallant Fox's Kentucky Derby win of 1930 stands out. He prefaced his account of the race with twenty-seven lines of verse immortalizing Earl Sande in print, somewhat as the great rider immortalized himself in the saddle.

Say, have they turned the pages
    Back to the past once more?
Back to the racin' ages
    An' a Derby out of the yore?
Say, don't tell me I'm daffy,
    Ain't that the same ol' grin?
Why it's that handy
Guy named Sande,
Bootin' a winner in!

Say, don't tell me I'm batty!
    Say, don't tell me I'm blind!
Look at that seat so natty!
    Look how he drives from behind!
Gone is the white of the Ranco,
    An' the white band under his chin—
Still he's that handy
Guy named Sande,
Bootin' a winner in!

Maybe he ain't no chicken,
    Maybe he's gettin' along,
But the ol' heart's still a-tickin',
    And the ol' bean's goin' strong.
Roll back the years! Yea, roll 'em!
    Say, but I'm young agin',
Watchin' that handy
Guy named Sande,
Bootin' a winner in.

AT RIGHT: *Earl Sande and Buddy Ensor, April 1932* [UPI]

BELOW: *After retiring in 1933, Sande returned to racing twenty years later. He is shown on his first mount, Honest Bread.* [UPI]

Seabiscuit

JOHN HERVEY

In a sense John Hervey's account of the closing years of Seabiscuit's racing career is an anti-climax. His earlier prowess as a runner is best detailed in the historic War Admiral–Seabiscuit Match Race at Pimlico. However, given space, the truest account of Seabiscuit's remarkable racing career is contained in B. K. Beckwith's Saga of Seabiscuit. *If the Beckwith opus is still in print, then buy it; if it is not and you can snag a copy, then do so and treasure it.*

O F great horses, as of great men, it may be said that contemporary judgments are often faulty, that not until they have receded in point of time to allow perspective are they to be seen in their true proportions. And then earlier verdicts are frequently reversed. The tumult and the shouting have died away, the dust of conflict has settled, and the heat of controversy, pro and con, has been replaced by a more judicial temper.

This is the generally accepted conservative viewpoint. It is not, however, universal among horsemen. There are many who hold a somewhat contrary opinion and in defense of it urge facts that cannot be overlooked. One is that no great race horse can be correctly assessed except by those who have beheld his actual performances, known him in the flesh and been able, at first hand, to study his individuality and estimate his capacities, not upon the basis of printed data but upon personal knowledge.

For this, also, there is plausibility. Confronted by the living animal, conceptions formed from hearsay, written descriptions or ideas gathered at second hand often prove unfounded. It is true, in a very special sense, that John E. Madden uttered a precept when he said, as regarded race horses: "Opinions die. Only the records live." But mere records may be misleading. Who, for example, could have obtained a more nearly correct impression of Boston or Lexington, Ormonde or St. Simon, from reading the summaries of their races than from seeing them perform?

Taking everything into consideration, it seems probable that neither the one criterion nor the other is infallible and that the most intelligent assessment is by balancing them against each other and using them as mutual means of ascertaining the truth.

We have been led to these reflections as we approach the task of composing a farewell appreciation of the horse whose name heads the page. It is no easy one. Few will seriously deny his title to greatness. Nobody will wish, on the one hand, to see it exaggerated or, on the other, minimized. The words of "Old Ironsides," "Paint me as I am!"—not omitting the mole that disfigured his countenance—may here well apply. The record of Seabiscuit exhibits its flaws and its disfigurements. But behind them, with the imposing bulk of the Lord Protector, towers the horse himself; a monument to the breed that produced him, beside whom most of its members seem pygmies indeed.

Seabiscuit first appeared in this series of annual volumes in that for the season of 1937, when, as a four-year-old he occupied the stellar position, being the leading money-winning Thoroughbred of the year, with a credit of $168,642.50.

For the season of 1938 he was accorded the still more coveted title of "Horse of the Year," with special awards from various donors of trophies significant of that honor. Concerning all these facts the reader is referred to these volumes, in which they are described in complete detail. We will, therefore, now complete the record and round out the recital, at its close dismissing the hero from our purview as he passes into history, his turf career ended in such a blaze of glory as no other Thoroughbred has ever achieved.

When he retired to winter quarters following his defeat of War Admiral in their memorable match at Pimlico on November 1, 1938, Seabiscuit, then five years old, had won a total of $340,480 in four seasons of campaigning. On the world's roster of great money-winners but one name stood above his; that of Sun Beau, with a credit of $376,744. Sun Briar's son had held the pride of place for seven years, since his retirement at the close of the season of 1931, and had successfully resisted the attempts of such titans as Equipoise, Gallant Fox, Phar Lap and others to wrest it from him.

Now there was a new Richmond in the field. Turf circles, fully alive to it, found their most absorbing topic of conversation, in the outlook for 1939, to be: "Can Seabiscuit dethrone Sun Beau? He has but $36,260 to go. In 1937 he won $168,580. In 1938 he won $130,395. He retired sound after the match. He will be profusely supplied with opportunities for big winnings the coming season, for he is the best drawing card upon the American turf. He needs to win but one really big race to go over the top. It is good betting that he will do so before summer comes. Twice he has lost the $100,000 Santa Anita Handicap by a nose only. He will try for it again in March. If he holds his form, what is there in sight that can beat him? With any sort of luck he should turn the trick then and there."

But the part which luck plays in racing was about to be demonstrated. Seabiscuit, arriving home in California early in the winter of 1938–39, after a short indulgence resumed training for his third attempt to win the world's richest race, now only about three months distant. His preparation progressed in satisfying style, on the whole, though there were from time to time rumors that his underpinning, in the past troublesome at intervals, was under suspicion. These rumors, however, were discounted as propaganda aimed to lengthen the very short odds against him in the ante-post betting, where, from the outset, he had been a top-heavy favorite.

On February 14—the $100,000 race being due upon March 4—the public was given its first sight of him for that season, the vehicle chosen being an allowance race at one mile for a purse of $1,900. There would be but three starters; himself, carrying 128 pounds; the celebrated mare Marica, with 113; and the veteran gelding Today, with but 107 aboard. As Merica had not been training any too well, she was at 6½ to 1. Today was at 4¾ to 1. So certain was Seabiscuit assumed to be of winning that he was at but one to five.

The result was a facer. Seabiscuit set the pace around the lower turn, but entering the back stretch Today, hard ridden, passed him and took a short lead, the quarter being run in :22⅗. They were then only heads apart, but as they raced through the back stretch Seabiscuit began to lose ground and Today was half a length ahead at the half in the lightning time of :45⅗ (track record for that distance :46⅘). He then went on past and, rounding the upper turn, kept drawing away until at the three-quarters, run in 1:10⅖, he had a lead of three lengths. Through the home stretch Wall kept riding him vigorously and when Woolf went to the whip with Seabiscuit he was able to make up but half a length of the distance, being beaten two and a half lengths as Today won in 1:35⅗, lowering the track record from 1:35⅘, scored by Top Row in 1935; it was to prove the fastest mile run during the entire year of 1939 in North America.

Considering this, the fact that it was Seabiscuit's first race in nearly four months and that he was giving the winner 24 pounds, it marked an excellent effort by him and, ordinarily, would have led to the assumption that by March 4 he would be cherry ripe. But as he returned to the stand—he had come out for the race wearing four bandages—it was observed that he was limping. Next morning's papers carried the headlines: "Seabiscuit Lame! May Not Start in Big Race!" Squads of interviewers beat a path to his stable and gave his owner, Charles S. Howard, and his trainer, "Silent Tom" Smith, no rest for the next few days in their quest for the truth. There was apprehension among the speculators. Was anything really wrong with the horse? Or was this merely a maneuver to get better odds against him?

The sequel proved that Messrs. Howard and Smith were wise men rather than intriguing ones. It was Seabiscuit's left foreleg that was in trouble. X-rayed, it showed a slight inflammation of the suspensory ligament. His lameness was slight. Many owners undoubtedly would have resorted to heroic methods and sent him to the post on March 4, for the odds had lengthened from five to two to ten to one and there was a great chance for a coup. But Messrs. Howard and Smith were not of that persuasion. Seabiscuit would have to carry 133 pounds, giving great lumps of weight to everything else in a big field. The time was too short in which to indulge him, then make him taut again; the risk of a breakdown at any moment would be imminent.

Repeatedly Messrs. Howard and Smith had declined to take such chances with the horse and events had approved their course. In this instance they did not hesitate. Seabiscuit was scratched from the $100,000 race and the dependence of the stable rested upon its Argentine four-year-old, Kayak II, who came through in magnificent style and record-breaking time. "Howard luck! Nobody ever saw anything like it!" was the unanimous exclamation of the regulars. . . . Possibly . . . And, one surmises, something more.

Seabiscuit remained with the Howard stable at Santa Anita through the meeting, then accompanied it north to Tanforan, which closed on April 22. He was then sent to Mr. Howard's farm, at Willitts, in Mendocino county, about 125 miles north of San Francisco, the owner's home city, was bred to seven mares within the next few weeks, spent the summer and early fall under treatment for his tendon trouble, which, never serious, was soon overcome. He was apparently sound when he arrived at the farm, and on October 24 rejoined the stable at Tanforan to re-enter active training, again with the $100,000 handicap as his objective.

For this event he had once more been assigned the top weight; 130 pounds. When originally conceived and first offered, in 1935, it had been decreed by the management that top weight should be 130 pounds and no more. This had been maintained until 1939, when, owing to continuous criticism, the limit was lifted to 133 pounds; which, as aforesaid, had been given Seabiscuit. This concession was, however, but a momentary waver. The fact was that in no case had a winner carried more than 126 pounds (Rosemont in 1937), he being moreover the only one that had carried more than 117 pounds. Also that Seabiscuit himself was the sole and only horse that had ever been able to carry 130 pounds and run into a place (second in 1938)—concrete evidence that the criticisms were ill-founded and unworthy of deference. So for 1940 the limit of 130 pounds was restored and for the third consecutive season Seabiscuit accorded the high but perilous honor of top of the handicap. Kayak II, his stablemate, who had substituted for him the previous spring so ably, was placed second with 129 pounds, and Challedon, winner of the title "Horse of the Year" for 1939, given 128 pounds.

It may be said that the expert consensus at this particular juncture was that Seabiscuit's attempt at a comeback was predestined to failure. The reasoning may be outlined as follows: First of all, the son of Hard Tack was admittedly a cripple, a patched-up horse. Second, he had been down and out for practically a year, and during that period had been placed in stud service. Third, he was now seven years of age, had already run the great number of 85 races, campaigning all over the continent from the Atlantic to the Pacific. Fourth, his unsound leg was in front, where the heavy weight he must carry would bring the severest strain upon it. These were all, in the abstract, weighty and cogent arguments.

But over and above them there was the final one, considered in effect the clincher. It was that he was attempting the impossible, for in the past many famous horses had made similar attempts—and failed. Once in a great while some remarkable comeback had been registered, as in the case of Old Rosebud. But even with him—a horse of very high class—the ordeal had been far less severe. He was a gelding, and in the process of rejuvenation a much longer time had been allotted him; nor was he asked, when he resumed racing, to undertake any such feat as that which was facing Seabiscuit. In the entire range of turf history, American and foreign, there was no instance to compare with his, hence it was thoroughly improbable that he could reverse the record and succeed where all the others had failed.

Had Messrs. Howard and Smith listened to these arguments and been impressed by them, Seabiscuit undoubtedly would never have resumed his turf career. But they refused to be swerved from their purpose and accepted the issue.

The little horse, when he reappeared at Santa Anita late in November of 1939, was, it had to be admitted, looking well and moving freely. No trace of lameness was perceptible; neither had his demure demeanor and perfect manners been affected by his use at stud. He was still the same Seabiscuit, so far as appearances went. But the pessimists declined to be deceived. "Just wait till they begin to step him up," they asserted.

The first real move asked of him was not until December 19, when he was breezed a half in :49. The final three furlongs were galloped in :34⅕—and right then it was evident that he had not lost his speed. There was wet weather at Santa Anita about this time and not until New Year's Day was he again attracting the clockers—and then he scampered five furlongs in 1:01⅕ without ever being out of a "snug." He had always been an object of intense interest and curiosity, and this was now redoubled; for everything went to indicate that those who had given him the count had another guess coming.

Continuous rain and mud was now the order for a considerable period in Southern California and the work of the horses at the Arcadia course was much interfered with. Finally on January 7 Seabiscuit and Kayak broke together and ran a quarter in :24⅖, three furlongs in :37⅕, half in :49⅗, five furlongs in 1:02⅗, six furlongs in 1:15⅘, when Kayak went on and the little bay horse was taken back to finish the mile under a heavy pull in 1:44⅗ and then gallop out an additional furlong. Rain was falling and the track was bad, but it was felt that work must be done.

Another stretch of bad weather now set in, so persistent that the next workout, on January 15, had to be done over the five-furlong Anita Chiquita training track and not the main course. It was in poor condition, but when, again accompanied by Kayak, Seabiscuit romped to the quarter in :23⅗, half in :48⅕, five furlongs in 1:00⅖ and three-quarters in 1:13, it was considered sensational. He was known not to like such going, but finished unextended and pulled up bright and gay.

Up to that time—it was almost certain that Challedon would not come west for the $100,000 race—Kayak had been the favorite in the winter

Seabiscuit, with Jockey J. Pollard in the saddle, at Belmont Park in May 1938. [MORNING TELEGRAPH]

books at odds of four to one, while so little faith was felt in Seabiscuit's ability to come back that he was at ten to one. There was now a hasty revision of the figures and the 'Biscuit was dropped down almost to a parity with his stable companion, especially when it was known next morning that he had cooled out perfectly sound. On January 18 he was out again, finding his first opportunity to work over the main oval when it was fast, and reeled off three furlongs in :36⅖. This was followed by another six furlong spin on the 19th in 1:12⅖.

His progress had been so steady, also rapid, that it was reported his *rentrée* might be made on the 27th in the $10,000-added San Felipe Handicap, which, being at six furlongs, was well suited for that purpose. On the 23rd he was galloped three furlongs in :36⅗, in company with Kayak. It was also announced that he had been named to start in a six-furlong allowance race next day, but rain bringing a muddy track he was scratched. The same fate befell him when he was re-entered to race the following one. Owing to the fact that 16 horses were named for the San Felipe he was drawn out of that also and instead of racing was given a trial of seven furlongs in 1:25⅖, displaying form that was impressive.

For the fourth time he was named to start on January 31 in a mile purse event, but again it was the same old story, "rain and mud," and again he was scratched. Brought out next morning despite the conditions he worked through the slop and outside the "dogs" in 1:42⅖, just breezing, with Kayak prompting him; the fractions being :24⅘, :48⅘, 1:14⅘.

It had now become a by-word at Santa Anita that "Seabiscuit will-won't go today." The management was unable to throw any light on the subject and referred all queries to Mr. Howard. That gentleman in turn referred them to the weather clerk, saying he had been anxious to race his horse for two weeks past, but would not do so under adverse circumstances. Not until February 6 did he get good conditions to work under, when, there being no racing that day, he sprinted three furlongs in :35 and the notes read: "Displayed brilliant speed, looks and acts good." Two days later he was out again and this time electrified the clockers by dashing off five furlongs in flat :59.

At length, on February 9, he effected his oft-postponed return to the post. The event was a graded handicap at seven furlongs, for $2,000, for which he was top weight at 128 pounds, seven others starting, whom he gave from 10 to 26 pounds each. Made favorite at even money, he finished third as Heelfly (118 pounds) won by a length from Sun Egret (115 pounds), with Seabiscuit two lengths farther back. The chart spoke of his effort as follows: "Wearing four bandages, he broke well, was in rather tight quarters next the rail on the back stretch when he lacked the early speed to keep up, but continued to save ground and was going steadily at the finish." It was a very fast race, the time being :22⅘, :45⅘, 1:10⅗, 1:23; track record 1:22⅖. He pulled up sound and Trainer Smith announced himself pleased with the effort.

His next outing was planned for the $10,000-added San Carlos Handicap, seven furlongs, to be run February 17, and in preparation for it he was worked a mile in 1:38 on the 13th, accompanied by Kayak, the fractions being :24, :47⅖, 1:12, pulling up sound but "appeared tired in the final eighth"; this was the first time since his return to training that he had been sent a mile at speed. The rail-birds agreed that if he was going to be ready to race a mile and a quarter in his best form by March 2 he was badly in need of both racing and intensive work in the interim. Meanwhile more food for gossip was provided by Handicapper Webb Everett, who assigned the 'Biscuit but 127 pounds for the San Carlos, while giving Kayak 130.

Both horses went to the post for that event, along with nine others and so great was their prestige that they were favored at four to five, though giving much weight to all the others. Their showing came as a shock. Seabiscuit finished sixth, beaten seven lengths, with Kayak eighth, though lapped upon him and Ligaroti, seventh. Specify (115 pounds) won from Lassator (105 pounds) and Viscounty (109 pounds). The time was :22⅗; :45⅗; 1:10⅗; 1:23⅖. Of Seabiscuit's performance the chart said: "Running in four bandages, he soon raced into a contending position (second), but, in close quarters in the back stretch, dropped back, then continued on the inside and, while not abused, was going gamely at the end."

The result produced the reaction to be expected. Seabiscuit was set down as a hopeless back number. Kayak was denounced as without any excuse whatever. The odds against both horses for the great race now so near lengthened appreciably. Those against several of the other eligibles shortened proportionately.

Seabiscuit again cooled out sound. But now the course pursued with him puzzled the experts. He had performed poorly on February 17, in the San Carlos Handicap, over seven furlongs. He was next engaged in the San Antonio Handicap, $10,000 added, to be run on February 24, over a mile and a sixteenth, which was to be virtually a dress rehearsal for the $100,000 handicap to be run March 2 and in which a large field, almost exclusively eligibles for that event, was sure to start. If he were seriously intended, would it not be reasonable to "pop it to him" in his work during the intervening week? However, nothing of the kind was done. Instead he did mere cantering exercise. The newsmongers were mystified. "Silent Tom" had little to say and that merely to the effect that Seabiscuit was all right and would start unless the track was muddy. But heads were wagged and the word passed around that something must be wrong. How could a horse that tailed off in trying to go seven furlongs last Saturday be got ready to go a mile and a sixteenth next Saturday by staying in the stable all week or just doing jog work?

The sequel came like a thunderclap. Seabiscuit ran off with the San Antonio Handicap with an ease that was astounding—especially in view of the fact that he defeated 12 of the best handicap horses in training, gave them all except his stable companion, Kayak, lumps of weight, won in a romp without being asked for his best, and equaled the track record for the distance! To many of those who witnessed the performance it was incredible. Breaking from the No. 12 stall, he was taken at once close to the leaders, from fifth at the quarter had raced into second place at the half, lapping the leader, Vino Puro, to his girths, moved on past him rounding the upper turn, and in the stretch came away with such speed and strength that he seemed just beginning to race. This despite the blazing pace—quarter in :23⅕, half in :46⅘, three-quarters in 1:11⅕, mile in 1:36⅖ and mile and a sixteenth in 1:42⅖. He pulled up "looking for horses" and came cantering back to pose before the cheering throng fresh as the traditional daisy.

After getting away slowly and running far back for the best part of a mile, Kayak, when let loose of, came hurtling through the field like a belated express and finished second, two and a half lengths off Seabiscuit. Just what it all meant was not lost even upon the most dazed spectators . . . "Seabiscuit is himself again! As for the big race—why, Howard has it all sewed up right now!"

For four years past Seabiscuit had been the most popular horse owned and raced in California since the revival of the sport there. The public, regardless of the "inside dope," had sent him and Kayak to the post for the San Antonio Handicap big favorites at 1¾ to 1.

Just one more week remained before the $100,000 race. The excitement that reigned throughout its course mounted steadily while the odds against the Howard pair shortened. Their magnificent form had a depressing effect upon the owners and trainers of the other entrants and as the days passed it became apparent that the field would be smaller than expected. It proved to be the smallest on record—but 13 horses. When the inaugural Santa Anita Handicap was run, it brought out 20, and until now 15 had been the smallest number. This was a compliment to Seabiscuit, from the sporting standpoint, but a left-handed one financially, as it meant that the net to the winner would also be the smallest yet: $86,650, as against the $91,100 which Kayak had netted a year before. As a matter of fact at one interval it looked as if but ten horses would go to the post. Then the local patriotism of several California owners prompted them to add three more, just in honor of the year's biggest turf event.

The most uncertain note was that sounded by the weather. Mud would mean the scratching of Seabiscuit—that was certain. The atmosphere was "catchy" and when, after thoroughly resting out from their race of the previous Saturday, the time for their formal trial for the grand event came, on Thursday, February 29, he and Kayak were confronted by a track so bad that double "dogs" had been laid down, making it necessary for them to keep out beyond the middle of the course. Going separately and not together, as usual, Seabiscuit worked five furlongs in the very fast time of 1:00⅗, with fractions in :23 and :48⅕, seeming not at all bothered by the going. Kayak did his turn in 1:01⅕ just as cleverly.

The day before the race *Daily Racing Form*'s special commissioner interviewed "ten representative men connected with the racing business" (names not specified—for which they must subsequently have been thankful) and they lined up as follows: three for Heelfly, three for Whichcee, two for Seabiscuit, one for Kayak and one for Don Mike. That is to say, the consensus was that Seabiscuit had but two chances in ten to win. The reporter, for his part, commented: "The answer is that despite the fact that the Howard entry of Seabiscuit and Kayak II will go to the post heavily backed favorites, many horsemen, who the book says should know better, are going out on the limb to try to beat them." . . . Something not at all uncommon at the races. The consensus of *D.R.F.'s* own corps of selectors, six strong, gave Seabiscuit a rating of 32 points, Kayak 20 and Whichcee, as third, 14. As they finished in precisely that order, we must accord these selectors a deserved bouquet.

Experiencing a change of heart, the weather man brought out the sun on Friday and promised a perfect day and fast track for Saturday. And for his final work before going to the post, Smith asked nothing of Seabiscuit but a leisurely gallop of a mile the previous morning.

The management had anticipated a record-breaking day if conditions favored and they were not disappointed. The attendance was placed, officially, at 74,000, including celebrities unnumbered from all over the U.S.A. and foreign lands. The parking space for 22,000 cars had been exhausted before post time for the first race. The grated windows saw $1,707,200 passed through them during the afternoon—a new high for Santa Anita as against 1939's $1,701,760. Of that amount, $328,700 was bet upon the feature event, which fell short of the previous year's $375,685, this being attributable to the extreme partiality of the public for the Howard entry.

The shortest-priced favorite in the previous history of the $100,000 handicap had been Discovery, in 1936, he starting at 1½ to 1 and running unplaced. In the inaugural, of 1935, Equipoise had started favorite at 17 to 10, likewise running unplaced. In 1938 Seabiscuit had been at the same odds and was beaten a nose by Stagehand, the three-year-old to which he was giving 30 pounds actual weight. Still the flood of money poured in upon him and Kayak, coupled, as the rules provide, and sent them to the post at but seven to ten; Mr. Howard, also as the rules permitted, declared to win with Seabiscuit.

The enthusiasm first broke loose when, prior to entering the saddling paddock, Seabiscuit was breezed through the home stretch. He was a horse easily recognized and wave after wave of applause burst from the stands and followed him until he left the track. This was renewed and redoubled when he reappeared in the post parade, until it swelled into thunderous volume—leaving no doubt that the crowd was placing its money where its heart had gone. But in his usual way the little bay horse walked modestly along, with low-held head and dapper steps. The experts, however, noted one unusual fact and commented upon it to each other. Though, measured by the rules of the trade, "Silent Tom" had not given him a heroic preparation, he had lost the full-fleshed, rounded form for which he had been so famous. Gone was that plump and dimpled outline, being replaced by one from which every pound of surplus weight had been eliminated, leaving the tremendous muscular equipment which he possessed to stand forth fully revealed. For the first time he looked an athlete, taut to the last notch and grimly ready. Another thing was also missing—the four bandages he had worn in his three previous races at the meeting. He was now clean-legged and without an extra ounce to carry.

In the draw for positions the Howard entry spanned the track. Kayak was in the No. 2 stall, down almost next the rail. Seabiscuit was in No. 12, with only one horse, the three-year-old Royal Crusader, outside him. It had been feared that he might get an inside place, hence perhaps fare badly in the jump-off. When it was learned that his luck was otherwise, the stable's confidence rose higher still.

According to the talent, there was only one other horse among the baker's dozen lining up with a real chance to win; Whichcee, who the year before had run a brilliant second to Kayak. He was now carrying two pounds more, with a burden of 114 (Basil James) but his form recently had been high and his following backed him down to four to one. Nothing else was as good as ten to one, Heelfly, third choice, being at slightly longer odds.

It was 4:23½ P.M. when the 13 Thoroughbreds entered the stalls. Starter Palmer, anxious that the getaway should be perfect, kept them there for three minutes, then gave the signal and they were off. The four-year-old Wedding Call, longest-priced member of the party, whose showing was perhaps the surprise of the race, was one of the first away yet the speedy Specify outbroke him. A few more strides and Whichcee had taken the lead, while Seabiscuit, placed under a drive by Pollard, responded with such a rush that, hurtling across from his outer position, he almost reached the leader and as they passed the stands the first time was running strongly just behind him. With him carrying top weight it seemed risky to make such use of him thus early in the race but in planning how it should be ridden it had been decided to keep the little horse out of harm's reach at all hazards and the only way to do so was to take him at once to the front or near it.

The first quarter had been negotiated in flat :23, which, for a mile-and-a-quarter race, was dizzy. As they rounded the clubhouse turn Whichcee was leading, closely pressed by Seabiscuit, upon whom Specify was lapped to his middle, with Royal Crusader at his throatlatch, the four being just well clear of Wedding Call and Ra II, who were heads apart. In this formation they passed the half in :47⅕ and set sail up the back stretch. Shortly Wedding Call took a fresh burst of speed and passing everything but the two leaders, drew up to them. At the three-quarters (the half-mile pole, well up the back stretch), passed in 1:11⅕, Whichcee was still leading, a half length in front of Seabiscuit, while Wedding Call had ranged along outside, pinning the 'Biscuit in between himself and Whichcee in perilous quarters, for they were speeding toward

OPPOSITE

Seabiscuit's triumphs culminated in an honor accorded few race horses. His statue in bronze, by sculptor Hulette "Tex" Wheeler, was unveiled at Santa Anita race track in February 1941. Seabiscuit and his likeness are shown here with the famous horse's owner, Charles S. Howard.

the far turn. It began to look as if the favorite might be pinched off there and, possibly, forced back to a position from which it would be difficult for him to come through and win.

Whichcee sped along like a hunted hare, and Wedding Call hung on with surprising speed and determination. All the way into the far turn the three contenders raced so close together that a blanket might have covered them and now the friends of Seabiscuit commenced to show anxiety. The crucial moment was at hand and in a furlong his fate might be sealed. The struggle continued with unabated fury and midway of the upper oval the battling trio were heads apart, Whichcee still leading, Seabiscuit second, Wedding Call third. Then a great roar went up from the watching thousands. Wedding Call, reaching his limit, faltered. Seabiscuit sprung forward and deprived Whichcee of the lead! They flashed past the mile post in 1:36 and an instant later swung into the stretch.

As the favorite's head showed in front the grandstand shook with the colossal roar that went up as his backers began shouting frantically: "Come on, Seabiscuit!" But while he was now in command it was by a narrow margin only, for Whichcee was hanging on gamely and by no means done. His 16 pounds' advantage was serving him well and while in the past he had shown that in a race of such length the final furlong was just about that much too far, the stubbornness with which he contended was amazing. Almost head and head, but with Seabiscuit slightly in advance they started through the final straightaway. And not until the last furlong pole was reached was the gelding raced into submission. Then, amid another roar of jubilation, the favorite began drawing past. At the sixteenth pole he was clear and Pollard shot him over to the rail.

It was now plain that he was out of danger and, as this was seen, renewed outbursts of cheers, shouts and screams such as Santa Anita never before had heard broke forth. It seemed as if all 74,000 throats in the overwrought throng had joined in one spontaneous cry. On and on he came, running free and strong, Pollard steadying him and only mildly riding him, his stride rhythmic, his ears playing, his flight straight and true.

Now the wire is reached, the post passed. He sweeps by in the clear. Whichcee is back in third place, three lengths arear, for in the final dash Kayak, far behind until entering the home stretch, has come whirling through to the finish an easy second. The chart says he was beaten by but a length, but the photo shows Seabiscuit with open space between them, almost a half length of it. An open half-length behind Whichcee comes Wedding Call, fourth, lapped by War Plumage, the only mare in the field, who came from eighth place at

the top of the stretch, making a splendid run.

The time for the mile and a quarter is 2:01⅕, lowering the record for the event and for the track, which Kayak had established at 2:01⅖ in 1939. Only once in American turf history has it been authentically beaten, in the memorable International at Latonia, in 1924, when Sarazen, 3 years, 120 pounds, stopped the watches at 2:00⅘. On one other occasion only has it been equaled: by Discovery when, in the Arlington Handicap of 1935, at Arlington Park, under the crusher of 135 pounds he ran in just 2:01⅕.

Seabiscuit has returned to the stand and as Pollard pulls him up and prepares to guide him into the winner's enclosure the ovation swells to a deafening crescendo then suddenly breaks and is replaced by a vast, tumultuous chorus of "Oh's" and a groundswell of repressed outcries as there is perceived upon the neon bulletin board directly across from the stand in the infield the ominous word, in letters of red: PROTEST. The unofficial placing of the horses had been flashed as soon as they finished: 12-2-6-1. It shone forth above the ominous red word, as yet unconfirmed. And now—?

Then it is observed that Basil James, in 1936 America's champion jockey, having hustled Whichcee back to the finish as fast as possible, has mounted into the stewards' stand to prefer the charge that when, well inside the final furlong, Pollard swung Seabiscuit across in front of him and took the rail, "he almost knocked my horse's legs from under him."

Thus avers the defeated rider. The plea, if allowed by the officials, will mean the disqualification of both Seabiscuit and Kayak and the awarding of the race to his own mount.

The presiding steward is Christopher J. Fitz-Gerald, dean of the profession, who has occupied that position ever since the Santa Anita track was opened and was one of the fathers of the $100,000 race. His associates are J. F. Gallagher and J. C. McGill, together with E. J. Brown, official representative of the California State Horse Racing Board and former president of the National Association of State Racing Commissioners.

They listen to James's allegation and then inform him that it is groundless. The alleged foul, had it occurred, must have taken place directly under their glasses, as well as the concentrated gaze of the entire assemblage, and they saw nothing of the kind. In making his final run, Seabiscuit, when passing Whichcee, had lightly grazed him, as often happens when two horses are laying along close together. But there had been no interference. The official confirmation of the placing is announced.

"Red" Pollard rides Seabiscuit sedately into the enclosure, "Silent Tom" takes his place at the horse's head. Owner Howard makes his way there. Now Pollard dismounts and stands between them, the great shawl of red and white roses prepared for the victor draped about his short, slim figure and blending perfectly with the colors that he wears: "red, white 'H' in triangle, front and back, white sleeves, red and white cap." President Hal Roach of the Los Angeles Turf Club joins the group, carrying the magnificent gold cup provided for the winning owner, which he presents, with a few appropriate words, to Mr. Howard, who responds briefly. Feminine spectators, present by the tens of thousands, wonder why Mrs. Howard has not entered the picture—unaware that so great was her anxiety over the outcome of the contest that she remained secluded at the stable while it was being run, getting only a distant glimpse of the horses as they rounded the upper turn. "I just could not bear to watch the race from the clubhouse," she told an inquiring reporter, "among a crowd of people. I wanted to be alone, for I wasn't sure I could hold myself together."

It is all over. Seabiscuit, officially the winner, has earned the sum of $86,650, which, together with his former credit of $351,080 brings his grand total up to $437,730, as against Sun Beau's record of $376,744. For the first time in turf history a race horse has crossed the $400,000 mark—done so in a manner so thrilling, against a background so eventful and romantic that nothing in the annals of sport can approach it.

Telegrams rain in upon the owner of this unprecedented animal expressing the enthusiasm of sports-lovers throughout America over him and his performance. Among them is the following:

Mr. and Mrs. Charles S. Howard:

The victory of your great horse on Saturday must be a wonderful satisfaction to both of you. It was your faith in his ability and your perseverance in the face of discouraging setbacks which finally won the title. We are elated to think that such a great champion had such splendid and purposeful owners. Your example will be an inspiration. To you and to Mr. Tom Smith we offer our sincere congratulations and we are sure that Sun Beau would have us extend his best wishes to his successor Seabiscuit.

Mr. and Mrs. Willis Sharpe Kilmer

In this graceful and heartfelt manner the dethroned king did homage to his successor.

Little horse, what next?

This was the question propounded by sportsmen the morning after. Along with the account of his achievement the headlines featured it. What next for Seabiscuit? He has come out of his supreme effort unscathed. With the opportunities that racing associations will be only too glad to provide for him, it should be easy for him to reach the $500,000—the half-million—mark.

So the reporters sought Mr. Howard and asked him what his plans were. He responded that he was uncertain, having not yet thought them out; it was possible the public might have further opportunities to see Seabiscuit in action. They also sought out "Silent Tom." His response was prompt and unequivocal.

"Seabiscuit has done enough. He should never be saddled for another race. His place henceforth is in the stud. My wish is for his immediate and permanent retirement."

Reflection convinced Mr. Howard that this was the correct position and he authorized the publication of the statement that the horse would be gradually let down and then sent to the farm at Willitts to be conditioned for active stud duty in 1941, at a fee of $2,500. Undoubtedly he was moved to make this decision by three things: (1) The widely expressed opinion of real sportsmen that further racing by Seabiscuit, no matter what the result, would be an anticlimax and an injustice to the horse; (2) the similar belief of Trainer Smith; (3) the remarkable aptitude for stud duties that the stallion had already displayed. The previous spring, during his vacation from training while being brought back to soundness, he had been bred to seven mares owned by Mr. Howard. Every one was heavy—and, it may here be added, shortly afterward delivered a sound and healthy living foal.

As this is the last time that Seabiscuit will appear in these annual volumes, unless in years to come as the sire of some performer chosen for inclusion, as a matter of record the following statistical résumé of his complete winnings, the various stakes that he won and his best time at various distances, is appended:

MONEY WINNINGS OF SEABISCUIT

Year	Age	Races	1st	2nd	3rd	Unpl.	Winnings
1935............	2	35	5	7	5	18	$ 12,510
1936............	3	23	9	1	5	8	28,995
1937............	4	15	11	2	1	1	168,580
1938............	5	11	6	4	1	0	130,395
1939............	6	1	0	1	0	0	400
1940............	7	4	2	0	1	1	96,850
Totals.......		89	33	15	13	28	$437,730

STAKE EVENTS WON BY SEABISCUIT

Date	Track	Event	Dist.	Time	Wt.	Value
		1935—Two Years				
June 26	Narragansett Park	*Watch Hill	⅝ m.	:59⅗	108	$2,795
Oct. 16	Agawam	Springfield	¾	1:11⅖	109	2,030
Oct. 23	Empire City	Ardsley	5¾ f.	1:08⅘	112	2,835
		1936—Three Years				
Aug. 3	Saratoga	*Mohawk	1 m.	1:38⅖	109	2,960
Sept. 7	Detroit	Governor's	1⅛	1:50⅘	109	4,290
Sept. 26	Detroit	Hendrie	1 1/16	1:44⅖	115	2,010
Oct. 24	Empire City	Scarsdale	1 70 yds.	1:44	116	5,570
Nov. 28	Bay Meadows	Bay Ridge	1 m.	1:36	116	1,970
Dec. 12	Bay Meadows	World's Fair	1 3/16	1:55⅘	114	8,000
		1937—Four Years				
Mar. 6	Santa Anita	San Juan Cap'rano	1⅛	1:48⅘	120	9,200
Apr. 17	Tanforan	Marchbank	1⅛	1:48⅘	124	8,200
May 22	Bay Meadows	Bay Meadows	1 1/16	1:44⅗	127	7,530
June 26	Aqueduct	Brooklyn	1⅛	1:50⅕	122	18,025
July 10	Empire City	Butler	1 3/16	1:58⅗	126	18,025
July 24	Empire City	Yonkers	1 1/16	1:44⅕	129	8,225
Aug. 7	Suffolk Downs	Massachusetts	1⅛	1:49	130	51,705
Oct. 12	Jamaica	Continental	1 1/16	1:44⅘	130	9,250
Oct. 16	Laurel	†Laurel	1	1:37⅖	126	4,270
Nov. 5	Pimlico	Riggs	1 3/16	1:57⅖	130	10,025
		1938—Five Years				
Mar. 27	Agua Caliente	Agua Caliente	1⅛	1:50⅖	130	8,600
Apr. 16	Bay Meadows	Bay Meadows	1⅛	1:49	133	11,270
July 16	Hollywood	Hollywood Gold Cup	1¼	2:03⅘	133	37,150
Aug. 12	Del Mar	Match, Ligaroti	1⅛	1:49	130	25,000
Sept. 28	Havre de Grace	Havre de Grace	1⅛	1:50	128	8,175
Nov. 1	Pimlico	Match, War Admiral	1 3/16	1:56⅗	120	15,000
		1940—Seven Years				
Feb. 24	Santa Anita	San Antonio	1 1/16	1:42⅖	124	10,000
Mar. 2	Santa Anita	Santa Anita	1¼	2:01⅕	130	86,650

** Claiming.* *† Dead Heat.*

This is not the record number of stake events credited to an American Thoroughbred. Twenty-seven are listed above, as against 34 to the credit of Exterminator; while Kingston won 33. However, Exterminator started 100 times and Kingston 138. Of Seabiscuit's 27, one was a dead heat for the Laurel Stakes of 1937 with Heelfly. This was also the only "straight" stake race in the table. Otherwise those listed were all handicaps—with the exceptions of the two matches against Ligaroti and War Admiral in 1938.

The scenes of his triumphs extended from the Atlantic to the Pacific and he was one of the most tireless travelers ever campaigned, on the Atlantic Coast appearing all the way from New Hampshire to Florida, and on the Pacific, from Tanforan to Agua Caliente. Through the Middle West he ranged from Detroit to Cincinnati—but, curiously enough, never was started over a track in Kentucky, the state of his birth.

Altogether he performed on 21 different major tracks located in 11 different states. During the season of 1938 alone he twice crossed the continent from west to east and from east to west.

As a weight-carrier he deserves to rank with such heroes as Exterminator, Discovery and Equipoise, on eight occasions carrying from 130 to 133 pounds successfully and making enormous concessions to beaten horses. His feat of giving 30 pounds to so good a colt as Stagehand, himself carrying 130 and that colt but 100, in the Santa Anita Handicap of 1938 and being beaten by a nose only, was one of the grandest in handicap history.

From the time standpoint his brilliance was equal. In his first winning race, as a two-year-old, he equaled the Narragansett track record for five furlongs, 1:00⅗; in his next, but four days later, he lowered it a full second, to :59⅗. Such performances were of constant recurrence through his different campaigns.

At the beginning of 1940 he held three different track records at Bay Meadows: the mile at 1:36; 1⅛ miles at 1:49 (under 133 pounds) and

1¹⁄₁₆ miles at 1:55⅘; that for 1⅛ miles at Del Mar, 1:49 (under 130 pounds); that for 1³⁄₁₆ miles at Pimlico, 1:56⅗; that for 1⅛ miles at Santa Anita, 1:48⅘; and that for 1⅛ miles at Suffolk Downs, 1:49 (under 130 pounds); while in his two farewell appearances he equaled the Santa Anita mark of 1:42⅖ for 1¹⁄₁₆ miles and lowered that for 1¼ miles to 2:01⅕. During his four full and two partial seasons before the public he broke numerous other records.

The table below speaks for itself.

No performer, however successful, brilliant or renowned, can hope to escape criticism, disparagement or challenge. The fact that Seabiscuit never won beyond a mile and a quarter caused accusations of his inability to go such distances. The longest one he ever essayed was a mile and five furlongs, the Bowie Handicap of 1937 at Pimlico in which, carrying 130 pounds, he was beaten a nose by the grand mare Esposa, to whom he was giving 15 pounds; the time, 2:45⅕, a new track record.

In 1938 he attempted to win the Manhattan Handicap at Belmont Park, over a mile and a half, and, carrying 128 pounds, was beaten into third place by Isolater, 108 pounds, and Regal Lily, 108 pounds, over a muddy track. In the former race he gave a fine exhibition, though defeated. In the latter he was started, as it were, under protest, his dislike for the mud having been established.

He was emphatically not a "mudder" and on two other notable occasions was beaten because of it. In the Narragansett Special of 1937, burdened with 132 pounds, he ran third to Calumet Dick, 115 pounds, and Snark, 117 pounds. In the Stars and Stripes Handicap of 1938, at Arlington Park, this being his only appearance at a Chicago meeting, with 130 pounds up, he was beaten by War Minstrel, 107 pounds. Speaking conservatively, in good going he could hardly have lost these races.

A third and final doubt of his greatness has been expressed because of his two-year-old career. Not until he had faced the starter no less

than 18 times did he "break his maiden"; and of 35 races which he ran at that age, he won but five, while in 18 was he unplaced. It has been contended that such a showing is incompatible with the criteria of true greatness in a race horse.

In weighing the accusation it will be well to recall that many turf titans have been very ordinary two-year-olds, some of them even less than that, showing no glint of their future form. In the case of Seabiscuit, upon his behalf it may be said that repeatedly throughout his juvenile campaign he displayed extreme speed and high class, but that no comprehension whatever appears to have been entertained of his real caliber in his stable.

He was at that age a small, somewhat slight and even weedy-looking colt, one of the four foals got by an untried sire in his first stud season and from a mare not thought good enough to be bred to a fashionable stallion. (He is by Man o' War's son Hard Tack, for whom it was almost impossible to get mares at first, out of Swing On, by Whisk Broom II.) He was run in claiming races as early as June of that year, and "weeded out" at the first good opportunity.

The transformation that then almost immediately took place in him resembled nothing so much as that in a stage spectacle when a beggar boy is at the touch of a wizard's wand metamorphosed into a fairy prince. In his case the wizard was Tom Smith. As aforesaid, Seabiscuit had run unplaced 18 times as a two-year-old, while at three, before coming into Smith's charge he had run unplaced six times more. *During his entire subsequent career, embracing 42 additional races, he ran unplaced but four times.*

Two of these, moreover, were starts made by him within the first few weeks after Smith took him over and before he had a chance fully to size him up. The majority of the races for which Smith saddled him were against the best horses in training and for the turf's richest prizes, whereas up to that time he had been contending chiefly against animals of the lower grades for overnight purses and minor stakes.

Seabiscuit is a solid bay horse without white,

RECORDS MADE BY SEABISCUIT

Year	Age	Track	Distance	Weight	Jockey	Time
1935	2	Narragansett	⅝ mile	108	F. Horn	:59⅗
1935	2	Empire City	5¾ furlongs	112	F. Kopel	1:08⅘
1935	2	Agawam	¾ mile	109	J. Stout	1:11⅖
1936	3	Bay Meadows	1 mile	116	J. Pollard	1:36
1936	3	Empire City	1 m. 70 yds.	116	J. Pollard	1:44
1940	7	Santa Anita	1¹⁄₁₆ mile	124	J. Pollard	1:42⅖
1937	4	Santa Anita	1⅛ mile	120	J. Pollard	1:48⅘
1937	4	Tanforan	1⅛ mile	124	J. Pollard	1:48⅘
1936	3	Bay Meadows	1³⁄₁₆ mile	114	J. Pollard	1:55⅘
1940	7	Santa Anita	1¼ mile	130	J. Pollard	2:01⅕

of a rich shade and with black points. In the spring of his five-year-old form he was carefully measured and weighed by Dr. Harry C. Crawford, V.S., and was found to be precisely 15½ hands tall and to weigh 1,040 pounds. He girthed 72 inches, was 17 inches across the chest, 17½ inches around the forearm at the swell, 36 inches around the stifle and 17 around the gaskin, or second thigh. The width between his eyes was 9 inches and around the muzzle he measured 18.

As a two-year-old and through the early part of his three-year-old career Seabiscuit was a slim, slight colt, but then began to thicken up and take on a robust, masculine appearance, which finally culminated in the full-made, muscular, brawny form for which he was conspicuous, causing the remark that he was a big horse on short legs.

His "quality" is admirable. His head is deep through the jowls, with taper muzzle, clean and bloodlike, with a full, clear eye and good ear, well set and carried; his neck is of good length and nicely crested, shoulders well laid and running well back, body short rather than long, coupling very smooth, croup with little slope and the quarters round, full and deep. His bone is heavy for a horse of his size.

When returned to training after nine months of stud duty and idleness in 1939, he weighed 1,080 pounds, but when, about four months later, he crowned his career by his supreme performance at Santa Anita he probably did not weigh 1,000 pounds.

As a racing tool he had few weaknesses. With extreme speed from the barrier, he could be rated and placed at will in a field of horses, could sprint at a dizzy clip when asked to, and would hold on at the finish with gameness and tenacity whether overmatched or not. His sire was a notorious "bad actor" at the post and in an interview Smith was quoted as saying that "the 'Biscuit" was inclined to be fractious there, but he had no difficulty in curing him of it, his manners becoming exemplary. He was intelligent, tractable, quiet and self-contained, a perfect trouper, standing long shipments without loss of form and seldom or never missing a feed.

The record of his races shows that Jimmy Stout rode him when he débuted as a two-year-old at Hialeah on January 19, 1935, and oftenest during his protracted campaign that season, which did not close until November 11 at Pimlico. But he had many other jockeys during its course, including F. Horn, M. Peters, Raymond Workman, J. Burke, Johnny Gilbert, George Woolf, F. Kopel and C. Rosengarten. In his 12 races at three, previous to his sale to Mr. Howard, he was ridden variously by Ira Hanford, Stout, Kopel and K. Knott.

Immediately upon passing into the Howard stable he became the regular mount of J. ("Red") Pollard, who rode him exclusively thereafter through the rest of 1936 and all of 1937, or in 26 consecutive starts. Early in 1938 Pollard suffered a broken collarbone in a track accident which placed him on the sidelines. He was just coming back to action the next summer when he was thrown from a horse at Boston and had a leg broken, in consequence of which he was incapacitated until the past season and resumed riding Seabiscuit only after the latter's comeback began.

Pressure was placed upon both Mr. Howard and Trainer Smith to employ some more famous jockey in 1940, it being argued that after his double injury and long absence from the saddle, Pollard would be unable to do the horse justice, but they remained loyal to the rider and he came through in triumph. During Pollard's enforced inactivity, Seabiscuit was ridden in nine races, including his matches against War Admiral and Ligaroti, by Woolf, and once each by Workman and N. Richardson.

It was announced shortly after his farewell at Santa Anita last March that a biography of Seabiscuit was being written and would be published in book form. It is by B. K. Beckwith and is a most attractive little volume. The interested reader will find all the essential facts about him embodied in the present sketch and those narrated in the volumes of this series for 1938 and 1939. The whole forms a "romance of reality" without parallel in the annals of the turf.

Swaps—Nashua

EVAN SHIPMAN

J. Sam Perlman, impresario of the Triangle Publications—the Daily Racing Form *and the* Morning Telegraph—*was totally uncompromising in urging the inclusion of the following accounts of the famed Swaps–Nashua match race by his staff man, the late Evan Shipman. I am sure you will agree, as I now do after reading them, that Sam is correct. I hope that my friend Evan knew the high regard his boss had for him and particularly for this piece of reporting.*

WASHINGTON PARK, HOMEWOOD, ILLINOIS, Aug. 31, 1955—Marking time until the big race this afternoon, we can look back on the last few days spent in Chicago as a pleasant interlude. Speaking professionally, I'd say that Ben Lindheimer and his associates here at Washington Park have done everything possible to render the task of covering the big match race agreeable to the visiting turf journalist, and you may believe us that the fraternity is on hand from far and wide. Indeed, national interest in this long-awaited encounter of the Kentucky Derby winner, Swaps, with his runner-up in that classic, the eastern champion, Nashua, far transcends the strictly local stir caused by the race, and we are at a loss to assign a reason for the relative apathy of the Chicagoans. Right from the start it appeared to us and to the majority of our tribe that if Lindheimer had a perfect "natural" with this match, and if Chicago is not now what is known as a "good race town," an event of this type is ideally designed to make it so. The feeling is strong that Washington Park is making a valuable contribution to the entire sport in this country, and it would be boorish not to express gratitude for the dignified, gracious manner in which a superlative spectacle has been offered the American racing public.

If all preliminaries and arrangements for the match proceeded in an atmosphere of unvaried good nature and good will, you will pardon us for remarking that it was not always thus. No, not by any means. Match racing in the not-too-distant past has been the cause of much bad blood, and your old-time horseman, faced with the prospect of a match, was quite prepared to toss good manners and fair play to the winds. It is not necessary to cite instances to anybody whose memory goes back a few years, but we assure you that "biting and gouging in the clinches" was once an accepted part of the routine. No more marked contrast to that rough-and-tumble style could exist than the prerace conduct of the principals in this match. The respect and regard that both camps expressed for each other was not a mere lip-service, and for once there was no taint of hypocrisy attached to the hope expressed on each side: "May the better colt win!"

Modern notions of publicity, these including the exposure of every nook and cranny "backstage" to the public view and ear by means of television, demand that a good many of our picturesque traditions undergo a process of sterilization. Some of us may deplore the loss of color, feeling, in paying our debt to the public, that we are at the mercy of some huge and anonymous abstraction. Nevertheless, racing—and the kind of racing that was typified by the old-fashioned match—could stand a little sprucing up. A little attention to both manners and morals has done not one iota of harm so far as the essentials of good, healthy sport are concerned.

Divergent as Swaps and Nashua may be from the point of view of the locales that they represent and where they were bred, the background of their respective owners and trainers and the methods that have been employed to bring them to their peak, these two superb colts nonetheless share one important characteristic. In tail male inheritance, both represent powerful European families, families whose influence is world-wide and of infinitely more importance in the universal picture than any of our native strains. Swaps, through Rex Ellsworth's Khaled and Lord Derby's famed Hyperion, is one of the mighty tribe of the English Gainsborough, while Nashua, a son of the imported Nasrullah, he by the great Italian from the late Federico Tesio's stud, Nearco, is a member of the Phalaris clan. Close up in the pedigrees of both Khaled and Nasrullah we find the name of The Tetrarch, the "Spotted Wonder" of the English turf whose descendants have played such a vital role in modern American turf history.

Charged with emphasizing Nashua's inheritance from his dam's sire, Johnstown, at the expense of the Belair colt's own sire, Nasrullah, we can only reply that we were at pains to reinforce our own recollection of Johnstown with that of Mr. Fitz. Having developed and trained both Nashua and his maternal grandsire, Johnstown, Mr. Fitz certainly knows what he is talking about, and we can do no better in this respect than to quote the veteran horseman. "I never saw Nasrullah, and, of course, I cannot speak about him," Mr. Fitz told us. "But Nashua seems to me like a bigger edition of Johnstown in conformation—yes, even to the lop ears. They have much the same head; a little plain, but plenty of common sense. They are the same type of horse, give the same picture, but Nashua is bigger, stouter. Then the disposition is much the same. They are both what we call 'clever' colts; plenty of sense. Johnstown was more 'businesslike' than this fellow, never any nonsense about him. Nashua loves to play. Not a mean hair in his hide, mind you; he's like a big kid. When he nips my coat, he doesn't mean any harm, but I always think he may get a little flesh along with the cloth. Maybe the most important thing," Mr. Fitz concluded, as he cast a fond gaze in the direction of the playful Nashua, "is that they both have the same type of speed, and I can tell you one thing: Johnstown was a very fast horse!"

WASHINGTON PARK, HOMEWOOD, ILLINOIS, Sept. 2—Underneath all the surface amenities, the smiles for the TV cameras and the gracious quotes for the press, Wednesday's match race that resulted in a smashing victory for the eastern champion, Nashua, and consequently a sound drubbing for the Kentucky Derby winner Swaps, was a deadly serious business, particularly for a professional horseman. The $100,000 winner-take-all purse offered by the management of Washington Park was, of course, not to be sneezed at, but in these days of fantastic values for stallions, Wednesday's match had an importance as regards the careers of both Nashua and Swaps that far transcends the immediate accounting in terms of dollars and cents. Realizing all that, we are on guard to weigh carefully any statements concerning the race and its participants emanating from either camp.

When, last May, Swaps, the colt from California, humbled our eastern champion, Nashua, in a truly run Kentucky Derby, nary an excuse or alibi was offered by owner William Woodward, Jr.; the veteran trainer, doyen of his profession, Mr. Fitz, or the country's pre-eminent jockey, Eddie Arcaro. They nursed their wounds in silence, and until the time came when Nashua could meet his conqueror again, let the Derby result speak for itself. In other words, Nashua's entourage behaved in trying circumstances in the tradition of good sportsmanship and good manners. Unfortunately, this has not been the case with the Swaps crowd now that Nashua, to their utter astonishment, has completely turned the tables. No, the dust had barely settled on the racing strip before Rex Ellsworth, Meshach Tenney and everybody connected with the chestnut three-year-old from the Coast began a campaign of excuses designed to disparage Nashua and to whitewash the tarnished reputation of their colt, hitherto undefeated this season and just recently seriously compared with such greats of American turf history as Man o' War and Citation.

Before the running of the match, never a word was said implying even faintly that Swaps was not at his best. Those who have seen this good colt a number of times, as has this observer, never saw the handsome, big son of Khaled in such perfect trim as when he was saddled Wednesday on the turf in front of the Washington Park grandstand. Both Nashua and Swaps presented ideal pictures of equine condition, and the California colt's supple action was everywhere applauded as he took his preliminary canter on the upper stretch. So far as the eye could discern, Swaps went to the post sound, and after a grueling race over a strip that was soggy and holding under deceptive dust on top, he came back sound, nobody commenting at that

Willie Shoemaker drives Swaps to the finish line to win the 81st running of the Kentucky Derby at Churchill Downs. Close behind is Nashua, with Eddie Arcaro up. The running time was 2:01⅘. [UPI]

time on the colt's favoring a foot. Nor did Ellsworth or Tenney or little Willie Shoemaker, who had the mount on the western sensation, say anything about "lameness" or a bad foot when they were exhaustively questioned immediately following the running. All that came later.

Shoemaker, who is not noted for his loquacity, did tell us that Swaps seemed to be laboring, and that the colt's action was not as free during the match as in previous races. This conformed well enough with what we had just seen, but we put it down to the fact that in Swaps's previous races under our observation he had been running freely, under more or less of a restraining hold, on the head end. This time there was a very important difference to take into account. This time, Swaps was vainly trying to match strides with a rival who was outrunning him every time Shoemaker chose to make a bid. Shoemaker made three powerful runs at Nashua, and all three were foiled. The early pace, considering the condition of the Washington Park strip that afternoon, was wicked, first half in :46 flat, initial three-quarters in 1:10%, and this was considerably faster than excellent sprinters on the same card were capable of doing. If Swaps was "laboring," he had good reason to labor. There is a whale of a difference between tooling along in front with everything going your way, and mustering your strength for successive challenges, each and every one of them repulsed.

Now, mind you, not a hint of "lameness" in all the talk back and forth that followed Swaps's defeat. Ellsworth did say that Swaps "could not have been right," and also that the colt "certainly had not run his race," but we simply put that down to a disgruntled loser who didn't know enough to keep his mouth shut when the tide turned against him, as it must against all of us in this sport, one time or another. It was not until the next morning—Thursday morning—that we heard talk of lameness and that bad foot. Yesterday morning it was all over the race track, and Ellsworth told Bill Boniface, racing editor of the Baltimore Sunpapers, that Swaps was "dead lame." We confess that, in our naiveté, we were ready to swallow even this, since we did know that Swap's training had been temporarily suspended just prior to the Santa Anita Derby last winter because of a bad front foot, and we also knew, or had heard, that the foot still troubled the colt as close as a few days before the Kentucky Derby. So, in our innocence, we absorbed yesterday morning's story of the bad foot, incorporating back-stretch rumors that we had heard of a shoe being cast during a recent extra-fast work, and this all formed a part of our today's column. Later, we happened upon Washington Park's official track veterinary.

What Warren L. Skinner, veterinarian here for the State of Illinois, told us was not only simple, but simply damning. He said neither more nor less than that he had seen Swaps walked on the track and back from the track to his stable beside a lead pony at 10 o'clock in the morning, or approximately one hour after Ellsworth had told Boniface with a straight face that his colt was "dead lame." When Dr. Skinner watched Swaps walk—and not just a few steps, either—the colt showed no signs of lameness; he did not "point" and he did not "nod," the usual indications. True, Dr. Skinner did not—we repeat, *did not*—make any examination of Swaps; he was not asked to do so. After telling us this, Dr. Skinner suddenly realized that he might find himself smack in the middle of an unwelcome controversy, and, in our presence, he telephoned steward Keene Daingerfield, representing the Illinois State Racing Board, to inquire whether "he would allow Shipman to quote him." It would, of course, have been our duty to quote Dr. Skinner in any case, but Daingerfield "had no objection," once we promised to make it clear that Dr. Skinner's report depended on *observation* and not on examination. The point is, we hope and trust inescapably, that Ellsworth, ever since he had seen his colt beaten and well beaten, was in frantic search for an alibi. Maybe too frantic, because this one will simply not go down, or at least not east of California.

Clockers Are Little Men

RED SMITH

*Choosing the best of Red Smith is as difficult as judging the Miss America Beauty Pageant—
they are all beauties. I crossed the infield with Red and Frank Graham, as Bill Winfrey escorted
Native Dancer to be saddled for the Kentucky Derby of 1953. As we ducked under the rail a
youngster called to Winfrey: "Hey mister! Dark Star's gonna beat you!" We all heard the
remark but paid no attention; that is, no one except Red, who made it the theme of his column
the next day, after Dark Star did beat Native Dancer. Anyway, the following is a little story,
about little men, telling little about which there is little to tell, except that it catches exactly
how little there is to gain by getting up early to clock the horses.*

ACCORDING to the best traditions, sunrise on a spring morning is supposed to make a guy glad to be alive. But at sunrise, how can a guy tell he's alive? There is a law in the benighted state of New York which bars children from race tracks in the afternoon, the archaic theory being that frequenting a gambling hell is an occasion of sin for minors. Wherefor a small boy, if he is to be reared properly, must be taken to the track for the morning works.

There were only a few sets on the training track at Belmont when the small boy got out of the car and walked along the outside rail toward the glass-fronted shed which is supposed to furnish shelter to frostbitten trainers, but is always filled with clockers. It had been explained what a clocker was, how highly skilled his job, which demands that he recognize any one of maybe a thousand horses that will be working unidentified by silks.

"Why don't they call 'em timekeepers?" the boy asked.

There was a Palomino pony with one of the sets on the track, and the boy pointed him out joyfully.

"Look!" he said. "He looks just like Trigger!"

A horse working alone galloped by.

"Black Beauty!" the small boy said. Might have been too.

A stable swipe came walking along the rail with his head down. He passed the small boy just as a horse drove by working nice, reaching out and grabbing ground.

"Lookit 'im go!" the boy said.

"He ain't goin' so fast," the swipe said without lifting his head or breaking his stride. "About thirteen and a half."

The clockers were all standing down in front of the little house, because by this time the sun was warm on their shoulders. They were swapping notes and telling lies. The small boy stood a little way off from them and watched. After a while he said:

"Clockers are all little men. Look, there's even a midget."

"They don't have to be big," he was told.

"Just have good eyes," he said.

Big Jim Healey was there watching his horses. Not the same Healey the man was telling a story about, how he raced his string one meeting in New Orleans and, on returning, was asked how it had gone.

"It was all right," this other Healey said, this having been his first visit to the home of Antoine and Arnaud and Galatoire and Broussard and oysters Rockefeller and *pompano en papillote*.

"It was all right," this other Healey said, "but there wasn't any good place to eat."

"I found a place just before I left," he said. "If you're ever down there, try it. Morrissey's Cafeteria."

A. G. Robertson, the trainer, was there. A man asked him which was the most improved three-year-old he'd seen.

"The only three-year-old I've seen," Robbie said, "is Citation. The rest are all eight years old."

"How about Coaltown?"

Robbie sighed. "There's nothing can catch that Coaltown. I wish I had something like him and nobody else in the world knew about him but me."

The small boy, who'd been sitting in the house to rest, came out and said it was colder in there than outside. Sammy Smith, who is called Dude Smith, nodded. He said it seemed like spring, but there was always a cold wind this time of year at Belmont.

"There was a clocker died here a few months ago," he said. "Guys used to say spring was here and it would seem like it was. That clocker would take a walk out in the infield and he'd come back shaking his head. No, he'd say, it wasn't here. Every day he'd take a walk out in the infield. Finally he'd come back and say, 'Spring is here.' He'd write it down on the rail here, 'Spring is here.' And it would be. It might be late, but spring wouldn't be here to stay till that day the clocker wrote it down on the rail here. He'd wait till he found blackberry bushes broken out in the infield, and then he'd know."

By now Ed Christmas had a set working that included Escadru, his Kentucky Derby prospect. The clockers came to attention when Escadru worked with a stablemate. One of them made like Freddy Capposella, giving it a call: "That's Escadru behind—Escadru moving up—he takes the lead—Escadru is doing some running, boys, I'll give you a tip."

The rider pulled Escadru up and the small boy walked back toward the car, passing Ed Christmas, who'd been off by himself watching his horse work.

"The clockers got excited," a man told Mr. Christmas.

"What did they catch 'im in?" Ed asked.

"They didn't say."

"This your boy?" Ed asked.

Not exactly changing the subject, you understand.

"Say, isn't that Mr. Dooley, our bookkeeper?"

DRAWING BY TEMES [© 1956 BY THE CURTIS PUBLISHING COMPANY]

A Very Pious Story

RED SMITH

The selection of this story is made easier—at least my conscience is easier—because Red Smith gives full credit to Walter Haight, of the Washington Post, in his very first sentence. This is one of those ridiculous stories which make the race track such a fun-place—where the lies are as long as the odds. Red's telling of this particular Piece of Haight suffers only from the audio and dimensional lack which Mr. Haight's presence adds to all his back-room sorties.

At the derby, Walter Haight, a well-fed horse author from Washington, told the story this way.

There's this horse player and he can't win a bet. He's got patches in his pants from the way even odds-on favorites run up the alley when he's backing them and the slump goes on until he's utterly desperate. He's ready to listen to any advice when a friend tells him: "No wonder you don't have any luck, you don't live right. Nobody could do any good the way you live. Why, you don't even go to church. Why don't you get yourself straightened out and try to be a decent citizen and just see then if things don't get a lot better for you?"

Now, the guy has never exactly liked to bother heaven with his troubles. Isn't even sure whether they have horse racing up there and would understand his difficulties. But he's reached a state where steps simply have to be taken. So, the next day being Sunday, he does go to church and sits attentively through the whole service and joins the hymn-singing and says "Amen" at the proper times and puts his buck on the collection plate.

All that night he lies awake waiting for a sign that things are going to get better; nothing happens. Next day he gets up and goes to the track, but this time he doesn't buy a racing form or

scratch sheet or Jack's Green Card or anything. Just gets his program and sits in the stands studying the field for the first race and waiting for a sign.

None comes so he passes up the race. He waits for the second race and concentrates on the names of the horses for that one, and again there's no inspiration. So again he doesn't bet. Then, when he's looking them over for the third, something seems to tell him to bet on a horse named Number 4.

"Lord, I'll do it," he says, and he goes down and puts the last fifty dollars on Number 4 to win. Then he goes back to his seat and waits until the horses come onto the track.

Number 4 is a little fractious in the parade, and the guy says, "Lord, please quiet him down. Don't let himself get hurt." The horse settles down immediately and walks calmly into the starting gate.

"Thank you, Lord," says the guy. "Now please get him off clean. He don't have to break on top, but get him away safe without getting slammed or anything, please." The gate comes open and Number 4 is off well, close up in fifth place and saving ground going to the first turn. There he begins to move up a trifle on the rail and for an instant it looks as though he might be in close quarters.

"Let him through, Lord," the guy says. "Please make them horses open up a little for him." The horse ahead moves out just enough to let Number 4 through safely.

"Thank you, Lord," says the guy, "but let's not have no more trouble like that. Have the boy take him outside." Sure enough, as they go down the back stretch the jockey steers Number 4 outside where he's lying fourth.

They're going to the far turn when the guy gets agitated. "Don't let that boy use up the horse," he says. "Don't let the kid get panicky, Lord. Tell him to rate the horse a while." The rider reaches down and takes a couple of wraps on the horse and keeps him running kind, just cooking on the outside around the turn.

Wheeling into the stretch Number 4 is still lying fourth. "Now, Lord," says the guy. "Now we move. Tell that kid to go to the stick." The boy outs with his bat and, as Ted Atkinson says, he really "scouges" the horse. Number 4 lays his ears back and gets to running.

He's up to third. He closes the gap ahead and now he's lapped on the second horse and now he's at his throatlatch and now he's past him. He's moving on the leader and everything behind him is good and cooked. He closes ground stride by stride with the boy working on him for all he's worth and the kid up front putting his horse to a drive.

"Please, Lord," the guy says. "Let him get out in front. Give me one call on the top end, anyway."

Number 4 keeps coming. At the eighth pole he's got the leader collared. He's past him. He's got the lead by two lengths.

"Thank you, Lord," the guy says, "I'll take him from here. Come on, you son of a bitch!"

"Wow! What a photo finish!"

DRAWING BY GEO. RECKAS [© 1945 BY THE CURTIS PUBLISHING COMPANY]

At a Paris Race Track

HAROLD E. STEARNS

This anecdote is taken from The Street I Knew, *the autobiography of Harold E. Stearns, American editor, critic and literary expatriate (1891–1943). It is included in this collection not so much as an example of great race writing, but because it typifies a condition of racing which, I feel, is one of its greatest attractions. In between the idle rich, lounging in their plush turf-club boxes, and the patched-pants denizens of the louse-ring, are the great mass of horse players— the mechanic, the office worker, the professor, the housewife, the farmer, the scientist—who, prove the old adage that ". . . under the turf and over the turf all men are equal." Mr. Stearns, a recognized intellectual, reveals in this account the same emotions you and I would reveal holding tickets on a long-shot winner.*

To EVERYBODY who follows the races regularly for any length of time there come, I am certain, winning days—and I make it plural, for every gambler knows that there are inexplicable "runs" of good luck, exactly as there are those of bad luck. There is no way of telling—ah, if there only were!—when a run is going to begin, or, which is more disconcerting, when it is going to end. The successful gambler has a kind of intuition about this, and plays very strong or weak accordingly. It is not, I hasten to point out, a question either of his knowledge or of his judgment. You will hear a man say at the track, after you argue with him about a horse, "Yes, I know it's the form horse; he ought to win; I see nothing to beat him. His price is good, too. But I'm not going to play him. I'm laying off the race. My luck is 'out' right now."

Nor will it much matter to him whether the horse in question wins or not in fact. For if he wins, after all he did so without the gambler's support, and nothing will convince the true plunger that, *had* he bet on him, the horse would not have lost. His bet is what would have made the difference; his bet—don't laugh—would goad the horse to lose, and if no other way was pos-

sible, by accident. Hence it is not deception at all when a gambler will often advise *you* to go heavy on a horse—and not bet a cent himself. *Your* luck is in; his is out. And you will even hear him say, after the race, "Glad I laid off that, old man, and gave you a chance to win." And he believes it, too. Sometimes—almost—so do I.

One day toward the end of March I came up to Jim's apartment for dinner late, after finishing my work at the office and duly giving my tips for the next day. Jim and I sat before the open fire talking horses and sipping—Jim, a brandy; myself, that "filthy sweetish liquor," as he used to call it, a *vielle cure*. Jim was busy studying Paris *Sport*, while I was reading an account of Fouchardière's inimitable and preposterous character, Le Bouif, at the snail races he had organized in Brittany.

Suddenly Jim looked up and asked, "Harold, do you remember that ancient mare we bet on in the handicap one of the last days of Longchamps in the fall?"

"Oh," I said, "you mean Belle of Zante? That name has stuck—and she ran a great race, too, for an old lady of her age, even if she only came in third. What about her? Is she dead? She was twelve or thirteen then."

"Dead, hell," said Jim. "Some owner I don't know has bought her and has evidently been training her all winter. By God, here she is down to run at Auteuil next week over the hurdles." He smiled: "Her *début en obstacles,* if you please."

I reflected a bit on this information, then said: "Why, damn it all, that's like asking your grand-mother to compete in a hundred-yard hurdle event. I never heard of such a thing."

Neither had Jim, but from that moment both of us knew that we were going to bet on Belle of Zante in that coming race.

In my day it was only 40 francs (around $2.00 then) to get into the paddock, but this was theoretical to me anyway, as I always had my press card—being France, with my photo-graph affixed—and usually, too, I had an invita-tion or two (the different French racing societies were very generous in this respect to accredited racing editors), so that for the most part Jim didn't have to pay to get in.

Once within the gates, Jim bought his pro-gram, which at all the French tracks is conven-tionally one franc. I walked to the *salon de la presse* to get my program, *gratuit.* I marked my card, as we call it, noting the scratches for the first race and rejoined Jim outside.

"Let's have a drink at the suicides' bar"—as he called the rather dark, ill-lighted one on the grandstand.

However, when we saw Belle in the paddock she looked half asleep; she walked gingerly and rather haltingly, almost as if she had a game right hind leg. When the jockey got on her back, he looked the picture of despondency. Merely to see him was to know that he felt he couldn't win—a delicate bit of histrionics, which I had seen too often before to be impressed, that is, to be discouraged from betting, or "thrown off," as it is called. Yet it really was not easy to work up much enthusiasm for that ambling, almost downcast-looking animal, who might well have been thinking of her happier, sunnier days as a filly of promise and beauty.

Jim looked at me with world-weary languor.

"You have to be a Christian and believe in miracles to do this," he said. And without an-other word—heedless of the odds, heedless of the curious looks from an interested group be-fore the "big" booth—Jim went over, and said, *"Le numéro quatorze, dix fois gagnant,"* stressing the *gagnant.*

Quite obviously skeptical, the clerk was yet proud of his customer's order. And when Jim repeated it, again emphasizing the "to win" phrase in French, the clerk—almost with an admiring gesture—slowly, reverentially, tore off

ten 500-franc tickets, stamped them, and handed them to Jim, who had put down the correct number of bank notes on the counter.

Interest in what we were doing had tricked us in our sense of time—hardly had Jim the tickets tucked away when the bell rang. They were off already. We walked briskly to the front of the stands and Jim remarked, "Come to think of it, Harold, probably we could buy the horse for not much more than our bet."

"Not after this race is over, we couldn't."

When we reached the front of the nearest stand the horses were wheeling and coming from left to right past the steeplechase water-jump in front of us. But they were turning aside a bit, on the flat turf, for this jump is not taken in a hurdle affair. They were fairly well bunched, and thus far not a horse had gone down—the fourteen that started (and Belle, being a debu-tante at this kind of race, had been given bottom weight, hence was number *"quatorze"* on the program) were still on their feet, all, seemingly, going easy and strong. But at the big hurdle jump way across the field, where some "bunching up" had already become noticeable and a few trailers were beginning to drag behind, two horses went down—and there were groans from the crowd, particularly from those who had bet on the unfortunate animals. Belle was neither of the two; we could see the green-and-yellow of her jockey's silks and the gray of his cap quite clearly "up with the bunch."

It was right after this critical jump that Belle began to take a bit of a lead—just enough to see daylight (as racing men put it) between her and the nearest horse.

"What imbecile is that out front?" roared a Frenchman beside me, and although it was not quite clear whether he was referring to the horse or the jockey, I somehow took umbrage at the remark, almost as if it were meant personally for me, and said in a quiet unnecessarily strident tone, and in my best slang French, "There are more imbeciles watching this race than there are in it."

The Frenchman glared at me, but we were both too interested in what was going on before our eyes to bother getting into a fight. I knew this, and hence didn't care if I was courageous. Nor could I help smiling a bit when Jim gave me an admiring glance.

Imbecile or not, Belle's jockey had chosen the right tactics—and at the right time. She had always been a horse, even on the flat, who liked to keep out ahead, what we term a "front run-ner." Over the jumps she liked the same thing; she didn't want any horse near her—and she wanted a clear field ahead of her. When she had negotiated the last hurdle, she was almost five lengths in the lead of her nearest competitor, and her jockey wisely eased her up on the short run-in to the finish, crossing the line almost at a walk and with the other horses straining at her heels, yet with plenty to spare. At the end the stands were curiously silent, for nobody had backed her and nobody had anything to cheer about. A few polite handclaps were all we heard. Fascinated, I watched while the number "14" went up over the judges' stand, and somehow my throat felt dry and strained.

Luckily the agony of waiting for the "all clear" bell—and it is precisely that under such circumstances, when you have backed a big outsider—was really short, though it seemed to me interminable. At last the bell rang, clear and firm, and as we gulped our champagne and turned to the announcements board, that magic little thin line of red—from whence comes the expression, *"le rouge est mis,"* meaning the die is cast, or something equivalent—snapped into place over the "14." Belle had won; it was legal; we were "on" her! There is no glow like it in the world—all the other pleasures, even sensuous ones, are not to be compared with it.

Jim was quite obviously trying to moderate his excitement. "There are two thrills at the French races," he observed. "The first is when your horse wins; the second is when the odds go up—especially if it's an outsider."

"Also a third, Jim—when you drink your ani-mal's health in champagne. Maybe some day we can do that in our own country."

As we solemnly pledged Belle, there was an audible murmur, growing into a chorus of *"Regarde-moi ça," "Incroyable,"* and *"Tiens, tiens."*

Jim turned to me—"Look at that *affichage*. Do you see what I see?"

"One thousand, two hundred and eighty-five francs, fifty centimes—that's what I see," I said, reading slowly, not quite believing my own eyes.

"We have gone insane," announced Jim with conviction. "That means a little over $50 for every forty cents we put up—well over 100 to 1. Can such things be?"

"Can be—and are," I said, making a valiant effort to *act* indifferent, but I felt a trifle dizzy. I realized that never before had I seen, let alone bet upon, such a long-shot miracle as Belle— and that, probably, never should I do so (perhaps never have the chance to do so) again. That is the kind of bet which comes only once— if it comes at all—in a lifetime.

"Harold," said Jim looking at me with mock severity, "quite aside from what you won this time—for half of it is yours—I can't afford being seen at the races with anybody dressed the way you are. We are going to my tailor's, when we leave here, and I am going to buy you some clothes. You owe it to God, to Belle, and to me. Not to mention yourself."

"Well, well, Charley Jones! Say, you look like you've put on a few ounces."

DRAWING BY DANA FRADON

Seeing Nellie Home

RAYMOND B. TOMKINS

The account of the 1924 Preakness by Raymond Tomkins is notable for its breezy style. It is sort of an early-day Dan Parker-Toney Betts story treatment, combining humor with iconoclasm.

LITTLE NELLIE MORSE, an innocent, girlish horse, won the Preakness yesterday and the diamond stickpin, the Woodlawn Vase, the $54,000 and the watery cheers of some 30,000 diving Venuses and Adonises, who went in swimming with all their clothes on.

Fourteen other horses—all males—also Preaknessed around the swamp. They were seeing Nellie home.

Nellie Morses' owner is Bud Fisher, well known as the artist who did not paint the Mona Lisa. He was in Europe taking the waters while his filly was at Pimlico taking the coin. Of course, he did not know his Nellie Morse had won the Preakness, and he does not know it yet. His trainer, Alex Gordon, doesn't know where in Europe Bud Fisher is.

He may not even know he has a horse named Nellie Morse, or that there is such a race as a Preakness. He is richer by $54,000 and he doesn't know that, either.

They can't cable him, wireless him or write him. He may be in Berlin, Rome, Paris or London. A whole city full of people, no more related to Nellie Morse than to Lady Godiva, went blah when the nags were coming round the bend, yet Nellie Morse's own ball and chain was as completely out of the picture as a bottle of near beer at a *Schatzenfest* in Brooklyn.

This doesn't often happen at a Preakness. Usually the place is crawling with owners. Yesterday it was crawling not only with owners but owners emeritus, like J. K. L. Ross, who once won two Preaknesses; Samuel D. Riddle, whom Man o' War made famous; R. T. Wilson, Jr., whose Pillory won two years ago, and Walter J. Salmon, whose Vigil won last year, to say nothing of Edward F. Whitney, owner of the only other suffrage horse ever to win a Preakness—Rhine Maiden, the victor in 1915.

Wearing large Gainsborough hats and carrying parasols they would have made a chic chorus of owners of ex-Preakness winners. There they were at the track with their victories behind them, while there was Bud Fisher's victory coming down the stretch, and Bud himself far, far away in heathen lands where they will think champagne is a drink. The situation has scarcely been paralleled in Preakness history.

But there were other unparalleled things besides that. Never before has the Preakness been run in six inches of thick waffle batter. It was as much a regatta as a horse race. It was simply a case of the skipjack. Nellie Morse, beating a lot of bugeyes that didn't carry sail enough.

Old horsemen said they should have postponed the Preakness and staged a race between the *Leviathan* and the *Majestic*. Other old horsemen were only prevented from sending their horses home to the stables and entering their speedboats instead by the earnest efforts of clearheaded friends. It was the wettest Preakness of all time.

Alex Gordon said afterwards he knew Nellie Morse was going to win by the way she left the dry dock. She took one of those sidewise launchings, and scarcely even splashed. In fact, so certain was Alex Gordon of everything that he never knew until a half hour later whether Governor Ritchie had presented him with a diamond stickpin or a penny savings bank, and he went away and left the Woodlawn Vase standing in the rain.

Alex and Johnny Loftus settled the Preakness early in the afternoon. Johnny Loftus, trainer for the Oak Ridge stable, with two horses in the big race himself, twice a Preakness-winning rider (on War Cloud in 1918 and on Sir Barton in 1919) convened with Alex Gordon (as trainers will) and talked the thing over.

"Nellie Morse will win in a walk, or shall we say a breast stroke?" Alex Gordon said.

"She hasn't a chance," replied Johnny Loftus. "It will be Apprehension, or perhaps Faenza; though most likely Apprehension."

"Ah, but you don't know the speed of this Nellie Morse in a heavy sea," warned Alex Gordon.

"Well, we'll toss a quarter and settle it," said Johnny Loftus.

So they tossed a quiet quarter, these two trainers did, there in a quiet nook at the wild race track; and Alex Gordon called "Heads!"

and it came "heads," proving that Nellie Morse would win.

And it doesn't look like a frame-up because Faenza, finished twelfth while Apprehension finished fifteenth, which was last.

This proved yesterday to the racing men who heard the story how foolish it is not to believe in signs or conju'ns. The case of the horse named Nautical was only the exception that proves it still more for, with his name, Nautical should have outrowed every other boat on the course, whereas in point of actual fact he finished next to last.

Nautical didn't go to the post a favorite, but a good many persons, believing in signs and conju'ns, bet on him. Nellie Morse was anything but a favorite: nice name—vine-clad cottages, old farmyard trysting gate by moonlight and everything—but no kind of horse for a race like this. Rustic was one favorite—Maryland horse. Maryland trainer and owner. Revenue Agent was another favorite.

Seven horses were scratched, including Wise Counsellor, the swift Kentucky babe, and Senator Norris, another Maryland horse. In fact it was "scratch day" for many horses. Their owners took one look at the cruel sea and said, "Heaven help the poor sailors on a track like that!" Even so, 15 horses lined up at the post was a bigger field than ever before in a Preakness.

"I never saw a horse take so much interest in a race."

DRAWING BY HERB WILLIAMS

Today Is 400 Years Old

UNANIMOUS

The author is a pardonable nom de course. *In fact this piece was the result of the collaborative efforts of Alfred G. Vanderbilt, Vaughn Flannery, the eminent artist, and myself, in an effort to get across to the racing public some idea of how much human thought and energy and patience go into the breeding of a Thoroughbred good enough to run in the Preakness. It applies equally to every breeder and to each and every race because it is the background of every horse and every race.*

FOUR long years ago a horse breeder worked late into the night. Under his study lamp were spread the pedigree records of the Thoroughbred horse.

These records have been called "the oldest social register in the world"—but this is a bit unfair to the Thoroughbred. Theirs is more than a record of ancestors, for only the worthy are deemed deserving enough to be reserved for breeding.

From these records and his experience the breeder hoped to select for his mare just the stallion to help produce a foal possessed of the quality of bone and muscle, and, above all, the disposition, the speed and the courageous racing heart to win the Preakness.

With the air of a man who has made up his mind, the breeder closed his books, and walked through the night to his stable for one final inspection. As he left he gave his favorite mare a goodnight pat as though to tell her the die had been cast. The decision the breeder made that night is recorded in the racing program in your hand—for under the name of the horse of your choice is set down the name of the father and mother.

The stallion chosen may have been the breeder's own, or a neighbor's, or even one miles away in another state. The breeder backed his judgment by paying a fat stud fee, the shipping expense and board for his mare, and by caring for her with all the concern of a fond and fussy grandmother. Remember, this was four years ago—long before Preakness Day.

The year slipped by. One spring night, the groom came to the house, called the breeder to the stables and there in the deep, clean straw of the foaling shed stood his Preakness hope—long-legged, wobbly-kneed, and with the timid eyes of a deer.

When the weary breeder tumbled back into bed, the Preakness must have seemed a long way off.

Three summers ago your Preakness choice was romping over the fields of a breeding farm somewhere in Virginia, Kentucky or Maryland, playing with other foals, slipping cautiously behind his mother when strangers appeared.

Came the fall and weaning time. The colt's mother was led away. Less than a year old—he was alone and on his own.

Came 1936—your favorite was running in a grassy paddock and growing like a weed. His breeder had worried over his food and feet and his disposition to nick and bump himself in his enthusiasm to run and play. Because all horses' birthdays are officially January 1, he is now a yearling and has been registered with the Jockey Club. He is ready to be "broken."

Thoroughbreds are not "broken" cowboy style—they are "gentled"—slowly—patiently. First they learn to be led, with only the weight of a hand resting where one day a jockey will sit. Gradually the weight is increased until he will carry a light saddle. The first to sit on our young colt's back was a wiry-legged lad of 100 pounds. In time the colt was ridden. Then, first school days over, he was turned out until spring.

A year ago this spring, a letter came from the Jockey Club notifying the owner that the name he had requested for his horse was now official. And we only wish you could know the study and imagination that went into his naming.

That spring this horse you've chosen as your favorite met his trainer, and was given long, easy gallops. Then one morning he was asked to run with all the speed he had. Probably, for a while, his shins were sore and tender. Probably he had a siege of coughing. Young horses, like children, must go through their childhood illnesses. But finally the colt was ready for a race.

In his first race, the chances are he ran "green"—for he was inexperienced and did not know what he was supposed to do. Oddly enough, horses have to learn to race.

But he did learn. At last he won a race. As a two-year-old he proved he was a horse of merit, and when he was retired for the winter, his owner had paid the first of a series of substantial fees to nominate him for the Preakness.

Today, a three-year-old, he comes up to the Preakness. Pimlico has offered a rich purse. If the colt didn't have a chance to win the Preakness, he would not be here. He is fit and ready— and you are here to see him run.

What will happen? Will he find the track to his liking? Will he get away badly? Will he be full of run but boxed in behind other horses? Will his chance to run come too late in the race? Or will he find that, try as he will, there is a better horse in the race? Remember, defeat may be by no more than the width of your little finger.

If you back him with a wager, please remember this: 400 years of breeding will have helped your choice vindicate your esteem. If he fails to win, be watching closely—for the chances are that 400 years of breeding will be trying with might and main. Remember, too, that the finest thing about a Thoroughbred is—a courageous heart.

Win or lose, let your choice be your choice and you will have witnessed one of the most thrilling events the tradition of racing affords. You will be seeing a race founded 65 years ago by our own Maryland Jockey Club and named in honor of the great horse Preakness.

Remember, too, though horses who race here today have pedigree and performance records that go back further than any other living creature, Thoroughbreds do not rest upon their laurels. The only way to prove whether a better horse has been bred is to race him.

Because such races are something to see, for centuries race courses have been established and regular racing meetings held. Once more Pimlico fulfills its function as a proving ground of Thoroughbred breeding and today stamina and courage will be tested in the Preakness.

The horses who prove themselves here may one day return to our breeding farms to carry on a tradition that began 400 years ago when Henry VIII founded the Royal Studs and enacted laws that brought the Thoroughbred horse into being.

All we ask of you is that you like horses. If you do you are one of us. Welcome to Pimlico! Welcome to the Preakness! If all the horse talk you will hear makes you feel like an outsider and a greenhorn—take heart. No one lives who knows all there is to know about the Thoroughbred.

There is real reason—you might even call it a selfish reason—for Maryland to welcome you here today. Who knows but that this day may make you a racing enthusiast for life?

One day you may attend a Maryland Yearling Sale and become a horse owner. Before long you may have your own lush Maryland acres and your first brood mare. Driving into Pimlico today behind big vans carrying horses they have bred are enthusiasts who not so long ago were seeing their first Preakness.

If we seem a bit certain about all this, remember it has been going on in Maryland for ages— and Maryland can wait for you.

For you, today began 400 years ago.

All these things had to happen before you could see this Preakness. We wanted you to know because the bugle has blown and in a moment the horses will begin the parade to the post. There's the lead pony. Here they come!

The Redemption Handicap

CHARLES E. VAN LOAN

If I didn't know better, and for a fact, that Damon Runyon had the liveliest and most originally creative of minds, I might have suspected he was an ardent reader of Charles E. Van Loan's wonderful Old Man Curry stories in his youth. Certainly it would be hard to deny an affinity between Van Loan's Bald-faced Kid and Runyon's Harry The Horse. Van Loan preceded Runyon by a decade or so, and each made a notable contribution not only to the realistic literature of the American turf but also to the mores of the first quarter of sporting life in this 20th century.

"WELL, old sport, are you going to slip another one over on 'em today?"

"What do you think of Jeremiah's chances, Mr. Curry?"

"Can this black thing of yours beat the favorite?"

"There's even money on Jeremiah for a place; shall I grab it?"

Old Man Curry, standing at the entrance to a paddock stall, lent an unwilling ear to these queries. He was a firm believer in the truth, but more firmly he believed in the fitness of time and place. The whole truth, spoken incautiously in the paddock, has been known to affect closing odds, and it was the old man's habit to wager at post time, if at all. Those who pestered the owner of the "Bible stable" with questions about the fitness of Jeremiah and his chances to be first past the post went back to the betting ring with their enthusiasm for the black horse slightly abated. Old Man Curry admitted, under persistent prodding, that if Jeremiah got off well, and nothing happened to him, and it was one of his good days, and he didn't get bumped on the turn, and the boy rode him just right, and he could stay in front of the favorite, he might win. Pressed further, a note of pessimism developed in the

patriarch's conversation; he became the bearded embodiment of reasonable doubt. Curry's remarks, rapidly circulating in the betting ring, may have made it possible for Curry's betting commissioner, also rapidly circulating at the last minute, to unload a considerable bundle of Curry's money on Jeremiah at odds of five and six to one.

One paddock habitué, usually a keen seeker after information, might have received a hint worth money had he come after it. Old Man Curry noted the absence of the Bald-faced Kid, and when the bugle sounded the call to the track he turned the bridle over to Shanghai, the Negro hostler, and ambled into the betting ring in search of his young friend. The betting ring was the Kid's place of business—if touting is classed as an occupation and not a misdemeanor—but Old Man Curry did not find him in the crowd. It was not until the horseman stepped out on the lawn that he spied the Kid, his elbows on the top rail of the fence, his chin in his hands, and his back squarely turned to the betting ring. He did not even look around when the old man addressed him.

"Well, Frank, I kind of expected you in the paddock."

The Kid was staring out across the track with the fixed gaze of one who sees nothing in particular; he grunted slightly, but did not speak.

"Jeremiah—he's worth a bet today."

"Uh-huh!" This without interest or enthusiasm.

"I saw some five to one on him just now."

The Kid swung about and glanced listlessly toward the betting ring. Then he looked at the horses on their way to the post. The old man read his thought.

"You've got a couple of minutes yet," said he. "Mebbe more; there's some bad actors in that bunch, and they'll delay the start."

The Kid looked again at the betting ring; then he shook his head. "Aw, what's the use?" said he irritably. "What's the use?"

Old Man Curry's countenance took on a look of deep concern.

"What ails you, son? Ain't you well?"

"Well enough, I guess. Why?"

"Because I never see you pass up a mortal cinch before."

The Kid chuckled mirthlessly. "Old-timer," said he, "I'm up against a cinch of my own—but it's a cinch to lose."

He returned to his survey of the open field, but Old Man Curry lingered. He stroked his beard meditatively.

"Son," said he at length, "Solomon says that a brother is born for adversity. I don't know what a father is born for, but I reckon it's to give advice. Where you been the last week or ten days? It's mighty lonesome round the stable without you."

"I'm in a jam, and you can't help me."

"Mebbe not, but it might do some good to talk it all out of your system. You know the number, Frank."

"You mean well, old-timer," said the Kid, "and your heart's in the right place, but you—you don't understand."

"No, and how can I 'less you open up and tell me what's the matter? If you've done anything wrong—"

"Forget it!" said the Kid shortly. "You're barking up the wrong tree. I'm trying to figure out how to do right!" . . .

That night the door of Old Man Curry's tack room swung gently open, and the aged horseman, looking up from his well-thumbed copy of the Old Testament, nodded to an expected visitor.

"Set down, Frank, and take a load off your feet," said he hospitably. "I sort of thought you'd come."

For a time they talked horse, usually an engrossing subject, but after a bit the conversation flagged. The Kid rolled many cigarettes which he tossed away unfinished, and the old man waited in silence for that which he knew could not long be delayed. It came at last in the form of a startling question. "Old-timer," said the Kid abruptly, "you—you never got married, did you?"

Old Man Curry blinked a few times, passed his fingers through his beard, and stared at his questioner. "Why, no, son." The old man spoke slowly, and it was plain that he was puzzled. "Why, no, I never did."

"Did you ever think of it—seriously, I mean?"

Old Man Curry met this added impertinence without resentment, for the light was beginning to dawn on him. He drew out his packet of fine cut and studied its wrappings carefully.

"I'm not kidding, old-timer. Did you ever think of it?"

"Once," was the reply. "Once, son, and I've been thinking about it ever since. She was the right one for me, but she got the notion I wasn't the right one for her. Sometimes it happens that way. She found the man she thought she wanted, and I took to runnin' round the country with race horses. After that she was sure I was a lost soul and hell-bent for certain. This was a long time ago—before you was born, I reckon."

After a silence, the Kid asked another question:

"Well, at that, the race-track game is no game for a married man, is it?"

"M-m-well," answered the patriarch thoughtfully, "that's as how a man's wife looks at it. Some of 'em think it ain't no harm to gamble s'long's you can win, but the average woman, Frank, she don't want the hosses runnin' for her bread and butter. You can't blame her for that, because a woman is dependent by nature. If the Lord had figured her to git out an' hustle with the men, He'd have built her different, but He made her to be p'tected and shelteredlike. A single man can hustle and bat round an' go hungry if he wants to, but he ain't got no right to ask a woman to gamble her vittles on any proposition whatever."

"Ain't it the truth!" ejaculated the Bald-faced Kid, with a depth of feeling quite foreign to his nature. "You surely spoke a mouthful then!" Old Man Curry raised one eyebrow slightly and continued his discourse.

"For a man even to figger on gettin' married, he ought to have something comin' in steady—something that bad hosses an' worse men can't take away from him. He oughtn't to bet at all, but if he does it ought to be on a mortal cinch. There ain't many real cinches on a race track, Frank; not the kind that a married man'd be justified in bettin' the rent money on. Yes, sir, a man thinkin' 'bout gettin' married ought to have a job—and stick to it!"

"And that job oughtn't to be on a race track either," supplemented the Kid, his eyes fixed on the cigarette which he was rolling. "But that ain't

all I wanted to ask you about, old-timer. Suppose, now, a fellow had a girl that was too good
for him—a girl that wouldn't wipe her feet on a
gambler if she knew it, and was brought up to
think that betting was wrong. And suppose now
that this fellow wasn't even a gambler. Suppose
he was a hustler—a tout—but he'd asked the
girl to marry him without telling her what he
was, and she'd said she would. What ought that
fellow to do?"

Old Man Curry took his time about answering;
took also a large portion of fine cut and stowed
it away in his cheek.

"Well, son," said he gently, "it would depend
a lot on which the fellow cared the most for—
the race track or the girl."

The Kid flung the cigarette from him and
looked up, meeting the old man's eyes for the
first time. "I beat you to it, old-timer! Win or
lose, I'm through at the end of this meeting.
There's a fellow over in Butte just about my age.
He was a hustler too, and a pal of mine, but two
years ago he quit, and now he's got a little gents'
furnishing-goods place—nothing swell, of course,
but the business is growing all the time. He's been
after me to come in with him on a percentage of
the profits, and last night I wrote him to look for
me when they get done running here. That part
of it is settled. No more race track in mine. But
that ain't what I was getting at. Have I got to tell
the girl what I've been doing the last five years?"

"Would you rather have her find out from
someone else, Frank?"

"No-o."

"If you want to start clean, son, the best place
to begin is with the girl."

"But what if she throws me down?"

"That's the chance you'll have to take. You've
been taking 'em all your life."

"Yes, but nothing ever meant as much to me
as this does."

"Well, son, the more a woman cares for a man
the more she'll forgive."

"Did Solomon say that?" demanded the Kid.

"No, I said it. You see, Frank, it was this way
with Solomon: he had a thousand wives, more or
less, and I reckon he never had time to strike
a general average. He wrote a lot 'bout women,
first and last, but it seems he only remembered
two kinds—the ones that was too good to live
and the ones that wasn't worth killin'. It would
have been more helpful to common folks if he'd
said something 'bout the general run of women.
You'd better tell her, Frank."

The Bald-faced Kid sighed.

"I'd rather take a licking. You're sure about
that forgiving business, old-timer?"

"It's the one best bet, my son."

"Pull for it to go through, then. Goodnight—
and thank you."

Left alone, Old Man Curry turned the pages
for a time, then read aloud:

" 'There be three things which are too wonderful for me, yea, four which I know not: The
way of an eagle in the air; the way of a serpent
upon a rock; the way of a ship in the midst of
the sea, and the way of a man with a maid—*the
way of a man with a maid.*' Well, after all, the
straight way is the best way, and the boy's on
the right track."

A few days later Old Man Curry, sunning himself in the paddock, caught sight of the Kid. That
engaging youth had a victim pinned in a corner
and, program in hand, was pointing the way to
prosperity.

"Now, listen," he was saying. "You ain't taking a chance when you bet on this bird today.
Didn't I tell you that the boy that rides him is
my cousin? And ain't the owner my pal? What
better do you want than that? This tip comes
straight from the barn, and you can get twenty
to one for all your money!"

The victim squirmed and wriggled and twisted
and would have broken away but for the Kid's
compelling eye. At last he thought of something
to say:

"If this here Bismallah is such a hell-clinkin'
good race horse, how come they ain't *all* bettin'
on him?"

"Why ain't they?" the Kid fairly squealed. "Because we've been lucky enough to keep him under
cover from everybody! That's why! Nobody
knows what he can do; the stable money won't
even be bet here for fear of tipping him off; it'll
be bet in the pool rooms all over the Coast.
He'll walk in, I tell you—just *walk* in! Why,
say! You don't think I'd tell you this if I didn't
know it was *so?* Here comes the owner. I'll go
talk with him. You wait right here!"

It was really the owner of Bismallah, who,
speaking out of the corner of his mouth, told the
Bald-faced Kid to go to a warmer clime. The
hustler returned to his victim instead.

"He says it's all fixed up; everything framed;
play him across the board. Come on!"

The victim allowed himself to be dragged in
the direction of the betting ring, and Old Man
Curry watched the proceedings with a whimsical
light in his eye. Later he found a chance to dis-
cuss the matter with the Kid. The last race was
over, and Frank was through for the day.

"You're persuadin' 'em pretty *strong,* ain't
you son?" asked the old man. "You used to
give advice; now you're makin' 'em *take* it
whether they want to or not."

"Where do you get that stuff?" demanded the
Kid, bristling immediately.

"Why, I saw you working on that big fellow
in the gray suit. I was afraid you'd have to hit

him on the head and go into his pocket after it. Looked to me like he wasn't exackly crazy to gamble."

"Oh, him!" The tout spat contemptuously. "Do you know what that piker wanted to bet? Six dollars, across the board! I made him loosen up for fifteen, and he howled like a wolf."

"The hoss—lost?" By the delicate inflection and the pause before the final word, Old Man Curry might have been inquiring about the last moments of a departed friend. The Kid was looking at the ground, so he missed the twinkle in the old man's eyes.

"He ran like an apple woman," was the sullen response. "Confound it, old-timer, I can't pick 'em every time!"

"No, I reckon not," said the patriarch. "I—reckon—not." He lapsed into silence.

"Aw, spit it out!" said the Kid after a time. "I'd rather hear you say it than feel you thinking it!"

Old Man Curry smiled one of his rare smiles, and his big, wrinkled hand fell lightly on the boy's shoulder.

"What I was thinking wasn't much, son," said he. "It was this: if you can make total strangers open up and spend their substance for something they only think is there, you ought to get rid of an awful lot of shirts and socks and flummery—the things that folks can see. If you can sell stuff that *ain't,* you surely can sell stuff that *is!*"

"I'm sick of the whole business!" The words ripped out with a snarl. "I used to like this game for the excitement in it—for the kick. I used to like to see 'em run. Now I don't give a damn, so long as I can get some coin together quick. And the more you need it the harder it is to get! Today I had four suckers down on different horses in the same race, and a sleeper woke up on me. Four bets down and not a bean!"

The twinkle had gone from the old man's eyes.

"Four hosses in one race, eh? Do you need the money that bad, son?"

For answer the Kid plunged his hand into his pocket and brought out a five-dollar gold piece and a small collection of silver coins which he spread upon his palm. "There's the bank roll," said he, "and don't tell me that Solomon pulled that line about a fool and his money!"

The old man calmly appraised the exhibit of precious metals before he spoke.

"How come you to be down so low, son?"

"I was trying to win myself out a little stake," was the sulky answer, "but they cleaned me. That's why I'm hustling so hard. It's a rotten game, but it owes me something, and I want to collect it before I quit!"

"Ah, hah!" said Old Man Curry, stroking his beard meditatively. "Ah, hah! You haven't told her yet."

"No, but I'm going to. That's honest."

"I believe you, son, but did it ever strike you that mebbe she wouldn't want you to make a fresh start on money that you got this way? Mebbe she wouldn't want to start with you."

"Dough is dough." The Bald-faced Kid stated this point in the manner of one forestalling all argument. "At one time and another I've handled quite a lot of it that I got different ways, but I never yet had any trouble passing it off on folks, and they didn't hold their noses when they took it either. Anything that'll spend is good money, and don't you forget it!"

"But this girl, now—mebbe she won't think so."

"What she don't know won't hurt her."

"Son, what a woman don't know she guesses and feels, and she may have the same sort of a feelin' that I've got—that some kinds of money never bring anybody luck. A while ago you said this game was rotten, and yet you're tryin' to cash in your stack and pick up all the sleepers before you quit. Seems to me I'd want to start *clean.*"

"Dough is dough, I tell you!" repeated the Kid stubbornly. He turned and shook his fist at the distant betting ring where the cashiers were paying off the last of the winning tickets. "Look out for me, all of you sharks!" said the boy. "From now till the end of the meeting it's packing-house rules, and everything goes!"

" 'A wise son heareth his father's instruction,' " quoted Old Man Curry.

"I hear you, old-timer," said the Kid, "but I don't get you. Next thing I suppose you'll pull Solomon on me and tell me what he says about tainted money!"

"I can do that too. Let's see, how does it go? Oh, yes. 'There is that maketh himself rich, *yet hath nothing;* there is that maketh himself poor, yet hath great riches.' That's Solomon on the money question, my boy."

"Huh!" scoffed the unregenerate one. "Solomon was a king, wasn't he, with dough to burn? It's mighty easy to talk—when you've got yours. I haven't got mine yet, but you watch my smoke while I go after it!"

Old Man Curry trudged across the infield in the wake of the good horse Elisha. Another owner, on the day of an important race, might have been nervous or worried; the patriarch maintained his customary calm; his head was bent at a reflective angle, and he nibbled at a straw. Certain gentlemen, speculatively inclined, would have given much more than a penny for the old man's thoughts; having bought them at any price, they would have felt themselves defrauded.

Elisha, the star performer of the Curry stable, had been combed and groomed and polished within an inch of his life, and there were blue ribbons in his mane, a sure sign of the confidence of Shanghai, the hostler. He was also putting this confidence into words and telling the horse what was expected of him.

"See all them folks, 'Lisha? They come out yere to see you win anotheh stake an' trim that white hoss from Seattle. Gray Ghost, thass whut they calls him. When you hooks up with him down in front of that granstan', he'll think he's a ghost whut's mislaid his graveyard, yes, indeedy! They tells me he got lots of that ol' early speed; they tells me he kin go down to the half-mile pole in nothin', flat. Let him *do* it; 'tain't early speed whut wins a mile race; it's *late* speed. Ain't no money hung up on that ol' half-mile pole! Let that white fool run his head off; he'll come back to you. Lawdy, all them front runners comes back to the reg'lar hosses. Run the same like you allus do, an' eat 'em up in the stretch, 'Lisha! Gray Ghost—pooh! I neveh seen *his* name on no lamp post! I bet befo' you git th'ough with him he'll wish he'd saved some that ol' early speed to finish on. You ask me, 'Lisha, I'd say we's spendin' this yere first money right *now!*"

It was the closing day of the meeting, always in itself an excuse for a crowd, but the management had generously provided an added attraction in the shape of a stake event. Now, a Jungle Circuit stake race does not mean great wealth as a general thing, but this was one of the few rich plums provided for the horsemen. First money would mean not less than $2,000, which accounted for the presence of the Gray Ghost. The horse had been shipped from Seattle, where he had been running with and winning from a higher grade of Thoroughbreds than the Jungle Circuit boasted, and there were many who professed to believe that the Ghost's victory would be a hollow one. There were others who pinned their faith on the slow-beginning Elisha, for he was, as his owner often remarked, "an honest hoss that always did his level best." Eight other horses were entered, but the general opinion seemed to be that there were only two contenders. The others, they said, would run for Sweeney— and third money.

Old Man Curry elbowed his way through the paddock crowd, calmly nibbling at his straw. He was besieged by men anxious for his opinion as to the outcome of the race; they plucked at the skirts of his rusty black coat; they caught him by the arms. Serene and untroubled, he had but one answer for all.

"Yes, he's ready, and we're tryin'."

In the betting ring Gray Ghost opened at even money with Elisha at seven to five. The Jungle speculators went to the Curry horse with a rush that almost swept the block men off their stands, and inside of three minutes Elisha was at even money with every prospect of going to odds-on,

and the gray visitor was ascending in price. The sturdy big stretch-runner from the Curry barn had not been defeated at the meeting; he was the known quantity and could be depended upon to run his usual honest race.

The Ghost's owner also attracted considerable attention in the paddock. He was a large man, rather pompous in appearance, hairless save for a fringe above his ears, and answered to the name of "Con" Parker, the Con standing for concrete. He had been in the cement business before taking to the turf, and there were those who hinted that he still carried a massive sample of the old line above his shoulders. When cross-examined about the gray horse, he blunted every sharp inquiry with polite evasions, but he looked wiser than any human could possibly be, and the impression prevailed that he knew more than he would tell. Perhaps this was true.

The saddling bell rang, and the jockeys trooped into the paddock, followed by the roust-abouts with the tackle. Old Man Curry, waiting quietly in the far corner of Elisha's stall, saw the Bald-faced Kid wriggling his way through the crowd. He came straight to the old man.

"Elisha's four to five now," he announced breathlessly, "and they're still playing him hard. The other one is five to two. Looks like a false price on the Ghost, and I know that Parker is going to set in a chunk on him at post time. What do you think about it?"

"You goin' to bet your own money, son?"

"I've got to do it—make or break right here."

"How strong are you?"

"Just about two hundred bones."

"Ah, hah!" Old Man Curry paused a moment for thought and sucked at his straw. "Two hundred at five to two—that'd make seven hundred, wouldn't it? Pretty nice little pile."

The Kid's eyes widened. "Then you don't think Elisha can beat the Ghost today?"

"I ain't bettin' a cent on him," said the old man. "Not a cent." And the manner in which he said it meant more than the words.

"Then, shall I—?"

Old Man Curry glanced over at the gray horse, standing quietly in his stall.

"Play that one, son," he whispered.

After the Kid had gone rocketing back to the betting ring, Curry turned to Jockey Moseby Jones.

"Mose," said he, "don't lay too far out of it today. This gray hoss lasts pretty well, so begin working on 'Lisha sooner than usual. He's ready to stand a long, hard drive. Bring him home in front, boy!"

"Sutny will!" chuckled the little Negro. "At's bes' thing I do!"

When the barrier rose, a gray streak shot to the front and went skimming along the rail, opening an amazingly wide gap on the field. It was the Ghost's habit to make every post a winning one; he liked to run in front of the pack.

As he piloted the big bay horse around the first turn into the back stretch, Jockey Mose estimated the distance between his mount and the flying Ghost, taking no note of the other entries. Then he began to urge Elisha slightly.

"Can't loaf much today, hawss!" he coaxed. "Shake yo'self! Li'l mo' steam!"

The men who had played the Curry horse to odds on and thought they knew his running habits were surprised to see him steadily moving up on the back stretch. It was customary for Elisha to begin to run at the half-mile pole—usually from a tail-end position—but today he was mowing down the outsiders even before he reached that point, and on the upper turn he went thundering into second place—with the Ghost only five lengths away. The imported jockey on Parker's horse cast one glance behind him, and at the head of the stretch he sat down hard in his saddle and began hand riding with all his might. Close in the rear rose a shrill whoop of triumph.

"No white hawss eveh was *game*, 'Lisha! Sic him, you big red rascal! Make him dawg it!"

But the Ghost was game to the last ounce. More than that, he had something left for the final quarter, though his rider had not expected to draw upon that reserve so soon. The Ghost spurted, for a time maintaining his advantage. Then, annihilating incredible distances with his long, awkward strides and gathering increased momentum with every one, Elisha drew alongside. Again the Ghost was called on and responded, but the best he had left and all he had left, was barely sufficient to enable him to hold his own. Opposite the paddock inclosure, with the grandstand looming ahead, the horses were running nose and nose; ten yards more and the imported jockey drew his whip. Moseby Jones cackled aloud.

"You ain't *stuck* on 'is yere white sellin' plater, is you, 'Lisha? What you hangin' round him faw, then? Bid him goodnight *an' goodbye!*"

He drove the blunt spurs into Elisha's sides, and the big bay horse leaped out and away in a whirlwind finish that left the staggering Ghost five lengths behind and incidentally lowered the track record for one mile.

It was a very popular victory, as was attested by the leaping, howling dervishes in the grandstand and on the lawn, but there were some who took no part in the demonstration. Some, like Con Parker, were hit hard.

There was one who was hit hardest of all, a youth of pleasing appearance who drew several pasteboards from his pocket and scowled at them for a moment before he ripped them to bits and hurled the fragments into the air.

"Cleaned out! Busted!" ejaculated the Bald-faced Kid bitterly. "The old scoundrel double-crossed me!"

The last race of the meeting was over when Old Man Curry emerged from the track office of the Racing Association. The grandstand was empty, and the exits were jammed with a hurrying crowd. The betting ring still held its quota, and the cashiers were paying off the lines with all possible speed. As they slapped the winning tickets upon the spindle, they exchanged pleasantries with the fortunate holders.

"Just keep this till we come back again next season," said they. "We're lending it to you—that's all."

Old Man Curry made one brisk circle of the ring, examining every line of ticket holders, then he walked out on the lawn. The Bald-faced Kid was sitting on the steps of the grandstand smoking a cigarette. Curry went over to him. "Well, Frank," said he cheerfully, "how did you come out on the day?"

The boy stared up at him for a moment before he spoke.

"You ought to know," said he slowly. "You told me to bet on that gray horse—and then you went out and beat him to death!"

"Ah, hah!" said the old man.

"I was crazy for a minute," said the Kid. "I thought you'd double-crossed me. I've cooled out since then; now I'm only sorry that you didn't know more about what your own horse could do. That tip made a tramp out of me, old-timer."

"Exackly what I hoped it would do, son," and Old Man Curry fairly beamed.

"What's that?" The cigarette fell from the Kid's fingers, and his lower jaw sagged. "You thought Elisha could *win*—and you went and touted me onto the other one?"

Old Man Curry nodded, smiling.

As the boy watched him, his expression changed to one of deep disgust. He dipped into his vest pocket and produced his silver stop watch. "Here's something you overlooked," he sneered. "Take it, and I'll be cleaned right!"

Old Man Curry sat down beside him, but the Kid edged away. "I wouldn't have thought it of you, old-timer," said he.

"Frank," said the old man gently, "you don't understand. You don't know what I was figgerin' on."

"I know this," retorted the Kid: "if it hadn't been for you, I wouldn't have to go to Butte alone!"

"You've told her, then?"

"Last night."

"And I was right about the forgivin' business, son?"

"Didn't I say she was going to Butte with me? We had it all fixed to get married, but now—"

"Well, I don't see no reason for callin' it off." Old Man Curry's cheerfulness had returned, and as he spoke he drew out his old-fashioned leather wallet. "You know what I told you 'bout bad money, son—tainted money? You wouldn't take my word for it that gamblers' money brings bad luck; I just nachelly had to fix up some scheme on you so that you wouldn't have no bad money to start out with." He opened the wallet and extracted a check upon which the ink was scarcely dry—the check of the Racing Association for the winner's portion of the stake just decided. "I wouldn't want you to have bad luck, son," the old man continued. "I wanted you to have good luck—and a clean start. Here's some money that it wouldn't hurt anybody to handle—an honest hoss went out and run for it and earned it, an' he was runnin' for you every step of the way! Here, take it." He thrust the check into the boy's hand—and let it stand to his credit that he answered before looking at it.

"I—I had you wrong, old-timer," he stammered—"wrong from the start. I—I can't take this. I ain't a pauper, and I—I——"

"Why of course you can take it, son," urged the old man. "You said this game owed you a stake, and maybe it does, but the only money you can afford to start out with is clean money, and the only clean money on a race track is the money that an honest hoss can go out and run for—and win. No, I can't take it back; it's indorsed over to you."

Then, and not before, did the Kid look at the figures on the check.

"Why," he gasped, "this—this is for twenty-four hundred and something! I don't *need* that much! I—we—*she* says three hundred would be plenty! I—"

"That's all right," interrupted Old Man Curry. "Money—clean money—never comes amiss. You can call the three hundred the stake that was owin' to you; the rest, well, I reckon that's just my weddin' present. Goodbye, son, and good luck!"

"For a boy who was brought up on a farm, you know very little about horses!"

Upset Beats Man o' War

FRED VAN NESS

Well, it happened this way . . .

SARATOGA, N. Y. Aug. 13, 1919 THE Glen Riddle Farm's great two-year-old, Man o' War, met with his first defeat here today in the running of the Sanford Memorial. He was forced to bow to Harry Payne Whitney's Upset in a neck-and-neck finish in this six-furlong dash, but he had the satisfaction of quite definitely triumphing over the widely heralded Golden Broom, which he easily beat into submission and which finished third, four lengths back.

Though defeated, Man o' War was not discredited. On the contrary, the manner in which he ran this race stamped him, in the opinion of horsemen, as the best of his division without question. Though failing to get his nose in front, he stood out as the best horse in the race by a large margin, for he had all the worst of the racing luck. Beginning with a very bad start, he came on to give battle to a horse which had a start of three to four lengths on him. There was scarcely a witness of this race who did not believe after it was all over that Man o' War would have walked home, with anything like a fair chance.

The Sanford Memorial, for which John Sanford donated a cup on this occasion because of the presence of Man o' War and Golden Broom, was by far the most interesting event that has been held during the Saratoga meeting. One of the largest crowds of the meeting, about 20,000 persons, saw the running of the race.

After two of the original entries had been scratched, John E. Madden added Captain Alcock; and seven horses went to the post. As was expected, Man o' War was an odds-on favorite, the prevailing price being one to two.

Golden Broom was offered as two to one while Upset, regarded at all times as the third choice, was seven to one to win but only two to five to show.

Golden Broom had an inside position, with Ambrose again in the saddle, while Man o' War was next to the outside with Loftus up. Golden Broom, which seems to be a very shy and green colt, had to be led out of the paddock with a pony and so conducted throughout the parade past the stands and to the starting post. Upon arriving there he began to act up, apparently through anxiety to be away winging.

For those who had hoped for a pretty race without anything to mar it, it was unfortunate that Mars Cassidy was ill and was not able to act as starter. C. H. Pettingill, one of the placing judges, acted in his place and did very badly all day, getting only two really good starts on a program of seven events.

One of the worst starts was that in the Sanford Memorial. Golden Broom broke through the barrier three times, while Upset, which was near him, also was trying to beat the barrier. Willie Knapp was the rider of Upset. Man o' War acted very calmly but was on his toes. Pettingill spent several minutes trying to get the horses lined up and then sent them away with only those near the rail ready for the start. The start was responsible for the defeat of Man o' War, it turned out.

Golden Broom, showing the speed which he had twice flashed here, was away with a bound and was two lengths in front in the first sixteenth. Upset, also away like a shot out of a gun,

[295

took after the leader, with G. W. Loft's Donnacona running third. Man o' War, one of the fastest breakers among the two-year-olds, and one which had always been able to break with the first of the field, was left almost at the post. As the horses straggled away Man o' War was next to last to leave, having to get set after the others were under way.

Golden Broom cut out a decidedly fast race, Ambrose having in mind the easy victory he gained as a front runner a few days before. He also had in mind, no doubt, the fact that just such a pace, sustained to the wire, was needed to beat the favorite. At the first turn Golden Broom was leading, with Upset second, two lengths back, and Donnacona third, and at that point it seemed Mrs. Jeffords' fine colt would win.

In the meantime Man o' War was beginning to show what a really great horse he was. Off almost last, he gained his speed in a few strides and then started to pass horses all along the back stretch. Armistice and The Swimmer were soon disposed of, and making the turn the Glen Riddle Farm's racer drew up to fourth.

At this point Donnacona gave up the chase, and on the last part of the turn into the stretch Man o' War took third position, about two lengths back of Upset.

The Whitney colt was running a fine race but had not yet gained on Golden Broom. A few strides down the stretch Golden Broom suddenly gave up, and Upset raced past him. In another instant Man o' War had dashed by his chestnut rival and it became a question whether Upset could last to win. Man o' War received a fine ride from Loftus, who gave the colt every assistance within his power. Steadily Man o' War drew up on Upset. A hundred feet from the wire he was three-fourths of a length away. At the wire he was a scant neck out of the first position and in another 20 feet he would have passed the Whitney horse. Golden Broom lasted to take third, while Captain Alcock rushed up for fourth. All but the first three were badly beaten.

What made the race of Man o' War so impressive was the fact that he came from so far behind and that also he conceded 15 pounds to Upset. On the very performance of the two today the Whitney horse would not appear to have a chance to win under an even break.

Man o' War vs. John P. Grier

FRED VAN NESS

. . . and then it happened this way!

I NEW YORK, July 11, 1920
N what veteran race-goers declared the greatest
horse race that has been seen on the American
turf in more than a decade, Samuel D. Riddle's
mighty Man o' War won the undisputed right
to the three-year-old crown at Aqueduct yesterday when he defeated Harry Payne Whitney's
John P. Grier in the $6,000 Dwyer Stakes at a
mile and a furlong and established a new world
record for the distance. The time was 1:49⅕, a
fifth of a second faster than the previous record
made by H. P. Whitney's Borrow over the same
course in 1917, and equaled in the same season,
at Aqueduct, by Boots.

To more than 25,000 persons who witnessed
the whirlwind battle of speed and stamina, it provided a thrill such as is seldom experienced in any
horse race, no matter how close the finish may
be. The great thrill came from the fact that Man
o' War was finally put to a real test against a
three-year-old which in any other year would be
a champion and was forced to do his best over a
greater part of the distance to gain, finally, the
decision. He won the heartbreaking contest only
after a great struggle through the stretch in which
he ran John P. Grier out to the very last ounce.
The champion then went on to win by two
lengths.

Man o' War has been referred to as the champion throughout this season, but all the while
there was this one colt which he had not met as
a three-year-old, and it was necesary to beat him
to have undisputed claim to the title. John P.
Grier was the last of the good ones of his age to
be sent after the mighty son of Fair Play, and

now that he has failed, Man o' War has reached
the point where he has no more worlds to con-
quer while he remains in races exclusively for
horses of his age.

It was a smashing race viewed from any angle.
It was a struggle between two really great horses;
a match race, as only these two went to the post,
and while the majority of those in the stands felt
quite confident of the outcome, they saw Man o'
War forced to run his very best, his rider obliged
to go to the whip in the stretch drive after the
contestants had set such a dazzling pace from the
very start that they seemed fairly to fly through
space rather than to touch ground. Some idea of
the speed they maintained over the entire course
can be had from the fractional times. The six
furlongs were run in 1:09⅗, which is a new
American record for the distance, while the mile
was covered in 1:35⅗, one-fifth of a second
faster than the mark made by Man o' War at
Belmont Park, where he established a new American record for a race in competition.

John P. Grier came out of the race defeated
but covered with laurels, for his performance
was one that probably no other horse save Man
o' War could duplicate. The Whitney colt established himself as a remarkably fine racer, undoubtedly the best in the Whitney string, and
justified the opinion of those who classed him as
the second best of the juveniles last year when
he finished second to Man o' War in the Futurity.

The Whitney colt was game to the core. He
ran with every ounce of speed and courage he
could command to the very limit of his ability.
He fairly collapsed about fifty yards from the

[297

Man o' War pulls ahead of John P. Grier near the finish of the race [UPI]

finish when he reached the extent of his endurance. Up to that time he was never more than half a length back of the champion and at one time he actually got his nose in front of Man o' War.

Because of the presence of John P. Grier there was opportunity for considerable speculation on the race. Man o' War was first quoted at one to three, while his rival was offered at two to one. There was a rush to support the champion at this price and the odds quickly dropped to one to five. Not a few wagered on the Whitney colt but altogether the speculation on the race was not heavy. The thousands who had gathered at Aqueduct were there to see a great race and to admire two great horses.

Man o' War received the usual welcome as he came out on parade, this time accompanied by a lead pony. It would seem that Man o' War fully realizes his own importance in the racing world, for on parade he is at his very best, always high-spirited and gifted with all the attributes of a real show animal. John P. Grier was very tame on parade, but when he reached the barrier he became frisky and with the two high-spirited colts to handle Starter Cassidy did not spring the barrier for two minutes.

The pair popped out of the chute at the head of the back stretch and into view of those in the stands almost on even terms, with Man o' War running on the rail. They went fo top speed at the very first jump and the pace was never slackened. John P. Grier attempted to go to the front in the first sixteenth, but Kummer let out his mount and Man o' War took the lead by less than half a length, and thus the two went through the long run of the back stretch, neither ever giving an inch in the great struggle.

At the turn Man o' War showed about half a length in front. Halfway around the turn Ambrose began to move up with the Whitney colt. When the horses turned into the stretch there was probably slightly less than half a length between them. At no time in the race up to the final fifty yards did daylight ever show between them.

Kummer had Man o' War under a hand ride but was letting his mount go at top speed through the first sixteenth of the stretch run.

Suddenly there was a murmur in the crowd. The blue silks which encased Ambrose were seen to come up until the two racers were on what appeared from the stands to be even terms. There was a cry that John P. Grier had passed the champion and was winning, and for just a fraction of a second it seemed this might prove true.

Kummer had not made a move up to this time, but now he turned and applied his whip to Man o' War. One lash and the great colt sprang out, and in two or three strides had taken a lead of three-quarters of a length. The race now seemed over, but it was not. Ambrose lashed John P. Grier, and that colt, responding with amazing gameness, moved up again, made a mighty effort as if fully realizing the importance of the duel and once more came to almost even terms with his rival.

The horses were in front of the stands by this time and the shouts and cheers of the great crowd might have been heard for a mile around. Men and women who are usually serene and dignified jumped up and down and waved arms frantically. For just a second there loomed the possibility of the horse of the century meeting defeat. It was a rather sickening thought to those who had raised this colt to a pedestal. The same crowd would have hailed a new champion in the next breath.

But Man o' War was not to disappoint anyone. The second challenge by John P. Grier proved to be his last and his greatest effort. Kummer went to the whip once more and gave Man o' War two lashes. Once more the son of Fair Play bounded forward, showing that he still had something left.

This final bound put an end to the race. John P. Grier had done his best. The last effort took all he had in reserve. He was then but fifty yards from the finish and as Man o' War responded to the lash John P. Grier fairly flattened out. He could no longer contend with the great horse which seemed never to be at the end of his speed and endurance. The Whitney colt was thoroughly exhausted. Man o' War bounded on to win by two lengths, gaining all this distance in the last few yards.

Clarence Kummer, who has ridden Man o' War in all of his five victories this season, was asked after the race if the champion was ridden out and if the Whitney colt did actually get in front.

"John P. Grier had his head in front for a moment at the eighth pole," said Kummer, "but the moment I went after him in earnest the race was over. As to whether Man o' War was all in, well, when horses run like they did from the start something has to crack and while I would not like to say how much Man o' War had left, it was enough so that he could have gone on to give another horse a battle had there been a third horse in the race. He ran a hard race, but he was not all in at the end."

THE JOCKEY CLUB
300 Park Avenue
New York 22, N. Y.

COLORS

ANNUAL FEE $5.00 FOR YEAR 19____ OR $25.00 LIFE

FRONT AND BACK OF JACKET MUST BE IDENTICAL

Date_____ 19____

IMPORTANT

LIFE COLORS will only be issued to those owners who have registered colors annually for three consecutive years and will be cancelled after five years unless The Jockey Club is advised every two years thereafter that they are still being used for racing purposes.

ANNUAL COLORS will not be reserved beyond one year after expiration.

DRAW DESIGN ON SKETCH ➡

Samples of color materials must be furnished

Complete description of jacket, including number and width of sashes, hoops, stripes and any other design on body or sleeve, must be given below: Definitions appear on reverse side of application.

Jacket_____
            (Front and back must be identical)
_____

Sleeves_____

Cap_____

Full Name_____
            (colors must be registered in one name only)

Permanent Address_____

Business_____

Business Address_____

Name of Your Trainer_____

Date Paid	Entered on Cards	Published	Remarks

DEFINITIONS.

Ball — Circle 8" in diameter.

Blocks — 4" square.

Braces — 2" vertical band running over shoulders and down front and back to bottom of jacket.

Cross — 4" panel and 4" hoop.

Diagonal Quarters — 4 triangles joining in a point at the center of the jacket.

Diagonal V Stripes — 1½" running downward from both shoulders to center of jacket.

Diamonds — 4" horizontally, 5" vertically.

Dots — 2½" in diameter.

Halves — horizontal only.

Hoops — horizontal bands running completely around jacket or sleeves; one hoop 4", more than one, 2½".

Panel — 5" vertical stripe running from collar to waist.

Sash — 4" diagonal stripe running from left shoulder to right hip.

Cross sashes — 4" diagonal stripes running from shoulders to hips crossing at center of front and back.

Stars — 3" in diameter, having 5 points.

Stripes — 1½" vertical or diagonal.

Yoke — 4" from shoulder seam.

FRONT AND BACK MUST BE IDENTICAL

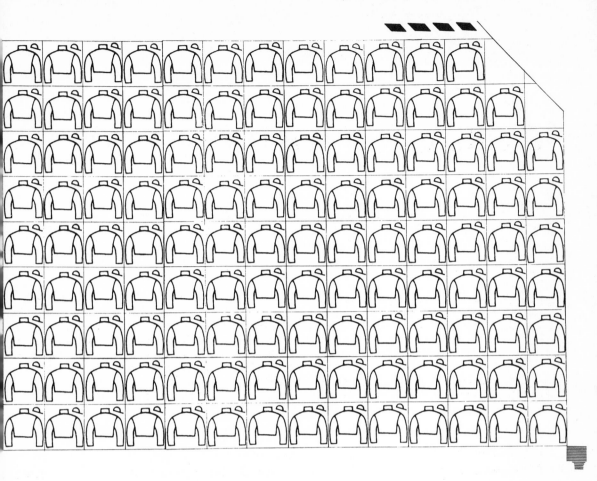

The brilliant racing silks worn by jockeys to distinguish one Thoroughbred racing stable from another are not chosen haphazardly by the stable owners. To avoid duplication, racing colors must be registered with the Jockey Club on the forms shown here. They are kept on file at the Jockey Club's offices in New York City, and new registrants are informed of colors and designs that have been previously issued. More than 2,500 stables have registered racing colors. Designs must be easily identifiable in motion (extremely rapid motion, the stable owner hopes). They are usually chosen from the following markings: balls, blocks, braces, quarters, diamonds, dots, hoops (on sleeves), panels, sashes, stars, and stripes. Some exceptions: the running W brand of the famous King Ranch and the trumpet insignia of the stable of Mrs. Angelina Prima, mother of band leader Louis Prima.

The Race from *Ben-Hur*

LEW WALLACE

My father, a notable gentleman but not a notable follower of the races—I believe he witnessed the Dixie Handicap at Pimlico some years ago—suggested the inclusion in this collection of the chariot race from Ben-Hur. *I am grateful to him for that and, I believe, many students of form and result will also be grateful. It has occurred to me that the latter group have probably been wondering for years "Who win it?" whenever Ben-Hur's great race is mentioned. Well, here it is, fellows, Ben-Hur was the jockey. Move over, Arcaro and Shoemaker et al.*

THE competitors were now under view from nearly every part of the Circus, yet the race was not begun; they had first to make the chalked line successfully.

The line was stretched for the purpose of equalizing the start. If it were dashed upon, discomfiture of man and horses might be apprehended; on the other hand, to approach it timidly was to incur the hazard of being thrown behind in the beginning of the race; and that was certain forfeit of the great advantage always striven for— the position next the division wall on the inner line of the course.

This trial, its perils and consequences, the spectators knew thoroughly; and if the opinion of old Nestor, uttered what time he handed the reins to his son, were true—

"It is not strength, but art, obtained the prize,
And to be swift is less than to be wise"—

all on the benches might well look for warning of the winner to be now given, justifying the interest with which they breathlessly watched for the result.

The arena swam in a dazzle of light; yet each driver looked first thing for the rope, then for the coveted inner line. So, all six aiming at the same point and speeding furiously, a collision seemed inevitable; nor that merely. What if the editor, at the last moment dissatisfied with the start, should withhold the signal to drop the rope? Or if he should not give it in time?

The crossing was about two hundred and fifty feet in width. Quick the eye, steady the hand, unerring the judgment required. If now one look away! or his mind wander! or a rein slip! And what attraction in the ensemble of the thousands over the spreading balcony! Calculating upon the natural impulse to give one glance—just one— in sooth of curiosity or vanity, malice might be there with an artifice; while friendship and love, did they serve the same result, might be as deadly as malice.

The divine last touch in perfecting the beautiful is animation. Can we accept the saying, then these latter days, so tame in pastime and dull in sports, have scarcely anything to compare to the spectacle offered by the six contestants. Let the reader try to fancy it; let him first look down upon the arena, and see it glistening in its frame of dull-gray granite walls; let him then, in this perfect field, see the chariots, light of wheel, very graceful, and ornate as paint and burnishing can make them—Messala's rich with ivory and gold; let him see the drivers, erect and statuesque, undisturbed by the motion of the cars, their limbs naked, and fresh and ruddy with the healthful polish of the baths—in their right hands goads, suggestive of torture dreadful to the thought—in their left hands, held in careful separation, and high, that they may not interfere with view of the steeds, the reins passing taut from the fore ends of the carriage-poles; let him see the fours, chosen for beauty as well as speed; let him see them in magnificent action, their masters not more conscious of the situation and all that is asked and hoped for them—their heads tossing, nostrils in play, now distent, now contracted—limbs too dainty for the sand which they touch but to spurn—limbs slender, yet with impact crushing as hammers—every muscle of the rounded bodies instinct with glorious life, swelling, diminishing, justifying the world in taking from them its ultimate measure of force; finally, along with chariots, drivers, horses, let the reader see the accompanying shadows fly; and, with such distinctness as the picture comes, he may share the satisfaction and deeper pleasure of those to whom it was a thrilling fact, not a feeble fancy. Every age has its plenty of sorrows; heaven help where there are no pleasures!

The competitors having started each on the shortest line for the position next the wall, yielding would be like giving up the race; and who dared yield? It is not in common nature to change a purpose in midcareer; and the cries of encouragement from the balcony were indistinguishable and indescribable: a roar which had the same effect upon all the drivers.

The fours neared the rope together. Then the trumpeter by the editor's side blew a signal vigorously. Twenty feet away it was not heard. Seeing the action, however, the judges dropped the rope, and not an instant too soon, for the hoof of one of Messala's horses struck it as it fell. Nothing daunted, the Roman shook out his long lash, loosed the reins, leaned forward, and, with a triumphant shout, took the wall.

"Jove with us! Jove with us!" yelled all the Roman faction, in a frenzy of delight.

As Messala turned in, the bronze lion's head at the end of his axle caught the foreleg of the Athenian's right-hand trace-mate, flinging the brute over against its yoke-fellow. Both staggered, struggled, and lost their headway. The ushers had their will at least in part. The thousands held their breath with horror; only up where the consul sat was there shouting.

"Jove with us!" screamed Drusus, frantically.

"He wins! Jove with us!" answered his associates, seeing Messala speed on.

Tablet in hand, Sanballat turned to them; a crash from the course below stopped his speech, and he could not but look that way.

Messala having passed, the Corinthian was the only contestant on the Athenian's right, and to that side the latter tried to turn his broken four; and then, as ill fortune would have it, the wheel

of the Byzantine, who was next on the left, struck the tailpiece of his chariot, knocking his feet from under him. There was a crash, a scream of rage and fear, and the unfortunate Cleanthes fell under the hoofs of his own steeds: a terrible sight against which Esther covered her eyes.

On swept the Corinthian, on the Byzantine, on the Sidonian.

Sanballat looked for Ben-Hur, and turned again to Drusus and his coterie.

"A hundred sestertii on the Jew!" he cried.

"Taken!" answered Drusus.

"Another hundred on the Jew!" shouted Sanballat.

Nobody appeared to hear him. He called again; the situation below was too absorbing, and they were too busy shouting, "Messala! Messala! Jove with us!"

When the Jewess ventured to look again, a party of workmen were removing the horses and broken car; another party were taking off the man himself; and every bench upon which there was a Greek was vocal with execrations and prayers for vengeance. Suddenly she dropped her hands; Ben-Hur, unhurt, was to the front, coursing freely forward along with the Roman! Behind them, in a group, followed the Sidonian, the Corinthian and the Byzantine.

The race was on; the souls of the racers were in it; over them bent the myriads.

When the dash for position began, Ben-Hur, as we have seen, was on the extreme left of the six. For a moment, like the others, he was half blinded by the light in the arena; yet he managed to catch sight of his antagonists and divine their purpose. At Messala, who was more than an antagonist to him, he gave one searching look. The air of passionless hauteur characteristic of the fine patrician face was there as of old, and so was the Italian beauty, which the helmet rather increased; but more—it may have been a jealous fancy, or the effect of the brassy shadow in which the features were at the moment cast, still the Israelite thought he saw the soul of the man as through a glass, darkly: cruel, cunning, desperate; not so excited as determined—a soul in a tension of watchfulness and fierce resolve.

In a time not longer than was required to turn to his four again, Ben-Hur felt his own resolution harden to a like temper. At whatever cost, at all hazards, he would humble this enemy! Prize, friends, wagers, honor—everything that can be thought of as a possible interest in the race was lost in the one deliberate purpose. Regard for life even should not hold him back. Yet there was no passion, on his part; no blinding rush of heated blood from heart to brain, and back again; no impulse to fling himself upon fortune: he did not believe in fortune; far otherwise. He had his plan, and, confiding in himself, he settled to the task never more observant, never more capable. The air about him seemed aglow with a renewed and perfect transparency.

When not halfway across the arena, he saw that Messala's rush would, if there was no collision, and the rope fell, give him the wall; that the rope would fall, he ceased as soon to doubt; and, further, it came to him, a sudden flashlike insight, that Messala knew it was to be let drop at the last moment (prearrangement with the editor could safely reach that point in the contest); and it suggested, what more Romanlike than for the official to lend himself to a countryman who, besides being so popular, had also so much at stake? There could be no other accounting for the confidence with which Messala pushed his four forward the instant his competitors were prudentially checking their fours in front of the obstruction—no other except madness.

It is one thing to see a necessity and another

Charlton Heston plays Ben-Hur in the most recent film version of the classic equine epic.
[UPI]

to act upon it. Ben-Hur yielded the wall for the time.

The rope fell, and all the fours but his sprang into the course under urgency of voice and lash. He drew head to the right, and, with all the speed of his Arabs, darted across the trails of his opponents, the angle of movement being such as to lose the least time and gain the greatest possible advance. So, while the spectators were shivering at the Athenian's mishap, and the Sidonian, Byzantine, and Corinthian were striving, with such skill as they possessed, to avoid involvement in the ruin, Ben-Hur swept around and took the course neck and neck with Messala, though on the outside. The marvelous skill shown in making the change thus from the extreme left across to the right without appreciable loss did not fail the sharp eyes upon the benches: the Circus seemed to rock and rock again with prolonged applause. Then Esther clasped her hands in glad surprise; then Sanballat, smiling, offered his hundred sestertii a second time without a taker; and then the Romans began to doubt, thinking Messala might have found an equal, if not a master, and that in an Israelite!

And now, racing together side by side, a narrow interval between them, the two neared the second goal.

The pedestal of the three pillars there, viewed from the west, was a stone wall in the form of a half-circle, around which the course and opposite balcony were bent in exact parallelism. Making this turn was considered in all respects the most telling test of a charioteer; it was, in fact, the very feat in which Orestes failed. As an involuntary admission of interest on the part of the spectators, a hush fell over all the Circus, so that for the first time in the race the rattle and clang of the cars plunging after the tugging steeds were distinctly heard. Then, it would seem, Messala observed Ben-Hur, and recognized him; and at once the audacity of the man flamed out in an astonishing manner.

"Down Eros, up Mars!" he shouted, whirling his lash with practiced hand—"Down Eros, up Mars!" he repeated, and caught the well-doing Arabs of Ben-Hur a cut the like of which they had never known.

The blow was seen in every quarter, and the amazement was universal. The silence deepened; up on the benches behind the consul the boldest held his breath, waiting for the outcome. Only a moment thus: then, involuntarily, down from the balcony, as thunder falls, burst the indignant cry of the people.

The four sprang forward affrighted. No hand had ever been laid upon them except in love; they had been nurtured ever so tenderly; and as they grew, their confidence in man became a lesson to men beautiful to see. What should such dainty natures do under such indignity but leap as from death?

Forward they sprang as with one impulse, and forward leaped the car. Past question, every experience is serviceable to us. Where got Ben-Hur the large hand and mighty grip which helped him now so well? Where but from the oar with which so long he fought the sea? And what was this spring of the floor under his feet to the dizzy eccentric lurch with which in the old time the trembling ship yielded to the beat of staggering billows, drunk with their power? So he kept his pace, and gave the four free rein, and called to them in soothing voice, trying merely to guide them round the dangerous turn; and before the fever of the people began to abate, he had back the mastery. Nor that only; on approaching the first goal, he was again side by side with Messala, bearing with him the sympathy and admiration of everyone not a Roman. So clearly was the feeling shown, so vigorous its manifestation, that Messala, with all his boldness, felt it unsafe to trifle further.

As the cars whirled round the goal, Esther caught sight of Ben-Hur's face—a little pale, a little higher raised, otherwise calm, even placid.

Immediately a man climbed on the entablature at the west end of the division wall, and took down one of the conical wooden balls. A dolphin on the east entablature was taken down at the same time.

In like manner, the second ball and second dolphin disappeared.

And then the third ball and third dolphin.

Three rounds concluded: still Messala held the inside position; still Ben-Hur moved with him side by side; still the other competitors followed as before. The contest began to have the appearance of one of the double races which became so popular in Rome during the later Cæsarean period—Messala and Ben-Hur in the first, the Corinthian, Sidonian, and Byzantine in the second. Meantime the ushers succeeded in returning the multitude to their seats, though the clamor continued to run the rounds, keeping, as it were, even pace with the rivals in the course below.

In the fifth round the Sidonian succeeded in getting a place outside Ben-Hur, but lost it directly.

The sixth round was entered upon without change of relative position.

Gradually the speed had been quickened—gradually the blood of the competitors warmed with the work. Men and beasts seemed to know alike that the final crisis was near, bringing the time for the winner to assert himself.

The interest which from the beginning had centered chiefly in the struggle between the Roman and the Jew, with an intense and general sympathy for the latter, was fast changing to anxiety on his account. On all the benches the spectators bent forward motionless, except as their faces turned following the contestants. Ilderim quitted combing his beard, and Esther forgot her fears.

"A hundred sestertii on the Jew!" cried Sanballat to the Romans under the consul's awning.

There was no reply.

"A talent—or five talents, or ten; choose ye!" He shook his tablets at them defiantly.

"I will take thy sestertii," answered a Roman youth, preparing to write.

"Do not so," interposed a friend.

"Why?"

"Messala hath reached his utmost speed. See him lean over his chariot-rim, the reins loose as flying ribbons. Look then at the Jew."

The first one looked.

"By Hercules!" he replied, his countenance falling. "The dog throws all his weight on the bits. I see, I see! If the gods help not our friend, he will be run away with by the Israelite. No, not yet. Look! Jove with us, Jove with us!"

The cry, swelled by every Latin tongue, shook the *velaria* over the consul's head.

If it were true that Messala had attained his utmost speed, the effort was with effect; slowly but certainly he was beginning to forge ahead. His horses were running with their heads low down; from the balcony their bodies appeared actually to skim the earth; their nostrils showed blood-red in expansion; their eyes seemed straining in their sockets. Certainly the good steeds were doing their best! How long could they keep the pace? It was but the commencement of the sixth round. On they dashed. As they neared the second goal, Ben-Hur turned in behind the Roman's car.

The joy of the Messala faction reached its bound; they screamed and howled, and tossed their colors; and Sanballat filled his tablets with wagers of their tendering.

Malluch, in the lower gallery over the Gate of Triumph, found it hard to keep his cheer. He had cherished the vague hint dropped to him by Ben-Hur of something to happen in the turning of the western pillars. It was the fifth round, yet the something had not come; and he had said to himself, the sixth will bring it; but, lo! Ben-Hur was hardly holding a place at the tail of his enemy's car.

Over in the east end, Simonides' party held their peace. The merchant's head was bent low. Ilderim tugged at his beard, and dropped his brows till there was nothing of his eyes but an occasional sparkle of light. Esther scarcely breathed. Iras alone appeared glad.

Along the home stretch—sixth round—Messala leading, next him Ben-Hur, and so close it was the old story:

Thus to the first goal, and round it. Messala, fearful of losing his place, hugged the stony wall with perilous clasp; a foot to left, and he had been dashed to pieces; yet, when the turn was finished, no man, looking at the wheel tracks of the two cars, could have said, here went Messala, there the Jew. They left but one trace behind them.

As they whirled by, Esther saw Ben-Hur's face again, and it was whiter than before.

Simonides, shrewder than Esther, said to Ilderim, the moment the rivals turned into the course, "I am no judge, good sheik, if Ben-Hur be not about to execute some design. His face hath that look."

To which Ilderim answered, "Saw you how clean they were and fresh? By the splendor of God, friend, they have not been running! But now watch!"

One ball and one dolphin remained on the entablatures; and all the people drew a long breath, for the beginning of the end was at hand.

First, the Sidonian gave the scourge to his four, and, smarting with fear and pain, they dashed desperately forward, promising for a brief time to go to the front. The effort ended in promise. Next, the Byzantine and Corinthian each made the trial with like result, after which they were practically out of the race. Thereupon, with a readiness perfectly explicable, all the factions except the Romans joined hope in Ben-Hur, and openly indulged their feeling.

"Ben-Hur! Ben-Hur!" they shouted, and the blent voices of the many rolled overwhelmingly against the consul stand.

From the benches above him as he passed, the favor descended in fierce injunctions.

"Speed thee, Jew!"

"Take the wall now!"

"On! Loose the Arabs! Give them rein and scourge!"

"Let him not have the turn on thee again. Now or never!"

Over the balustrade they stooped low, stretching their hands imploringly to him.

Either he did not hear, or could not do better, for halfway round the course and he was still following; at the second goal even still no change!

And now, to make the turn, Messala began to draw in his left-hand steeds, an act which necessarily slackened their speed. His spirit was high; more than one altar was richer of his vows; the Roman genius was still president. On the three pillars only six hundred feet away were fame, increase of fortune, promotions, and a triumph ineffably sweetened by hate, all in store for him! That moment Malluch, in the gallery, saw Ben-Hur lean forward over his Arabs, and give them the reins. Out flew the many-folded lash in his hand; over the backs of the startled steeds it writhed and hissed, and hissed and writhed again and again; and though it fell not, there were both sting and menace in its quick report; and as the man passed thus from quiet to resistless action, his face suffused, his eyes gleaming, along the reins he seemed to flash his will; and instantly not one, but the four as one, answered with a leap that landed them alongside the Roman's car. Messala, on the perilous edge of the goal, heard, but dared not look to see what the awakening portended. From the people he received no sign. Above the noises of the race there was but one voice, and that was Ben-Hur's. In the old Aramaic, as the sheik himself, he called to the Arabs.

"On, Atair! On, Rigel! What, Antares! dost thou linger now? Good horse—oho, Aldebaran! I hear them singing in the tents. I hear the children singing and the women—singing of the stars, of Atair, Antares, Rigel, Aldebaran, victory!—and the song will never end. Well done! Home tomorrow, under the black tent—home! On, Antares! The tribe is waiting for us, and the master is waiting! 'Tis done! 'tis done! Ha, ha! We have overthrown the proud. The hand that smote us is in the dust. Ours the glory! Ha, ha!— steady! The work is done—so ho! Rest!"

There had never been anything of the kind more simple; seldom anything so instantaneous.

At the moment chosen for the dash, Messala was moving in a circle round the goal. To pass him, Ben-Hur had to cross the track, and good strategy required the movement to be in a forward direction; that is, on a like circle limited to the least possible increase. The thousands on the benches understood it all: they saw the signal given—the magnificent response; the four close outside Messala's outer wheel, Ben-Hur's inner wheel behind the other's car—all this they saw. Then they heard a crash loud enough to send a thrill through the Circus, and, quicker than thought, out over the course a spray of shining white and yellow flinders flew. Down on its right side toppled the bed of the Roman's chariot. There was a rebound as of the axle hitting the hard earth; another and another: then the car went to pieces; and Messala, entangled in the reins, pitched forward headlong.

To increase the horror of the sight by making death certain, the Sidonian, who had the wall next behind, could not stop or turn out. Into the wreck full speed he drove; then over the Roman, and into the latter's four, all mad with fear. Presently, out of the turmoil, the fighting of horses, the resound of blows, the murky cloud of dust and sand, he crawled, in time to see the Corinthian and Byzantine go on down the course after Ben-Hur, who had not been an instant delayed.

The people arose, and leaped upon the benches, and shouted and screamed. Those who looked that way caught glimpses of Messala, now under the trampling of the fours, now under the abandoned cars. He was still; they thought him dead; but far the greater number followed Ben-Hur in his career. They had not seen the cunning touch of the reins by which, turning a little to the left, he caught Messala's wheel with the iron-shod point of his axle, and crushed it; but they had seen the transformation of the man, and themselves felt the heat and glow of his spirit, the heroic resolution, the maddening energy of action with which, by look, word, and gesture, he so suddenly inspired his Arabs. And such running! It was rather the long leaping of lions in harness; but for the lumbering chariot, it seemed the four were flying. When the Byzantine and Corinthian were halfway down the course, Ben-Hur turned the first goal.

And the race was WON!

The consul arose; the people shouted themselves hoarse; the editor came down from his seat, and crowned the victors.

The fortunate man among the boxers was a low-browed, yellow-haired Saxon, of such brutalized face as to attract a second look from Ben-Hur, who recognized a teacher with whom he himself had been a favorite at Rome. From him the young Jew looked up and beheld Simonides and his party on the balcony. They waved their hands to him. Esther kept her seat; but Iras arose, and gave him a smile and a wave of her fan—favors not the less intoxicating to him because we know, O reader, they would have fallen to Messala had he been the victor.

The procession was then formed, and, midst the shouting of the multitudes which had had its will, passed out of the Gate of Triumph.

And the day was over.

War Admiral

JOHN HERVEY

Despite my personal feelings for War Admiral—I never was one of his enthusiasts—he had a tremendous appeal for many thousands. I was forcefully reminded of this the day he went down to defeat by Seabiscuit in the Pimlico Special, when the cheers of the winner's fans were tempered by the mournful mien of War Admiral's backers, many of whom wept unabashedly.

AT THE CLOSE OF THE SEASON OF 1937, in our previous volume of this series, War Admiral, three-year-old son of Man o' War and Brushup, by Sweep, bred and owned by Samuel D. Riddle, of Glen Riddle, Pennsylvania, Glen Riddle Farm, Berlin, Maryland, and Faraway Farm, Lexington, Kentucky, and trained by George Conway, was accorded the position of honor as The Horse of the Year.

War Admiral was also accorded that honor in a nationwide poll of leading turf writers and critics of racing conducted by *Turf & Sport Digest,* of Baltimore; in this poll his near relative Seabiscuit was the close runner-up. In another instance, advised by a small group of prominent horsemen, the magazine *Horse & Horseman,* of New York, selected Seabiscuit as The Horse of the Year with War Admiral second.

These circumstances in a way foreshadowed what was to come during the season of 1938—to wit, the struggle between them for the kingship of the American turf, which finally culminated in the match to decide it, run at Pimlico on November 1 and won by Seabiscuit.

As we write another nationwide poll is being taken by the *Digest* for the purpose of awarding the title of "The Horse of the Year" for 1938. Its result will not be announced in time to be chronicled in this book, but there is every reason to believe that this time the title will go to Seabiscuit, but perhaps by no wider a margin than that by which he was relegated to second place the year before.

For, despite his defeat in the match, War Admiral retains an army of admirers who refuse to allow a single race to alter their judgment,

taking the position that "one swallow does not make summer" and that nothing but a series of meetings, or at best, a return match, would enable a correct verdict.

War Admiral is the only horse in the present volume, Esposa alone excepted, that has appeared in our two previous ones as well, he having been accorded a place among the leading two-year-olds of 1936, while in 1937 he was the undefeated champion three-year-old and was also acclaimed as the best horse in training, of any age or either sex. This being the case, we will not here review his performances during those seasons, but refer the reader to the chapters devoted to him in those volumes, in which the full details, profusely illustrated, will be found. We will proceed at once to narrate his adventures during 1938, more stirring and memorable than any that hitherto had befallen him.

Of the two farms which Mr. Riddle maintains for the carrying on of his racing and breeding activities, Faraway, at Lexington, Kentucky, with Man o' War at its head, is devoted to stud purposes, under the management of Harrie B. Scott, who assumed that position several seasons before War Admiral was foaled there. Glen Riddle, at Berlin, Maryland, in the "Eastern Shore" country, is an estate chosen by Mr. Riddle because the climate is especially favorable for the wintering of his racing stable, while it is also in a famous hunting and fishing region and he is an ardent devotee of those sports.

For over twenty years past his Thoroughbreds, at the close of the season, have been returned to Glen Riddle Farm for the winter, also receiving their early preparation in the spring before returning to the races, there being a good training track and all other facilities.

It was to Maryland that War Admiral was sent as a yearling, from Kentucky, to be broken and begin his training under the watchful eye of Conway, and there he has wintered annually ever since. His stay in 1937–38, however, was comparatively short, for he did not finish his three-year-old campaign until November 3, when he won the Pimlico Special. As he was scheduled to race in the $50,000-added Widener Cup Handicap at Hialeah, on March 5, 1938, but four months away, his sojourn at the farm was of necessity abbreviated. Just before New Year he was again entrained, reaching Hialeah on December 31, where he took quarters in Barn G, to remain for the next ten weeks, preparing for and filling his engagement.

From the moment of his arrival he became the chief center of interest in the Peninsular turf scheme, the swarm of sightseers, reporters and photographers that haunted his vicinity often making it difficult for the stable to carry on normally or the colt get the rest that he required. Neither he nor anyone connected with him could, it seemed, make the slightest move without being watched, chronicled and criticized. Of course, this is the "penalty of greatness" everywhere, but it proved doubly so at the greatest winter resort on the Atlantic seaboard, with its throngs of visitors and tourists, all eager for a glimpse of the premier Thoroughbred of the country.

It had been the intention to race War Admiral at least a couple of times at Hialeah preceding the Widener, in order that he might come to it fit and ready, but this plan of campaign was cramped by the difficulty of finding any suitable opportunities. He had been named in several minor handicaps, but Mr. Riddle declined to race him in any of them because the colt was assessed the same weight for them, 130 pounds, that he was to carry in the $50,000 race. He declared that it was unfair to ask him to assume such a burden so early in the year, and for a comparatively insignificant event, and that it was impossible properly to season him under such circumstances—his position being practically the same as that of Charles S. Howard, the owner of Seabiscuit, who was experiencing similar difficulties in California at the same time in his attempts to find some preparatory races for that horse.

It was during this interval that the owner of War Admiral, whose speech is often salty, expressed to an interviewer a sentiment that immediately took its place among the imperishable epigrams of the turf. "All the handicappers know about a horse," said he crisply, "is that one end bites and the other end kicks."

It therefore so fell out that previous to the big stake, War Admiral went to the post but once at Hialeah, this being in a $1,100-purse race at seven furlongs, an allowance affair, run on February 19, not at all the kind of an outing that was desired but the only one that presented itself. It called upon him to carry 122 pounds, with the five that opposed him allotted from 110 to 116 pounds each. After displaying his rooted aversion to the stalls most decidedly, he was placed outside them, was taken away moderately, took the lead when ready and won as he pleased by a length and a half from Sir Oracle, 116 pounds, with Caballero II (110) six lengths farther back. The time was :23, :45⅗, 1:10⅕, 1:23⅘. His display of extreme speed and facile ease was convincing evidence that if nothing adverse occurred, he would strip for the Widener in fine form. His odds had been three to ten.

His work continued uninterruptedly and was of a very satisfactory sort. To gratify the public he was several times given special trials staged during the regular races of the afternoon programs at Hialeah. The last of these occurred on February 26, when he was sent a mile in 1:39⅕, with quarters in :24, :48, 1:12 and 1:25⅗. On March 1, he received his distance trial, 1¼ miles, in 2:06, which was without any special feature. On March 4, the day before the race, he was breezed a half in :50⅖ and then pronounced ready.

March 5 proved as radiant a day as Florida could be asked to provide and the attendance at Hialeah, which from that standpoint cannot and does not attempt to compete with the great centers of population, was 21,000, a capacity crowd (the grandstand seating but 5,500), that wagered over $750,000, breaking all previous records for the meeting. As there had been a shower the previous night, however, the track was not so fast as usual.

For the $50,000 race, though almost at the same hour another field of 18 of the best handicap horses in America were coming out for the $100,000 race at Santa Anita, there were 13 contenders, which, under the circumstances was all and more than could have been hoped for. So overshadowing, however, was War Admiral in class and prestige that with his top weight of 130 pounds, and none of the other dozen carrying more than 114 pounds, from which the imposts scaled down to 101½ (Bourbon King), with an average for the entire party of about 108 pounds, he was at but 3½ to 10, with nothing in the field at shorter odds than 10½ to 1 (Tatterdemalion, five years, 107 pounds).

The post parade was a brilliant spectacle, staged as it was in the picturesquely exotic setting which, owing to the artistic taste of Joseph

E. Widener, is unequaled on this continent. Post time was 4:30 and at 4:38 the horses entered the stalls. There was a delay of five minutes, during which the Admiral again refused to take his place in the No. 7 compartment assigned him, so once more he was taken outside. They were then soon on their way, the colt getting off like a skyrocket to go almost immediately to the lead and make in effect a runaway race of it, as, after rating along a length in advance to the three-quarters, Kurtsinger let loose of him and he opened up a gap of five by the time he reached the stretch. He retained this advantage until nearing home, when, seeing that nothing could get near him, he was taken up and allowed Zevson to finish an open half-length back as he galloped under the wire amid an uproarious outburst of cheering. War Minstrel was half a length behind Zevson, with Corinto fourth, a length farther back.

The reader is referred to the official chart, printed elsewhere, for full details of the manner in which the race was run by the entire field, but as a matter of fact it was a one-horse affair from start to finish, the winner "stealing the show." The time, 2:03⅘, with quarters in :23⅗, :47⅕, 1:11⅗ and 1:37, was two seconds off the record for the stake, 2:01⅘, established in 1936 by Mantagna, 109 pounds, and equaled the next year by Columbiana, a four-year-old carrying 103 pounds. It should be noted, however, that in the interim the Hialeah track had been resurfaced and considerably slowed in the process, this being done because of the criticisms that its previous great speed was due to an insufficient cushion, hard on the legs and feet of horses racing over it.

War Admiral came out of the race showing little sign of any effort and was rested up over Sunday and then on Monday shipped home to Maryland to lay up there until the resumption of his campaign in the North.

And now arose a strange situation. War Admiral was proclaimed on all sides the champion race horse. The majority opinion designated him the best seen in America since his sire, nearly twenty years before. The public was a-tiptoe with anxiety to see him perform. But it began to appear as if they might to a large extent go ungratified unless the prevailing conditions changed.

The root of the matter lay in the fact that owing to the abuse of rational racing policy, practically all valuable or important events for horses three years old and upward on the American turf today are handicaps; weight-for-age and similar stakes have been with but few exceptions eliminated from the programs of all associations, large and small, high and low. It has become handicaps or nothing, unless an owner wishes to limit himself to just four stake events, these being the Whitney, the Wilson, the Saratoga Cup, at Saratoga, and The Jockey Club Gold Cup at the Belmont Park fall meeting. Of these the first two are worth only about $3,000 to the winner, and the last two about $6,000 each.

In other words, if a horse won all four, he would not earn as much as he could by running second in a single handicap (the Santa Anita, which pays $20,000 to the placed horse). In addition, the two cups are over such long routes as to be beyond the tether of the typical handicap horse, including most of the best.

The victory of War Admiral in the $50,000 Widener Cup, coming on top of his unbeaten three-year-old career, meant that henceforth if raced in handicaps he would have to assume the most severe penalties. What this signified had been vividly illustrated a couple of seasons ago when the handicappers piled such enormous weights upon Discovery that they first subjected him to a series of unmerited defeats and then all but broke him down. Of these things Mr. Riddle was mindful. He had already voiced his objection to letting War Admiral follow the same path Discovery had been obliged to pursue, as the result would be inevitably the same.

He now declared that the colt would not be started when the weights were, in his opinion, excessive, for in addition to the other factors involved, he was a small horse, just a shade over 15½ hands tall and weighing considerably less than 1,000 pounds stripped for action. He wished to keep him sound and retire him so, nor would he recede from that position. He accordingly declared him from a number of his spring engagements in Maryland, for which he had been heavily handicapped, and stated that it was possible he might not again be seen in public until at Saratoga, in July.

But meanwhile the magnificent performance of Seabiscuit at Santa Anita, where in the $100,000 race he had been beaten a nose only by Stagehand, when carrying 130 pounds to but 100 pounds on the latter, and the time 2:01⅗, had proclaimed him a greater horse than ever. From all sides there came demands for a match between him and the Admiral for the kingship of the turf. These became so general that the owners of the two champions could not ignore them, and both, when interviewed, expressed themselves as willing for such a meeting.

Much space might be devoted to all the excursions and alarums, fanfares of publicity, of a thousand and one kinds, events and incidents which marked the course of the next six weeks, but that would not be history, it would be merely retailing what was ephemeral and unworthy of permanent record. Suffice it to say that after much preliminary firing, the Westchester Racing

War Admiral [MORNING TELEGRAPH]

Association came forward early in April with an offer of a purse of $100,000, "winner take all," for a match to be run at Belmont Park, on Memorial Day, May 30, which was accepted by Messrs. Riddle and Howard; the distance to be a mile and a quarter and the weights 126 pounds.

This was received by the general sporting public with acclamation and enthusiasm and the immediate prospect was for one of the greatest turf events ever consummated, for whose analogues it would be necessary to go back to the historic duels of a century ago between American Eclipse and Henry, Wagner and Grey Eagle, Boston and Fashion, and, in later times, the meetings of Miss Woodford and Freeland; Salvator and Tenny; Domino, Clifford and Henry of Navarre.

The advance interest indicated that on the day of the race Belmont Park would entertain the largest crowd that ever entered its gates, and that it would be representative of the entire American sporting world, gathered from all parts of the Union. Extensive preparations were made by the management to care for such an outpouring; while the event was yet weeks away the hotels in New York were filing away room reservations for the day. Everything pointed to a memorable occasion.

War Admiral took quarters at Belmont to prepare for the contest and Seabiscuit was shipped from California on April 21, arriving there on the 25th. On the 16th he had won the Bay Meadows Handicap of $15,000 added, carrying 133 pounds, in record-breaking time, indicating that he was never in better form. But he had not been long at Belmont before it was current gossip that he was not doing well. As time passed and the date of the match drew near, these rumors became public knowledge and finally it was found necessary to declare him and cancel the match, he being pronounced unfit to do himself justice.

The disappointment was extreme and nationwide. The high anticipations universally entertained had been completely blasted, all the preparations had gone for nought and what had looked like an immense success converted into a fiasco. This gave an opportunity for something that had previously made some headway but for the time being been drowned by the general enthusiasm.

From the moment the match first began to be agitated, there had been, from certain quarters, a raking fire of acrid and derogatory criticism. There was an evident effort and desire to "queer the race" in advance and prejudice the public against it. This had even gone so far that what were represented as authentic reports were published to the effect that Belmont Park would have nothing to do with the project, that such

affairs were detriments to the welfare of the turf, etc. Now, once the match had fallen through, these animadversions were brought forth and reiterated, and the Seabiscuit party, in especial, came in for scathing criticism.

War Admiral meanwhile had taken his preparation in the most satisfactory way. His work indicated that he was at the very peak of his form and that almost anything might be expected from him when asked for a supreme effort. Mr. Riddle was one of the most disappointed of men when at the eleventh hour the race had to be abandoned. He was himself at the time very unwell at his home at Glen Riddle, Pennsylvania, but in order as far as possible to provide a substitute for the match, he announced that the Admiral would be started in the Suburban Handicap, to be run on Saturday, May 28, or two days preceding the date of the match now definitely off. For this race he had been allotted 132 pounds, which was not excessive; the distance was the same set for the match, a mile and a quarter. He was as ready for it as if prepared expressly for that purpose.

The announcement that he was to start, opposing seven of the best handicap horses in training, including his old adversary Pompoon, Snark, Aneroid, etc., was received with great satisfaction by the public and one of Belmont's largest crowds assembled to witness the race. But in the night and early morning hours showers fell which left the track muddy. Mr. Riddle being confined to a sickbed at home, under his physician's care and with a high temperature, it was thought best to relieve him of all bother or anxiety. Trainer Conway suspended his final decision until nearly the last possible moment, 2 P.M., and then scratched the colt, not feeling willing to take the responsibility of racing him under the circumstances.

But, the afternoon proving bright and hot, the track dried out so well that when the Suburban was run, at 4:20, the winner, Snark, broke the race record, running in 2:01⅖, the fastest race of the year, as it proved, for the distance.

The immediate reaction was extraordinary. The announcement of the Admiral's withdrawal was received with hisses and boos. The Belmont Park management not only made a statement that it was in no way responsible for the action taken, but it was thought necessary for this to be supplemented by an elaborate manifesto issued on behalf of the New York State Racing Commission—which really did nothing but inflame the situation. Though this was by no means the first time that similar incidents had occurred in connection with famous horses and big races, the innocent bystander would have supposed it an unprecedented thing and a high crime and misdemeanor on the part of the Glen Riddle

Stable. Though Mr. Riddle was far from the scene of action and imprisoned in a sickroom, knowing nothing of what went on until it was all over, he was subjected to the most unseemly criticism, which in some instances was even venomous in its character.

According to his wont, he made no reply. Neither did Trainer Conway. Both felt that they had been very unjustly attacked but they declined to utter a syllable in apology or self-defense. They also felt that in such circumstances "actions spoke louder than words"—and in accordance therewith, War Admiral was prepared for the Queens County Handicap, to be run at Aqueduct on the following Saturday, June 6.

This stake, while of small value, comparatively speaking—net to winner $4,425—is old-established at one mile, was in its 33rd running and in the past had been won by many first-class horses, such as Roamer, Old Rosebud, Grey Lag, Zev, Mad Hatter, and others down to Snark, the winner of 1937. That horse, now trying for a double, was fresh from his Suburban victory and to him the Admiral was being asked to concede six pounds, assuming 132 to his 126. When it was known that the two cracks were to start, all other candidates but Danger Point, 112 pounds, and Rudie, 109, were scratched and it was left virtually a duel between them.

The attendance was estimated at 12,000, and when War Admiral appeared at the head of the post parade, having drawn the No. 1 stall, hisses and catcalls were heard along the quarter stretch, instead of the applause wont to greet him—so well had the propaganda against him done its work. But truly great horses, like great men, when tested, rise superior to such manifestations and such was now to be the case.

As if conscious of the responsibility resting upon him, this time the Admiral gave little trouble and broke from his stall with facility. However Kurtsinger, in view of his weight, had no intention of taking him to the front, but under strong restraint reined him in behind Rudie and let that fast colt do the pace-setting. The first quarter was run in :23, with Rudie three lengths ahead, and at the half in :46⅕ the distance had decreased only by a length. It was only by degrees that the Admiral cut it down, but at the three-quarters in 1:11⅗, he was at Rudie's haunches, while Snark was still four lengths back, waiting to make his run.

As they neared the home turn Kurtsinger loosened his rein and in a few strides had assumed the lead, while Rudie began falling back rapidly to finish last. At the same time Longden moved with Snark and, rushing up, was close behind War Admiral as they swung into the stretch. The latter was well out in the track, having come around Rudie to take the lead, while Snark had slipped through next the rail, saving considerable ground. Longden now asked him for all he had to give and he answered with a rush that for a time looked dangerous, as he gained visibly upon the Admiral and Kurtsinger was seen to be riding the favorite vigorously. He had gone back to the rail and it would be necessary for Snark to come out around to head him. Slowly Snark gained, but at the last sixteenth was still a length behind. Kurtsinger now moved the Admiral out slightly (the chart asserts that the colt swerved under pressure, but this is incorrect) and the struggle continued. Longden drew his whip and struck Snark repeatedly; Kurtsinger drew his but did not strike the Admiral, merely swishing it through the air. He kept steadily on and passed the post winner by a length. The time was 1:36⅘; record for the race, 1:36, in 1921, by John P. Grier, 4 years, 127 pounds, at which time the Aqueduct course was considered decidedly faster than it is today.

When he came back to scale War Admiral was cheered again and again, his performance having been such that it was impossible to withhold its due acknowledgment. He had given an older horse, and one of the fastest of recent times, six pounds, and a beating at his favorite distance and one considered by his own stable too short for him to show to the best advantage. The post odds were: Admiral, 11 to 20; Snark, 11 to 5.

The $50,000 Massachusetts Handicap's fourth running was to be decided at Boston on June 29. It had been won the previous season by Seabiscuit, who carried 130 pounds and ran the nine furlongs in 1:49, a new record for the course at Suffolk Downs. Both he and the Admiral were eligible for this renewal and each had been allotted 130 pounds. It was announced that Seabiscuit had come around from the off-form which caused his withdrawal from the match a month since, and that he would make an effort to execute a double in it. Mr. Riddle determined to send his colt on for the event as well, and fight out the issue that had previously gone by default of the adversary.

This, however, did not come to pass. Heavy storms, then recurrent in New England, left the track in very bad condition the morning of June 29, Mr. Howard reserved his decision as to starting Seabiscuit until the last moment permissible under the rules (45 minutes before post time), then, supported by a veterinary opinion that he was unfit to race, withdrew him. Mr. Riddle was unwilling to do anything similar with his colt, as an immense throng had gathered expecting to see the two rivals come together, but he started him against his own desires, realizing that the condition of the course and the immense concessions he was called upon to make placed the Admiral in a very bad spot.

War Admiral in typical fine form, winning the Belmont Stakes in 1938. [ACME]

This the result confirmed.

To the five that opposed him he was called upon to give from 29 to 23 pounds each; and among them was the swift three-year-old Menow, carrying but 107 pounds and known to be a good mud runner. The public, however, sent the brown colt to the post a two-to-five favorite. By a great effort he raced up to second place at the six-furlong mark, while Menow was bowling along in a romp that ended with him six lengths in front. The Admiral, a very tired colt, lost third money by a nose to War Minstrel. This left him technically unplaced for the first (and only) time in his career, though he received an award of $2,500.

As he had been in active training with but slight interruption now for six straight months, since January 1, during the next four weeks he was left untasked, being taken to Saratoga, where he was indulged for a time and then tightened up again in preparation for his engagements at the great summer meeting which began on July 25. The first of these was the Whitney Stakes, on July 27, one mile, weight for age, $3,000 added, with a valuable piece of plate to the winner. Under these conditions, only Fighting Fox, three years, 116 pounds, and Esposa, six years, 121 pounds, cared to face him, though the track was a mass of mire from recent rain; his weight was 126 pounds.

The feeling against him now again made itself conspicuous, and, encouraged by his defeat at Boston, there was much talk indulged in that Esposa was going to administer another to him. Her partisans were numerous and professed great confidence in her, to such an extent that she was sent to the post at the short odds of 11 to 5, the Admiral being three to five and the Fox's six to one. William Woodward's colt led off, but in the second quarter the Admiral moved to the front and spinning off the furlongs in a manner that made his pursuers dizzy, he won by eight lengths pulled up, in 1:39⅗, while Esposa, unable at any time to get within hailing distance, was beaten out by the Fox for the place by open daylight.

War Admiral reappeared only three days later for the 36th running of the Saratoga Handicap. He had been given 130 pounds, willingly accepted, for the added money was $7,500 and it was desired to make him the third winner of the stake by Man o' War, whose older sons Mars (1927) and Marine (1930) already figured on its honor roll. Only four were willing to line up with him, Esposa, 116 pounds, Isolater, 105½, Unfailing, 110, and Burning Star, 112. As before, the contention was advanced that Esposa was about to take his measure, as she had that of Seabiscuit the fall before in Maryland. On that occasion she was receiving 15 pounds from the Californian; now she was getting 14 from the Admiral, and her partisans predicted another sensational coup. It failed to materialize.

The two ran first and second all the way, the big mare not letting the little colt get more than an open length away from her at any stage. Coming home she set sail for him in earnest with Wall riding his hardest. The track was in bad shape from the storms then prevalent over the East and the powerful mare, at home in the going, responded resolutely to his urging. Kurtsinger had been instructed to win only by a safe margin and to take nothing unnecessary out of his mount and this he did, allowing Esposa to lap him at the finish. The official chart says that he won by a neck, but the photos show that her nose was barely past his girths, she being under the whip while he was not. The mile and a quarter, in the heavy going, was run in 2:06, with the first mile in 1:39. Net to winner $7,500. His odds were seven to ten, Esposa's six to one.

With determined persistence, then, on August 20, after a period of three weeks during which nothing had been done with the brown colt, while the iron-sided mare had been out twice, running unplaced in the Merchants' & Citizens' and winning the Champlain Handicap, she was still again set at him, this time in the weight-for-age Whitney Stakes at a mile and a quarter. As in the Wilson, Fighting Fox was the only other starter. This time the track was fast and the odds, Admiral one to three, Esposa four to one, the Fox eight to one. Man o' War's son made every post a winning one, passing the quarter in :23⅗, half in :47⅗, three-quarters in 1:12⅗, mile in 1:38 and full distance in 2:03⅘. The chart tells us that he was under strong restraint most of the way, but was placed under mild hand urging in the final eighth when Esposa, under the whip, endeavored to challenge but "could not menace" him. As Kurtsinger was laid up, the result of a terrible race-track accident, he was ridden by Wayne Wright.

Just a week later, on the closing day of the meeting, August 27, he completed his string of four consecutive victories at The Spa by his best performance there and one of the finest of his career. Its medium was the premier long-distance fixture of the American racing calendar, the Saratoga Cup, now in its 58th renewal, at a mile and three-quarters, weight for age. For the fourth time, also, it was Esposa that made what might be called a "dying effort" to estop him. Fighting Fox did not appear but instead his stable companion, the three-year-old filly Anaflame, completed the trio that went to the post. As one looks back over the previous showing she had made, it is almost inexplieable that Esposa should have been at such short odds as three to one, with the colt at one to three and Anaflame at 25 to 1. The year before she had been made favorite for the cup and run a poor third to Count Arthur and Matey. How she was going to beat the Admiral, who had just whipped her three times hand-running and was now essaying a distance all in his favor—well, it was a conundrum!

The moment the tape was sprung the colt darted to the front and measuring off the quarters with the precision and facility of a machine, rated away to the quarter in :24, half in :48⅘, three-quarters in 1:14, mile in 1:40⅕, mile and a quarter in 2:05⅕, mile and a half in 2:30⅖ (track record 2:31⅘), and finished coasting, a winner by four lengths in 2:55⅘; stake and track record, 2:55, by Reigh Count, three years, 118 pounds, in 1928; American record, 2:54⅗, by Chilhowee, three years, 126 pounds, at Latonia, Kentucky, in 1924.

It seemed certain that had he been ridden out the Admiral could have beaten both these marks. He had allowed Esposa to keep within a length and a half of him until entering the stretch, when Maurice Peters, who was now riding, Wright being unavailable and Kurtsinger still disabled, shook his whip at him and he bounded away as if the race was just beginning, was taken up in the last eighth, and finished under a pull.

So faultless an exhibition was it of all the qualities which go to constitute the race horse of the highest class that when he came prancing back to the stand, apparently unaffected by his effort, it "rose at him" and he was applauded to the echo.

Seabiscuit had been entered for the Saratoga Cup, but was in California when it was run, where he had been making a midsummer campaign, not returning east until the middle of September. Both he and the Admiral were engaged in The Jockey Club Gold Cup, to be run at Belmont Park on October 1, and for a time the idea was indulged that then their long-deferred meeting might take place. But the defeat of Seabiscuit in the Manhattan Handicap on September 20, while hardly a true bill, chilled any ardor that his stable might have held for an encounter over two miles with his younger rival and he was declared once more, leaving for Maryland where the handicaps looked more inviting.

As a consequence when, on the day appointed, War Admiral turned out for the longest stake race now run annually in America, with an endowment of $5,000 and a gold cup worth $2,500 additional for the winner, for company he had only the two three-year-olds, Magic Hour and Jolly Tar, each carrying 117 pounds and himself 124. Just a week previous Magic Hour had unexpectedly won the Realization, our longest three-year-old fixture, 1⅝ miles, and this had created the hope that, with his pull in the weights, he might offer stout resistance to the Admiral. But the layers of odds could not see it that way and he and Jolly Tar were each at 12 to 1, with the brown four-year-old at 1 to 12—perhaps the shortest odds in many seasons in such an event.

The race justified the odds. The official description reads as follows: "War Admiral moved into command at the start, was taken under snug restraint and rated along steadily. At no stage was he urged and was galloping along under restraint all through the stretch." Wright was now again riding him and his margin at the finish was three lengths over Magic Hour, with Jolly Tar ten lengths farther back. Fractional time, :25⅕, :52⅖, 1:18⅘, 1:44⅗, 2:09⅘, 2:34⅗, 2:59⅕, 3:24⅘. Thunders of applause came from the crowded stands as Conway led him into the winner's enclosure and Mr. Riddle was presented with the splendid trophy, won by War Admiral's sire when the stake was first contested in 1920, and in 1926 by that other great son of Man o' War, Crusader, thus making three of these massive gold cups grouped together in the trophy room at Glen Riddle.

This was the last race run by him previous to the Pimlico match precisely one month later, on November 1, of which a full account is presented in the piece on Seabiscuit, the victor on that great occasion. It may be said that Mr. Riddle was anxious for the match. His colt was being hailed as the king of the turf, but there remained the reservation that he had yet to defeat the Californian. That horse had persistently evaded a meeting with him; first in Maryland the previous fall; again in the match set for Memorial Day at Belmont Park; again in the $50,000 race at Boston; again in the Saratoga Cup; and still again, and for the fifth time, in The Jockey Club Gold Cup. On each of these occasions the Admiral was ready for the post and the older horse declined the combat.

As it was his intention to retire War Admiral to the stud in the spring of 1939, Mr. Riddle desired before doing so to test him against the only horse in America that was considered a fit antagonist for him on even terms. He had never deigned to reply to the sneers, the jeers, the contumely, the malicious gossip and criticism of which both horses and their owners and trainers had been made the targets ever since the springtime. But he felt and knew that the great sporting public had taken no part in the "smearing campaign," that it recognized the two horses for what they were, and would rise en masse if only given the opportunity to see them meet.

In this position he was joined by Alfred Gwynne Vanderbilt, leading spirit at Pimlico, who had not allowed himself to be misled by the adverse propaganda. He was as anxious to bring a match off as Mr. Riddle and was able to secure the agreement of Mr. Howard, with the result which is now a lasting page in our turf history.

The defeat of War Admiral by Seabiscuit was accepted by Mr. Riddle with a philosophic sportsmanship which few owners command. He offered no apologies or alibis, presented no explanation or attempt to minimize the reverse—but he did make the statement that he was ready and willing for another meeting between them. To show his good faith he sent War Admiral to

Narragansett Park and announced that he would be a certain starter for the $10,000-added Rhode Island Handicap there, to be run on November 12 and for which Seabiscuit was eligible; the distance being nine furlongs, or a half-furlong less than that of the match. The weights had not yet been announced, the conditions not calling for them until the ninth, three days before the race. Seabiscuit was then given 130 pounds and War Admiral 127; but while the management voluntarily agreed to increase the added money to $25,000 in case both horses started, Mr. Howard decided not to race the 'Biscuit and he remained in Maryland.

War Admiral had been shipped to Narragansett previous to the announcement of the weights and when race day came the opposition had narrowed down to five horses of which the two best were the veteran handicapper Mucho Gusto, now six years old but in very good form and the winner of eight races, chiefly stakes, during the season, his assignment being 115 pounds; and the four-year-old Busy K., with 112 pounds, the latter having run second, under 107 pounds, in the $50,000 handicap at Boston in June, when the Admiral ran fourth and Menow won. The others comprised Fair Stein, five years, 106 pounds, Gray Jack, five years, 108 pounds, and Palamede, seven years, 101 pounds.

The park was packed with spectators, for the Admiral had never before been seen at Providence and such was the confidence in his ability to win that he was at 1 to 20, odds that recalled those quoted against his sire when he was at the height of his career. Mucho Gusto and Palamede, coupled, were at 8½ to 1, the others at 11, 12 and 21 to 1. The Admiral drew the outer stall of the six, but refused to get off from it, was sent outside and then broke promptly. Mucho Gusto took the track, Kurtsinger keeping the Admiral back with open space between them until rounding into the back stretch, when he slightly relaxed his hold and he moved by on the outside and assumed the lead before reaching the half. Then he began leaving Mucho Gusto and, racing away, was six lengths in front at the home turn. All through the stretch he was galloping, was taken up in the last furlong, and won by 2½ lengths, Mucho Gusto beating Busy K. a length for the place, the last-named having both Fair Stein and Gray Jack lapped on him. The time was :23⅕, :47⅖, 1:11⅗, 1:37⅖, 1:51⅖; track record 1:49⅘ by Stagehand, the previous September 10.

This closed the colt's campaign and he was returned on Monday to Glen Riddle Farm, in Maryland, where he was scheduled to rusticate until about January 1, when he will, as a year ago, be sent to Hialeah, to prepare for his farewell appearance upon the turf in the renewal of the $50,000 Widener Handicap. When Mr. Widener first sponsored this stake, in 1936, he entitled it the Widener Challenge Cup and announced that a rich gold trophy would be awarded the owner of any horse taking it a second time. The Admiral having won it last March, he will try the coming one to take it back to Glen Riddle.

Under any circumstances this will be his adieu to the public as a race horse, for he is to begin stud duty at Faraway "in the Blue Grass" shortly afterward, his inaugural season's book of 20 mares for 1939 having been filled and closed almost as soon as it was opened last fall. He will stand beside his renowned sire in the new stallion barn recently built at the farm and under the management of Mr. Scott. As Man o' War is now 22 his covers will be strictly limited henceforth and War Admiral, at no distant date, will be the head of the stud so far as active service is concerned.

Should he succeed in again winning the big stake at Hialeah it will put him over the $300,000 mark, his record to January 1, 1938, reading: 25 starts, 20 wins, 3 seconds, 1 third, once unplaced (when fourth and earning $2,500) and a total of $272,140.

Whirlaway

JOHN HERVEY

Reading from l. to r., Whirlaway's races invariably found him out of the picture until the very end, and then it was invariably at the extreme right—on the winning end and having come from nowhere. He would have been as sensational a television star as Native Dancer was to be a decade later.

WHIRLAWAY, at the close of the campaign of 1942, was voted the title "Horse of the Year," in two polls of experts—race reporters, critics of form and class, handicappers and the like—his majority in each instance being decisive.

His right to the honor was well established. No other horse seen upon the turf during the year was so much a public idol. No other had so large or so demonstrative a following. No other occupied so much space or received so much attention in the press. No other, in the sum of his achievements, had risen to the same altitude. He was not without rivals, but none of them measured up to him in these attributes.

This, moreover, was the second time that he had won this high distinction. It had also been awarded him in 1941. He, therefore, equaled the feat of Challedon in the two previous seasons of 1939 and 1940, when that great performer carried the poll.

Whirlaway is a thoroughbred of many and varied achievements. He has been for three years before the public and from the early part of his first campaign, as a two-year-old, he was proclaimed a champion. His career has been extraordinary, in many respects unequaled, his achievements have been not only remarkable but of a sustained sensationalism such as has attended few famous race horses for three consecutive seasons. And he remains today sound, strong and apparently unscathed, despite his long-continued and Herculean labors.

Altogether, he may be pronounced a marvel of the course.

The best evidence of which, is the following tabular summary of his career to date, showing its progress from season to season and its grand results in their totality:

PERFORMANCES OF WHIRLAWAY

Year	Age	Races	First	Second	Third	Unpl.	Winnings
1940	2	16	7	2	4	3	$ 77,275
1941	3	20	13	5	2	0	272,386
1942	4	22	12	8	2	0	211,250
Totals		58	32	15	8	3	$560,911

When it is stated that no other Thoroughbred, American or foreign, has ever won more than $437,730—this being credited to the American Seabiscuit; that the English record is the $291,275 of Isinglass (from whom Whirlaway directly descends in tail-male); that the French record is $233,210 of Corrida; and that the Australian record is $332,250, assigned to Phar Lap; it will be seen that, as a money-winner, Whirlaway is not only in a class by himself but *is* a class by himself, being the first race horse in history to earn as much as half a million dollars.

He is likewise the first and only Thoroughbred, so far as research has revealed, that was the season's leading money-winner, first as a two-year-old, then as a three-year-old, and still again as a four-year-old (or all-aged) performer.

Quite a large number have led in two consecutive years, either as two- and three-year-olds, or three- and four-year-olds, in this country and abroad; but Whirlaway has the unique and superior distinction of having headed the handicap division in his four-year-old form, after having previously topped the roster as a juvenile and then as a classic, or Derby, colt.

While his titles to fame are many and varied, it is this above all that has earned for him the respect and the reputation that he enjoys. Today the gauge set upon almost everything mundane is money value. Before it everybody, with few exceptions, bows; by it, everything is judged. It was the avowed object for which Whirlaway strove, nothing that astute calculation, expert handling or unswerving management could suggest being omitted from his curriculum. It is his supreme merit that he rose to the ordeal in dauntless style and emerged from it triumphant.

The career of Whirlaway at two and three, together with the full particulars of his origin, ancestry, ownership, training and all connected details will be found recorded in the two previous volumes of *American Race Horses* for 1940 and 1941. To them the reader is referred if he wishes to familiarize himself with them or to refresh his memory. We will here pick up the thread where it was dropped a year ago and devote ourselves exclusively to his performances of 1942.

Before the season of 1941 had been completed, and despite his severe campaign of 20 races, the last one being that for The Jockey Club Gold Cup, at Belmont Park, in which he was beaten by a nose only by Market Wise in new American record time for two miles. Whirlaway was loaded upon the cars and started for California. His objective there was the 1942 renewal of the $100,000-added Santa Anita Handicap; which, if he won it, would place him within striking distance of Seabiscuit's money-won record of $437,-730. The expedition, however, proved abortive, as the outbreak of war with Japan soon after his arrival there caused the cancellation of the meeting under government orders, as well as all others for the year in the southern California sector. As it had been the calculation of Mr. Wright to retain his Calumet Farm Stable on the Pacific Coast throughout the entire winter and early spring, racing them there exclusively, no alternate provision had been made for such a debacle as occurred. It would therefore have been useless to return it to the East as no engagements had been secured at Hialeah, such as the $50,000 Widener would have provided for Whirlaway—and, upon the face of the returns, he might have won. So he did not retrace his steps across the continent until well along in the spring, when he reappeared at Keeneland for the April meeting, his debut for the season being made there on the 9th in the Phoenix Handicap, at six furlongs, $2,500 added.

His allotment for this event was 128 pounds (A. Craig), the other starters being the five-year-old Bay Carse (114), the four-year-old War Bugle (114) and the two three-year-olds Devil Diver (113½) and Sun Again (112), the last-named being Whirlaway's stable companion, with the pair coupled as selected winners at three to five. The result was a surprise, as Devil Diver led all the way and beat Whirlaway by a head in a rousing finish; the favorite found the distance too short for his stretch rush to prevail. The track was muddy and time slow, 1:13⅗.

On April 15, he started back in an overnight $1,500 handicap, also at six furlongs. There were eight starting, of a high grade, Whirlaway, however, at 126 pounds, conceding them from seven to 21 pounds each. He was once more coupled with Sun Again (109) and the pair were at one to two. They finished one-two with Sun Again first by a neck, though not on sufferance, as Craig rode Whirlaway out and was just unable to connect. In the stretch, he bore out considerably as he did at times in previous seasons. The time was 1:12⅕; track record, 1:10⅖. Track fast.

These efforts indicated what was already pretty well known—that Whirlaway, despite the intense speed he had exhibited in many of his races, is not a sprinter, per se. They were expected, however, to edge him up for bigger game in the near future and as such fulfilled their function.

From Keeneland he was taken to Louisville, for the Derby meeting at Churchill Downs, and there on April 25 appeared for the Clark Handicap, 1 1/16 miles, $2,500 added. Assuming 127 pounds (Eads), and against four opponents of such inferior class that he was asked to give them all much weight, he found an unexpectedly formidable antagonist in Aonbarr (115) and only in the final strides was he able to nail him and beat him a head, coming from far back in the early running. Time, 1:44⅘, first mile in 1:38; track record 1:44, flat. At post time, he had been backed down to but one to ten. Net of the stake to him, $2,150.

These affairs had been by way of preliminary to his first really serious engagement of the spring, the $20,000-added Dixie Handicap, at Pimlico, on May 6. The field that came out for it was the best thus far of the season, for with him at the top of the handicap at 128 pounds (Arcaro), there was a distinguished company to oppose him, consisting of Attention (who in their last previous meeting had defeated him in the Classic, at Arlington Park, in July of 1941), he having up 124 pounds, along with Mioland (126), Challedon (124), Best Seller (114), Impound (110), Air Master (112) and Sir Alfred (115).

Whirlaway, at 8¼ to 5 and Attention at four to one were the only ones seriously considered and when they turned into the home stretch it looked as if there was to be a repetition of the Classic, for Attention was leading Best Seller, who manifestly could not handle him, while

Whirlaway was lengths back in fifth position. It did not seem as if he could possibly get up in the distance still remaining—but he did so, amid thunderous shouts of encouragement from his backers. His rush home was tremendous, although at the end he was once more bearing out. But so irresistible was it, that he got up to beat Attention by three parts of a length, with Mioland lapped on the son of Equipoise. It was from all standpoints a grand effort, as the time, 1:57 for the $1\frac{3}{16}$ miles, was near the track mark of 1:56$\frac{3}{5}$ held by Seabiscuit, with the first mile in 1:37$\frac{4}{5}$. Net of the stake to him, $19,275, which brought him up almost even with the second-largest money-winner and former champion Sun Beau, whose credit is $376,744.

This demonstration seemed convincing, and Whirlaway was hailed with renewed enthusiasm as the best horse in training. He was then especially prepared for the Suburban, our most famous handicap, to be run at Belmont Park on May 30. Market Wise, though coming out of the race virtually broken down, in it administered to Whirlaway a still more decisive beating than he had the previous fall when they had last met in The Jockey Club Gold Cup.

It was followed by another reverse, this time in a race of quite a different description—the Carter Handicap, at Aqueduct, on June 13, in which the task was again essayed of showing that Whirlaway was (or is) a sprinter; that event, at seven furlongs, being one of the season's outstanding stakes for speed horses. The result demonstrated that while he could run very fast, he could not do so from flag-fall to finish, breathlessly, as a real sprinter must. It was Doublrab, the champion of the season over the short courses, that took the race. That real flyer beat Swing and Sway by a head, Whirlaway three parts of a length farther back, he carrying 130 pounds (Haas) and a big favorite at 23 to 10.

"Whirly" had now started six times since the season opened and been beaten four. His claim to exalted class was beginning to be questioned, for, it was argued, he had been beaten by four different horses—and that was not the kind of card that a champion should turn in. Nevertheless, his following remained faithful and when, on Monday, June 22 he was saddled for the $3,500 Celt Purse, an allowance race at Aqueduct intended for candidates in the coming Brooklyn Handicap to fledge their wings for, the distance being $1\frac{1}{8}$ miles, he was wagered upon as if all were over, being pounded down to one to three. One reason for this, of course, was the fact that for the first time since his campaign began he was carrying moderate weight, 122 pounds. Attention (117) was second choice at four to one, the other starters being Swing and Sway (113), The Rhymer (113) and Waller (113), all at long prices. Attracted by the splendid field, a crowd of 15,000 had turned out for the race.

This proved another characteristic set-to between Whirlaway and Attention, and at the finish the excitement was prodigious as the two fought for the mastery. Little Swing and Sway took the track and, setting a scorching pace, spun off the quarters as if he intended to take things over, with Attention close by, within striking distance. The favorite was not laying so far back, Woolf sending him up closer to the leaders than usual when the first half mile was covered. As they swung for home, Swing and Sway was still in front, with a scant length's advantage, but Attention, not yet asked for his best, was at his heels, with Whirlaway an open length back, and Woolf already driving him strongly. Through the stretch, the battle became thrilling. Swing and Sway hung on with tenacity and was still leading as the mile was passed in 1:37$\frac{2}{5}$, but Attention was wearing him down and shortly after headed him. Whirlaway meanwhile was being ridden by Woolf with all of that jockey's strength, and we have no stronger rider. Passing Swing and Sway, he drew up to Attention and made a furious challenge. Mrs. Corning's colt refused to yield but fought on, matching stride for stride with his adversary and keeping his head in front. They were now almost to the wire, and it looked as if Whirlaway was once more to be beaten. Under stress of their efforts, both contenders began to bear out as their riders drew their whips and asked for a supreme effort. Passing the post, it was impossible for the spectators to say who had won, or the judges, with certainty, it being necessary for the photo to decide. When developed, it showed the barest edge of Whirlaway's nostril in front of that of Attention, and amid great cheering he was announced the winner. The time, 1:49$\frac{2}{5}$, lowered, by nearly a second, the track record of 1:50, established in 1941 by Market Wise.

The result of this contest was hailed as evidence that Whirlaway had at length reached his top form and Brooklyn Handicap Day, Saturday, June 27, found him, regardless of his burden of 128 pounds, a topheavy favorite at a shade less than one to two. Attention (122) and Tola Rose (106) were coupled as second choice at $4\frac{1}{4}$ to 1, while Swing and Sway (110) and The Rhymer (112), coupled, came third at $5\frac{1}{4}$ to 1. The field was completed by Waller (111), Olympus (110) and Paperboy (105). There had been finer days for the historic handicap since its first running in 1886, as there were showers in the forenoon and prospects of more; but nevertheless the turnstiles showed a count of 22,054 in attendance. President Theodore Knapp of the Queens County Jockey Club announced that the profits of the day would be donated to the Army and Navy Relief Fund; and should they fall short of

The high spot of Whirlaway's career as a three-year-old—his ride to victory with Jockey Eddie Arcaro in the 1941 Kentucky Derby. Trainer Ben Jones holds the reins.

$100,000, that the Club would make good the deficiency.

When the gates were sprung, Swing and Sway was out like a flash and at once assumed the role that he had played the previous Monday, taking the track and showing the way. The 20-to-1 shot, Olympus, hot after him, outran Attention and took second place; Whirlaway, in characteristic style, back next to last. Like Attention a son of Equipoise, Swing and Sway is otherwise unlike him, being a small, compact colt on the dumpling order, while Attention is tall, rangy and commanding. Longden was riding him and set a steady pace, being at the quarter in :23⅘ and half in :49. At this point he had an open half length on Olympus but James, on the latter, then placed him under pressure and he raced up alongside until at the three-quarters in 1:13, he was at the leader's throatlatch. But this was a momentary effort, taking all he had, and he was shortly done and dropped back to finish last—hardly an Olympic performance. Attention then took his place and the two half brothers, again as on Monday, came into the stretch but a length apart. Paperboy was third, with an open gap showing between him and Attention. Whirlaway, beginning his run, was but a neck away, with Tola Rose fifth, on almost even terms.

When straight in the stretch, Woolf took Whirlaway out around the others and challenged. He responded with a grand rally and, passing Paperboy and Attention, tackled Swing and Sway. That colt tried bravely when the chestnut locked with him, but without avail and Blenheim's son, amid great roars of enthusiasm, went on past to win drawing away by a length and three-quarters, Swing and Sway being an open half-length before Attention, who, tiring, just saved third place from The Rhymer.

The full mile and a quarter was run in 2:02⅖, lowering the race record from the 2:03 of Isolater (119 pounds) made in 1940. The net of the stake, to which $30,000 had been added, was $23,650, making it the richest of the 54 Brooklyns that have gone into history. By this achievement, Whirlaway passed the $400,000 mark, his total reaching $404,486, and he had drawn within $33,244 of his goal, Seabiscuit's record.

As his next engagement, the following Saturday, July 4, was in the $30,000-added Butler Handicap, feature event of the Empire City summer meeting, it was the feeling that he was soon to take the honors.

But the uncertainties of racing were now due for a flaming example. Tola Rose, the 16-to-1 shot, in receipt of a year and 29 pounds from Whirlaway, galloped to victory by 2½ lengths, while a crowd of almost 35,000 looked on in stunned astonishment. The 132 pounds that had been assigned to the favorite proved too much for him to handle and it was with difficulty that he took second place from Swing and Sway by a neck. The character of his effort, however, is disclosed by the time, which lowered the track record for the distance, 1$\frac{3}{16}$ miles, from 1:57⅖ to 1:56⅘.

As one surveys the record of Whirlaway in its entirety it is discovered that, as a whole, it is a pattern of alternate victories and defeats. It does not show the long-sustained runs of success that have marked the careers of such horses as Luke Blackburn, Hindoo, Hanover, Man o' War and other champions of the past, but depicts him as, for the most part, pursuing a seesaw course, now up and now down, now in eclipse and now with a golden halo. Not of the all-conquering class, save in the amount of money that he has collected, he has won this by continuous comebacks to the winner's circle after being rudely thrust outside it, now taking fortune's buffets and now her rewards.

In most dramatic fashion, he was soon to pass from the former to the latter in the attainment of his quest, Seabiscuit's crown. Had he won the Butler, it would not have put him "over the top." But the last obstacle was to be cleared with his next stride upward.

The Butler was run on July 4. On July 15 came the seventh renewal of the $50,000-added Massachusetts Handicap at Boston, which, after the cancellation of the $100,000 Santa Anita Handicap, shared with the Widener the rank of richest all-aged event of 1942. It had been instrumental in Seabiscuit's taking of his title, for he had won it in 1937, the first season that saw it enriched with a $50,000 endowment; that wonderful little horse taking up 130 pounds to accomplish the feat in record-breaking time. In 1940, under the same burden, Challedon, endeavoring to pass him, had been beaten into third place by Eight Thirty and Hash. Now Whirlaway had received and accepted the same impost—top weight being conditioned at 130 pounds—and was to face a field that apparently was at his mercy. Attention (122) and Swing and Sway (113) were present, but both were beginning to show the wear and tear of their extreme but ineffectual efforts in the races just described. Of the six fielders, the one that was expected to make the most trouble was Belair's swift three-year-old, Apache, for he was in at but 107 pounds. So his odds were 3¼ to 1, Attention's 6¾ to 1, Swing and Sway's 9¾ to 1. But the sharps inclined to the opinion that if Whirlaway found trouble, it would come from the Irish-bred three-year-old, Rounders, in at 108 and known to be in high form. He was, however, at 8½ to 1, showing how little expectation was really indulged about him. As for Whirlaway, even money ruled.

With a fine day and fast track, a crowd officially in excess of 30,000 was in attendance. Massachusetts was represented by Governor Saltonstall, the stands and clubhouse were thronged with people of distinction. Of all those one might have expected to be present, only owner Warren Wright was not to be seen—he being detained in the West, hence missing what should have been one of the proudest moments of his career as a turfman.

The Massachusetts, seventh on the long nine-race program, was set for 4:45 Eastern War Time, and as he appeared upon the quarter stretch in the post parade, Whirlaway was greeted with prolonged applause. It was the critical opinion that he had never looked better and, as the sequel showed, he never was better unless it was upon that memorable Kentucky Derby Day when he had run the mile and a quarter in 2:01⅖ with its dazzling last quarter in flat :24. His work since the Butler had been such as to indicate that Trainer Ben Jones felt no necessity of keying him up any more tightly than he already was. He had rested after his defeat until Sunday, July 12, when he had been breezed five furlongs in 1:01⅗, then on Tuesday had been sent six furlongs in 1:13⅗, with the first five in :59⅘, after which he was eased off.

The line-up in the stalls was as follows: Transfigure, 1; Swing and Sway, 2; Rounders, 3; Blueberry Pie, 4; Attention, 5; Apache, 6; Whirlaway, 7. When released, Rounders and Apache, the two three-year-olds, went at once to the front, the pace being furious, and at the quarter the Irish colt led the son of Alcazar by a neck only in :23⅗. Stout then called upon Apache and he sped past, taking the lead and reaching the half in :46⅗ with daylight in his favor. Keeping on to the three-quarters he passed that point in 1:11⅖, but by that time was beginning to grow leg-weary. Rounders had drawn nearer to him, with Attention on almost even terms, Whirlaway 2½ lengths farther back, but coming fast.

They were now well around the upper turn and Apache was struggling vainly to hold his lead, then surrendered it and as they made the swing Attention, passing both him and Rounders (and bumping the latter as he did so), showed momentarily in front. But Woolf now came rushing up with Whirlaway and in a few strides more went to the lead, a great roar going up from the crowd as his scarlet-hooded head was seen in front. The mile was completed in 1:36 flat, equaling the track record for that distance—and the race, so far as first money was concerned, was over. Woolf, nevertheless, was taking no chances, but continued to ride Whirlaway the rest of the way to the wire, under which he darted winner by 2¼ lengths. Rounders, recovering from his bumping and coming strongly, outfinished Attention for the $10,000 second money by a length; Attention, in turn, being four the better of the weary Apache. The complete time, as was fitting, lowered the track record from 1:48⅗, made by War Relic (102) in 1941, to 1:48⅕.

Trainer Ben Jones, standing at the head of the colt that he had conditioned and managed with such skill and success, converting him from a moody, fractious, unreliable youngster with various bad habits into a phenomenal racing tool with the ransoms of several kings to his credit, received from Governor Saltonstall the gold trophy provided for the winner amid salvos of applause that continued until the colt was led away. The $43,850 which the stake netted him had raised his winnings to $454,336. He had at last deprived Seabiscuit of his hard-earned laurels with $16,606 to spare.

Seabiscuit was retired to the stud immediately following the epochal triumph at Santa Anita that placed him upon his pedestal. What now for Whirlaway? Something very different indeed. Almost in the same paragraph in which his success was recorded the sports writers were asking him to "go on up" and make himself the first $500,000 winner in history—for the moment only had he done enough. And when Ben Jones was interviewed, he agreed with them. "Whirlaway will not be done for a long while. He's the soundest horse in training, he's looking for horses, and $500,000 will be easy for him. We start next in the big handicap at Arlington Park, two weeks from now, and that'll put him within easy reach of a half-million. He's only four years old. No reason why he shouldn't race on for seasons yet. Who knows? He may make it a million before he's done!" And the interested reporters hastened to so inform the awe-struck public. . . . Yes, times have changed! It seems only yesterday to many since Man o' War made himself the first American Thoroughbred to win as much as $200,000. How wonderful it was! What superlatives were exhausted over him. . . . And now Whirly is knocking at the $500,000 door and they are talking of the million-dollar one opening before him!

But—those unguessabilities that make horse racing! August 1 is the date of the $25,000-added Arlington Handicap. It is a poor day for such a race, dismal, wet and dreary, with the track the proverbial sea of mud. But the king of money-winners has drawn an immense throng of Chicagoans to Arlington Park and, in anticipation of another such performance as he had given at Boston, they send him to the post at three to ten, for only four horses are willing to oppose them and none seems to have the ghost of a chance. One of them is Rounders, the colt that hails from the Emerald Isle by way of Texas and, as a three-year-old, he gets in at 103 pounds. When he goes right to the front and, opening up a long lead, begins scooting through the slush as if he loved it, there is no great surprise. Whirlaway, with Eddie Arcaro aboard, is keeping closer to the pace than usual and when he gets ready it will be easy for him to come through. But his 130 pounds, the mud and the class of the Celtic three-year-old prove too tough a proposition to handle. He is beaten 3½ lengths at the wire, and finishes staggering. The spectators sit as if stunned. . . . It is another misstep in the zigzag of his dizzy climb to the heights.

There is to be another $25,000 handicap raced at Chicago soon, at Washington Park, and it is announced that Whirlaway will be back then to retrieve his fortunes, but meanwhile he is returning east to Saratoga. Chicago, however, has seen the last of him for 1942, it transpires. The plans are changed and after resting until August 29, he appears at the new Garden State Park, where racing has been revived in New Jersey after a hiatus of half a century, and a $10,000-added handicap offers him some very easy money. He has only three victims to dispatch, and does so in short order, with nine furlongs in 1:50⅘, under 130 pounds (Eads); Rosetown (111), Aonbarr (117) and In Question (110), filing along behind him. With $8,500 added to his exchequer and not a hair turned, he is now well past the $460,000 mark.

It is two weeks more to the $25,000 Narragansett Special. A year before, War Relic there handed Whirlaway a most unexpected beating. This year—well, it looks as if he just can't lose. That is, unless Alsab is brought on from Chicago to battle him, in which event—well, there might be doings. Alsab is brought on, but come race day, after a great crowd has gathered to see the two heroes contend, he is scratched; and, surely enough, Whirly couldn't lose. Rounders, with 112 pounds this time, cannot get near him. As he sweeps under the wire after a brilliant mile and ³⁄₁₆ in 1:56⅖, first mile in 1:36⅗, he has two lengths on Boysy and there was never a time after he started his run that he was in a particle of danger. There is a net to him of $24,300, which brings his total up to $491,136. And that half-million mark? . . . Come, come! Let us talk now of millions!

But all is not serene in the Narragansett atmosphere. Management and public alike are dissatisfied at their supposed great attraction's having missed fire. The upshot is an offer of $25,000 for a "Championship Match Race" the next Saturday between the two rivals. Both accept—and the result surpasses all anticipations. The odds say that Whirlaway (126 pounds; Woolf) should leave Alsab (119 pounds; Bierman) down the course, they being three to ten and eight to five respectively. It is weight for age

and Whirly's customary 130 pounds has been discounted. Actually, Alsab leads all the way and wins by a nose with the time exactly that of the Special on the previous Saturday; 1:56⅖.

It is another zigzag to the left and that half-million must for the moment rate on the deferred-payment plan. But it should materialize the coming Saturday, when the champion money-winner is due at Belmont Park for the $10,000-added Manhattan Handicap, at 1½ miles, and a field that looks like feeble opposition, although his impost is to be 132 pounds. The odds say 3½ to 5 Whirlaway; but the finish sees him a couple of lengths behind the five-year-old Bolingbroke (still another of those sons of Equipoise that have infested his pathway) whose impost is 115 pounds and who covers the route in the new American record time of 2:27⅖. But let us add: Whirlaway was great in defeat—perhaps never greater.

Another week goes by and brings the annual Jockey Club Gold Cup, the renewal of the famous distance event in which a year before he had run his never-to-be-forgotten duel with Market Wise, beaten a nose in new-record two-mile time. This year there is another lion in his path—for Alsab will face him again. Bolingbroke will be there, and The Rhymer will make up a quartet. It is another weight-for-age event, and as before that calls for a seven-pound concession from him to Alsab, the latter carrying 117 pounds, the three older horses 124 pounds each. The odds posted upon the gigantic bulletin board in the Belmont Park infield nevertheless read: Whirlaway 5½ to 10; Alsab 2¾ to 1—the others not seriously regarded. How can that be after the race at Narragansett Park? Well, it's this way. In the first place—says the public, also the talent— we love Whirlaway. In the second place, that race at Narragansett wasn't a true one—our money says so right now. In the third place, we know that Whirly can go two miles in record time—he did it here last season. And we don't know that about Alsab. In fact, we have our doubts if he can get that far in winning style. He's got to show us before we will believe it. And, last, he was out here only last Tuesday and raced a mile and five furlongs in the Realization. There isn't any colt living that could do that and come right back today to beat Whirly at two miles.

Part of this may be questionable logic—but the closing clause is straight horse sense. Moreover, Alsab is not sagaciously ridden. He goes right out on the pace at the word, races The Rhymer to a standstill; then takes the lead, holds it until the last furlong but then, when Whirlaway, under punishment, comes at him, cannot hold his advantage and is beaten three parts of a length. It is not a record-breaking two miles, but it is a splendid one, run in 3:21⅗, which is faster

Whirlaway, ridden by Jockey G. Woolf, wins the Jockey Club Gold Cup at Belmont Park, November 3, 1942. Alsab, with C. Bierman up, is second. [UPI]

than the former mark of Exterminator that stood for twenty-one years until Whirlaway made Market Wise erase it.

Mr. Wright is ill in a hospital and cannot be there to see his colt revenge himself upon his whilom conqueror, and Ben Jones for him accepts the coveted and magnificent trophy which means so much to all true sportsmen. Moreover, first money, $18,350 (the endowment of the stake has been raised this year to $25,000) has put Whirlaway far over that $500,000 mark. He

has now zigzagged up to $511,486. But last year, whereas he had been retired directly after this same stake, no such intention is now entertained. The interviewers again seek Ben Jones and in his smiling, genial way he tells them: "Retire Whirlaway? Perhaps, after two or three more seasons—not before. That's the soundest colt alive. If he was mine he'd be racing when he was ten years old! There's a lot more money laying around for him to pick up yet this fall. And he's going to get it!"

The biggest piece of this money will be for contest the next Saturday at Belmont Park—the $25,000-added New York Handicap at 2 miles and a quarter. If Whirlaway is tireless, so is Alsab, and the pair make two of the field of 12 with Whirly (130: Westrope)at even money and Alsab (121: Bierman) at 4¼ to 1. The story of the race will be found in our piece on Alsab, who made it two out of three, turning into the stretch on almost even terms with his rival and racing him into submission in the final furlong, after which he stalled off the lightweight Obash to win in 3:47⅕, almost record time. Whirlaway comes third by open daylight. Another defeat— but another splendid effort.

The charts show that subsequent to this event Whirlaway was called upon to race five times more before it was called a year. These starts, however, were strictly for the purpose of swelling his cash winnings and not calls along the path of glory, and he was withheld from the special Victory Week at Belmont Park where the public was hoping to see him and Alsab meet once more; neither was he seen at the Empire City late fall meeting. His itinerary was therefore as follows:

At Laurel, on October 24, he won the Washington Handicap, $15,000 added, from a field of eight others, carrying 130 pounds (Woolf) 1¼ miles in 2:03⅖; Thumbs Up (110) and Riverland (118) second and third, with Equifox, Tola Rose, Aonbarr, Vagrancy, Equinox and Pictor making up the party. He was driving at the finish to win by half a length. His odds, 3½ to 5.

On October 28, he had a walk-over for the Pimlico Special, $10,000 and gold cup, winner take all, 1³⁄₁₆ miles. Ridden by Woolf at 126 pounds he cantered over the course in 2:05⅗.

On November 3 at Pimlico, he was beaten 2½ lengths by Riverland (115 pounds) in the Riggs Handicap, $10,000 added. Woolf rode him at 130 pounds; he was at 4½ to 10 in the betting and was never dangerous.

On November 11, at Pimlico, he won the Governor Bowie Handicap, $10,000 added, 1⅝ miles, carrying 129 pounds (Eads) and winning as he pleased by three lengths from Dark Discovery (106), Equifox (109½) and Skirmish (104). Time, 2:48⅕, track record 2:45⅕; track slow.·

On December 12, he won the Louisiana Handicap, $15,000 added, nine furlongs, at the Fair Grounds, New Orleans, an event arranged expressly for him, he carrying 130 pounds (Eads) and beating Heartman (120), Riverland (124), Corydon (120), Marriage (118) and three others in a drive but without trouble by 1½ lengths. Time, 1:53; track record, 1:50⅕; track slow. Net to him, $12,450.

Nothing further being in sight he was taken thence to Hialeah to prepare for the winter meeting there, with the possibility of a special being arranged for him at Tropical Park in advance of it; but the cancellation of the Florida season, due to the restriction of motor traffic, left him with nothing to remain for and he was returned to New Orleans; where he concluded wintering but did not appear again. Mr. Wright is said to be thinking of retiring him to the stud at the close of the season of 1943, or even before then should circumstances point that way. Ben Jones opposes the idea and hopes to be still campaigning him for years to come.

Of the 32 races won by Whirlaway, 24 have been stake events, the record number for an American Thoroughbred being 34 by Exterminator, while Kingston won 33 and Seabiscuit 27. The great difference in their earnings is explained by the similar differences in the stake values concerned. Moreover, Exterminator started 100 times, Kingston 138 and Seabiscuit 89, whereas thus far Whirlaway has but 58. On page 327 is the table of such races won by him.

The total amount tabulated there is $496,585; leaving $64,326, the remainder of Whirlaway's winnings, to come from place-moneys in stakes and other earnings in purse races. As a matter of record, only $12,575 of his entire credit of $560,911 has been won in purse events, all the rest ($548,336) representing stake money. In addition, he has received well toward twenty gold and silver trophies, whose value may reach $50,000, likewise breeder's and nominator's awards of above $5,000.

Whirlaway remained much the same colt through his four-year-old form as in his three-year-old. He had grown but little in height and thickened but little in bulk. His action remained the same—he still ran with the same low head, the same quick, nervous and not-too-well-regulated stroke forward and the same pistonlike, powerful and perfect rear propulsion, he still loitered by the way through the early furlongs and then came home like an express behind schedule, he still showed an inclination to bear out in the stretch, but along with it a determination to struggle to the bitter end that was heroic, the same consistency, the same iron constitution, the same legs of steel and heart of oak.

STAKE EVENTS WON BY WHIRLAWAY

1940—Two Years

Date	Track	Event	Dist.	Time	Wgt.	Value
Aug. 10	Saratoga	Saratoga Special	¾ m.	1:11 *1*	122	$9,750
Aug. 31	Saratoga	Hopeful	6½ f.	1:18	122	37,850
Oct. 19	Keeneland	Breeders' Futurity	¾ m.	1:11 *1*	122	7,835
Nov. 14	Pimlico	Walden	1¹⁄₁₆ m.	1:52 *1*	122	8,140

1941—Three Years

May 3	Louisville	Kentucky Derby	1¼ m.	2:01 *2*	126	61,275
May 10	Pimlico	Preakness	1³⁄₁₆ m.	1:58 *4*	126	49,365
June 7	Belmont Park	Belmont	1½ m.	2:31	126	39,770
June 21	Aqueduct	Dwyer	1¼ m.	2:03 *2*	126	8,075
Aug. 6	Saratoga	Saranac Handicap	1 m.	1:38	130	3,800
Aug. 16	Saratoga	Travers	1¼ m.	2:05 *4*	130	16,900
Aug. 23	Washington Park	American Derby	1¼ m.	2:04	126	44,975
Sept. 20	Belmont Park	Realization	1⅝ m.	2:44 *1*	126	23,050

1942—Four Years

April 25	Louisville	Clark Handicap	1¹⁄₁₆ m.	1:44 *4*	127	2,150
May 6	Pimlico	Dixie Handicap	1³⁄₁₆ m.	1:57	128	19,275
June 27	Aqueduct	Brooklyn Handicap	1¼ m.	2:02 *2*	128	23,650
July 15	Boston	Mass. Handicap	1⅛ m.	1:48 *1*	130	43,850
Aug. 29	Garden State	Trenton Handicap	1⅛ m.	1:50 *4*	130	8,500
Sept. 12	Narragansett	Narrgst. Special	1³⁄₁₆ m.	1:56 *2*	130	24,300
Oct. 3	Belmont Park	J. C. Gold Cup	2 m.	3:21 *3*	124	18,350
Oct. 24	Laurel	Washington Hdcp.	1¼ m.	2:03 *2*	130	14,350
Oct. 28	Pimlico	Pimlico Special	1³⁄₁₆ m.	2:05 *2*	126	10,000
Nov. 11	Pimlico	Gov. Bowie Hdcp.	1⅝ m.	2:48 *1*	129	8,625
Dec. 12	New Orleans	Louisiana Hdcp.	1⅛ m.	1:53	130	12,450

He Lies Where He Longed to Be

TOM WHITE

It is merely coincidental that in this horse story no mention of any particular horse is made. It's a nice story—in fact it won a Thoroughbred Racing Association prize—but the fact of the matter is that in first following it up Tom White, an otherwise erudite journalist, found an excuse to visit Pimlico. As an old intimate of Mr. White, I really believe he finds more stories than winners at the race track.

THEY buried him by the light of the moon and a flashlight in the Pimlico infield nine years ago and if ever a man found happiness in his final resting place it was Dillon Grey.

Tomorrow, on Old Hilltop's day of days, the infield will be opened to the public and anyone who takes a close look will see the slight rise in the turf at the base of the flagpole that marks the urn's location.

There are so many, many things that make Pimlico unique; so many bits and shreds of lore and tradition thereabouts that the sentimentalist is hard pressed to concentrate on the serious business of handicapping horses.

But for my money the little-known and seldom told story of "Dill" Grey deserves a special place in the memories of the track.

Only two persons were present for the interment that May night in 1949—"Dill's" daughter, Mrs. Mary Daniels of Columbus, Ohio, and an unidentified friend.

They showed up at Pimlico around 10 o'clock one night, carrying a shovel, a flashlight and the urn, asking permission to bury a horseman's ashes in the infield.

It was typical of Jack Needles, then secretary of the Maryland Jockey Club, that he granted permission forthwith, with no questions asked.

Next morning, however, Pimlico's publicity team of Dave Woods and Alice Doughton started asking plenty of questions—whose ashes were they, who was the woman and what was the story behind the strange burial?

Memory has been dimmed somewhat by the years, but in general this is the tale they unfolded:

"Dill" Grey was a horse trainer. He was a quiet, kindly man, immensely popular, but there was a sadness in his life.

"Dill" couldn't seem to make the big time. He was a half-mile trainer, spending his life around the smaller tracks and yearning for the day when he'd get to the winner's circle at the mile ovals.

The day never came and as "Dill" grew older he began to think that if he couldn't make Pimlico in life he would want nothing more than to be there in death. And so he imparted this wish to his daughter and to his many friends in the racing game.

In April of 1949, at the age of 55, "Dill" died of a heart attack while training at Charles Town, a half-mile track in West Virginia.

Remembering his request, his fellow horsemen went to the local funeral parlor and asked for his ashes, so they could be brought to Baltimore. To their consternation they learned that "Dill's" widow had wired that the urn should be shipped to Columbus for burial.

That seemed to be that and notices were duly published in the newspaper and "Dill' was headed for Ohio soil.

But it was then that the daughter, Mrs. Daniels, stepped into the picture. Her love for her father, her respect for his wish, were all she needed to persuade Mrs. Grey that "Dill" belonged at Pimlico.

That is how Dillon Grey finally found his way to the track he loved above all others.

There is no monument at the grave. Mrs. Daniels said there really was no need for one—that her father is still at the races in Maryland and that is all he wanted.

Any lines that could have been written for "Dill" Grey were penned long ago by Robert Louis Stevenson in his poem, "Requiem":

> This be the verse you grave for me—
> Here he lies where he longed to be.

[UPI]

Chinaman's Chance

DAVID F. WOODS

Well, nobody else ever asked me *permission to reprint it!*

Iᴛ's a dirty shame, bartender. And you wanna know why it's a dirty shame? Give me a shot and a beer chaser and I'll tell ya. Don't go away, 'cause you gotta hear the whole story and, anyway, nobody's comin' in this hot-box bar on a day like this.

Phew, I needed that!

The trouble is, they all look alike and they all sound alike.

Who? The Chinese, of course. And would ya mind fillin' it up again?

Well, I been takin' my laundry to Wing Lo's over on Second Avenue and I been noticin' for a long time how there's always a scratch sheet lyin' around.

I don't never pay much attention, though. When I'm workin', Saturdays is the only time I can get out to the track. Then I get laid off about three weeks ago and I got about a hundred bucks to last me until they put my old shift on again.

Like I say, I take my laundry in this mornin' to this Wing Lo's and there is one of them Chinamen readin' a scratch sheet. It comes to me all of a sudden that the Chinese is lucky gamblers and maybe I can do somethin' with the thirty-five bucks I got left between me and a relief check.

This guy in the laundry and me, we never had any conversation. I always just give him my dirty clothes and he hands me a slip, which I never know what it says, and when I come back he just points to a slip on the clean laundry where it says how much I owe him. I always figgered he couldn't speak nothin' but Chinese.

When I get back to my room I get to thinkin' about rabbit feet and rubbin' a hunchback and all them other good-luck things and, suddenly, I figger I never tried followin' a Chinaman. This guy at Wing Lo's must be goin' to Jamaica today because he was checkin' the entries. I change into a clean shirt and hurry back to the laundry so's I can follow him to the track and see what he plays.

Ya better fill 'em up again. Mmm. It sorta helps after what I went through.

Well, we got to the track and it ain't much trouble followin' him. He just walks along, this Chinaman, and I don't know if it's Wing Lo hisself or not 'cause I can't tell 'em apart. He don't seem to hear or see anythin' that's goin' on around him. I figger I'll just follow him for a few races, not makin' any bets but see how he does; if he's winnin'.

He don't play the daily double and that sort of surprises me 'cause I figger a Chinaman likes a bargain and if he's got 'em figgered out in a Chinese system he oughta follow it. He goes out to the paddock and just stands there lookin' at the horses for the first race. He moves along and studies each horse like he was gonna buy them.

When the horses go out on the track he looks at his program and then heads for the ten-dollar window. He shows the program to the guy and points to a number and the guy takes his dough and gives him a ticket.

I don't see what he's got but I follow him outside and soon the horses are runnin' and this Chinaman don't do nothin' at all. He just stares at the result board in the infield and when the race is over and the numbers go up he goes back under the stand and gets in line where they cash ten-dollar tickets.

I look at my program and see that the horse that wins is the favorite and pays a little better than even money. The Chinaman should get back twenty-two bucks.

Six to five ain't my kinda odds when all I got is thirty-five bucks, less what I shelled out for a round-trip ticket and to get in the track. I figger I'll stick with the Chinaman and see if he don't come up with somethin' at a price.

The second-race horses is in the paddock and the Chinaman goes out and examines each one like he was gonna buy them, too. Then he checks his program and goes to the ten-dollar window again, points to a number and gives the guy two ten-dollar bills and gets his tickets.

I stay on his heels to the front of the grandstand where he just stands and watches that board in the infield. The horses are runnin' and it's a real close finish but he never pays no attention until the winnin' number goes up and then turns around and heads for the ten-dollar cashier.

By this time I'm gettin' a little nervous because this winner pays off at eight to one and the Chinaman is now a hundred and seventy bucks ahead, and he don't even play the double. And I look up and see the double pays off at two hundred and sixty bucks for a deuce.

In the third race I keep followin' him and he goes through the whole same thing; to the paddock where he acts like he's gonna buy a horse, all of them; then to the fifty-dollar window where he points to a number on his program, gives the guy three fifties, gets his tickets and goes outside in front to watch the board while the horses is runnin'. The numbers go up and, so help me, if that laundry guy didn't do anythin' but turn around and head for the fifty-dollar cashier!

That horse paid nine to two and the Chinaman is gettin' himself a fat bankroll. I figger he's close to five hundred dollars winner, and I ain't made a bet yet and I'm gettin' more nervous.

It sorta comes to me that this guy can't keep pickin' winners all afternoon and, maybe, I already lost my chance. I get shaky and don't know what to do except I ain't gonna let him outta my sight.

The fourth race is one of them filly events and he don't even go to the paddock; just walks around lookin' like he was visitin' the zoo or somethin'. I figger his system don't include horses that are dames and I feel better 'cause I never did like 'em myself, and even a Chinaman with this guy's luck couldn't get me to put my roll on one of 'em.

Then the fifth race is comin' up and he goes out to the paddock and I'm tryin' to make up my mind what I'm gonna do when he goes to make a bet. If he goes to the fifty- or hundred-dollar window I'm gonna have trouble findin' out what he's bettin' on.

Anyway, he goes through all that stuff of actin' like he's gonna buy each horse in the race. Then he heads for the hundred-dollar window, points to a number on his program and gives the guy four hundred dollars, gets his tickets and goes out front.

I just stand there a couple minutes figgerin' how I'm gonna find out what horse the Chinaman bets on. The horses is nearin' the startin' place and I decide I'll just ask the guy at the hundred-dollar window what that Chinaman bet on. So I go up to the window and I asks the guy and he just looks at me and says: "What Chinaman?" And the bell rings and the horses is runnin' and I run, too, to find the Chinaman and see what happens.

It's a dirty shame, bartender. Fill 'em up again, will ya?

He watches the board and when the numbers go up he just turns around and heads straight for the hundred-dollar cashier! The winner pays off at three to one and my Chinaman's got more dough in one afternoon 'n he can make runnin' a string of laundries. He's got at least twelve hundred bucks!

By this time I'm beginnin' to get the jitters and my shirt is wet and the starch the Chinee laundry puts in my collars makes it wrinkle and I feel like I'm gonna lose my lunch, only I ain't had anythin' to eat since coffee at breakfast.

I follow him out to the paddock and the sixth race is the big one, with all the best horses, and the crowd is thicker, with owners and trainers talkin' with friends just out to see the big race. Those people is just sentimental players.

But the Chinaman acts just the same with these horses like he did with them others; like he was gonna buy 'em from the way he went close as he could to each.

Right now I'm gettin' desperate. I gotta find out what horse he's gonna bet on and I gotta get my own bet down. But I can't go to any window bigger than ten bucks and that would be too far from where the Chinaman's gonna bet 'cause it's a cinch he's gonna go to the hundred-dollar window again.

Before I know it, I'm walkin' right alongside of the Chinaman and I puts my hand on his arm and he stops, and turns around and looks at me, and smiles. I say, when I see he recognizes me, "What do you like in this race?" He points to his program and puts his finger on number six horse. "Thanks," I tell him and I move away to the ten-dollar window.

I look up at the odds board and see Number Six horse is ten to one, which I figger will give me a profit of about ninety bucks for the day.

I get reckless and buy two ten-dollar tickets on Number Six. As I pass the hundred-dollar window I see the Chinaman handin' over a stack of bills. But this time I'm gonna watch the race, and not the Chinaman. So, I don't follow him.

The horses is in the gate and they start at once. I follow my Number Six and he seems to be runnin' good. They come into the stretch and he is neck 'n' neck with another. They come down to the finish line and, suddenly, my horse looks like he run out of breath and the other horse wins by a length.

If you don't mind, bartender, I gotta have another. And this is the part ya gotta hear, 'cause it's a dirty shame.

I get back to town feelin' terrible. But I go over to Wing Lo's laundry 'cause I gotta find out what did that Chinaman think about losin' all that dough. When I get there one of them is just closin' the joint; I never know which one 'cause I can't tell them Chinamen one from another. This one looks like the guy I followed at the track, so I go up to him and ask how he made out at the races.

He looks at me sorta funny, for a couple seconds, and says, "Oh, you mean my brother, Lee!" I'm a little surprised 'cause his English is so good. Anyway, I say I saw his brother at the track and thought he was makin' a lot of money but then lost it all back.

Then this Chinaman, I guess it was Wing Lo, starts to laugh. Then he asks me did I bet on his brother's horses; the one Lee Lo bet on. I says no, except in the sixth race and that was the only one got beat.

Wing Lo starts to laugh again, and then says, "My brother just left a few minutes ago. He said he was goin' over to take a course at night school."

Then I say, "What's that got to do with anything?" and start to turn away when he calls me back and says, "My brother is goin' to take a course in Spanish."

When I started to say again what's that got to do with anythin', this Chinaman says, "My brother Lee Lo is an expert lip-reader.

"He goes to the track a lot and has good luck 'cause he gets close to the trainers, jockeys and owners in the paddock and can read their lips what they're sayin' and figgers from that what horses to bet on."

I says to Wing Lo, "That's fine, but what the hell happened to your brother in the sixth race today?"

Then he just smiles at me and says. "That's what my brother Lee is goin' to study Spanish for. The trainer and jockey of the horse which win the sixth race today are from Argentina and my brother couldn't read what they were sayin' with their lips."

A dirty shame, bartender. Guess there's enough left outta my last sawbuck for another shot and chaser. Now, ain't it a dirty shame?

Appendix

WANNA MAKE BOOK?

FROM *The American Racing Manual*

"The price is right" is not a television program; it's the hour of decision for the horse player. The following is the formula for "making a book"—the basis for making up the morning line. A "book" must add up to approximately 100, using the totals of percentages and adding to that figure the percentage of pari-mutuel take-out by the track and state. A 113 book is about average for American racing, although in some areas the take-out is as high as 16 per cent.

BETTING PERCENTAGE TABLE

Odds	Pct.	Odds	Pct.	Odds	Pct.	Odds	Pct.
1–1	50.00	19–1	5.00	12–5	29.41	45–100	68.97
2–1	33.33	20–1	4.76	13–5	27.78	11–20	64.52
2½–1	28.57	25–1	3.85	14–5	26.31	55–100	
5–2		30–1	3.23	16–5	23.81	13–20	60.60
3–1	25.00	40–1	2.44	17–5	22.72	65–100	
3½–1	22.23	50–1	1.96	18–5	21.73	15–20	57.14
7–2		60–1	1.64	19–5	20.83	75–100	
4–1	20.00	75–1	1.32	21–5	19.23	17–20	54.06
4½–1	18.19	80–1	1.24	22–5	18.53	85–100	
9–2		100–1	.99	1–10	90.91	19–20	51.28
5–1	16.67	150–1	.66	3–10	76.92	95–100	
5½–1	15.39	200–1	.50	7–10	58.84	2–3	60.00
11–2		250–1	.38	9–10	52.63	2–7	77.80
6–1	14.29	300–1	.33	11–10	47.62	2–9	81.90
7–1	12.50	500–1	.20	13–10	43.47	3–4	57.14
8–1	11.11	1–5	83.33	15–10	40.00	8–15	65.20
9–1	10.00	2–5	71.42	3–2		17–15	46.95
10–1	9.09	3–5	62.50	17–10	37.04	1–2	66.67
11–1	8.33	4–5	55.55	19–10	34.47	1–3	75.00
12–1	7.69	6–5	45.45	1–20	95.20	1–4	80.00
13–1	7.14	7–5	41.67	3–20	86.95	1–6	85.68
14–1	6.66	8–5	38.46	15–100		1–7	87.50
15–1	6.25	9–5	35.71	7–20	74.07	1–8	88.89
16–1	5.88	11–5	31.25	35–100		1–9	90.00
17–1	5.55			9–20	68.97	1–10	90.91
18–1	5.26						

WHITHER THE WITHERS?

FROM *The American Racing Manual*

The people of racing are prone to talk a lingo of their own. Much of it is just plain race-trackese; and much of it is the free use of technical terms. The race horse, the Thoroughbred in particular, is a delicate albeit a powerful animal. Even a Cadillac can take only so much rough treatment before slowing down. Imagine the pounding the race horse takes, the shocks it absorbs, running at full speed for a mile. The accompanying diagram and text may prove enlightening and helpful in reading these pages and going racing.

WEIGHT OF A HORSE AND ITS DISTRIBUTION

Weight is one of the most important factors in horse racing. On the theory that "weight brings them all together," the handicapper imposes poundage calculated to effect that result, and his weight lists are studied carefully by owners, trainers and others engaged or interested in the sport. Weight is important, too, to the jockey. It determines the length of his career as a race rider.

But there is one phase of this subject that is seldom considered and that is the weight of the horse himself at various stages of his career. Horses come in "all sizes, shapes and colors," and when one speaks of size in a horse it must be linked with his weight and general conformation. In this article it is endeavored to give authentic data on a number of horses and arrive at an average. This is an approximation, except in the case of Gallant Fox, whose exact weight and measurements are definitely known.

Anyone who has visited a breeding farm knows that at birth, and as a foal, the body of a Thoroughbred is short and the legs long. When a human is born the announcement of the proud parents generally mentions the weight. In the Thoroughbred foal the breeder is more concerned with the conformation and general health than with poundage. At some farms little attention is paid to weight, even when the babes are yearlings and are being prepared for the sales ring. At others, as at Court Manor, the Virginia breeding establishment of the late Willis Sharpe Kilmer, a careful record was kept of yearlings over a period of years. The average was about 860 pounds, with some individuals attaining 900 pounds.

At the two-year-old stage the legs and body of a horse grow practically at the same pace.

It may be surprising, but the weight does not increase greatly. This is understandable when it is realized that yearlings often are fattened—especially market yearlings—and that this fat must be taken off the two-year-old who is trained into condition for racing. The weight at this age will range between 900 and 1,000 pounds.

When the horse is three the legs and also the withers have grown more rapidly, so at this age it is the height which is slightly in excess. The weight has increased. Phar Lap weighed 1,150 pounds, and in the fall of 1930—the year in which Gallant Fox won nine of his ten starts—the Belair three-year-old weighed 1,125 pounds.

In the race horse the distribution of weight is highly important. Let us take Gallant Fox as an example: he stood 16.1 hands, which is equivalent to 65 inches, at the withers. Man o' War was 65⅝ inches, with a longer leverage of hind-quarters, and this may account for his tremendous stride, which has been estimated, when at top speed, at from 25 to 28 feet, as compared with 24 for Gallant Fox. Phar Lap also had a tremendous stride. One veteran who witnessed his Agua Caliente triumph compared it with that of "Big Red."

The body of a horse can be separated into six parts—the trunk, the four legs and the neck with the head. Dr. S. H. Chubb, curator of the American Museum of Natural History, gave years to the study for horse measurements as compared with the distribution of weight. These few notes are not meant to be as exhaustive or as scientific as the research of Dr. Chubb, but rather to give the reader brief examples of weight distribution. Using Gallant Fox as the subject again, his 1,125 pounds are distributed as follows: the trunk, about 675 pounds; the head and neck, 115 pounds; and the four legs together, about 335 pounds.

During the Thoroughbred's four-year-old season the body lengthens but the legs have stopped growing. At the five-year-old stage the withers may grow fractionally but the body lengthens still further. When the horse is unwound and sent to the farm for stud duty, the end of the training grind means the gaining of more weight, many stallions scaling 1,300 pounds.

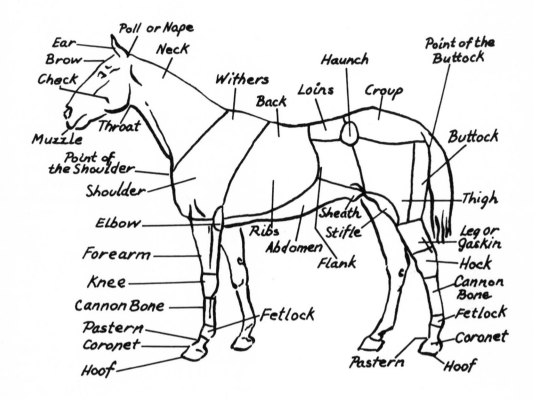

WHOSE MONEY?

FROM *The American Racing Manual*

For years I have heard, and will probably continue for as long as there is pari-mutuel wagering, the expressions: "I got the track's money today" or "The track got all my money." They are the sentiments of winners and losers. The fact is the track took just as much from the winners as from the losers. This analysis of a mythical horse race is appropriate reading for budding horse players; horse lovers can turn to Joe Palmer.

Years ago bookmaking was practically unknown in this country. Betting on the race tracks was wholly through auction pools and pari mutuels. In 1871 James E. Kelley of New York opened a winter book on the Belmont Stakes of that year, won by Harry Bassett at Jerome Park. He made book on various other events later. In 1873 or 1874 an English bookmaker named Stanford began bookmaking on New York tracks. He made money, and that induced others to embark in the new method of betting. Presently it became so popular that it monopolized speculation on the running turf and the auction pools and mutuels were banished to the trotting tracks. Gradually the pendulum swung the other way, and bookmaking now is almost unknown on this continent.

The distinguishing feature of mutuel betting is that it is the public that makes the odds. Other features are the absolute fairness of the system. It is the method used in such great racing countries as France, Australia and Argentina, and in these countries was welcome relief from abuses connected with or growing out of bookmaking. England also adopted it, though the bookmaker still prevails. By this method, each backer bets what he pleases on the horse of his choice.

Betting is done by purchasing tickets representing the horse of the buyer's selection. These tickets usually are $2 each, but $5, $10, $25, $50 and $100 tickets are on sale to accommodate persons who may desire to wager in large sums. Each ticket sold is registered by a machine as soon as it is sold. These machines show plainly the number of tickets sold on each horse and also the total sold on all the horses. Tickets by the purchase of which the bettor can back a horse to win, run second or third, are sold on all tracks where the mutuel system is used, these being called "straight," "place" and "show" tickets. There is no limit to the number of tickets one may buy, and if so minded one can purchase tickets on every horse in the race. When a race has been decided, a percentage (allowed by the states where pari-mutuels are legalized) of the whole sum invested is deducted for the association and the state. The remainder is at once divided properly and paid to the holders of winning tickets.

To show at a glance the process of this ascertainment of the pay-off due winning backers, a mythical 10-horse race is used for illustration, and methods and results are presented as follows:

Horse	$2 tickets
Old Rosebud	425
Roamer	415
Spur	268
King Gorin	184
Borrow	93
Ormesdale	105
Sasin	62
Rickety	315
Sunbonnet	187
Hendrie	49
Total	2,103

Suppose Old Rosebud was first, Roamer second and Borrow third. Then the following would be the method of ascertaining the value of the Old Rosebud straight tickets:

Total number of straight tickets sold 2,103
Convert to dollars (multiply by 2) ...... ×2
$4,206.00

$4,206.00 Deduct 10 per cent take-out .. −420.60
×.10
$ 420.60 Net for division $3,785.40

Divide $3,785.40 by the number of tickets sold on Old Rosebud (425):

```
425 ) 3,785.40 ( 8.90
      3,400
      3,854
      3,825
        290
```

Each $2 bet on Old Rosebud therefore returns the buyer $8.90. This sum includes the $2 paid for the ticket, making the net profit $6.90. Fractions of less than ten cents—five cents in some states (known as breakage)—are withheld and distributed in accordance with state laws.

Place tickets at $2 each were sold as follows:

Horse	$2 tickets
Old Rosebud	673
King Gorin	451
Roamer	258
Spur	302
Borrow	126
Ormesdale	245
Sasin	124
Rickety	420
Sunbonnet	117
Hendrie	89
Total	2,805

Place backers of Old Rosebud and **Roamer** would win and the calculation is made as follows:

Total number of place tickets sold 2,805
Convert to dollars (multiply by 2) ...... ×2
$5,610.00
$5,610.00 Deduct 10 per cent take-out .. −561.00
×.10
$ 561.00 Gross for division $5,049.00

Add together number of tickets sold
on Old Rosebud   673
and Roamer   258
931
Convert to dollars (multiply by 2)   ×2
$1,862
Deduct total from total net value $1,862.00

Net for division $3,187.00
Divide $3,187.00 into halves:
2) 3,187.00 ($1,593.50

Divide one-half by the number of tickets sold on Old Rosebud and the other half by the number of tickets sold on Roamer, thus:

Old Rosebud	Roamer
673) 1,593.50 (2.36	258) 1,593.50 (6.17
1,346	1,548
2,475	455
2,019	258
4,560	1,970
4,038	1,806
522	164

To the results thus obtained of $2.36 for Old Rosebud and $6.17 for Roamer must now be added $2, which in each case was paid for the ticket. This brings the actual result that backers of Old Rosebud for place would be entitled to, a return of $4.36 for each $2 invested, and similarly the place backers of Roamer would be entitled to $8.17. As the odd cents are withheld, they would be paid $4.30 and $8.10, respectively.

Where horses are backed to run third, or "show," the method of calculation is as in the case of place betting, except that the net sum remaining after the deduction of the track's and state's take-out and the aggregate of the sales of tickets to "show" on the three place horses is divided into three equal parts instead of two. Each of these three parts is then divided by the respective number of tickets sold on the three placed horses, and with $2 added to the results the value of the "show" tickets is obtained, thus:

Calculation of "show" ticket prices:

Horse	$2 tickets
Old Rosebud	901
King Gorin	612
Spur	423
Roamer	364
Borrow	245
Ormesdale	336
Sasin	197
Rickety	528
Sunbonnet	189
Hendrie	110
Total	3,905

In this the buyer of "show" tickets on Old Rosebud, Roamer and Borrow are the winners and their dividends are ascertained in the following manner:

Total number of "show" tickets sold.... 3,905
Convert to dollars (multiply by 2)...... ×2
$7,810.00
$7,810.00 Deduct 10 per cent take-out. −781.00
×.10
$ 781.00 Gross for division......... $7,029.00

Add together number of tickets sold on
Old Rosebud   901
on Roamer   364
and Borrow   245
1,510
Convert to dollars (multiply by 2)   ×2
$3,020
Deduct total from total net value....... $3,020.00
Net for division................ $4,009.00

Divide $4,009.00 into three equal parts:
3) 4,009.00 (1,336.33.
Divide each of these thirds by the number of tickets sold on Old Rosebud, Roamer and Borrow, respectively, thus:

Old Rosebud	Roamer
901) 1,336.33 (1.48	364) 1,336.33 (3.67
901	1,092
4,353	2,443
3,604	2,184
7,493	2,593
7,208	2,548
285	45

Borrow
245) 1,336.33 (5.45
1,225
1,113
980
1,333
1,225
108

To the results in each case $2 is to be added for the purchase of tickets, making the exact value of each Old Rosebud ticket to the buyer $3.48, of each Roamer ticket $5.67, and of each Borrow ticket $7.45. The odd cents are withheld, and the respective returns to the backers would be $3.40, $5.60 and $7.40.

When two horses run a dead heat for first place, whether the purse be or not be divided, the money bet is divided as in the calculations for place betting. Should the dead heat be run off, it shall be the subject of a new and distinct pool and bear no relation to the original contest.

When two horses run a dead heat for second place the winning horse is given his full share of one-half of the place money and each of the two dead heat place horses takes one-half of the remainder: that is, one-fourth of the whole.

In case no ticket is sold on a horse and that horse wins, all the straight money goes to the horse which is placed second. The place and show pools, however, are not affected hereby and remain unchanged so long as there is a participating ticket in either.

A mutuel field is two or more horses grouped and sold as a single horse.

In various states certain contingencies are governed by special rules.

"Mr. Rosebury has some sort of repair business. He fixes horse races."

DRAWING BY **PEARSON**   [© 1951 BY FAWCETT PUBLICATIONS, INC.]

Index

NOTE: *The editor has limited the entries in this index to items that seemed to him to have some historical importance or special significance, and has not attemped to supply an exhaustive index. This is particularly true of the names of the horses (appearing in small capitals) included in the list.*

Page numbers in italic type refer to illustrations.

About the Editor

David F. Woods was born in St. Louis, Missouri, in 1909 and attended schools in New York and Wisconsin. During a long career in advertising and publicity, he has served as the Director of Public Relations for Belmont Park, New York; Hialeah Race Course, Florida; Fair Grounds Race Course, New Orleans; Delaware Park, Delaware; Pimlico Race Course, Maryland; and The Thoroughbred Racing Associations of the United States (comprising 52 race tracks). From 1930 to the present time, with the exception of two years' service in the U.S. Cavalry at Ft. Riley, Kansas, during World War II, Mr. Woods has lived in Baltimore, where he is currently working as a free-lance writer and real estate broker. He is married and has two children and five grandchildren.